AS-Level
Mathematics

AS Maths is seriously tricky — no question about that.
To do well, you're going to need to revise properly and practise hard.

This book has thorough notes on everything in modules C1, C2, S1, M1 and D1.
It'll help you learn the stuff you need and take you step-by-step through loads of examples.

It's got practice questions... lots of them. For every topic there are warm-up and exam-style questions. Plus there are two full practice exams at the end of each module.

And of course, we've done our best to make the whole thing vaguely entertaining for you.

Complete Revision and Practice
Exam Board: OCR

Contents

Core Mathematics C1

C1 Section 1 — Algebra Fundamentals
A Few Definitions and Things 1
Laws of Indices 2
Surds 3
Multiplying Out Brackets 4
Taking Out Common Factors 5
Algebraic Fractions 6
Simplifying Expressions 7
Practice Questions 8

C1 Section 2 — Quadratic Equations
Sketching Quadratic Graphs 10
Factorising a Quadratic 11
Completing the Square 13
The Quadratic Formula 15
The Discriminant 16
Cows 18
'Almost' Quadratic Equations 19
Practice Questions 20

C1 Section 3
— Inequalities and Simultaneous Equations
Linear Inequalities 22
Quadratic Inequalities 23
Simultaneous Equations 24
Simultaneous Equations with Quadratics 25
Geometric Interpretation 26
Practice Questions 27

C1 Section 4
— Coordinate Geometry and Graphs
Coordinate Geometry 29
Equations of Straight Lines 31
Curve Sketching 32
Graph Transformations 33
Circles 34
Practice Questions 36

C1 Section 5 — Differentiation
Differentiation 39
Finding Tangents and Normals 41
Stationary Points 42
Increasing and Decreasing Functions 43
Curve Sketching 44
Real-Life Problems 45
Practice Questions 46

C1 Practice Exams
C1 — Practice Exam One 49
C1 — Practice Exam Two 51

Core Mathematics C2

C2 Section 1 — Polynomials
Factorising Cubics 53
Algebraic Division 54
The Remainder and Factor Theorems 55
Practice Questions 56

C2 Section 2 — Sequences and Series
Sequences 57
Arithmetic Progressions 59
Arithmetic Series and Sigma Notation 60
Geometric Progressions 61
Sequence & Series Problems 64
Binomial Expansions 65
Practice Questions 68

C2 Section 3 — Circles and Trigonometry
Arc Length and Sector Area 71
The Trig Formulas You Need to Know 73
Using the Sine and Cosine Rules 74
Graphs of Trig Functions 75
Transformed Trig Graphs 76
Solving Trig Equations in a Given Interval 77
Practice Questions 81

C2 Section 4 — Logs and Exponentials
Logs 84
Exponentials and Logs 85
Practice Questions 87

C2 Section 5 — Integration
Integration 89
The Trapezium Rule 92
Areas Between Curves 94
Practice Questions 95

C2 Practice Exams
C2 — Practice Exam One 98
C2 — Practice Exam Two 100

Statistics S1

S1 Section 1 — Representation of Data
Histograms 102
Stem and Leaf Diagrams 103
Location: Mean, Median and Mode 104
Variation: Interquartile Range 106
Cumulative Frequency Graphs 107
Variation: Standard Deviation 108
Variation and Outliers 109
Coding 110
Comparing Distributions 111
Practice Questions 112

Contents

S1 Section 2 — Probability
Random Events and Venn Diagrams 115
Tree Diagrams 117
Conditional Probability 118
Independent Events 119
Arrangements and Selections 120
Practice Questions 123

S1 Section 3 — Discrete Random Variables
Probability Distributions 125
Expected Values, Mean and Variance 127
The Geometric Distribution 128
The Binomial Probability Function 129
The Binomial Distribution 130
Using Binomial Tables 131
Mean and Variance of $B(n, p)$ 132
Binomial Distribution Problems 133
Practice Questions 134

S1 Section 4 — Bivariate Data
Correlation 137
Linear Regression 139
More About Regression and Correlation 141
Practice Questions 142

S1 Practice Exams
S1 — Practice Exam One 144
S1 — Practice Exam Two 147
Statistical Tables 150

Mechanics M1

M1 Section 1 — Vectors and Forces
Vectors 156
Forces and Modelling 158
Forces are Vectors 160
Friction 163
Practice Questions 164

M1 Section 2 — Kinematics
Constant Acceleration Equations 167
Motion Graphs 169
Displacement, Velocity and Acceleration 171
Practice Questions 173

M1 Section 3 — Dynamics
Newton's Laws 175
Friction and Inclined Planes 176
Connected Particles 178
Momentum 181
Practice Questions 182

M1 Practice Exams
M1 — Practice Exam One 185
M1 — Practice Exam Two 188

Decision Maths D1

D1 Section 1 — Algorithms
Algorithms 191
Flow Charts 193
Sorting 194
Packing 196
Practice Questions 197

D1 Section 2 — Graph Theory
Graphs 199
Minimum Spanning Trees 202
Dijkstra's Algorithm 205
Practice Questions 207

D1 Section 3 — The Route Inspection Problem
Traversable Graphs 209
Route Inspection Problems 210
Practice Questions 213

D1 Section 4
— The Travelling Salesperson Problem
Travelling Salesperson Problem 215
Practice Questions 218

D1 Section 5 — Linear Programming
Linear Programs 220
Feasible Regions 221
Optimal Solutions 222
Optimal Integer Solutions 224
The Simplex Method 225
Practice Questions 228

D1 Practice Exams
D1 — Practice Exam One 231
D1 — Practice Exam Two 234

C1 — Answers 237
C2 — Answers 251
S1 — Answers 267
M1 — Answers 280
D1 — Answers 293

Index 305

Editors:
Josephine Gibbons, Paul Jordin, Sharon Keeley-Holden, Simon Little, Sam Norman, Ali Palin,
Andy Park, David Ryan, Lyn Setchell, Caley Simpson, Jane Towle, Jonathan Wray, Dawn Wright

Contributors:
Andy Ballard, Charley Darbishire, Claire Jackson, Tim Major, Mark Moody,
Garry Rowlands, Mike Smith, Claire Thompson, Julie Wakeling, Kieran Wardell, Chris Worth

Proofreaders:
Alastair Duncombe, Allan Graham, Helen Greaves

Published by CGP

ISBN: 978 1 84762 582 3

Groovy Website: www.cgpbooks.co.uk

Printed by Elanders Ltd, Newcastle upon Tyne.

Based on the classic CGP style created by Richard Parsons.

A Few Definitions and Things

Yep, this is a pretty dull way to start a book. A list of definitions. But at least it gets it out of the way right at the beginning — it would be a bit mean of me to try and sneak it in halfway through and hope you wouldn't notice.

Polynomials

POLYNOMIALS are expressions of the form $a + bx + cx^2 + dx^3 + ...$

$5y^3 + 2y + 23$ ← Polynomial in the variable y.

$1 + x^2$

$z^4 + 3z - z^2 - 1$ ← Polynomial in the variable z.

An expression is made up of <u>terms</u>.

E.g: z^4, $3z$, $-z^2$ and -1

x, y and z are always VARIABLES
They're usually what you solve equations to find. They often have more than one possible value.

Letters like a, b, c are always CONSTANTS
Constants never change. They're fixed numbers — but can be represented by letters. π is a good example. You use the symbol π, but it's just a number = 3.1415...

Functions

FUNCTIONS take a value, do something to it, and output another value.

$f(x) = x^2 + 1$ ← function f takes a value, squares it and adds 1.

$g(x) = 2 - \sin 2x$ ← function g takes a value (in degrees), doubles it, takes the sine of it, then takes the value away from 2.

You can plug values into a function — just replace the variable with a certain number.

$f(-2) = (-2)^2 + 1 = 5$

$f(0) = (0)^2 + 1 = 1$

$f(252) = (252)^2 + 1 = 63505$

$g(-90°) = 2 - \sin(-180°) = 2 - 0 = 2$

$g(0°) = 2 - \sin 0° = 2 - 0 = 2$

$g(45°) = 2 - \sin 90° = 2 - 1 = 1$

Exam questions use functions all the time. They generally don't have that much to do with the actual question. It's just a bit of terminology to get comfortable with.

Multiplication and Division

There's three different ways of showing MULTIPLICATION:

1) with good old-fashioned "times" signs (×):

$f(x) = (2x \times 6y) + (2x \times \sin x) + (z \times y)$

The multiplication signs and the variable x are easily confused.

2) or sometimes just use a little dot:

$f(x) = 2x.6y + 2x.\sin x + z.y$

Dots are better for long expressions — they're less confusing and easier to read.

3) but you often don't need anything at all:

$f(x) = 12xy + 2x \sin x + zy$

And there's three different ways of showing DIVISION:

1) $\dfrac{x+2}{3}$

2) $(x+2) \div 3$

3) $(x+2)/3$

Equations and Identities

This is an IDENTITY:

$x^2 - y^2 \equiv (x+y)(x-y)$

Make up any values you like for x and y, and it's always true. The left-hand side always equals the right-hand side.

But this is an EQUATION:

$y = x^2 + x$

This has at most two possible solutions for each value of y. e.g. if y = 0, x can only be 0 or -1.

The difference is that the identity's true for all values of x and y, but the equation's only true for certain values.

NB: If it's an identity, use the $\equiv$ sign instead of =.

Laws of Indices

You use the laws of indices a helluva lot in maths — when you're integrating, differentiating and ...er... well loads of other places. So take the time to get them sorted <u>now</u>.

Three mega-important *Laws of Indices*

You <u>must</u> know these three rules. I can't make it any clearer than that.

$$a^m \times a^n = a^{m+n}$$

If you <u>multiply</u> two numbers — you <u>add</u> their powers.

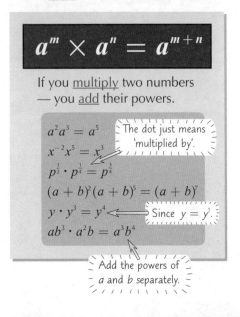

$a^2a^3 = a^5$
$x^{-2}x^5 = x^3$
$p^{\frac{1}{2}} \cdot p^{\frac{1}{4}} = p^{\frac{3}{4}}$
$(a+b)^2(a+b)^5 = (a+b)^7$
$y \cdot y^3 = y^4$ ← Since $y = y^1$.
$ab^3 \cdot a^2b = a^3b^4$

The dot just means 'multiplied by'.

Add the powers of a and b separately.

$$\frac{a^m}{a^n} = a^{m-n}$$

If you <u>divide</u> two numbers — you <u>subtract</u> their powers.

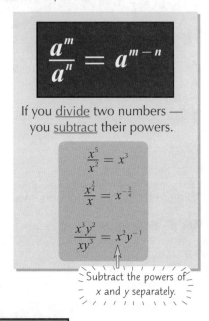

$\dfrac{x^5}{x^2} = x^3$

$\dfrac{x^{\frac{3}{4}}}{x} = x^{-\frac{1}{4}}$

$\dfrac{x^3y^2}{xy^3} = x^2y^{-1}$

Subtract the powers of x and y separately.

$$(a^m)^n = a^{mn}$$

If you have a <u>power</u> to the <u>power of something else</u> — <u>multiply</u> the powers together.

$(x^2)^3 = x^6$
$\{(a+b)^3\}^4 = (a+b)^{12}$
$(ab^2)^4 = a^4(b^2)^4 = a^4b^8$

This power applies to both bits inside the brackets.

Other important stuff about *Indices*

You can't get very far without knowing this sort of stuff. Learn it — you'll definitely be able to use it.

$$a^{\frac{1}{m}} = \sqrt[m]{a}$$

You can write <u>roots</u> as powers...

EXAMPLES
$x^{\frac{1}{5}} = \sqrt[5]{x}$
$4^{\frac{1}{2}} = \sqrt{4} = 2$
$125^{\frac{1}{3}} = \sqrt[3]{125} = 5$

$$a^{\frac{m}{n}} = \sqrt[n]{a^m} = \left(\sqrt[n]{a}\right)^m$$

A power that's a <u>fraction</u> like this is the <u>root of a power</u> — or the <u>power of a root</u>.

EXAMPLES
$9^{\frac{3}{2}} = (9^{\frac{1}{2}})^3 = (\sqrt{9})^3 = 3^3 = 27$
$16^{\frac{3}{4}} = (16^{\frac{1}{4}})^3 = (\sqrt[4]{16})^3 = 2^3 = 8$

It's often easier to work out the root first, then raise it to the power.

$$a^{-m} = \frac{1}{a^m}$$

A <u>negative</u> power means it's on the bottom line of a fraction.

EXAMPLES
$x^{-2} = \dfrac{1}{x^2}$
$2^{-3} = \dfrac{1}{2^3} = \dfrac{1}{8}$
$(x+1)^{-1} = \dfrac{1}{x+1}$

$$a^0 = 1$$

This works for <u>any</u> number or letter.

EXAMPLES
$x^0 = 1$
$2^0 = 1$
$(a+b)^0 = 1$

Indices, indices — de fish all live indices...

What can I say that I haven't said already? Blah, blah, important. Blah, blah, learn these. Blah, blah, use them all the time. Mmm, that's about all that needs to be said really. So I'll be quiet and let you get on with what you need to do.

Surds

A surd is a number like $\sqrt{2}$, $\sqrt[3]{12}$ or $5\sqrt{3}$ — one that's written with the $\sqrt{\ }$ sign. They're important because you can give <u>exact</u> answers where you'd otherwise have to round to a certain number of decimal places.

Surds are sometimes the only way to give an *Exact Answer*

Put $\sqrt{2}$ into a calculator and you'll get something like 1.414213562...
But square 1.414213562 and you get 1.999999999.

And no matter how many decimal places you use, you'll never get <u>exactly</u> 2.
The only way to write the exact, spot-on value is to <u>use surds</u>.

So, as you're not allowed a calculator for your C1 exam, leave your answer as a <u>surd</u>.

There are basically Three Rules for using Surds

There are three <u>rules</u> you'll need to know to be able to use surds properly. Check out the 'Rules of Surds' box below.

EXAMPLES   (i)   Simplify $\sqrt{12}$ and $\sqrt{\frac{3}{16}}$.   (ii)   Show that $\frac{9}{\sqrt{3}} = 3\sqrt{3}$.   (iii)   Find $(2\sqrt{5} + 3\sqrt{6})^2$.

(i)   <u>Simplifying</u> surds means making the number in the $\sqrt{\ }$ sign <u>smaller</u>, or getting rid of a <u>fraction</u> in the $\sqrt{\ }$ sign.

$$\sqrt{12} = \sqrt{4 \times 3} = \sqrt{4} \times \sqrt{3} = 2\sqrt{3} \qquad \sqrt{\frac{3}{16}} = \frac{\sqrt{3}}{\sqrt{16}} = \frac{\sqrt{3}}{4}$$

Using $\sqrt{\frac{a}{b}} = \frac{\sqrt{a}}{\sqrt{b}}$.

Using $\sqrt{ab} = \sqrt{a}\sqrt{b}$.

(ii)   For questions like these, you have to write a number (here, it's 3) as $3 = (\sqrt{3})^2 = \sqrt{3} \times \sqrt{3}$

$$\frac{9}{\sqrt{3}} = \frac{3 \times 3}{\sqrt{3}} = \frac{3 \times \sqrt{3} \times \sqrt{3}}{\sqrt{3}} = 3\sqrt{3}$$

Cancelling $\sqrt{3}$ from the top and bottom lines.

(iii) Multiply surds very <u>carefully</u> — it's easy to make a silly mistake.

$$(2\sqrt{5} + 3\sqrt{6})^2 = (2\sqrt{5} + 3\sqrt{6})(2\sqrt{5} + 3\sqrt{6})$$
$$= (2\sqrt{5})^2 + 2 \times (2\sqrt{5}) \times (3\sqrt{6}) + (3\sqrt{6})^2$$
$$= (2^2 \times \sqrt{5}^2) + (2 \times 2 \times 3 \times \sqrt{5} \times \sqrt{6}) + (3^2 \times \sqrt{6}^2)$$
$$= 20 + 12\sqrt{30} + 54$$
$$= 74 + 12\sqrt{30}$$

$= 4 \times 5 = 20$ $= 12\sqrt{5}\sqrt{6} = 12\sqrt{30}$ $= 9 \times 6 = 54$

Rules of Surds

There's not really very much to remember.
$$\sqrt{ab} = \sqrt{a}\sqrt{b}$$
$$\sqrt{\frac{a}{b}} = \frac{\sqrt{a}}{\sqrt{b}}$$
$$a = (\sqrt{a})^2 = \sqrt{a}\sqrt{a}$$

Remove surds from fractions by Rationalising the Denominator

Surds are pretty darn complicated.

So they're the last thing you want at the bottom of a fraction.

But have no fear — <u>Rationalise the Denominator</u>...

Yup, you heard... (it means getting rid of the surds from the bottom of a fraction).

EXAMPLE   Rationalise the denominator of $\frac{1}{1 + \sqrt{2}}$

Multiply the top and bottom by the denominator (but change the sign in front of the surd).

$$\frac{1}{1 + \sqrt{2}} \times \frac{1 - \sqrt{2}}{1 - \sqrt{2}}$$

$$\frac{1 - \sqrt{2}}{(1 + \sqrt{2})(1 - \sqrt{2})} = \frac{1 - \sqrt{2}}{1^2 + \sqrt{2} - \sqrt{2} - \sqrt{2}^2}$$

This works because: $(a + b)(a - b) = a^2 - b^2$

$$\frac{1 - \sqrt{2}}{1 - 2} = \frac{1 - \sqrt{2}}{-1} = -1 + \sqrt{2}$$

Surely the pun is mightier than the surd...

You'll need to work with surds in your <u>non-calculator C1 exam</u>, as roots are nigh on impossible (well, very tricky) to work out without a calculator. Learn the rules in the box so you can write them down without thinking — then get <u>loads</u> of practice.

Multiplying Out Brackets

In this horrific nightmare that is AS-level maths, you need to manipulate and simplify expressions <u>all the time</u>.

Remove brackets by **Multiplying** them out

Here are the basic types you have to deal with. You'll have seen them before. But there's no harm in reminding you, eh?

<u>Multiply Your Brackets Here — we do all shapes and sizes</u>

Single Brackets

$$a(b + c + d) = ab + ac + ad$$

Squared Brackets

$$(a + b)^2 = (a + b)(a + b) = a^2 + 2ab + b^2$$

Use the middle stage until you're comfortable with it. Just <u>never</u> make this <u>mistake</u>: $(a + b)^2 = a^2 + b^2$

Double Brackets

$$(a + b)(c + d) = ac + ad + bc + bd$$

Long Brackets

Write it out again with <u>each term</u> from one bracket separately multiplied by the <u>other bracket</u>.
Then <u>multiply out each</u> of these <u>brackets</u>, one at a time.

$$(x + y + z)(a + b + c + d)$$
$$= x(a + b + c + d) + y(a + b + c + d) + z(a + b + c + d)$$

Single Brackets

$$3xy(x^2 + 2x - 8)$$

Multiply all the terms inside the brackets by the bit outside — separately.

$$(3xy \times x^2) + (3xy \times 2x) + (3xy \times (-8))$$

All the stuff in the brackets now needs sorting out. Work on each bracket separately.

I've put brackets round each bit to make it easier to read.

$$(3x^3y) + (6x^2y) + (-24xy)$$

Multiply the numbers first, then put the x's and other letters together.

$$3x^3y + 6x^2y - 24xy$$

Squared Brackets

Either write it as two brackets and multiply it out...

$$(2y^2 + 3x)^2$$

$$(2y^2 + 3x)(2y^2 + 3x)$$

The dot just means 'multiplied by' — the same as the × sign.

$$2y^2.2y^2 + 2y^2.3x + 3x.2y^2 + 3x.3x$$

From here on it's simplification — nothing more, nothing less.

$$4y^4 + 6xy^2 + 6xy^2 + 9x^2$$

$$4y^4 + 12xy^2 + 9x^2$$

...or do it in one go.

$$(2y^2)^2 + 2(2y^2)(3x) + (3x)^2$$
$$\quad a^2 \qquad\quad 2ab \qquad\quad b^2$$

$$4y^4 + 12xy^2 + 9x^2$$

Long Brackets

$$(2x^2 + 3x + 6)(4x^3 + 6x^2 + 3)$$

Each term in the first bracket has been multiplied by the second bracket.

$$2x^2(4x^3 + 6x^2 + 3) + 3x(4x^3 + 6x^2 + 3) + 6(4x^3 + 6x^2 + 3)$$

Now multiply out each of these brackets.

$$(8x^5 + 12x^4 + 6x^2) + (12x^4 + 18x^3 + 9x) + (24x^3 + 36x^2 + 18)$$

Then simplify it all...

$$8x^5 + 24x^4 + 42x^3 + 42x^2 + 9x + 18$$

Go forth and multiply out brackets...

OK, so this is obvious, but I'll say it anyway — if you've got 3 or more brackets together, multiply them out 2 at a time. Then you'll be turning a really hard problem into two easy ones. You can do that loads in maths. In fact, writing the same thing in different ways is what maths is about. That and sitting in classrooms with tacky 'maths can be fun' posters...

Taking Out Common Factors

Common factors need to be hunted down, and taken outside the brackets. They are a danger to your exam mark.

Spot those Common Factors

A bit which is in each term of an expression is a <u>common factor</u>.

Spot Those Common Factors	$2x^3z + 4x^2yz + 14x^2y^2z$

Look for any bits that are in each term.

<u>Numbers:</u>   there's a common factor of 2 here because 2 divides into 2, 4 and 14.

<u>Variables:</u>   there's at least an x^2 in each term and there's a z in each term.

So there's a <u>common factor of $2x^2z$</u> in this expression.

And Take Them Outside a Bracket

If you spot a common factor you can "<u>take it out</u>":

$$2x^2z(x + 2y + 7y^2)$$

Write the common factor outside a bracket.

and put what's left of each term inside the bracket.

Afterwards, always <u>multiply back out</u> to check you did it right:

Check by Multiplying Out Again

$$2x^2z(x + 2y + 7y^2) = 2x^3z + 4x^2yz + 14x^2y^2z$$

But it's not just numbers and variables you need to look for...

Brackets: $(y + a)^2(x - a)^3 + (x - a)^2$

$(x-a)^2$ is a common factor — it comes out to give:

$$(x - a)^2((y + a)^2(x - a) + 1)$$

Look for Common Factors when Simplifying Expressions

EXAMPLE   Simplify... $(x + 1)(x - 2) + (x + 1)^2 - x(x + 1)$

There's an $(x + 1)$ factor in each term, so we can take this out as a common factor (hurrah).

$$(x + 1)\{(x - 2) + (x + 1) - x\}$$

The terms inside the big bracket are the old terms with an $(x + 1)$ removed.

At this point you should check that this multiplies out to give the original expression. (You can just do this in your head, if you trust it.)

Then simplify the big bracket's innards:

$$(x + 1)(\cancel{x} - 2 + x + 1 - \cancel{x})$$

$$= (x + 1)(x - 1)$$

$$= x^2 - 1$$

Get this answer by multiplying out the two brackets (or by using the "difference of two squares").

Bored of spotting trains or birds? Try common factors...

You'll be doing this business of taking out common factors a lot — so get your head round this. It's just a case of looking for things that are in all the different terms of an expression, i.e. <u>bits they have in common</u>. And if something's in all the different terms, save yourself some time and ink, and write it once — instead of two, three or more times.

Algebraic Fractions

No one likes fractions. But just like Mondays, you can't put them off forever. Face those fears. Here goes...

The first thing you've got to know about fractions:

$$\frac{a}{x} + \frac{b}{x} + \frac{c}{x} \equiv \frac{a+b+c}{x}$$

You can just add the stuff on the top lines because the bottom lines are all the same.

x is called a common denominator — a fancy way of saying 'the bottom line of all the fractions is x'.

Add fractions by putting them over a **Common Denominator**...

Finding a common denominator just means 'rewriting some fractions so all their bottom lines are the same'.

EXAMPLE Simplify $\frac{1}{2x} - \frac{1}{3x} + \frac{1}{5x}$

You need to rewrite these so that all the bottom lines are equal. What you want is something that all these bottom lines divide into.

Put It over a Common Denominator

30 is the lowest number that 2, 3 and 5 go into. So the common denominator is $30x$.

$$\frac{15}{30x} - \frac{10}{30x} + \frac{6}{30x}$$

Always check that these divide out to give what you started with.

$$\frac{15 - 10 + 6}{30x} = \frac{11}{30x}$$

...even **horrible** looking ones

Yep, finding a common denominator even works for those fraction nasties — like these:

EXAMPLE Simplify $\frac{3}{x+2} + \frac{5}{x-3}$

Find the Common Denominator

Take all the individual 'bits' from the bottom lines and multiply them together. Only use each bit once unless something on the bottom line is squared.

The individual 'bits' here are $(x+2)$ and $(x-3)$.

$$(x+2)(x-3)$$

Put Each Fraction over the Common Denominator

Make the denominator of each fraction into the common denominator.

$$\frac{3(x-3)}{(x+2)(x-3)} + \frac{5(x+2)}{(x+2)(x-3)}$$

Multiply the top and bottom lines of each fraction by whatever makes the bottom line the same as the common denominator.

Combine into One Fraction

Once everything's over the common denominator you can just add the top lines together.

$$= \frac{3(x-3) + 5(x+2)}{(x+2)(x-3)}$$

All the bottom lines are the same — so you can just add the top lines.

All you need to do now is tidy up the top.

$$= \frac{3x - 9 + 5x + 10}{(x+2)(x-3)} = \frac{8x+1}{(x+2)(x-3)}$$

So much prettier now all the terms are _together_. Simple.

Well put me over a common denominator and pickle my walrus...

Adding fractions — turning lots of fractions into one fraction. Sounds pretty good to me, since it means you don't have to write as much. Better do it carefully, though — otherwise you can watch those marks shoot straight down the toilet.

Simplifying Expressions

I know this is basic stuff but if you don't get really comfortable with it you <u>will</u> make silly mistakes. You will.

Cancelling stuff on the top and bottom lines

Cancelling stuff is good — because it means you've got rid of something, and you don't have to write as much.

EXAMPLE Simplify $\dfrac{ax + ay}{az}$

You can do this in two ways. Use whichever you prefer — but make sure you understand the ideas behind both.

Factorise — then Cancel

$$\frac{ax + ay}{az} = \frac{a(x + y)}{az}$$ *Factorise the top line.*

Cancel the 'a'. $$\frac{\cancel{a}(x + y)}{\cancel{a}z} = \frac{x + y}{z}$$

Split into Two Fractions — then Cancel

$$\frac{ax + ay}{az} = \frac{ax}{az} + \frac{ay}{az}$$ *This is an okay thing to do — just think what you'd get if you added these.*

$$= \frac{\cancel{a}x}{\cancel{a}z} + \frac{\cancel{a}y}{\cancel{a}z} = \frac{x}{z} + \frac{y}{z}$$ *This answer's the same as the one from the first box — honest. Check it yourself by adding the fractions.*

Simplifying complicated-looking **Brackets**

EXAMPLE Simplify the expression $(x - y)(x^2 + xy + y^2)$

There's only one thing to do here.... Multiply out those brackets!

$$(x - y)(x^2 + xy + y^2) = x(x^2 + xy + y^2) - y(x^2 + xy + y^2)$$ *Multiplying each term in the first bracket by the second bracket.*

$$= (x^3 + x^2y + xy^2) - (x^2y + xy^2 + y^3)$$ *Multiplying out each of these two brackets.*

$$= x^3 + x^2y + xy^2 - x^2y - xy^2 - y^3$$ *Don't forget these become minus signs because of the minus sign in front of the bracket.*

And then the x^2y and the xy^2 terms disappear...

$$= x^3 - y^3$$

Sometimes you just have to do **Anything** you can think of and **Hope**...

Sometimes it's not easy to see what you're supposed to do to simplify something.
When this happens — just do anything you can think of and see what 'comes out in the wash'.

EXAMPLE Simplify $4x + \dfrac{4x}{x + 1} - 4(x + 1)$

There's nothing obvious to do — so do what you can. Try adding them as fractions...

$$4x + \frac{4x}{x + 1} - 4(x + 1) = \frac{(x + 1) \times 4x}{x + 1} + \frac{4x}{x + 1} - \frac{(x + 1) \times 4x(x + 1)}{x + 1}$$ *The common denominator is (x+1).*

$$= \frac{4x^2 + 4x + 4x - 4(x + 1)^2}{x + 1}$$ *Still looks horrible. So work out the brackets — but don't forget the minus signs.*

$$= \frac{4x^2 + 4x + 4x - 4x^2 - 8x - 4}{x + 1}$$

$$= -\frac{4}{x + 1}$$ *Aha — everything disappears to leave you with this. And this is definitely simpler than it looked at the start.*

Don't look at me like that...

Choose a word, any word at all. Like "Simple". Now stare at it. Keep staring at it. Does it look weird? No? Stare a bit longer. Now does it look weird? Yes? Why is that? I don't understand.

C1 Section 1 — Practice Questions

So that was the first section. Now, before you get stuck into Section Two, test yourself with these questions. Go on. If you thought this section was a doddle, you should be able to fly through them...

Warm-up Questions

1) Pick out the constants and the variables from the following equations:
   a) $(ax + 6)^2 = 2b + 3$
   b) $f(x) = 12a + 3b^3 - 2$
   c) $y = \dfrac{-b \pm \sqrt{b^2 - 4ac}}{2a}$
   d) $\dfrac{dy}{dx} = x^2 + ax + 2$

2) What symbol should be used instead of the equals sign in identities?

3) Which of these are identities (i.e. true for all variable values)?
   A $(x + b)(y - b) = xy + b(y - x) - b^2$
   B $(2y + x^2) = 10$
   C $a^2 - b^2 = (a - b)(a + b)$
   D $a^3 + b^3 = (a + b)(a^2 - ab + b^2)$

4) Simplify these:
   a) $x^3.x^5$
   b) $a^7.a^8$
   c) $\dfrac{x^8}{x^2}$
   d) $(a^2)^4$
   e) $(xy^2).(x^3yz)$
   f) $\dfrac{a^2b^4c^6}{a^3b^2c}$

5) Work out the following:
   a) $16^{\frac{1}{2}}$
   b) $8^{\frac{1}{3}}$
   c) $16^{\frac{3}{4}}$
   d) x^0
   e) $49^{-\frac{1}{2}}$

6) Find exact answers to these equations:
   a) $x^2 - 5 = 0$
   b) $(x + 2)^2 - 3 = 0$

7) Simplify:
   a) $\sqrt{28}$
   b) $\sqrt{\dfrac{5}{36}}$
   c) $\sqrt{18}$
   d) $\sqrt{\dfrac{9}{16}}$

8) Show that a) $\dfrac{8}{\sqrt{2}} = 4\sqrt{2}$, and b) $\dfrac{\sqrt{2}}{2} = \dfrac{1}{\sqrt{2}}$

9) Find $(6\sqrt{3} + 2\sqrt{7})^2$

10) Rationalise the denominator of: $\dfrac{2}{3 + \sqrt{7}}$

11) Remove the brackets and simplify the following expressions:
    a) $(a + b)(a - b)$
    b) $(a + b)(a + b)$
    c) $35xy + 25y(5y + 7x) - 100y^2$
    d) $(x + 3y + 2)(3x + y + 7)$

12) Take out the common factors from the following expressions:
    a) $2x^2y + axy + 2xy^2$
    b) $a^2x + a^2b^2x^2$
    c) $16y + 8yx + 56x$
    d) $x(x - 2) + 3(2 - x)$

13) Put the following expressions over a common denominator:
    a) $\dfrac{2x}{3} + \dfrac{y}{12} + \dfrac{x}{5}$
    b) $\dfrac{5}{xy^2} - \dfrac{2}{x^2y}$
    c) $\dfrac{1}{x} + \dfrac{x}{x + y} + \dfrac{y}{x - y}$

14) Simplify these expressions:
    a) $\dfrac{2a}{b} - \dfrac{a}{2b}$
    b) $\dfrac{2p}{p + q} + \dfrac{2q}{p - q}$
    c) "A bird in the hand is worth two in the bush"

C1 Section 1 — Practice Questions

The warm-up questions should have been a <u>walk in the park</u>, so now for the main event — <u>exam-style questions</u>.
The questions on this page are like the ones you'll get <u>in your exam</u>, so make sure you can do them before moving on.

Exam Questions

1   a)   Write down the value of $27^{\frac{1}{3}}$.

(1 mark)

      b)   Find the value of $27^{\frac{4}{3}}$.

(2 marks)

2   Simplify

      a) $(5\sqrt{3})^2$

(1 mark)

      b) $(5 + \sqrt{6})(2 - \sqrt{6})$

(2 marks)

3   Given that $10000\sqrt{10} = 10^{k}$, find the value of k.

(3 marks)

4   Express $\dfrac{5 + \sqrt{5}}{3 - \sqrt{5}}$ in the form $a + b\sqrt{5}$, where a and b are integers.

(4 marks)

5   Factorise completely

$$2x^4 - 32x^2.$$

(3 marks)

6   Write

$$\frac{x + 5x^3}{\sqrt{x}}$$

   in the form $x^m + 5x^n$, where m and n are constants.

(2 marks)

7   Show that

$$\frac{(5 + 4\sqrt{x})^2}{2x}$$

   can be written as $\dfrac{25}{2}x^{-1} + Px^{-\frac{1}{2}} + Q$, and find the value of the integers P and Q.

(3 marks)

Sketching Quadratic Graphs

If a question doesn't seem to make sense, or you can't see how to go about solving a problem, try drawing a <u>graph</u>. It sometimes helps if you can actually <u>see</u> what the problem is, rather than just reading about it.

Sketch the graphs of the following quadratic equations:

① $y = 2x^2 - 4x + 3$ ② $y = 8 - 2x - x^2$

Quadratic graphs are **Always** u-shaped or n-shaped

A The first thing you need to know is whether the graph's going to be u-shaped or n-shaped (upside down). To decide, look at the <u>coefficient of x^2</u>.

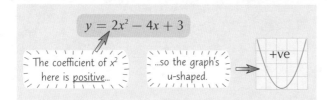

The coefficient of x^2 here is <u>positive</u>... ...so the graph's u-shaped.

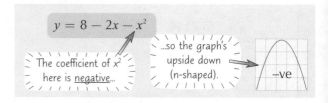

The coefficient of x^2 here is <u>negative</u>... ...so the graph's upside down (n-shaped).

B Now find the places where the graph crosses the <u>axes</u> (both the y-axis and the x-axis).

(i) Put $x = 0$ to find where it meets the <u>y-axis</u>.

$y = 2x^2 - 4x + 3$

$y = (2 \times 0^2) - (4 \times 0) + 3$ so $y = 3$

That's where it crosses the y-axis.

(ii) Solve $y = 0$ to find where it meets the <u>x-axis</u>.

$2x^2 - 4x + 3 = 0$

$b^2 - 4ac = -8 < 0$

You could use the formula. But first check $b^2 - 4ac$ to see if $y = 0$ has any roots.

So it has no solutions, and doesn't cross the x-axis.

For more info, see page 16.

(i) Put $x = 0$.

$y = 8 - 2x - x^2$

$y = 8 - (2 \times 0) - 0^2$ so $y = 8$

(ii) Solve $y = 0$.

$8 - 2x - x^2 = 0$

$\Rightarrow (2 - x)(x + 4) = 0$

$\Rightarrow x = 2$ or $x = -4$

This equation factorises easily...

C Finally, find the <u>minimum</u> or <u>maximum</u> (i.e. the <u>vertex</u>).

Since $y = 2(x - 1)^2 + 1$

By <u>completing the square</u> (see page 13).

the minimum value is $y = 1$, which occurs at $x = 1$.

The minimum or maximum of the graph is always at $x = \dfrac{-b}{2a}$

The maximum value is <u>halfway</u> between the roots — the graph's symmetrical.

The maximum value is at $x = -1$

So the maximum is $y = 8 - (2 \times -1) - (-1)^2$

i.e. the graph has a maximum at the point (–1, 9).

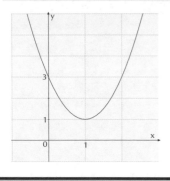

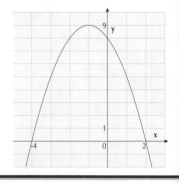

Sketching Quadratic Graphs

A) <u>up or down</u> — decide which direction the curve points in.

B) <u>axes</u> — find where the curve crosses them.

C) <u>max / min</u> — find the vertex.

Van Gogh, Monet — all the greats started out sketching graphs...

So there are <u>three steps</u> here to learn. Simple enough. You can do the third step (finding the max/min point) by either a) completing the square, which is covered a bit later, or b) using the fact that the graph's symmetrical — so once you've found the points where it crosses the x-axis, the point halfway between them will be the max/min. It's all laughs here...

Factorising a Quadratic

Factorising a quadratic means putting it into two brackets — and is useful if you're trying to draw a graph of a quadratic or solve a quadratic equation. It's pretty easy if $a = 1$ (in $ax^2 + bx + c$ form), but can be a real pain otherwise.

$$x^2 - x - 12 = (x - 4)(x + 3)$$

Factorising's not so bad when **a = 1**

EXAMPLE Solve $x^2 - 8 = 2x$ by factorising.

A Put into $ax^2 + bx + c = 0$ Form

$x^2 - 2x - 8 = 0$ ⟵ So $a = 1$, $b = -2$, $c = -8$.

Write down the two brackets with x's in: $x^2 - 2x - 8 = (x \quad)(x \quad)$

B Find the Two Numbers

Find two numbers that multiply together to make c but which also add or subtract to give b (you can ignore any minus signs for now).

1 and 8 multiply to give 8 — and add / subtract to give 9 and 7.
2 and 4 multiply to give 8 — and add / subtract to give 6 and 2.

This is the value for b you're after — so this is the right combination: 2 and 4.

C Find the Signs

Now all you have to do is put in the plus or minus signs.

It must be +2 and –4 because $2 \times (-4) = -8$ and $2 + (-4) = 2 - 4 = -2$

If c is negative, then the signs must be different.

$x^2 - 2x - 8 = (x \quad 4)(x \quad 2)$

$x^2 - 2x - 8 = (x + 2)(x - 4)$

D Solve the Equation

All you've done so far is to factorise the equation — you've still got to solve it.

$(x + 2)(x - 4) = 0$

$\Rightarrow x + 2 = 0$ or $x - 4 = 0$

Don't forget this last step. The factors aren't the answer.

$\Rightarrow x = -2$ or $x = 4$

Factorising Quadratics

A) Rearrange the equation into the standard $ax^2 + bx + c$ form.

B) Write down the two brackets:
$(x \quad)(x \quad)$

C) Find two numbers that multiply to give 'c' and add / subtract to give 'b' (ignoring signs).

D) Put the numbers in the brackets and choose their signs.

Another **Example**...

EXAMPLE Solve $x^2 + 4x - 21 = 0$ by factorising.

This equation is already in the standard format — you can write down the brackets straight away.

$x^2 + 4x - 21 = (x \quad)(x \quad)$

This is the value of 'b' you're after — 3 and 7 are the right numbers.

1 and 21 multiply to give 21 — and add / subtract to give 22 and 20.
3 and 7 multiply to give 21 — and add / subtract to give 10 and 4.

$x^2 + 4x - 21 = (x + 7)(x - 3)$

And solving the equation to find x gives... $\Rightarrow x = -7$ or $x = 3$

Scitardauq Gnisirotcaf — you should know it backwards...

Factorising quadratics — this is very basic stuff. You've really got to be comfortable with it. If you're even slightly rusty, you need to practise it until it's second nature. Remember why you're doing it — you don't factorise simply for the pleasure it gives you — it's so you can solve quadratic equations. Well, that's the theory anyway...

Factorising a Quadratic

It's not over yet...

Factorising a quadratic when $a \neq 1$

These can be a real pain. The basic method's the same as on the previous page — but it can be a bit more awkward.

EXAMPLE   Factorise $3x^2 + 4x - 15$

A Write Down Two Brackets

As before, write down two brackets — but instead of just having x in each, you need two things that will multiply to give $3x^2$.

It's got to be $3x$ and x here.

$$3x^2 + 4x - 15 = (3x \quad)(x \quad)$$

B The Fiddly Bit

You need to find two numbers that multiply together to make 15 — but which will give you $4x$ when you multiply them by x and $3x$, and then add / subtract them.

$(3x \quad 1)(x \quad 15) \Rightarrow x$ and $45x$ which then add or subtract to give $46x$ and $44x$.

$(3x \quad 15)(x \quad 1) \Rightarrow 15x$ and $3x$ which then add or subtract to give $18x$ and $12x$.

$(3x \quad 3)(x \quad 5) \Rightarrow 3x$ and $15x$ which then add or subtract to give $18x$ and $12x$.

$(3x \quad 5)(x \quad 3) \Rightarrow 5x$ and $9x$ which then add or subtract to give $14x$ and $4x$.

This is the value you're after — so this is the right combination.

C Add the Signs

You know the brackets must be like these... $\Rightarrow (3x \quad 5)(x \quad 3) = 3x^2 + 4x - 15$

So all you have to do is put in the plus or minus signs.

'c' is negative — that means the signs in the brackets are different.

You've only got two choices — if you're unsure, just multiply them out to see which one's right.

$$(3x + 5)(x - 3) = 3x^2 - 4x - 15$$

or...

$$(3x - 5)(x + 3) = 3x^2 + 4x - 15 \quad \Longleftarrow \text{ So it's this one.}$$

Sometimes it's best just to **Cheat** and use the **Formula**

Here are two final points to bear in mind:

1)   It <u>won't</u> always factorise.

2)   Sometimes factorising is so <u>messy</u> that it's easier to just use the quadratic formula...

So if the question doesn't tell you to factorise, don't assume it will factorise.
And if it's something like this thing below, don't bother trying to factorise it...

EXAMPLE   Solve $6x^2 + 87x - 144 = 0$

This <u>will</u> actually factorise, but there are 2 possible bracket forms to try.
$(6x \quad)(x \quad)$ or $(3x \quad)(2x \quad)$ And for each of these, there are 8 possible ways of making 144 to try.

And you can quote me on that...

"He who can properly do quadratic equations is considered a god."
Plato

"Quadratic equations are the music of reason."
James J Sylvester

Completing the Square

Completing the Square is a handy little trick that you should <u>definitely</u> know how to use.
It can be a bit fiddly — but it gives you <u>loads</u> of information about a quadratic really quickly.

Take any old quadratic and put it in a **Special Form**

Completing the square can be really confusing. For starters, what does "Completing the Square" <u>mean</u>?
<u>What</u> is the square? <u>Why</u> does it need completing? Well, there is <u>some</u> logic to it:

1) The <u>square</u> is something like this: $(x + \text{something})^2$ — It's basically the factorised equation (with the factors both the same), but there's something missing...

2) ...So you need to '<u>complete</u>' it by adding a number to the square to make it equal to the original equation. $(x + \text{something})^2 + d$

You'll start with something like this... ...sort the x-coefficients... ...and you'll end up with something like this.

$2x^2 + 8x - 5$ ⟹ $2(x + 2)^2 + ?$ ⟹ $2(x + 2)^2 - 13$

Lovely!

Make completing the square a bit **Easier**

There are only a few stages to completing the square — if you can't be bothered trying to understand it,
just <u>learn how to do it</u>. But I reckon it's worth spending a bit more time to get your head round it <u>properly</u>.

A) Take Out a Factor of 'a'

— take a factor of a out of the x^2 and x terms.

$f(x) = 2x^2 + 3x - 5$ ← This is in the form $ax^2 + bx + c$

This '2' is an 'a'.

$f(x) = 2\left(x^2 + \frac{3}{2}x\right) - 5$ ← Check that the bracket multiplies out to what you had before.

This is $\frac{b}{a}$

B) Rewrite the Bracket — rewrite the bracket as one bracket squared.

The number in the brackets is <u>always</u> half the old number in front of the x. $\frac{b}{2a}$

$f(x) = 2\left(x + \frac{3}{4}\right)^2 + d$ ← d is a number you have to find to make the new form equal to the old one.

Don't forget the 'squared' sign.

C) Complete the Square — find d.

To do this, <u>make the old and new equations equal each other</u>...

$2\left(x + \frac{3}{4}\right)^2 + d = 2x^2 + 3x - 5$

...and you can find d.

$2x^2 + 3x + \frac{9}{8} + d = 2x^2 + 3x - 5$

The x^2 and x bits are the same on both sides, so they can disappear.

$\frac{9}{8} + d = -5$

$\Rightarrow d = -\frac{49}{8}$

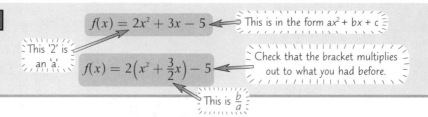

Completing the Square

A) **THE BIT IN THE BRACKETS IS ALWAYS** — $a\left(x + \frac{b}{2a}\right)^2$

B) **CALL THE NUMBER AT THE END d** — $a\left(x + \frac{b}{2a}\right)^2 + d$

C) **MAKE THE TWO FORMS EQUAL** — $ax^2 + bx + c = a\left(x + \frac{b}{2a}\right)^2 + d$

D) So the Answer is:

$f(x) = 2x^2 + 3x - 5 = 2\left(x + \frac{3}{4}\right)^2 - \frac{49}{8}$

Complete your square — it'd be root not to...

Remember — you're basically trying to write the expression as one bracket squared, but it doesn't quite work. So you have to add a number (d) to make it work. It's a bit confusing at first, but once you've learnt it you won't forget it in a hurry.

Completing the Square

Once you've completed the square, you can very quickly say <u>loads</u> about a quadratic function. And it all relies on the fact that a squared number can <u>never</u> be less than zero... <u>ever</u>.

*Completing the square can sometimes be **Useful***

This is a quadratic written as a completed square. As it's a quadratic function and the coefficient of x^2 is positive, it's a u-shaped graph.

This is a square — it can never be negative. The smallest it can be is 0.

$$f(x) = 3x^2 - 6x - 7 = 3(x - 1)^2 - 10$$

A

Find the Minimum — make the bit in the brackets equal to zero.

When the squared bit is zero, $f(x)$ reaches its minimum value. This means the graph reaches its lowest point.

$f(x) = 3(x - 1)^2 - 10$

This number here is the minimum.

$f(1) = 3(1 - 1)^2 - 10$

$f(1)$ means using $x = 1$ in the function

$f(1) = 3(0)^2 - 10 = -10$

So the minimum is -10, when $x = 1$

B

Where Does f(x) Cross the *x*-axis? — i.e. find x.

Make the completed square function equal zero.

$3(x - 1)^2 - 10 = 0$

Solve it to find where $f(x)$ crosses the x-axis.

$\Rightarrow (x - 1)^2 = \dfrac{10}{3}$

da-de-dah ... rearranging again.

$\Rightarrow x - 1 = \pm\sqrt{\dfrac{10}{3}}$

$\Rightarrow x = 1 \pm\sqrt{\dfrac{10}{3}}$

So $f(x)$ crosses the x-axis when...

$x = 1 + \sqrt{\dfrac{10}{3}} \quad \text{or} \quad x = 1 - \sqrt{\dfrac{10}{3}}$

These notes are all about graphs with positive coefficients in front of the x^2. But if the coefficient is negative, then the graph is flipped upside down (n-shaped, not u-shaped).

With this information, you can easily sketch the graph...

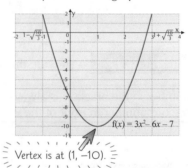

$f(x) = 3x^2 - 6x - 7$

Vertex is at (1, –10).

*Some functions don't have **Real Roots***

By completing the square, you can also quickly tell if the graph of a quadratic function ever crosses the x-axis. It'll only cross the x-axis if the function changes sign (i.e. goes from positive to negative or vice versa). Take this function...

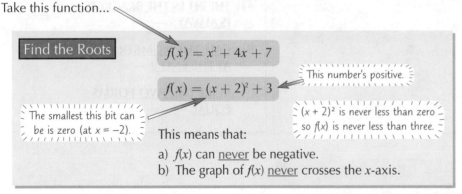

Find the Roots

$f(x) = x^2 + 4x + 7$

This number's positive.

$f(x) = (x + 2)^2 + 3$

The smallest this bit can be is zero (at $x = -2$).

$(x + 2)^2$ is never less than zero so $f(x)$ is never less than three.

This means that:

a) $f(x)$ can <u>never</u> be negative.
b) The graph of $f(x)$ <u>never</u> crosses the x-axis.

If the coefficient of x^2 is negative, you can do the same sort of thing to check whether $f(x)$ ever becomes positive.

Don't forget — two wrongs don't make a root...

You'll be pleased to know that that's the end of me trying to tell you how to do something you probably really don't want to do. Now you can push it to one side and run off to roll around in a bed of nettles... much more fun.

The Quadratic Formula

Unlike factorising, the quadratic formula <u>always</u> works... no ifs, no buts, no butts, no nothing...

The **Quadratic Formula** — a reason to be cheerful, but careful...

If you want to solve a quadratic equation $ax^2 + bx + c = 0$,
then the answers are given by this formula:

$$x = \frac{-b \pm \sqrt{b^2 - 4ac}}{2a}$$

The formula's a godsend — but use the power wisely...

If any of the coefficients (i.e. if *a*, *b* or *c*) in your quadratic equation are negative — be <u>especially</u> careful.

Always take things nice and <u>slowly</u> — don't try to rush it.

It's a good idea to write down what *a*, *b* and *c* are <u>before</u> you start plugging them into the formula.

There are a couple of minus signs in the formula — which can catch you out if you're not paying <u>attention</u>.

I shall teach you the ways of the **Formula**

EXAMPLE: Solve the quadratic equation $3x^2 - 4x = 8$, leaving your answer in surd form.

The mention of surds is a <u>big</u> clue that you should use the formula.

A **Rearrange the Equation**

Get the equation in the standard $ax^2 + bx + c = 0$ form.

$3x^2 - 4x = 8$

$3x^2 - 4x - 8 = 0$

B **Find *a*, *b* and *c***

Write down the coefficients *a*, *b* and *c* — making sure you don't forget minus signs.

$3x^2 - 4x - 8 = 0$

$a = 3 \quad b = -4 \quad c = -8$

C **Stick Them in the Formula**

Very carefully, plug these numbers into the formula. It's best to write down each stage as you do it.

$$x = \frac{-b \pm \sqrt{b^2 - 4ac}}{2a}$$

$$x = \frac{-(-4) \pm \sqrt{(-4)^2 - 4 \times 3 \times (-8)}}{2 \times 3}$$

$$x = \frac{4 \pm \sqrt{16 + 96}}{6}$$

$$x = \frac{4 \pm \sqrt{112}}{6}$$

Simplify your answer as much as possible, using the rules of surds (see page 3).

The $\pm$ sign means that we have two different expressions for *x* — which you get by replacing the $\pm$ with + and −.

$$x = \frac{2 \pm 2\sqrt{7}}{3}$$

$$x = \frac{2 + 2\sqrt{7}}{3} \quad \text{or} \quad x = \frac{2 - 2\sqrt{7}}{3}$$

Using this magic formula, I shall take over the world... ha ha ha...

Okay, maybe it's not <u>quite</u> that good... but it's really important. So learn it properly — which means spending enough time until you can just say it out loud the whole way through, with no hesitations. Or perhaps you could try singing it as loud as you can to the tune of your favourite cheesy song. Sha-la-la-la-la-la-la-ha... La-di-da... Sha-la-la-la-la-la-la-ha...

The Discriminant

By using part of the quadratic formula, you can quickly tell if a quadratic equation has two solutions, one solution, or no solutions at all. Tell me more, I hear you cry...

How Many Roots? Check the b² – 4ac bit...

$$x = \frac{-b \pm \sqrt{b^2 - 4ac}}{2a}$$

When you try to find the roots of a quadratic function, this bit in the square-root sign ($b^2 - 4ac$) can be positive, zero, or negative. It's <u>this</u> that tells you if a quadratic function has two roots, one root, or no roots.

The $b^2 - 4ac$ bit is called the <u>discriminant</u>.

<u>Because</u> — if the discriminant is positive, the formula will give you two different values — when you add or subtract the $\sqrt{b^2 - 4ac}$ bit.

<u>But</u> if it's zero, you'll only get one value, since adding or subtracting zero doesn't make any difference.

<u>And</u> if it's negative, you don't get any (real) values because you can't take the square root of a negative number.

Well, not in C1. In some areas of maths, you can actually take the square root of negative numbers and get 'imaginary' numbers. That's why we say no 'real' roots — because there are 'imaginary' roots!

It's good to be able to picture what this means:

A root is just the value of x when $y = 0$, so it's where the graph touches or crosses the x-axis.

$b^2 - 4ac > 0$	$b^2 - 4ac = 0$	$b^2 - 4ac < 0$
Two roots	One root	No roots

So the graph crosses the x-axis twice and these are the roots:

The graph just touches the x-axis from above (or from below if the x^2 coefficient is negative).

The graph doesn't touch the x-axis at all.

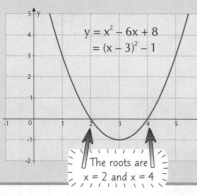

$y = x^2 - 6x + 8$
$= (x - 3)^2 - 1$

The roots are $x = 2$ and $x = 4$

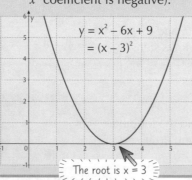

$y = x^2 - 6x + 9$
$= (x - 3)^2$

The root is $x = 3$

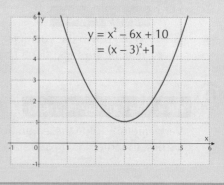

$y = x^2 - 6x + 10$
$= (x - 3)^2 + 1$

Identify a, b and c to find the Discriminant

The <u>first</u> thing you have to do when you're given a quadratic is to <u>work out</u> what a, b and c are. Make sure you get them the <u>right way round</u> — it's easy to get mixed up if the quadratic's in a <u>different order</u>.

EXAMPLE   Find the discriminant of $15 - x - 2x^2$. How many real roots does $15 - x - 2x^2$ have?

First, identify a, b and c: $a = -2$, $b = -1$ and $c = 15$ (NOT $a = 15$, $b = -1$ and $c = -2$).

Then put these values into the formula for the discriminant:

$$b^2 - 4ac = (-1)^2 - (4 \times -2 \times 15) = 1 + 120 = 121.$$

The discriminant is > 0, so $15 - x - 2x^2$ has two distinct real roots.

ha ha ha ha haaaaaa...   ha ha ha...   ha ha ha...   ha ha ha........

The Discriminant

The discriminant often comes up in exam questions — but sometimes they'll be sneaky and not actually tell you that's what you have to find. Any question that mentions roots of a quadratic will probably mean that you need to find the discriminant.

a, *b* and *c* might be **Unknown**

In exam questions, you're often given a quadratic where one or more of *a*, *b* and *c* are given in terms of an unknown (usually *k*, but sometimes *p* or *q*). This means that you'll end up with an equation or inequality for the discriminant in terms of the unknown — you might have to solve it to find the value or range of values of the unknown.

EXAMPLE Find the range of values of *k* for which: a) f(*x*) has 2 distinct roots,   b) f(*x*) has 1 root,
c) f(*x*) has no real roots, where f(*x*) = $3x^2 + 2x + k$.

First, decide what *a*, *b* and *c* are: $a = 3, b = 2, c = k$

Then work out what the discriminant is:
$$b^2 - 4ac = 2^2 - 4 \times 3 \times k$$
$$= 4 - 12k$$

These calculations are exactly the same. You don't need to do them if you've done a) because the only difference is the (in)equality symbol.

a) Two distinct roots means:
$$b^2 - 4ac > 0 \Rightarrow 4 - 12k > 0$$
$$\Rightarrow 4 > 12k$$
$$\Rightarrow k < \tfrac{1}{3}$$

b) One root means:
$$b^2 - 4ac = 0 \Rightarrow 4 - 12k = 0$$
$$\Rightarrow 4 = 12k$$
$$\Rightarrow k = \tfrac{1}{3}$$

c) No roots means:
$$b^2 - 4ac < 0 \Rightarrow 4 - 12k < 0$$
$$\Rightarrow 4 < 12k$$
$$\Rightarrow k > \tfrac{1}{3}$$

You might have to **Solve** a **Quadratic Inequality** to find *k*

When you put your values of *a*, *b* and *c* into the formula for the discriminant, you might end up with a quadratic inequality in terms of *k*. You'll have to solve this to find the range of values of *k* — there's more on this on p.23.

EXAMPLE The equation $kx^2 + (k + 3)x + 4 = 0$ has two distinct real solutions.
Show that $k^2 - 10k + 9 > 0$, and find the set of values of *k* which satisfy this inequality.

Identify *a*, *b* and *c*: $a = k, b = (k + 3)$ and $c = 4$

Then put these values into the formula for the discriminant:

$$b^2 - 4ac = (k + 3)^2 - (4 \times k \times 4) = k^2 + 6k + 9 - 16k = k^2 - 10k + 9.$$

The original equation has two distinct real solutions, so the discriminant must be > 0.

So $k^2 - 10k + 9 > 0$.

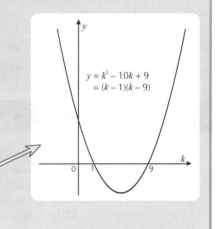

$y = k^2 - 10k + 9$
$= (k - 1)(k - 9)$

Now, to find the set of values for *k*, you have to factorise the quadratic:

$$k^2 - 10k + 9 = (k - 1)(k - 9).$$

The solutions of this equation are $k = 1$ and $k = 9$. From the graph, you can see that this is a u-shaped quadratic which is > 0 when

$k < 1$ or when $k > 9$.

I'll try not to discriminate...

Don't panic if you're not sure how to solve quadratic inequalities — they're covered in more detail on p.23. Chances are you'll get a discriminant question in the exam, so you need to know what to do. Although it might be tempting to hide under your exam desk and hope it doesn't find you, there's no escaping these questions — so get practising.

Cows

The stuff on this page isn't strictly on the syllabus. But I've included it anyway because I reckon it's really important stuff that you ought to know.

There are loads of Different Types of Cows

Dairy Cattle

Every day a dairy cow can produce up to 128 pints of milk — which can be used to make 14 lbs of cheese, 5 gallons of ice cream, or 6 lbs of butter.

The Jersey

The Jersey is a small breed best suited to pastures in high rainfall areas. It is kept for its creamy milk.

Advantages
1) Can produce creamy milk until old age.
2) Milk is the highest in fat of any dairy breed (5.2%).
3) Fairly docile, although bulls can't be trusted.

Disadvantages
1) Produces less milk than most other breeds.

The Holstein-Friesian

This breed can be found in many areas. It is kept mainly for milk.

Advantages
1) Produce more milk than any breed.
2) The breed is large, so bulls can be sold for beef.

Disadvantages
1) Milk is low in fat (3.5%).

Beef Cattle

Cows are sedentary animals who spend up to 8 hours a day chewing the cud while standing still or lying down to rest after grazing. Getting fat for people to eat.

The Angus

The Angus is best suited to areas where there is moderately high rainfall.

Advantages
1) Early maturing.
2) High ratio of meat to body weight.
3) Forages well.
4) Adaptable.

The Hereford

The Hereford matures fairly early, but later than most shorthorn breeds. All Herefords have white faces, and if a Hereford is crossbred with any other breed of cow, all the offspring will have white or partially white faces.

Advantages
1) Hardy.
2) Adaptable to different feeds.

Disadvantages
1) Susceptible to eye diseases.

Milk comes from Cows

This is really important — try not to forget it.

Milk is an emulsion of butterfat suspended in a solution of water (roughly 80%), lactose, proteins and salts. Cow's milk has a specific gravity of around 1.03.

It's pasteurised by heating it to 63° C for 30 minutes. It's then rapidly cooled and stored below 10° C.

Louis Pasteur began his experiments into 'pasteurisation' in 1856. By 1946, the vacuum pasteurisation method had been perfected, and in 1948, UHT (ultra heat-treated) pasteurisation was introduced.

cow + grass = fat cow

fat cow + milking machine ⇒ milk

You will often see cows with pieces of grass sticking out of their mouths.

SOME IMPORTANT FACTS TO REMEMBER:
- A newborn calf can walk on its own an hour after birth.
- A cow's teeth are only on the bottom of her mouth.
- While some cows can live up to 40 years, they generally don't live beyond 20.

Pantomime Cows aren't Real

If you go to see a pantomime around Christmas time, you may see a cow on stage. Don't get concerned about animal rights and exploitation of animals — it's not a real cow. Pantomime cows are just two people wearing a cow costume. Sometimes it'll be a pantomime horse instead.

The Cow
The cow is of the bovine ilk;
One end is moo,
the other, milk.
— Ogden Nash

Famous Cows and Cow Songs

Famous Cows
1) Ermintrude from the Magic Roundabout.
2) The Laughing Cow.
3) Other TV commercial cows — Anchor, Dairylea
4) The cow that jumped over the moon.
5) Greek mythology was full of gods turning themselves and their girlfriends into cattle.

Cows in Pop Music
1) Boom Boom Cow — Black Eyed Peas
2) Saturday Night at the Moo-vies — The Drifters
3) I Kissed a Cow — Katy Perry
4) Take a Cow — Rihanna
5) Cows Don't Lie — Shakira

Where's me Jersey — I'm Friesian...

Cow-milking — an underrated skill, in my opinion. As Shakespeare once wrote, 'Those who can milk cows are likely to get pretty good grades in maths exams, no word of a lie'. Well, he probably would've written something like that if he was into cows. And he would've written it because cows are helpful when you're trying to work out what a question's all about — and once you know that, you can decide the best way forward. And if you don't believe me, remember the saying of the ancient Roman Emperor Julius Caesar — 'If in doubt, draw a cow'.

'Almost' Quadratic Equations

Sometimes you'll be asked to solve equations that look really difficult, like the ones on this page. But with a bit of rearrangement and fiddling you can get them to look just like an ordinary quadratic you can solve.

Some **Nasty-looking** equations are just **Quadratics**

$$x^4 - 6x^2 + 9 = 0$$

Arrrgh. How on earth are you supposed to solve something like that? Well the answer is... with great difficulty — that's if you don't spot that you can turn it into quadratic form like this:

$$(x^2)^2 - 6(x^2) + 9 = 0$$

It still looks weird. But, if those x^2's were y's:

$$y^2 - 6y + 9 = 0$$

Now it's just a simple quadratic that you could solve in your sleep — or the exam, which would probably be more useful.

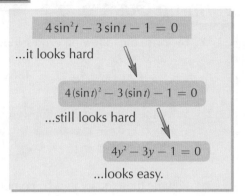

$$4\sin^2 t - 3\sin t - 1 = 0$$

...it looks hard

$$4(\sin t)^2 - 3(\sin t) - 1 = 0$$

...still looks hard

$$4y^2 - 3y - 1 = 0$$

...looks easy.

Just make a **Substitution** to **Simplify**

EXAMPLE: $2x^6 - 11x^3 + 5 = 0$

1 **Spot That It's a Quadratic**

Put it in the form: a(something)² + b(same thing) + (number) = 0.

$$2(x^3)^2 - 11(x^3) + 5 = 0$$

Now substitute x^3 for y to make it like a normal quadratic.

2 **Substitute**

let $x^3 = y$ $2y^2 - 11y + 5 = 0$

And solve this quadratic to find the values of y.

3 **Solve it**

$$2y^2 - 11y + 5 = 0$$
$$(2y - 1)(y - 5) = 0$$
$$y = \tfrac{1}{2}, \text{ or } 5$$

Now you've got the values of y, you can get the values of x.

4 **Find the Original Unknown x**

$y = \tfrac{1}{2}$, or 5   but... $y = x^3$ ← This comes from stage 2.

Which means... $x^3 = \tfrac{1}{2}$, or 5

So the answer is... $x = \sqrt[3]{\tfrac{1}{2}}, \text{ or } \sqrt[3]{5}$

Be careful with the number of solutions you get here. Depending on your substitution, you might get more than one solution <u>for each value of y</u>. e.g. if you make the subsitution $y = x^2$, there's a good chance you'll get <u>four</u> possible values for x. You have been warned...

Disguised Quadratics

1) **Put the equation in the FORM :**
a(something)²+b(same thing)+(number)=0

2) **SUBSTITUTE a new variable for the something in the brackets to get a normal-looking quadratic.**

3) **SOLVE the quadratic in the usual way — i.e. by factorising or using the quadratic formula.**

4) **Stick your answers in the substitution equation to get the values for the ORIGINAL unknown.**

Almost quadratics — almost worthwhile, almost interesting, almost...

Quadratics with delusions of grandeur. Whatever next. Anyway, there isn't much to add to what's already on this page. All you need to do is spot the substitution you can use to make your life easier — then things will be, well, easier.

C1 Section 2 — Practice Questions

Mmmm, well, quadratic equations — not exactly designed to make you fall out of your chair through laughing so hard, are they? But (and that's a huge 'but') they'll get you <u>plenty of marks</u> come that fine morning when you march confidently into the exam hall — if you know <u>what you're doing</u>. Time for some <u>practice questions</u> methinks...

Warm-up Questions

1) Factorise the following expressions. While you're doing this, <u>sing a jolly song</u> to show how much you enjoy it.
   a) $x^2 + 2x + 1$,   b) $x^2 - 13x + 30$,   c) $x^2 - 4$,   d) $3 + 2x - x^2$,
   e) $2x^2 - 7x - 4$,   f) $5x^2 + 7x - 6$.

2) Solve the following equations. And <u>sing verse two</u> of your jolly song.
   a) $x^2 - 3x + 2 = 0$,   b) $x^2 + x - 12 = 0$,   c) $2 + x - x^2 = 0$,   d) $x^2 + x - 16 = x$,
   e) $3x^2 - 15x - 14 = 4x$,   f) $4x^2 - 1 = 0$,   g) $6x^2 - 11x + 9 = 2x^2 - x + 3$.

3) Rewrite these quadratics by <u>completing the square</u>. Then state their <u>maximum</u> or <u>minimum</u> value and the <u>value of x</u> where this occurs. Also, say if and where they <u>cross the x-axis</u> — just for a laugh, like.
   a) $x^2 - 4x - 3$,   b) $3 - 3x - x^2$,   c) $2x^2 - 4x + 11$,   d) $4x^2 - 28x + 48$.

4) How many <u>roots</u> do these quadratics have? <u>Sketch</u> their graphs.
   a) $x^2 - 2x - 3 = 0$,   b) $x^2 - 6x + 9 = 0$,   c) $2x^2 + 4x + 3 = 0$.

5) Solve these quadratic equations, leaving your answers in <u>surd form</u> where necessary.   Have a peek at p.23 for help on solving a quadratic inequality.
   a) $3x^2 - 7x + 3 = 0$,   b) $2x^2 - 6x - 2 = 0$,   c) $x^2 + 4x + 6 = 12$.

6) If the quadratic equation $x^2 + kx + 4 = 0$ has <u>two roots</u>, what are the possible values of k?

7) Solve the equation $4x^4 - 5x^2 + 1 = 0$.

The warm-up questions will only get you as far as the <u>third floor</u>. And you'll have to use the stairs. To get all the way to the <u>top floor</u>, you need to take the <u>express lift</u> that is this lovely set of exam questions...

Exam Questions

1   The equation $x^2 + 2kx + 4k = 0$, where k is a non-zero integer, has equal roots.

     Find the value of k.

                                            (4 marks)

2   The equation $px^2 + (p + 3)x + 4 = 0$ has 2 distinct real solutions for x (p is a constant).

   a)   Show that $p^2 - 10p + 9 > 0$.

                                            (3 marks)

   b)   Hence find the range of possible values for p.

                                            (4 marks)

C1 Section 2 — Practice Questions

Two exam questions are <u>never enough</u> — so here are a few more...

3   Given that

$$5x^2 + nx + 14 \equiv m(x + 2)^2 + p,$$

find the values of the integers m, n and p.

(3 marks)

4   a)   Rewrite $x^2 - 12x + 15$ in the form $(x - a)^2 + b$, for integers a and b.

(2 marks)

b)   (i)   Find the minimum value of $x^2 - 12x + 15$.

(1 mark)

(ii)   State the value of x at which this minimum occurs.

(1 mark)

5   a)   Use the quadratic formula to solve the equation $x^2 - 14x + 25 = 0$.
       Leave your answer in simplified surd form.

(3 marks)

b)   Sketch the curve of $y = x^2 - 14x + 25$, giving the coordinates of the
       point where the curve crosses the x- and y-axis.

(3 marks)

c)   Hence solve the inequality $x^2 - 14x + 25 \leq 0$.

(1 mark)

6   a)   (i)   Express $10x - x^2 - 27$ in the form $-(m - x)^2 + n$, where m and n are integers.

(2 marks)

(ii)   Hence show that $10x - x^2 - 27$ is always negative.

(1 mark)

b)   (i)   State the coordinates of the maximum point of the curve $y = 10x - x^2 - 27$.

(2 marks)

(ii)   Sketch the curve, showing where the curve crosses the y-axis.

(2 marks)

7   Solve the equation $2x^{\frac{2}{5}} - 3x^{\frac{1}{5}} - 2 = 0$.

(4 marks)

Linear Inequalities

Solving <u>inequalities</u> is very similar to solving equations. You've just got to be really careful that you keep the inequality sign pointing the <u>right</u> way.

> Find the ranges of x that satisfy these inequalities:
>
> (i) $x - 3 < -1 + 2x$ (ii) $8x + 2 \geq 2x + 17$ (iii) $4 - 3x \leq 16$ (iv) $36x < 6x^2$

Sometimes the inequality sign *Changes Direction*

Like I said, these are pretty similar to solving equations — because whatever you do to one side, you have to do to the other. But multiplying or dividing by <u>negative</u> numbers <u>changes</u> the direction of the inequality sign.

> <u>Adding</u> or <u>subtracting</u> doesn't change the direction of the inequality sign

> <u>Multiplying</u> or <u>dividing</u> by something <u>positive</u> doesn't affect the inequality sign

EXAMPLE If you <u>add</u> or <u>subtract</u> something from both sides of an inequality, the inequality sign <u>doesn't</u> change direction.

EXAMPLE Multiplying or dividing both sides of an inequality by a <u>positive</u> number <u>doesn't</u> affect the direction of the inequality sign.

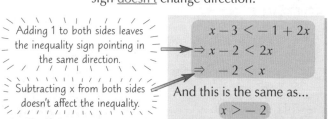

Adding 1 to both sides leaves the inequality sign pointing in the same direction.

Subtracting x from both sides doesn't affect the inequality.

$$x - 3 < -1 + 2x$$
$$\Rightarrow x - 2 < 2x$$
$$\Rightarrow -2 < x$$

And this is the same as...
$$x > -2$$

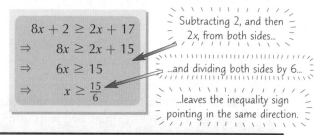

Subtracting 2, and then 2x, from both sides...

$$8x + 2 \geq 2x + 17$$
$$\Rightarrow \quad 8x \geq 2x + 15$$
$$\Rightarrow \quad 6x \geq 15$$
$$\Rightarrow \quad x \geq \frac{15}{6}$$

...and dividing both sides by 6...

...leaves the inequality sign pointing in the same direction.

But *Change* the inequality if you *Multiply* or *Divide* by something *Negative*

But multiplying or dividing both sides of an inequality by a <u>negative</u> number <u>changes</u> the direction of the inequality.

EXAMPLE
$$4 - 3x \leq 16$$
$$\Rightarrow -3x \leq 12$$
$$\Rightarrow \quad x \geq -4$$

Subtract 4 from both sides.

Then divide both sides by –3 — but <u>change</u> the direction of the inequality.

> The <u>reason</u> for the sign changing direction is because it's just the same as swapping everything from one side to the other:
> $-3x \leq 12 \Rightarrow -12 \leq 3x \Rightarrow x \geq -4$

Don't divide both sides by *Variables* — like *x* and *y*

You've got to be really careful when you divide by things that <u>might</u> be negative — well basically, don't do it.

EXAMPLE $36x < 6x^2$

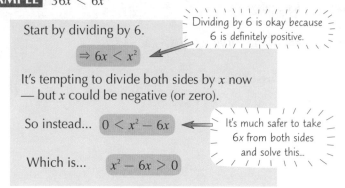

Start by dividing by 6.
$$\Rightarrow 6x < x^2$$

Dividing by 6 is okay because 6 is definitely positive.

It's tempting to divide both sides by x now — but x could be negative (or zero).

So instead... $0 < x^2 - 6x$

It's much safer to take 6x from both sides and solve this...

Which is... $x^2 - 6x > 0$

> ### *Two Types of Inequality Sign*
>
> There are two kinds of inequality sign:
>
> Type 1: $<$ — less than
>
> $>$ — greater than
>
> Type 2: $\leq$ — less than or equal to
>
> $\geq$ — greater than or equal to
>
> **Whatever type the question uses — use the same kind all the way through your answer.**

See the next page for more on solving quadratic inequalities.

So no one knows we've arrived safely — splendid...

So just remember — inequalities are just like normal equations except that you have to reverse the sign when multiplying or dividing by a negative number. And <u>don't</u> divide both sides by variables. (You should know not to do this with normal equations anyway because the variable could be <u>zero</u>.) OK — lecture's over.

Quadratic Inequalities

With quadratic inequalities, you're best off drawing the <u>graph</u> and taking it from there.

Draw a **Graph** to solve a **Quadratic** inequality

EXAMPLE Find the ranges of x which satisfy these inequalities:

① $-x^2 + 2x + 4 \geq 1$ ② $2x^2 - x - 3 > 0$

First rewrite the inequality with <u>zero</u> on one side.
$$-x^2 + 2x + 3 \geq 0$$

Then <u>draw</u> the graph of: $y = -x^2 + 2x + 3$

So find where it crosses the x-axis (i.e. where $y = 0$):
$$-x^2 + 2x + 3 \Rightarrow x^2 - 2x - 3 = 0$$
$$\Rightarrow (x + 1)(x - 3) = 0$$
$$\Rightarrow x = -1 \text{ or } x = 3$$

And the coefficient of x^2 is negative, so the graph is n-shaped. So it looks like this:

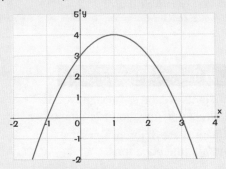

You're interested in when this is <u>positive or zero</u>, i.e. when it's above the x-axis.

From the graph, this is when x is <u>between –1 and 3</u> (including those points). So your answer is...

$-x^2 + 2x + 4 \geq 1$ when $-1 \leq x \leq 3$.

This one already has zero on one side, so <u>draw</u> the graph of $y = 2x^2 - x - 3$.

Find where it crosses the x-axis:
$$2x^2 - x - 3 = 0$$
$$\Rightarrow (2x - 3)(x + 1) = 0$$
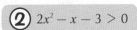 Factorise it to find the roots.
$$\Rightarrow x = \tfrac{3}{2} \text{ or } x = -1$$

And the coefficient of x^2 is positive, so the graph is u-shaped. And looks like this:

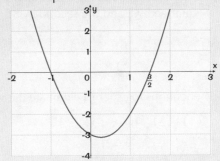

You need to say when this is <u>positive</u>. Looking at the graph, there are two parts of the x-axis where this is true — when x is <u>less than –1</u> and when x is <u>greater than 3/2</u>. So your answer is:

$2x^2 - x - 3 > 0$ when $x < -1$ or $x > \tfrac{3}{2}$.

EXAMPLE (REVISITED) On the last page you had to solve $36x < 6x^2$.

$$36x < 6x^2$$
equation 1 $\Rightarrow 6x < x^2$
$$\Rightarrow 0 < x^2 - 6x$$

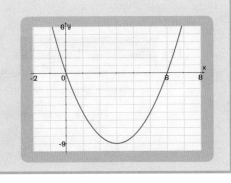

So draw the graph of
$$y = x^2 - 6x = x(x - 6)$$

And this is <u>positive</u> when $x < 0$ or $x > 6$.

If you divide by x in equation 1, you'd only get half the solution — you'd miss the $x < 0$ part.

That's nonsense — I can see perfectly...

Call me sad, but I reckon these questions are pretty cool. They look a lot more difficult than they actually are and you get to draw a picture. Wow! When you do the graph, the important thing is to find where it crosses the x-axis (you don't need to know where it crosses the y-axis) and make sure you draw it the right way up. Then you just need to decide which bit of the graph you want. It'll either be the range(s) of x where the graph is below the x-axis or the range(s) where it's above. And this depends on the inequality sign.

Simultaneous Equations

Solving simultaneous equations means finding the answers to two equations <u>at the same time</u> — i.e. finding values for x and y for which both equations are true. And it's one of those things that you'll have to do <u>again and again</u> — so it's definitely worth practising them until you feel <u>really confident</u>.

① $3x + 5y = -4$
② $-2x + 3y = 9$

This is how simultaneous equations are usually shown. It's a good idea to label them as equation ① and equation ② — so you know which one you're working with.

But they'll look different sometimes, maybe like this. Make sure you rearrange them as '$ax + by = c$'.

$4 + 5y = -3x$
$-2x = 9 - 3y$

rearrange as
$ax + by = c$

$3x + 5y = -4$
$-2x + 3y = 9$

Solving them by Elimination

Elimination is a lovely method. It's really quick when you get the hang of it — you'll be doing virtually all of it in your head.

EXAMPLE:

① $3x + 5y = -4$
② $-2x + 3y = 9$

To get the x's to match, you need to multiply the first equation by 2 and the second by 3:

①×2 $\quad 6x + 10y = -8$
②×3 $\quad -6x + 9y = 27$

Add the equations together to eliminate the x's.

①+② $\quad 19y = 19$
$\qquad\quad y = 1$

So y is 1. Now stick that value for y into one of the equations to find x:

$y = 1$ in ① $\Rightarrow 3x + 5 = -4$
$\qquad\qquad\qquad 3x = -9$
$\qquad\qquad\qquad x = -3$

So the solution is $x = -3$, $y = 1$.

But you should always...

A — Match the Coefficients

Multiply the equations by numbers that will make either the x's or the y's match in the two equations. (Ignoring minus signs.)

Go for the lowest common multiple (LCM). e.g. LCM of 2 and 3 is 6.

B — Eliminate to Find One Variable

If the coefficients are the <u>same</u> sign, you'll need to <u>subtract</u> one equation from the other.
If the coefficients are <u>different</u> signs, you need to <u>add</u> the equations.

C — Find the Variable You Eliminated

When you've found one variable, put its value into one of the original equations so you can find the other variable.

D — Check Your Answer

...by putting these values into the other equation.

② $-2x + 3y = 9$
$x = -3$
$y = 1$

$-2 \times (-3) + 3 \times 1 = 6 + 3 = 9$

If these two numbers are the same, then the values you've got for the variables are right.

Elimination Method

1) **Match the coefficients**
2) **Eliminate and then solve for one variable**
3) **Find the other variable (that you eliminated)**
4) **Check your answer**

Eliminate your social life — do AS-level maths

This is a fairly basic method that won't be new to you. So make sure you know it. The only possibly tricky bit is <u>matching the coefficients</u> — work out the lowest common multiple of the coefficients of x, say, then multiply the equations to get this number in front of each x.

Simultaneous Equations with Quadratics

Elimination is great for simple equations. But it won't always work. Sometimes one of the equations has not just x's and y's in it — but bits with x^2 and y^2 as well. When this happens, you can only use the substitution method.

Use Substitution if one equation is Quadratic

EXAMPLE:

$-x + 2y = 5$ ——— ① ← The linear equation — with only x's and y's in.

$x^2 + y^2 = 25$ ——— ② ← The quadratic equation — with some x^2 and y^2 bits in.

Rearrange the linear equation so that either x or y is on its own on one side of the equals sign.

$$① -x + 2y = 5$$
$$\Rightarrow x = 2y - 5$$

Substitute this expression into the quadratic equation...

Sub into ②: $x^2 + y^2 = 25$
$$\Rightarrow (2y - 5)^2 + y^2 = 25$$

...and then rearrange this into the form $ax^2 + bx + c = 0$, so you can solve it — either by factorising or using the quadratic formula.

$$\Rightarrow (4y^2 - 20y + 25) + y^2 = 25$$
$$\Rightarrow 5y^2 - 20y = 0$$
$$\Rightarrow 5y(y - 4) = 0$$
$$\Rightarrow y = 0 \text{ or } y = 4$$

One Quadratic and One Linear Eqn

1) **Isolate variable in linear equation**
   Rearrange the linear equation
   to get either x or y on its own.

2) **Substitute into quadratic equation**
   — to get a quadratic equation
   in just one variable.

3) **Solve to get values for one variable**
   — either by factorising or using
   the quadratic formula.

4) **Stick these values in the linear equation**
   — to find corresponding values
   for the other variable.

Finally put both these values back into the linear equation to find corresponding values for x:

When $y = 0$: $-x + 2y = 5$ ①
$$\Rightarrow x = -5$$

When $y = 4$: $-x + 2y = 5$ ①
$$\Rightarrow -x + 8 = 5$$
$$\Rightarrow x = 3$$

So the solutions to the simultaneous equations are: $x = -5$, $y = 0$ and $x = 3$, $y = 4$.

As usual, check your answers by putting these values back into the original equations.

Check Your Answer

$x = -5$, $y = 0$: $-(-5) + 2 \times 0 = 5$ ✓
$$(-5)^2 + 0^2 = 25 ✓$$

$x = 3$, $y = 4$: $-(3) + 2 \times 4 = 5$ ✓
$$3^2 + 4^2 = 25 ✓$$

$y = x^2$ — a match-winning substitution...

The quadratic equation above is actually a circle about the origin with radius 5. (There's more about circles on p34-35.) The linear equation is just a standard straight line. So what you're actually finding here are the two points where the line passes through the circle. And these turn out to be (–5, 0) and (3, 4). See the graph.
(I thought you might appreciate seeing a graph that wasn't a line or a parabola for a change.)

Geometric Interpretation

When you have to interpret something <u>geometrically</u>, you have to draw a picture and 'say what you see'.

Two Solutions — Two points of Intersection

EXAMPLE

$$y = x^2 - 4x + 5 \quad \text{①}$$
$$y = 2x - 3 \quad \text{②}$$

SOLUTION Substitute expression for y from ② into ①:

$$2x - 3 = x^2 - 4x + 5$$

Rearrange and solve:

$$x^2 - 6x + 8 = 0$$
$$(x - 2)(x - 4) = 0$$
$$x = 2 \text{ or } x = 4$$

In ② gives:
$$x = 2 \Rightarrow y = 2 \times 2 - 3 = 1$$
$$x = 4 \Rightarrow y = 2 \times 4 - 3 = 5$$

There are 2 pairs of solutions: $x = 2, y = 1$ and $x = 4, y = 5$

Geometric Interpretation

So from solving the simultaneous equations, you know that the graphs meet in <u>two places</u> — the points (2, 1) and (4, 5).

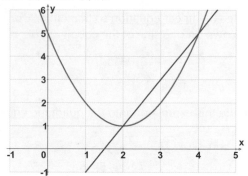

One Solution — One point of Intersection

EXAMPLE

$$y = x^2 - 4x + 5 \quad \text{①}$$
$$y = 2x - 4 \quad \text{②}$$

SOLUTION Substitute ② in ①:

$$2x - 4 = x^2 - 4x + 5$$

Rearrange and solve:
$$x^2 - 6x + 9 = 0$$
$$(x - 3)^2 = 0$$
$$x = 3$$

Double root — i.e. you only get 1 solution from the quadratic.

In Equation ② gives:
$$y = 2 \times 3 - 4$$
$$y = 2$$

There's 1 solution: $x = 3, y = 2$

Geometric Interpretation

Since the equations have only one solution, the two graphs only meet at one point — (3, 2). The straight line is a <u>tangent</u> to the curve.

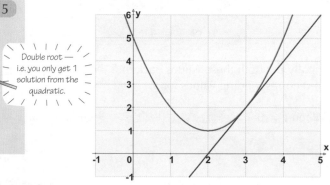

No Solutions means the Graphs Never Meet

EXAMPLE

$$y = x^2 - 4x + 5 \quad \text{①}$$
$$y = 2x - 5 \quad \text{②}$$

SOLUTION Substitute ② in ①:

$$2x - 5 = x^2 - 4x + 5$$

Rearrange and try to solve with the quadratic formula:
$$x^2 - 6x + 10 = 0$$
$$b^2 - 4ac = (-6)^2 - 4 \cdot 10$$
$$= 36 - 40 = -4$$

$b^2 - 4ac < 0$, so the quadratic has no roots.
So the simultaneous equations have no solutions.

Geometric Interpretation

The equations have no solutions — the graphs never meet.

Geometric Interpretation? Frankly my dear, I don't give a damn...

There are some lovely simultaneous equation practice questions on the next page.

C1 Section 3 — Practice Questions

What's that I hear you cry? You want practice questions — and <u>lots of them</u>. Well, it just so happens I've got a <u>few here</u>.
For quadratic inequalities, my advice is, 'if you're not sure, draw a picture — even if it's not accurate'.
And as for simultaneous equations — well, just <u>don't rush them</u>.

Warm-up Questions

1) Solve a) $7x - 4 > 2x - 42$,   b) $12y - 3 \leq 4y + 4$,   c) $9y - 4 \geq 17y + 2$.

2) Find the <u>ranges of x</u> that satisfy these inequalities:
     a) $x + 6 < 5x - 4$,   b) $4x - 2 > x - 14$,   c) $7 - x \leq 4 - 2x$

3) Find the <u>ranges of x</u> that satisfy the following inequalities. (And watch that you use the <u>right kind</u> of inequality sign in your answers.)
     a) $3x^2 - 5x - 2 \leq 0$,   b) $x^2 + 2x + 7 > 4x + 9$,   c) $3x^2 + 7x + 4 \geq 2(x^2 + x - 1)$.

4) Find the ranges of x that satisfy these <u>jokers</u>:
     a) $x^2 + 3x - 1 \geq x + 2$,   b) $2x^2 > x + 1$,   c) $3x^2 - 12 < x^2 - 2x$

5) Solve these sets of simultaneous equations:
     a) $3x - 4y = 7$ and $-2x + 7y = -22$,   b) $2x - 3y = \frac{11}{12}$ and $x + y = -\frac{7}{12}$

6) Find where possible (and that's a bit of a <u>clue</u>) the solutions to these sets of simultaneous equations. <u>Interpret</u> your answers <u>geometrically</u>.
     a) $y = x^2 - 7x + 4$ b) $y = 30 - 6x + 2x^2$ c) $x^2 + 2y^2 - 3 = 0$
        $2x - y - 10 = 0$ $y = 2(x + 11)$ $y = 2x + 4$

7) <u>A bit trickier</u> — find where the following lines <u>meet</u>:
a) $y = 3x - 4$ and $y = 7x - 5$
b) $y = 13 - 2x$ and $7x - y - 23 = 0$
c) $2x - 3y + 4 = 0$ and $x - 2y + 1 = 0$

I know, I know. Those questions <u>weren't enough</u> for you. Not to worry, there are plenty more
— and the next set are <u>exam-style</u> questions. Try to contain your excitement.

Exam Questions

1   For the inequalities below, find the set of values for x:

     a) $3x + 2 \leq x + 6$,
                                     (2 marks)

     b) $20 - x - x^2 > 0$,
                                       (4 marks)

     c) $3x + 2 \leq x + 6$ and $20 - x - x^2 > 0$.
                                       (1 mark)

C1 Section 3 — Practice Questions

The world is full of inequality and injustice. We need to <u>put a stop to it now</u>. The first thing we need to do is...
Oh, sorry, that's not what they meant by "solve the inequality". And I'd just come up with a solution for world peace.

2 Solve the inequalities:

　　a) $3 \leq 2p + 5 \leq 15$,

(3 marks)

　　b) $q^2 - 9 > 0$.

(4 marks)

3 a) Factorise $3x^2 - 13x - 10$.

(1 mark)

　　b) Hence, or otherwise, solve $3x^2 - 13x - 10 \leq 0$.

(3 marks)

4 Find the coordinates of intersection for the following curve and line:
$$x^2 + 2y^2 = 36, \quad x + y = 6$$

(6 marks)

5 The curve C has equation $y = -x^2 + 3$ and the line l has equation $y = -2x + 4$.

　　a) Find the coordinates of the point (or points) of intersection of C and l.

(4 marks)

　　b) Sketch the graphs of C and l on the same axes, clearly showing
　　　where the graphs intersect the x- and y- axes.

(5 marks)

6 The line l has equation $y = 2x - 3$ and the curve C has equation $y = (x + 2)(x - 4)$.

　　a) Sketch the line l and the curve C on the same axes, showing the coordinates
　　　of the x- and y- intercepts.

(5 marks)

　　b) Show that the x-coordinates of the points of intersection of l and C satisfy the equation
　　　$x^2 - 4x - 5 = 0$.

(2 marks)

　　c) Hence, or otherwise, find the points of intersection of l and C.

(4 marks)

Coordinate Geometry

Welcome to geometry club... nice — today I shall be mostly talking about straight lines...

Finding the equation of a line Through Two Points

If you get through your exam without having to find the equation of a line through two points, I'm a Dutchman.

EXAMPLE Find the equation of the line that passes through the points (–3, 10) and (1, 4), and write it in the forms:

$$y - y_1 = m(x - x_1)$$

$$y = mx + c$$

$$ax + by + c = 0$$

— where a, b and c are <u>integers</u>.

You might be asked to write the equation of a line in <u>any</u> of these forms — but they're all similar.
Basically, if you find an equation in one form — you can easily <u>convert</u> it into either of the others.

The **Easiest** to find is $y - y_1 = m(x - x_1)$...

Point 1 is (–3, 10) and Point 2 is (1, 4).

Label the Points Label Point 1 as (x_1, y_1) and Point 2 as (x_2, y_2).

Point 1 — $(x_1, y_1) = (-3, 10)$

Point 2 — $(x_2, y_2) = (1, 4)$

> It doesn't matter which way round you label them.

Find the Gradient Find the <u>gradient</u> of the line m — this is $m = \frac{y_2 - y_1}{x_2 - x_1}$.

$$m = \frac{4 - 10}{1 - (-3)} = \frac{-6}{4} = -\frac{3}{2}$$

> Be careful here, y goes on the top, x on the bottom.

Write Down the Equation <u>Write down</u> the equation of the line, using the coordinates x_1 and y_1 — this is just $y - y_1 = m(x - x_1)$.

$x_1 = -3$ and $y_1 = 10$ ⟹

$$y - 10 = -\frac{3}{2}(x - (-3))$$

$$y - 10 = -\frac{3}{2}(x + 3)$$

...and **Rearrange** this to get the other two forms:

For the form $y = mx + c$, take everything except the y over to the right.

$$y - 10 = -\frac{3}{2}(x + 3)$$

$$\Rightarrow y = -\frac{3}{2}x - \frac{9}{2} + 10$$

$$\Rightarrow y = -\frac{3}{2}x + \frac{11}{2}$$

Equations of Lines

1) **LABEL** the points (x_1, y_1) and (x_2, y_2).

2) **GRADIENT** — find it and call it m.

3) **WRITE DOWN THE EQUATION** using $y - y_1 = m(x - x_1)$

4) **CONVERT** to one of the other forms, if necessary.

To find the form $ax + by + c = 0$, take everything over to one side — and then get rid of any fractions.

> Multiply the whole equation by 2 to get rid of the 2's on the bottom line.

$$y = -\frac{3}{2}x + \frac{11}{2}$$

$$\Rightarrow \frac{3}{2}x + y - \frac{11}{2} = 0$$

$$\Rightarrow 3x + 2y - 11 = 0$$

> If you end up with an equation like $\frac{3}{2}x - \frac{4}{3}y + 6 = 0$, where you've got a 2 and a 3 on the bottom of the fractions — multiply everything by the <u>lowest common multiple</u> of 2 and 3, i.e. 6.

There ain't nuffink to this geometry lark, Mister...

This is the sort of stuff that looks hard but is actually pretty easy. Finding the equation of a line in that first form really is a piece of cake — the only thing you have to be careful of is when a point has a <u>negative coordinate</u> (or two). In that case, you've just got to make sure you do the subtractions properly when you work out the gradient. See, this stuff ain't so bad...

Coordinate Geometry

This page is based around two really important facts that you've got to know — one about <u>parallel lines</u>, one about <u>perpendicular lines</u>. It's really a page of unparalleled excitement...

Two more lines...

Line l_1
$3x - 4y - 7 = 0$
$y = \frac{3}{4}x - \frac{7}{4}$

Line l_2
$x - 3y - 3 = 0$
$y = \frac{1}{3}x - 1$

...and two points...

Point A $(3, -1)$

Point B $(-2, 4)$

Parallel lines have equal *Gradient*

That's what makes them parallel — the fact that the gradients are the same.

EXAMPLE Find the line parallel to l_1 that passes through the point A $(3, -1)$.

Parallel lines have the <u>same gradient</u>.

The original equation is this: $y = \frac{3}{4}x - \frac{7}{4}$

So the new equation will be this: $y = \frac{3}{4}x + c$

We just need to find c.

We know that the line passes through A, so at this point x will be 3, and y will be -1.

Stick these values into the equation to find c.

$$-1 = \frac{3}{4} \times 3 + c$$

$$\Rightarrow c = -1 - \frac{9}{4} = -\frac{13}{4}$$

So the equation of the line is... $y = \frac{3}{4}x - \frac{13}{4}$

And if you're only given the $ax + by + c = 0$ form it's even easier:

The <u>original</u> line is: $3x - 4y - 7 = 0$

So the <u>new</u> line is: $3x - 4y - k = 0$

Then just use the values of x and y at the point A to find k...

$$3 \times 3 - 4 \times (-1) - k = 0$$

$$\Rightarrow 13 - k = 0$$

$$\Rightarrow k = 13$$

So the equation is: $3x - 4y - 13 = 0$

The gradient of a *Perpendicular* line is: $-1 \div$ the Other Gradient

Finding <u>perpendicular</u> lines (or '<u>normals</u>') is just as easy as finding parallel lines — as long as you remember the gradient of the perpendicular line is <u>$-1 \div$ the gradient of the other one</u>.

EXAMPLE Find the line perpendicular to l_2 that passes through the point B $(-2, 4)$.

l_2 has equation: $y = \frac{1}{3}x - 1$

So if the equation of the new line is $y = mx + c$, then

$$m = -1 \div \frac{1}{3}$$

$$\Rightarrow m = -3$$

Since the gradient of a perpendicular line is: $-1 \div$ the other one.

Also... $4 = (-3) \times (-2) + c$

$$\Rightarrow c = 4 - 6 = -2$$

Putting the coordinates of B(−2, 4) into $y = mx + c$.

So the equation of the line is...

$$y = -3x - 2$$

Or if you start with: l_2 $\quad x - 3y - 3 = 0$

To find a perpendicular line, swap these two numbers around, and change the sign of <u>one of them</u>. (So here, 1 and −3 become 3 and 1.)

So the new line has equation...

$$3x + y + d = 0$$

Or you could have used $-3x - y + d = 0$.

But... $3 \times (-2) + 4 + d = 0$

$$\Rightarrow d = 2$$

Using the coordinates of point B.

And so the equation of the <u>perpendicular</u> line is...

$$3x + y + 2 = 0$$

Wowzers — parallel lines on the same graph dimension...

This looks more complicated than it actually is. All you're doing is finding the equation of a straight line through a <u>certain point</u> — the only added complication is that you have to find the gradient first. And there's another way to remember how to find the gradient of a normal — just remember that the gradients of perpendicular lines multiply together to make −1.

Equations of Straight Lines

Now you're all clued up on the equations of straight lines, it's time to move onto <u>line segments</u>. Instead of going on forever, a line segment is the <u>part of a line</u> between two <u>end points</u>, and there's all sorts of <u>cool stuff</u> you can find out about them.

Find the **Mid-Point** by finding the **Average** of the **End Points**

In the exam you could be asked to find the mid-point of a line segment.
To do this, just <u>add</u> the coordinates of the end-points of the line segment together, then <u>divide by two</u>:

> **EXAMPLE** Points A and B are given by the coordinates (7, 4) and (–1, –2) respectively.
> M is the mid-point of the line segment AB. Find the coordinates of M.

Take the coordinates of A and B and <u>add them</u> together:

$$(7, 4) + (-1, -2) = (7 - 1, 4 - 2) = (6, 2)$$

Now <u>divide by two</u>:

$$\left(\tfrac{6}{2}, \tfrac{2}{2}\right) = (3, 1)$$

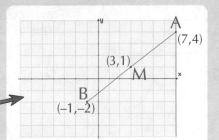

So the mid-point of AB has coordinates (3, 1)

Use **Pythagoras** to find the **Distance** between two points

You may also be asked to find the <u>distance</u> between two points, (i.e. the <u>length</u> of a line segment).
Luckily, there's a formula you can use:

$$d = \sqrt{(x_2 - x_1)^2 + (y_2 - y_1)^2}$$

The formula comes from using Pythagoras' theorem.

> **EXAMPLE** A line segment has endpoints P and Q, which have coordinates
> (6, 2) and (–1, 0) respectively. Find the length of PQ.

You'd get exactly the same answer if you took Q as (x_1, y_1) and P as (x_2, y_2).

Take point P as (x_1, y_1) and Q as (x_2, y_2).

So $x_1 = 6, x_2 = -1, y_1 = 2$ and $y_2 = 0$. Plugging these into the formula gives:

$$d = \sqrt{(-1 - 6)^2 + (0 - 2)^2} = \sqrt{(-7)^2 + (-2)^2} = \sqrt{49 + 4} = \sqrt{53}$$

So the length of PQ is $\sqrt{53}$

> **EXAMPLE** The point U has coordinates (3, k), and the point V has coordinates (15, 6).
> UV has length 13. Find all possible values of k.

Substituting into the equation gives: $13 = \sqrt{(15 - 3)^2 + (6 - k)^2} = \sqrt{12^2 + (6 - k)^2}$

Squaring both sides:
$$13^2 = 12^2 + (6 - k)^2$$
$$169 = 144 + (6 - k)^2$$
$$25 = (6 - k)^2$$
$$25 = 36 - 12k + k^2$$
$$k^2 - 12k + 11 = 0$$
$$(k - 1)(k - 11) = 0 \qquad \text{So } k = 1 \text{ or } k = 11$$

CGP — Coordinate Geometry Practitioners...

As long as you know how to add, subtract, square and square root then you should be fine with the stuff on this page. If not, then you could always try drawing the line and measuring it with a ruler — although it probably won't get you the right answer. Or any marks. Actually, you're best off steering clear of that method altogether.

Curve Sketching

A picture speaks a thousand words... and <u>graphs</u> are what pass for pictures in maths. They're dead useful in getting your head round tricky questions, and time spent learning how to sketch graphs is time well spent.

The graph of *y = kxⁿ* is a different shape for different *k* and *n*

Usually, you only need a <u>rough</u> sketch of a graph — so just knowing the basic shapes of these graphs will do.

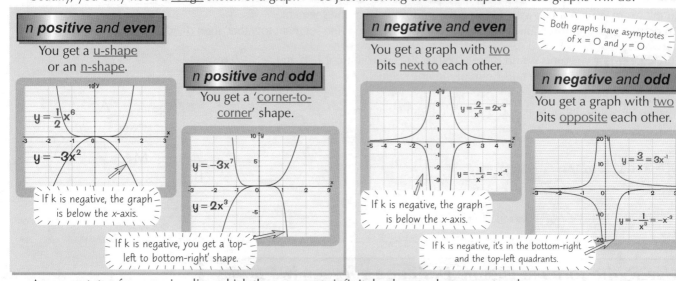

n positive and even

You get a <u>u-shape</u> or an <u>n-shape</u>.

$y = \frac{1}{2}x^6$

$y = -3x^2$

> If k is negative, the graph is below the x-axis.

n positive and odd

You get a 'corner-to-corner' shape.

$y = -3x^7$

$y = 2x^3$

> If k is negative, you get a 'top-left to bottom-right' shape.

n negative and even

You get a graph with <u>two</u> bits <u>next to</u> each other.

$y = \frac{2}{x^2} = 2x^{-2}$

$y = -\frac{1}{x^4} = -x^{-4}$

> If k is negative, the graph is below the x-axis.

> Both graphs have asymptotes of x = 0 and y = 0

n negative and odd

You get a graph with <u>two</u> bits <u>opposite</u> each other.

$y = \frac{3}{x} = 3x^{-1}$

$y = -\frac{1}{x^3} = -x^{-3}$

> If k is negative, it's in the bottom-right and the top-left quadrants.

An <u>asymptote</u> of a curve is a <u>line</u> which the curve gets <u>infinitely close</u> to, but <u>never touches</u>.

If you know the **Factors** of a cubic — the graph's easy to **Sketch**

A cubic function has an x^3 term in it, and all cubics have '<u>bottom-left to top-right</u>' shape — or a '<u>top-left to bottom-right</u>' shape if the coefficient of x^3 is <u>negative</u>.

If you know the <u>factors</u> of a cubic, the graph is easy to sketch — just find where the function is <u>zero</u>.

EXAMPLE Sketch the graphs of the following <u>cubic</u> functions.

(i) $f(x) = x(x-1)(2x+1)$ (ii) $g(x) = (1-x)(x^2-2x+2)$ (iii) $h(x) = (x-3)^2(x+1)$ (iv) $m(x) = (2-x)^3$

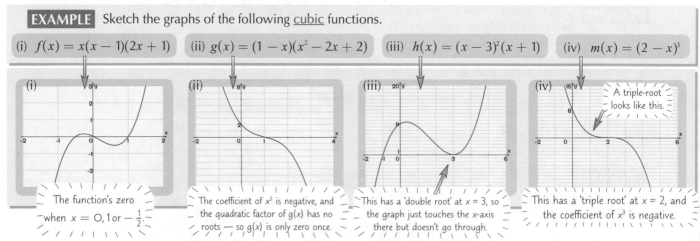

(i)

> The function's zero when $x = 0, 1$ or $-\frac{1}{2}$.

(ii)

> The coefficient of x^3 is negative, and the quadratic factor of g(x) has no roots — so g(x) is only zero once.

(iii)

> This has a 'double root' at $x = 3$, so the graph just touches the x-axis there but doesn't go through.

(iv)

> A triple-root looks like this.

> This has a 'triple root' at $x = 2$, and the coefficient of x^3 is negative.

The graph of *y = k√x* is a *u-shape* on its *Side*

The graph of $y = k\sqrt{x}$ is a <u>u-shape</u> on its side. Kind of like a <u>c-shape</u>. This makes sense really, because if $y = k\sqrt{x}$, then $x = \frac{1}{k^2}y^2$ — and this is just a normal <u>quadratic</u> with the x and y switched round.

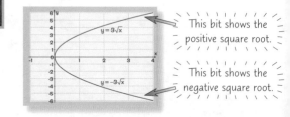

$y = 3\sqrt{x}$

$y = -3\sqrt{x}$

> This bit shows the positive square root.

> This bit shows the negative square root.

Graphs, graphs, graphs — you can never have too many graphs...

It may seem like a lot to remember, but graphs can really help you get your head round a question — a quick sketch can throw a helluva lot of light on a problem that's got you completely stumped. So being able to draw these graphs won't just help with an actual graph-sketching question — it could help with loads of others too. Got to be worth learning.

Graph Transformations

Suppose you start with any old function f(x). Then you can transform (change) it in three ways — by translating it, stretching or reflecting it.

$$y = f(x)$$

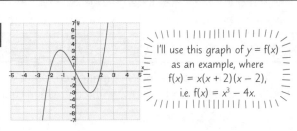

I'll use this graph of $y = f(x)$ as an example, where $f(x) = x(x + 2)(x - 2)$, i.e. $f(x) = x^3 - 4x$.

Translations are caused by Adding things

$y = f(x) + a$

Adding a number to the whole function translates the graph in the y-direction.

1) If a > 0, the graph goes upwards.

2) If a < 0, the graph goes downwards.

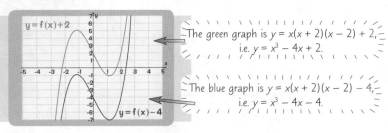

The green graph is $y = x(x + 2)(x - 2) + 2$, i.e. $y = x^3 - 4x + 2$.

The blue graph is $y = x(x + 2)(x - 2) - 4$, i.e. $y = x^3 - 4x - 4$.

$y = f(x + a)$

Writing '$x + a$' instead of 'x' means the graph moves sideways ("translated in the x-direction").

1) If a > 0, the graph goes to the left.

2) If a < 0, the graph goes to the right.

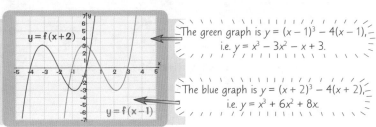

The green graph is $y = (x - 1)^3 - 4(x - 1)$, i.e. $y = x^3 - 3x^2 - x + 3$.

The blue graph is $y = (x + 2)^3 - 4(x + 2)$, i.e. $y = x^3 + 6x^2 + 8x$.

Stretches and Reflections are caused by Multiplying things

$y = af(x)$

Multiplying the whole function stretches, squeezes or reflects the graph vertically.

1) Negative values of 'a' reflect the basic shape in the x-axis.

2) If a > 1 or a < -1 (i.e. |a| > 1) the graph is stretched vertically.

3) If -1 < a < 1 (i.e. |a| < 1) the graph is squashed vertically.

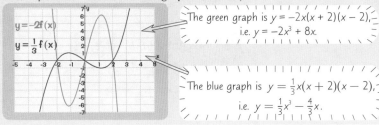

The green graph is $y = -2x(x + 2)(x - 2)$, i.e. $y = -2x^3 + 8x$.

The blue graph is $y = \frac{1}{3}x(x + 2)(x - 2)$, i.e. $y = \frac{1}{3}x^3 - \frac{4}{3}x$.

$y = f(ax)$

Writing 'ax' instead of 'x' stretches, squeezes or reflects the graph horizontally.

1) Negative values of 'a' reflect the basic shape in the y-axis.

2) If a > 1 or a < -1 (i.e. if |a| > 1) the graph is squashed horizontally.

3) If -1 < a < 1 (i.e. if |a| < 1) the graph is stretched horizontally.

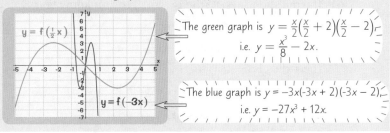

The green graph is $y = \frac{x}{2}\left(\frac{x}{2} + 2\right)\left(\frac{x}{2} - 2\right)$, i.e. $y = \frac{x^3}{8} - 2x$.

The blue graph is $y = -3x(-3x + 2)(-3x - 2)$, i.e. $y = -27x^3 + 12x$.

Circles

I always say a <u>beautiful shape</u> deserves a <u>beautiful formula</u>, and here you've got one of my favourite double-acts...

Equation of a circle: $(x - a)^2 + (y - b)^2 = r^2$

The equation of a circle looks complicated, but it's all based on Pythagoras' theorem.
Take a look at the circle below, with centre (6, 4) and radius 3.

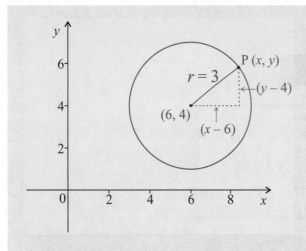

Joining a point P (x, y) on the circumference of the circle to its centre (6, 4), we can create a <u>right-angled triangle</u>.

Now let's see what happens if we use <u>Pythagoras' theorem</u>:

$$(x - 6)^2 + (y - 4)^2 = 3^2$$

or: $(x - 6)^2 + (y - 4)^2 = 9$

This is the equation for the circle. It's as easy as that.

In general, a circle with radius r and centre (a, b) has the equation: $(x - a)^2 + (y - b)^2 = r^2$

EXAMPLE:

i) What is the centre and radius of the circle with equation $(x - 2)^2 + (y + 3)^2 = 16$

ii) Write down the equation of the circle with centre (–4, 2) and radius 6.

SOLUTION:

i) Comparing $(x - 2)^2 + (y + 3)^2 = 16$ with the general form:

$$(x - a)^2 + (y - b)^2 = r^2$$

then $a = 2$, $b = -3$ and $r = 4$.

So the centre (a, b) is: (2, –3)

and the radius (r) is: 4.

And as if by magic, here it is.

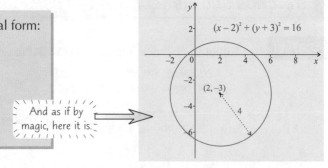

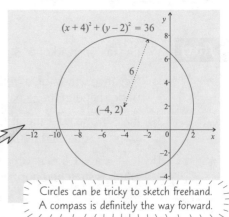

ii) The question says, 'Write down...', so you know you don't need to do any working.

The centre of the circle is (–4, 2), so $a = -4$ and $b = 2$.

The radius is 6, so $r = 6$.

Using the general equation for a circle $(x - a)^2 + (y - b)^2 = r^2$

you can write: $(x + 4)^2 + (y - 2)^2 = 36$

Circles can be tricky to sketch freehand. A compass is definitely the way forward.

This is pretty much all you need to learn. Everything on the next page uses stuff you should know already.

Circles

Rearrange the equation into the **familiar form**

Sometimes you'll be given an equation for a circle that doesn't look much like $(x - a)^2 + (y - b)^2 = r^2$.
This is a bit of a pain, because it means you can't immediately tell what the **radius** is or where the **centre** is.
But all it takes is a bit of **rearranging**.

Let's take the equation: $x^2 + y^2 - 6x + 4y + 4 = 0$

You need to get it into the form $(x - a)^2 + (y - b)^2 = r^2$.

This is just like completing the square.

Have a look at C1 Section 2 for more on completing the square.

$$x^2 + y^2 - 6x + 4y + 4 = 0$$
$$x^2 - 6x + y^2 + 4y + 4 = 0$$
$$(x - 3)^2 - 9 + (y + 2)^2 - 4 + 4 = 0$$
$$(x - 3)^2 + (y + 2)^2 = 9 \implies$$ This is the recognisable form, so the centre is **(3, –2)** and the radius is $\sqrt{9} = 3$.

Don't forget the Properties of Circles

You will have seen the circle rules at GCSE. You'll sometimes need to dredge them up in your memory for these circle questions. Here's a reminder of a few useful ones.

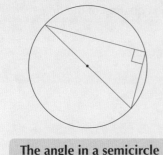

The angle in a semicircle is a right angle.

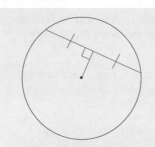

The perpendicular from the centre to a chord bisects the chord.

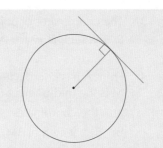

A radius and tangent to the same point will meet at right angles.

Use the Gradient Rule for Perpendicular Lines

Remember that the tangent at a given point will be perpendicular to the radius at that same point.

EXAMPLE: Point A (6, 4) lies on a circle with the equation $x^2 + y^2 - 4x - 2y - 20 = 0$.
    i) Find the centre and radius of the circle.
    ii) Find the equation of the tangent to the circle at A.

SOLUTION:

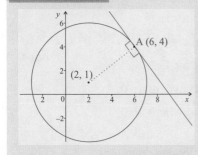

i) Rearrange the equation to show it as the sum of 2 squares:
$$x^2 + y^2 - 4x - 2y - 20 = 0$$
$$x^2 - 4x + y^2 - 2y - 20 = 0$$
$$(x - 2)^2 - 4 + (y - 1)^2 - 1 - 20 = 0$$
$$(x - 2)^2 + (y - 1)^2 = 25$$
This shows the centre is (2, 1) and the radius is 5.

ii) The tangent is at right angles to the radius at (6, 4).
Gradient of radius at $(6, 4) = \dfrac{4 - 1}{6 - 2} = \dfrac{3}{4}$

Gradient of tangent $= \dfrac{-1}{\frac{3}{4}} = -\dfrac{4}{3}$

Using $\quad y - y_1 = m(x - x_1)$
$$y - 4 = -\tfrac{4}{3}(x - 6)$$
$$3y - 12 = -4x + 24$$
$$3y + 4x - 36 = 0$$

So the chicken comes from the egg, and the egg comes from the chicken...

Well folks, at least it makes a change from all those straight lines and quadratics.
I reckon if you know the <u>formula</u> and <u>what it means</u>, you should be absolutely fine with questions on circles.

C1 Section 4 — Practice Questions

There you go then... a section on <u>various geometrical things</u>. And in a way it was quite exciting, I'm sure you'll agree. Though as you're probably aware, we mathematicians take our excitement from wherever we can get it. Anyway, I'll leave you alone now to <u>savour</u> these practice questions. <u>Don't skip the warm-up</u> — you don't want to hurt yourself...

Warm-up Questions

1) Find the <u>equations</u> of the <u>straight lines</u> that pass through the points
   a) $(2, -1)$ and $(-4, -19)$,   b) $\left(0, -\frac{1}{3}\right)$ and $\left(5, \frac{2}{3}\right)$.
   Write each of them in the forms
   i) $y - y_1 = m(x - x_1)$,
   ii) $y = mx + c$,
   iii) $ax + by + c = 0$, where a, b and c are integers.

2) a) The line l has equation $y = \frac{3}{2}x - \frac{2}{3}$. Find the equation of the lovely, cuddly line <u>parallel to l</u>, passing through the point with coordinates $(4, 2)$. Name this line <u>Lilly</u>.
   b) The line m (whose name is actually Mike) passes through the point $(6, 1)$ and is <u>perpendicular</u> to $2x - y - 7 = 0$. What is the equation of m?

3) The coordinates of points R and S are $(1, 9)$ and $(10, 3)$ respectively. Find the equation of the line <u>perpendicular</u> to RS, passing through the point $(1, 9)$.

4) Point A has coordinates $(2, 5)$ and point B has coordinates $(12, -1)$.
   M is the mid-point of the line segment AB. Find:
   a) The coordinates of M,
   b) The length of AM, leaving your answer in surd form.

5) It's lovely, lovely <u>curve-sketching time</u> — so draw rough sketches of the following curves:
   a) $y = -2x^4$,   b) $y = \frac{7}{x^2}$,   c) $y = -5x^3$,   d) $y = -\frac{2}{x^5}$.

6) Admit it — you <u>love</u> curve-sketching. We all do — and like me, you probably can't get enough of it. So more power to your elbow, and sketch these <u>cubic graphs</u>:
   a) $y = (x - 4)^3$,   b) $y = (3 - x)(x + 2)^2$,
   c) $y = (1 - x)(x^2 - 6x + 8)$,   d) $y = (x - 1)(x - 2)(x - 3)$.

7) Right — now it's time to get serious. Put your <u>thinking head on</u>, and use the graph of $f(x)$ to sketch what these graphs would look like after they've been '<u>transformed</u>'.

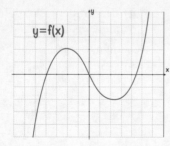

   a) $y = f(ax)$,   where   (i) $a > 1$,
                              (ii) $0 < a < 1$,
   b) $y = af(x)$,   where   (i) $a > 1$,
                              (ii) $0 < a < 1$,
   c) (i) $y = f(x + a)$,   (ii) $y = f(x - a)$, where $a > 0$,
   d) (i) $y = f(x) + a$,   (ii) $y = f(x) - a$, where $a > 0$.

8) Give the radius and the coordinates of the centre of the circles with the following equations:
   a) $x^2 + y^2 = 9$ b) $(x - 2)^2 + (y + 4)^2 = 4$ c) $x(x + 6) = y(8 - y)$

C1 Section 4 — Practice Questions

The excitement continues on this page, with a <u>thrilling selection</u> of the finest exam questions <u>money can buy</u>.
If you're asked to sketch a graph in your exam, it's worth taking a bit of time. They won't expect your graph to be <u>100% accurate</u>, but just make sure you've got the <u>general shape</u> right and that it crosses the axes in the <u>right places</u>.

Exam Questions

1 The line L has equation $4x + 3y = 15$.

   a) Find the gradient of L.

(2 marks)

   b) The point R lies on L and has coordinates $(3, 1)$. Find the equation of the line which passes through the point R and is perpendicular to L, giving your answer in the form $y = mx + c$.

(3 marks)

2 The curve C has the equation $y = (2x + 1)(x - 2)^2$.

  Sketch C, clearly showing the points at which the curve meets the x- and y- axes.

(4 marks)

3

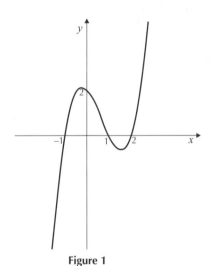

Figure 1

Figure 1 shows a sketch of the function $y = f(x)$. The function crosses the x-axis at $(-1, 0)$, $(1, 0)$ and $(2, 0)$, and crosses the y-axis at $(0, 2)$.

On separate diagrams, sketch the following:

   a) $y = f\left(\tfrac{1}{2}x\right)$.

(3 marks)

   b) $y = f(x - 4)$.

(2 marks)

On each diagram, label any known points of intersection with the x- or y- axes.

4 The line PQ satisfies the equation $2x - 14y + 6 = 0$.

  Points P and Q have coordinates $(-3, 0)$ and $(k, 1)$ respectively.

   a) Find the value of k.

(2 marks)

   b) Find the length of PQ, leaving your answer in surd form.

(3 marks)

   c) Find the equation of the line through Q which is parallel to the line $2x + y + 5 = 0$.

(3 marks)

C1 Section 4 — Practice Questions

Worry ye not, I'm not going to leave you wanting more — here are a few more exam questions for you to sink your teeth into.

5   a)   Sketch the curve $y = f(x)$, where $f(x) = x^2 - 4$, showing clearly the points of intersection with the x- and y- axes.

(2 marks)

      b)   Describe fully the transformation that transforms the curve $y = f(x)$ to the curve $y = -2f(x)$.

(2 marks)

      c)   The curve $y = f(x)$ is translated vertically two units upwards. State the equation of the curve after it has been transformed, in term of $f(x)$.

(1 mark)

6   The line l passes through the point $S(7, -3)$ and has gradient -2.

      a)   Find an equation of l, giving your answer in the form $y = mx + c$.

(3 marks)

      b)   The point T has coordinates $(5, 1)$. Show that T lies on l.

(1 mark)

7   C is a circle with the equation: $x^2 + y^2 - 2x - 10y + 21 = 0$.

      a)   Find the centre and radius of C.

(5 marks)

The line joining $P(3, 6)$ and $Q(q, 4)$ is a diameter of C.

      b)   Show that $q = -1$.

(3 marks)

      c)   Find the equation of the tangent to C at Q, giving your answer in the form $ax + by + c = 0$, where a, b and c are integers.

(5 marks)

8

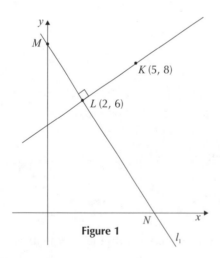

Figure 1

The points L and K have coordinates $(2, 6)$ and $(5, 8)$ respectively. The line l_1 passes through the point L and is perpendicular to the line LK, as shown in **Figure 1**.

      a)   Find an equation for l_1 in the form $ax + by + c = 0$, where a, b, and c are integers.

(4 marks)

          The line l_1 intersects the y-axis at the point M and the x-axis at the point N.

      b)   Find the coordinates of M.

(2 marks)

      c)   Find the coordinates of N.

(2 marks)

Differentiation

Brrrrrr... differentiation is a bad one — it really is. Not because it's that hard, but because it comes up all over the place in exams. So if you don't know it perfectly, you're asking for trouble. <u>Differentiation</u> is a great way to work out <u>gradients</u> of graphs. You take a function, differentiate it, and you can quickly tell <u>how steep</u> a graph is. It's magic.

Use this formula to differentiate *Powers of x*

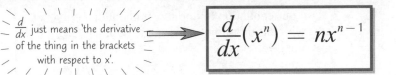

$\frac{d}{dx}$ just means 'the derivative of the thing in the brackets with respect to x'.

$$\frac{d}{dx}(x^n) = nx^{n-1}$$

Derivative just means 'the thing you get when you differentiate something'.

Equations are much easier to differentiate when they're written as <u>powers of x</u> — like writing $\sqrt{x}$ as $x^{\frac{1}{2}}$.

When you've done this, you can use the formula (the thing in the red box above) to differentiate the equation.

Use the differentiation formula...

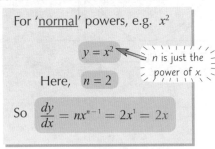

For '<u>normal</u>' powers, e.g. x^2

$$y = x^2$$

n is just the power of x.

See page 2 for more on negative powers.

Here, $n = 2$

So $\dfrac{dy}{dx} = nx^{n-1} = 2x^1 = 2x$

For <u>negative</u> powers, e.g. $\frac{1}{x^2} = x^{-2}$

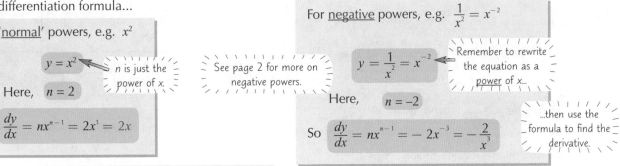

$$y = \frac{1}{x^2} = x^{-2}$$

Remember to rewrite the equation as a <u>power of x</u>...

Here, $n = -2$

So $\dfrac{dy}{dx} = nx^{n-1} = -2x^{-3} = -\dfrac{2}{x^3}$

...then use the formula to find the derivative.

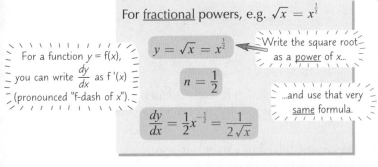

For <u>fractional</u> powers, e.g. $\sqrt{x} = x^{\frac{1}{2}}$

For a function $y = f(x)$, you can write $\frac{dy}{dx}$ as $f'(x)$ (pronounced "f-dash of x").

$$y = \sqrt{x} = x^{\frac{1}{2}}$$

Write the square root as a <u>power</u> of x...

$$n = \frac{1}{2}$$

...and use that very <u>same</u> formula.

$$\frac{dy}{dx} = \frac{1}{2}x^{-\frac{1}{2}} = \frac{1}{2\sqrt{x}}$$

<u>Power Laws:</u>
Differentiation's much easier if you know the Power Laws really well. Like knowing that
$$x^1 = x \quad \text{and} \quad \sqrt{x} = x^{\frac{1}{2}}$$
See page 2 for more info.

A constant always differentiates to 0 — see below.

Differentiate each term in an equation *Separately*

This formula is better than cake — even better than that really nice sticky black chocolate one from that place in town.

Even if there are loads of terms in the equation, it doesn't matter. Differentiate each bit separately and you'll be fine.

Here are a couple of examples...

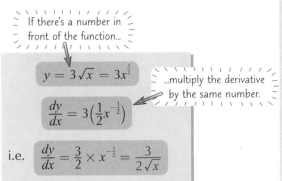

If there's a number in front of the function...

$$y = 3\sqrt{x} = 3x^{\frac{1}{2}}$$

...multiply the derivative by the same number.

$$\frac{dy}{dx} = 3\left(\frac{1}{2}x^{-\frac{1}{2}}\right)$$

i.e. $\dfrac{dy}{dx} = \dfrac{3}{2} \times x^{-\frac{1}{2}} = \dfrac{3}{2\sqrt{x}}$

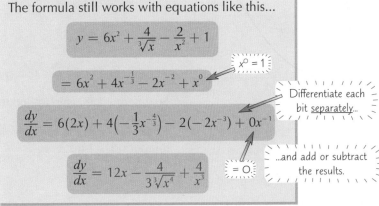

The formula still works with equations like this...

$$y = 6x^2 + \frac{4}{\sqrt[3]{x}} - \frac{2}{x^2} + 1$$

$$= 6x^2 + 4x^{-\frac{1}{3}} - 2x^{-2} + x^0$$

$x^0 = 1$

$$\frac{dy}{dx} = 6(2x) + 4\left(-\frac{1}{3}x^{-\frac{4}{3}}\right) - 2(-2x^{-3}) + 0x^{-1}$$

Differentiate each bit <u>separately</u>...

$= 0$

...and add or subtract the results.

$$\frac{dy}{dx} = 12x - \frac{4}{3\sqrt[3]{x^4}} + \frac{4}{x^3}$$

Dario Gradient — differentiating Crewe from the rest...

If you're going to bother doing maths, you've got to be able to differentiate things. Simple as that. But luckily, once you can do the simple stuff, you should be all right. Big long equations are just made up of loads of simple little terms, so they're not really that much harder. Learn the formula, and make sure you can use it by practising all day and all night forever.

Differentiation

Differentiation is what you do if you need to find a gradient. Excited yet?

Differentiate to find **Gradients**...

EXAMPLE Find the gradient of the graph $y = x^2$ at $x = 1$ and $x = -2$...

You need the gradient of the graph of...

$$y = x^2$$

So differentiate this function to get...

$$\frac{dy}{dx} = 2x$$

Now when $x = 1$, $\frac{dy}{dx} = 2$,

And so the gradient of the graph at $x = 1$ is 2.

And when $x = -2$, $\frac{dy}{dx} = -4$,

So the gradient of the graph at $x = -2$ is -4.

Use differentiation to find the gradient of a curve — which is the same as the gradient of the tangent at any given point.

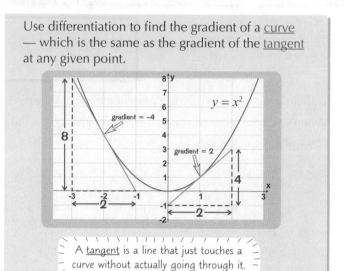

A tangent is a line that just touches a curve without actually going through it.

...which tell you **Rates of Change**...

So, you've differentiated an equation and found the gradient at a point — which is really useful because this tells you the rate of change of the curve at that point (e.g. from distance vs. time graphs you can work out speed).

EXAMPLE A sports car pulls off from a junction and drives away, travelling s metres in t seconds. For the first 10 seconds, its path can be described by the equation $s = 2t^2$.

Find: a) the speed of the car after 8 seconds and b) the car's acceleration during this period.

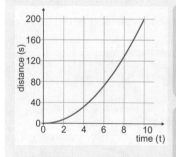

a) You can work out the speed by calculating the gradient of the curve $s = 2t^2$.

Differentiate to give: $\frac{ds}{dt} = 4t$ When $t = 8$, $\frac{ds}{dt} = 32$

So, the car is travelling at 32 ms^{-1} after 8 seconds.

b) Acceleration is the rate that speed (v) changes (i.e. it is the gradient of $v = 4t$).

So differentiate again to find the acceleration: $\frac{d^2s}{dt^2} = 4$

This means that the car's acceleration during this period is 4 ms^{-2}

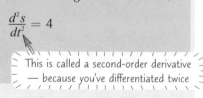

This is called a second-order derivative — because you've differentiated twice

Help me Differentiation — You're my only hope...

There's not much hard maths on this page — but there are a couple of very important ideas that you need to get your head round pretty darn soon. Understanding that differentiating gives the gradient of the graph is more important than washing regularly — AND THAT'S IMPORTANT. The other thing on the page you need to know is that the gradient tells you the rate of change of a function — which is also vital when working out what a question is after.

Finding Tangents and Normals

What's a tangent? Beats me. Oh no, I remember, it's one of those thingies on a curve. Ah, yes... I remember now...

Tangents *Just* touch a curve

To find the equation of a tangent or a normal to a curve, you first need to know its <u>gradient</u> —
so differentiate. Then complete the line's equation using the <u>coordinates</u> of one point on the line.

EXAMPLE Find the tangent to the curve $y = (4 - x)(x + 2)$ at the point (2, 8).

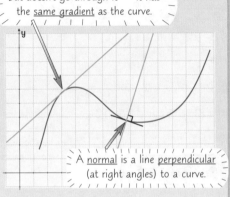

Tangents and Normals...

A <u>tangent</u> just touches the curve but doesn't go through it — it has the <u>same gradient</u> as the curve.

A <u>normal</u> is a line <u>perpendicular</u> (at right angles) to a curve.

To find the curve's (and the tangent's) <u>gradient</u>, first write the equation in a <u>form</u> you can differentiate...

$$y = 8 + 2x - x^2$$

...and then <u>differentiate</u> it.

$$\frac{dy}{dx} = 2 - 2x$$

The <u>gradient</u> of the tangent will be the gradient of the curve at $x = 2$.

At $x = 2$, $\frac{dy}{dx} = -2$,

So the tangent has <u>equation</u>,

$$y - y_1 = -2(x - x_1)$$

in $y - y_1 = m(x - x_1)$ form.
See page 29.

And since it passes through the <u>point</u> (2, 8), this becomes

$$y - 8 = -2(x - 2), \text{ or } y = -2x + 12.$$

You can also write it in $y = mx + c$ form.

Normals are at *Right Angles* to a curve

EXAMPLE Find the normal to the curve $y = \dfrac{(x + 2)(x + 4)}{6\sqrt{x}}$ at the point (4, 4).

There's more info on parallel and perpendicular lines on p.30.

Write the equation of the curve in a <u>form</u> you can differentiate.

$$y = \frac{x^2 + 6x + 8}{6x^{\frac{1}{2}}} = \frac{1}{6}x^{\frac{3}{2}} + x^{\frac{1}{2}} + \frac{4}{3}x^{-\frac{1}{2}}$$

Dividing everything on the top line by everything on the bottom line.

<u>Differentiate</u> it...

$$\frac{dy}{dx} = \frac{1}{6}\left(\frac{3}{2}x^{\frac{1}{2}}\right) + \frac{1}{2}x^{-\frac{1}{2}} + \frac{4}{3}\left(-\frac{1}{2}x^{-\frac{3}{2}}\right)$$

$$= \frac{1}{4}\sqrt{x} + \frac{1}{2\sqrt{x}} - \frac{2}{3\sqrt{x^3}}$$

Find the <u>gradient</u> at the point you're interested in. At $x = 4$,

$$\frac{dy}{dx} = \frac{1}{4} \times 2 + \frac{1}{2 \times 2} - \frac{2}{3 \times 8} = \frac{2}{3}$$

Because the gradient of the <u>normal</u> multiplied by the gradient of the <u>curve</u> must be −1.

So the <u>gradient</u> of the <u>normal</u> is $-\frac{3}{2}$.

And the <u>equation</u> of the normal is $y - y_1 = -\frac{3}{2}(x - x_1)$.

Finally, since the normal goes through the <u>point</u> (4, 4), the equation of the
normal must be $y - 4 = -\frac{3}{2}(x - 4)$, or after rearranging, $y = -\frac{3}{2}x + 10$.

Finding Tangents and Normals

1) **Differentiate the function.**

2) **Find the gradient, m, of the tangent or normal. This is,**

   for a <u>tangent</u>:   the gradient of the curve

   for a <u>normal</u>: $\dfrac{-1}{\text{gradient of the curve}}$

3) **Write the equation of the tangent or normal in the form**
   $y - y_1 = m(x - x_1)$, or $y = mx + c$.

4) **Complete the equation of the line using the coordinates of a point on the line.**

Repeat after me... "I adore tangents and normals..."

Examiners can't stop themselves saying the words 'Find the tangent...' and 'Find the normal...'. They love the words.
These phrases are music to their ears. They can't get enough of them. I just thought it was my duty to tell you that.
And so now you know, you'll definitely be wanting to learn how to do the stuff on this page. Of course you will.

Stationary Points

Differentiation is how you find gradients of curves. So you can use differentiation to find a <u>stationary point</u> (where a graph 'levels off') — that means finding where the <u>gradient</u> becomes <u>zero</u>.

Stationary Points are when the gradient is **Zero**

EXAMPLE   Find the stationary points on the curve $y = 2x^3 - 3x^2 - 12x + 5$, and work out the nature of each one.

A <u>stationary point</u> can be...

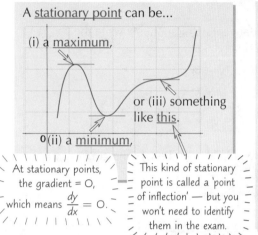

(i) a <u>maximum</u>,

or (iii) something like <u>this</u>.

O (ii) a <u>minimum</u>,

At stationary points, the gradient = 0, which means $\frac{dy}{dx} = 0$.

This kind of stationary point is called a 'point of inflection' — but you won't need to identify them in the exam.

You need to find where $\frac{dy}{dx} = 0$. So first, <u>differentiate</u> the function.

$$y = 2x^3 - 3x^2 - 12x + 5 \Rightarrow \frac{dy}{dx} = 6x^2 - 6x - 12$$

This is the expression for the gradient.

And then set this derivative equal to <u>zero</u>.

$$6x^2 - 6x - 12 = 0 \Rightarrow x^2 - x - 2 = 0$$
$$\Rightarrow (x-2)(x+1) = 0$$
$$\Rightarrow x = 2 \text{ or } x = -1$$

So the graph has <u>two</u> stationary points, at $x = 2$ and $x = -1$.

The stationary points are actually at $(2, -15)$ and $(-1, 12)$.

Substitute the x values into the function to find the y-coordinates.

Decide if it's a *Maximum* or a *Minimum* by differentiating **Again**

Once you've found where the stationary points are, you have to decide whether each of them is a <u>maximum</u> or <u>minimum</u> — this is all a question means when it says, '...determine the nature of the turning points'.

A turning point is another name for a maximum or a minimum.

To decide whether a stationary point is a <u>maximum</u> or a <u>minimum</u> — just differentiate again to find $\frac{d^2y}{dx^2}$.

For a function $f(x)$, $\frac{d^2y}{dx^2}$ can be written $f''(x)$

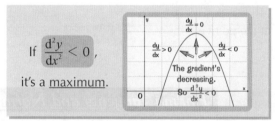

If $\frac{d^2y}{dx^2} < 0$, it's a <u>maximum</u>.

If $\frac{d^2y}{dx^2} > 0$, it's a <u>minimum</u>.

But if $\frac{d^2y}{dx^2} = 0$, you can't tell what type of stationary point it is.

You've just found that $\frac{dy}{dx} = 6x^2 - 6x - 12$.

So differentiating again gives $\frac{d^2y}{dx^2} = 12x - 6$.

Stick in the x-coordinates of the stationary points.

At $x = -1$, $\frac{d^2y}{dx^2} = -18$, which is <u>negative</u> — so $x = -1$ is a <u>maximum</u>.

And at $x = 2$, $\frac{d^2y}{dx^2} = 18$, which is <u>positive</u> — so $x = 2$ is a <u>minimum</u>.

And since a cubic graph (where the coefficient of x^3 is <u>positive</u>) goes from <u>bottom-left to top-right</u>...

...you can draw a rough sketch of the graph, even though the roots would be hard to find.

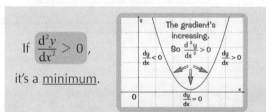

Stationary Points

1) **Find stationary points by solving**
    $$\frac{dy}{dx} = 0.$$

2) **Differentiate again to decide whether a point is a maximum or a minimum.**

3) **If** $\frac{d^2y}{dx^2} < 0$ — **it's a maximum.**

    If $\frac{d^2y}{dx^2} > 0$ — **it's a minimum.**

An anagram of differentiation is "Perfect Insomnia Cure"...

No joke, is it — this differentiation business — but it's a dead important topic in maths. It's so important to know how to find whether a stationary point is a max or a min — but it can get a bit confusing. Try remembering MINMAX — which is short for 'MINUS means a MAXIMUM'. Or make up some other clever way to remember what means what.

Increasing and Decreasing Functions

Differentiation is all about finding gradients. Which means that you can find out where a graph is going up...
...and where it's going down. Lovely.

Find out if a function is **Increasing** or **Decreasing**

You can use differentiation to work out exactly where a function is <u>increasing</u> or <u>decreasing</u> — and how quickly.

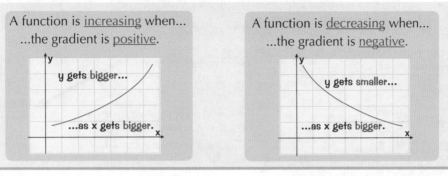

A function is <u>increasing</u> when...
...the gradient is <u>positive</u>.

y gets bigger...
...as x gets bigger.

A function is <u>decreasing</u> when...
...the gradient is <u>negative</u>.

y gets smaller...
...as x gets bigger.

And there's more...

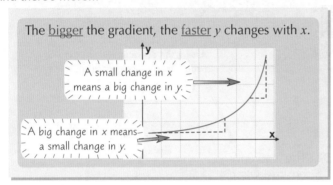

The <u>bigger</u> the gradient, the <u>faster</u> y changes with x.

A small change in x means a big change in y.

A big change in x means a small change in y.

Differentiation and Gradients

<u>Differentiate the equation</u> of the curve to find an expression for its gradient.

1) An increasing function has a <u>positive</u> gradient.

2) A decreasing function has a <u>negative</u> gradient.

EXAMPLE The path of a ball thrown through the air is described by the equation $y = 10x - 5x^2$, where y is the height of the ball above the ground and x is the horizontal distance from its starting point. Find where the height of the ball is increasing and where it's decreasing.

You have the equation for the path of the ball, and you need to know where y is increasing and where it's decreasing. That makes this a question about <u>gradients</u> — so <u>differentiate</u>.

$$y = 10x - 5x^2 \text{ so } \frac{dy}{dx} = 10 - 10x$$

This is an <u>increasing</u> function when: $10 - 10x > 0$, i.e. when $x < 1$, so the ball's height is increasing for $0 \le x < 1$.

And it's a <u>decreasing</u> function when: $10 - 10x < 0$, i.e. when $x > 1$, so its height decreases for $x > 1$ (until it lands).

Just to check: The gradient of the ball's path is given by $\frac{dy}{dx} = 10 - 10x$.

There's a turning point (i.e. the ball's flight levels out) when $x = 1$.

Differentiating again gives $\frac{d^2y}{dx^2} = -10$, which is <u>negative</u> — and so the turning point is a <u>maximum</u>.

This is what you'd expect — the ball goes <u>up then down</u>, not the other way round.

Decreasing function — also known as ironing...

Basically, you can tell whether a function is getting bigger or smaller by looking at the derivative. To make it more interesting, I wrote it as a nursery rhyme: the f(*duke of york*) = 10 000x, and when they were up the derivative was positive, and when they were down the derivative was negative, and when they were only halfway up at a stationary point the derivative was neither negative nor positive, it was zero. Catchy eh?

Curve Sketching

You'll even be asked to do some drawing in the exam... but don't get too excited — it's just drawing graphs... great.

Find where the curve crosses the **Axes**...

Sketch the graph of $f(x) = \frac{x^2}{2} - 2\sqrt{x}$, for $x \geq 0$.

The curve crosses the _y-axis_ when $x = 0$ — so put $x = 0$ in the expression for y.

When $x = 0$, $f(x) = 0$ — and so the curve goes through the <u>origin</u>.

The curve crosses the _x-axis_ when $f(x) = 0$. So solve

$$\frac{x^2}{2} - 2\sqrt{x} = 0$$
$$\Rightarrow x^2 - 4x^{\frac{1}{2}} = 0$$
$$\Rightarrow x^{\frac{1}{2}}(x^{\frac{3}{2}} - 4) = 0 \quad \boxed{\text{Factorising}}$$
$$\Rightarrow x^{\frac{1}{2}} = 0 \ \Rightarrow \ x = 0$$
$$\text{or: } x^{\frac{3}{2}} = 4 \ \Rightarrow \ x = 4^{\frac{2}{3}} = \sqrt[3]{4^2} = \sqrt[3]{16} \approx 2.5$$

And so the curve crosses the _x-axis_ when $x = 0$ (you knew this one already) and when $x \approx 2.5$.

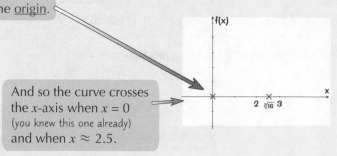

...**Differentiate** to find **Gradient** info...

Differentiating the function gives...

$$f(x) = \frac{1}{2}x^2 - 2x^{\frac{1}{2}}$$
$$\Rightarrow f'(x) = \frac{1}{2}(2x) - 2\left(\frac{1}{2}x^{-\frac{1}{2}}\right) = x - x^{-\frac{1}{2}} = x - \frac{1}{\sqrt{x}}$$

Using the derivative — you can find stationary points and tell when the graph goes 'uphill' and 'downhill'.

1) So there's a <u>stationary point</u> when...

$$x - \frac{1}{\sqrt{x}} = 0$$
$$\Rightarrow x = \frac{1}{\sqrt{x}}$$
$$\Rightarrow x^{\frac{3}{2}} = 1 \Rightarrow x = 1$$

And at $x = 1$, $f(x) = \frac{1}{2} - 2 = -\frac{3}{2}$.

2) The gradient's <u>negative</u> when...

$$x - \frac{1}{\sqrt{x}} < 0$$
$$\Rightarrow x < \frac{1}{\sqrt{x}}$$
$$\Rightarrow x^{\frac{3}{2}} < 1 \Rightarrow x < 1$$

So the function <u>decreases</u> when $0 \leq x < 1$...

3) The gradient's <u>positive</u> when...

$$x - \frac{1}{\sqrt{x}} > 0$$
$$\Rightarrow x > 1$$

...and <u>increases</u> for $x > 1$.

This is often the quickest way to check if something's a max or a min.

You could check that $x = 1$ is a <u>minimum</u> by differentiating again.

$$f''(x) = 1 - \left(-\frac{1}{2}x^{-\frac{3}{2}}\right) = 1 + \frac{1}{2\sqrt{x^3}}$$

This is <u>positive</u> when $x = 1$, and so this is definitely a minimum.

...and find out what happens when x gets **Big**

You can also try and decide what happens as x gets very <u>big</u> — in both the positive and negative directions.

Factorise f(x) by taking the <u>biggest</u> power outside the brackets...

$$\frac{x^2}{2} - 2\sqrt{x} = x^2\left(\frac{1}{2} - 2x^{-\frac{3}{2}}\right) = x^2\left(\frac{1}{2} - \frac{2}{x^{\frac{3}{2}}}\right)$$

As x gets large, this bit disappears — and the bit in brackets gets closer to $\frac{1}{2}$.

And so as x gets larger, f(x) gets closer and closer to $\frac{1}{2}x^2$ — and this just keeps growing and growing.

And the graph looks like this...

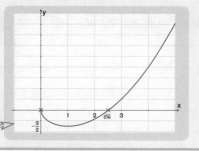

Curve sketching's important — but don't take my word for it...

Curve sketching — an underrated skill, in my opinion. As Shakespeare once wrote, 'Those who can do fab sketches of graphs and stuff are likely to get pretty good grades in maths exams, no word of a lie'. Well, he probably would've written something like that if he was into maths. And he would've written it because graphs are helpful when you're trying to work out what a question's all about — and once you know that, you can decide the best way forward. And if you don't believe me, remember the saying of the ancient Roman Emperor Julius Caesar, 'If in doubt, draw a graph'.

Real-Life Problems

Differentiation isn't just mathematical daydreaming. It can be applied to <u>real-life</u> problems. For instance, you can use differentiation to find out the <u>maximum possible volume</u> of a box, given a limited amount of cardboard. Thrilling.

Finding **Maximum / Minimum Values** for **Volume** and **Area**

To find the maximum for a shape's volume, all you need is an equation for the volume <u>in terms of only one variable</u> — then just <u>differentiate as normal</u>. But examiners don't hand it to you on a plate — there's usually one too many variables chucked in. So you've got to know how to manipulate the information to get rid of that unwanted variable.

EXAMPLE   A jewellery box with a lid and dimensions $2x$ cm by x cm by y cm is made using a total of 300 cm² of wood.

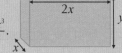

a) Show that the volume of the box can be expressed as: $V = \dfrac{300x - 4x^3}{3}$.

b) Use calculus to find the maximum volume.

a)   You know the basic equation for volume: $V = \text{width} \times \text{height} \times \text{depth}$
$$= x \times 2x \times y$$

But the question asks for volume in terms of x only — you don't want that pesky y in there. So you need to find y <u>in terms of x</u> and substitute that in. Use the given dimensions and surface area value to find y in terms of x:

① First, write an expression for the surface area:
$$2 \times [(2x \times x) + (2x \times y) + (x \times y)] = 300$$
$$\Rightarrow 4x^2 + 6xy = 300$$

Be careful when adding up the sides — here there's a lid so there are two of each side, but sometimes you'll get an open-topped shape.

② Then, rearrange to find an expression for y: $y = \dfrac{300 - 4x^2}{6x}$
$$y = \dfrac{50}{x} - \dfrac{2x}{3}$$

③ Finally, substitute the new expression for y into the equation for V, so that it's all in terms of x...
$$V = x \times 2x \times y = 2x^2 \times \left(\dfrac{50}{x} - \dfrac{2x}{3}\right)$$
$$= 100x - \dfrac{4x^3}{3} = \dfrac{300x - 4x^3}{3}$$
... and voila, the form the question asks for appears, as if by mathgic...

b)   Now it's just differentiating as normal, hurrah...

① Differentiate and find x when $\dfrac{dV}{dx} = 0$:
$$\dfrac{dV}{dx} = \dfrac{300 - 12x^2}{3} = 100 - 4x^2$$
$$100 - 4x^2 = 0 \Rightarrow 100 = 4x^2 \Rightarrow 25 = x^2 \Rightarrow x = 5$$
The other solution, $x = -5$ isn't relevant in this context.

② Check $x = 5$ is a maximum:
$$\dfrac{d^2V}{dx^2} = \dfrac{-24x}{3} = -8x$$
$$x = 5 \Rightarrow -8x = -40 < 0 \text{ so yes, it's a maximum}$$

③ Calculate V for $x = 5$:
$$V = 100 \times 5 - \dfrac{4 \times 5^3}{3} = 500 - \dfrac{500}{3} = \dfrac{1000}{3} = 333\tfrac{1}{3} \text{ cm}^3$$

Differentiation works for **Any Shape**

EXAMPLE   Ned uses a circular tin to bake his pies in. The tin is t cm high with a d cm diameter. The volume of the pie tin is 1000 cm³.

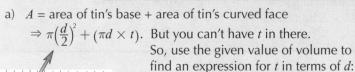

a) Prove that the surface area of the tin, $A = \dfrac{\pi}{4}d^2 + \dfrac{4000}{d}$.

b) Find the exact value of d which gives the minimum surface area of the tin.

a) $A = $ area of tin's base + area of tin's curved face
$$\Rightarrow \pi\left(\dfrac{d}{2}\right)^2 + (\pi d \times t).$$ But you can't have t in there.
So, use the given value of volume to find an expression for t in terms of d:

This shape is open-topped, so only count the area of the circle once.

$$V = \pi\left(\dfrac{d}{2}\right)^2 t = 1000$$
$$\Rightarrow t = \dfrac{1000}{\pi\left(\dfrac{d}{2}\right)^2} = \dfrac{4000}{\pi d^2}$$

Substitute your expression for t into the equation for surface area:
$$A = \dfrac{\pi}{4}d^2 + \left(\pi d \times \dfrac{4000}{\pi d^2}\right) \Rightarrow A = \dfrac{\pi}{4}d^2 + \dfrac{4000}{d}$$

b)   Differentiate and find the stationary point:
$$\dfrac{dA}{dd} = \dfrac{\pi}{2}d - \dfrac{4000}{d^2} \Rightarrow \dfrac{\pi}{2}d - \dfrac{4000}{d^2} = 0 \Rightarrow d^3 = \dfrac{8000}{\pi}$$
$$\Rightarrow d = \dfrac{20}{\sqrt[3]{\pi}}$$

Check it's a minimum:
$$\dfrac{d^2A}{dd^2} = \dfrac{\pi}{2} + \dfrac{8000}{d^3} = \dfrac{\pi}{2} + \dfrac{8000}{\left(\dfrac{8000}{\pi}\right)} = \dfrac{3\pi}{2}$$

Positive, so it is a minimum.

So the minimum surface area of the tin is found when $d = \dfrac{20}{\sqrt[3]{\pi}}$.

C1 Section 5 — Practice Questions

That's what <u>differentiation</u> is all about. Yes, there are <u>fiddly things</u> to remember — but overall, it's not as bad as all that. And just think of all the <u>lovely marks</u> you'll get if you can answer questions like these in the exam...

Warm-up Questions

1) <u>Differentiate</u> these functions with respect to x:
   a) $y = x^2 + 2$,
   b) $y = x^4 + \sqrt{x}$,
   c) $y = \dfrac{7}{x^2} - \dfrac{3}{\sqrt{x}} + 12x^3$

2) Find the <u>gradients</u> of these graphs at $x = 2$:
   a)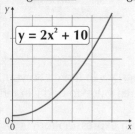

   $y = 2x^2 + 10$

   b)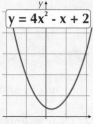

   $y = 4x^2 - x + 2$

   c)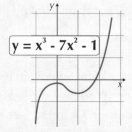

   $y = x^3 - 7x^2 - 1$

3) 1 litre of water is poured into a bowl.
   The <u>volume (v)</u> of water in the bowl (in ml) is defined by the <u>function</u>: $v = 17t^2 - 10t$
   Find the <u>rate</u> at which water is poured into the bowl when <u>$t = 4$ seconds</u>.

4) Yawn, yawn. Find the equations of the <u>tangent</u> and the <u>normal</u> to the curve $y = \sqrt{x^3} - 3x - 10$ at $x = 16$.

5) Show that the lines $y = \dfrac{x^3}{3} - 2x^2 - 4x + \dfrac{86}{3}$ and $y = \sqrt{x}$ <u>both go through</u> the point (4, 2), and are <u>perpendicular</u> at that point. Good question, that — <u>nice and exciting</u>, just the way you like 'em.

6) Find the stationary points of the function $y = x^3 + \dfrac{3}{x}$.
   Decide whether each stationary point is a <u>minimum</u> or a <u>maximum</u>.

7) The height (h m) a firework can reach is related to the mass (m g) of fuel it carries as shown below:
$$h = \frac{m^2}{10} - \frac{m^3}{900}$$
   Find the <u>mass of fuel</u> required to achieve the <u>maximum height</u> and state what the maximum height is.

If you get all the answers right, then well done... go <u>get yourself a pie</u>. But if you get any wrong, read the section again, work out where you went wrong, and then <u>try the questions again</u>.

Exam Questions

1 Given that $y = x^7 + \dfrac{2}{x^3}$, find:

   a) $\dfrac{dy}{dx}$

   (2 marks)

   b) $\dfrac{d^2y}{dx^2}$

   (2 marks)

2   Find the gradient of the curve $y = \frac{1}{\sqrt{x}} + \frac{1}{x}$ at the point $\left(4, \frac{3}{4}\right)$.

(5 marks)

3   a)   Show that the equation $\frac{x^2 + 3x^{\frac{3}{2}}}{\sqrt{x}}$ can be written in the form $x^p + 3x^q$, and state the values of p and q.

(3 marks)

b)   Now let $y = 3x^3 + 5 + \frac{x^2 + 3x^{\frac{3}{2}}}{\sqrt{x}}$. Find $\frac{dy}{dx}$, giving each coefficient in its simplest form.

(4 marks)

4   The curve C is given by the equation $y = 2x^3 - 4x^2 - 4x + 12$.

a)   Find $\frac{dy}{dx}$.

(2 marks)

b)   Write down the gradient of the tangent to the curve at the point where $x = 2$.

(1 mark)

c)   Hence or otherwise find an equation for the normal to the curve at this point.

(3 marks)

5   The curve C is given by the equation $y = mx^3 - x^2 + 8x + 2$, for a constant m.

a)   Find $\frac{dy}{dx}$.

(2 marks)

The point P lies on C, and has the x-value 5. The normal to C at P is parallel to the line given by the equation $y + 4x - 3 = 0$.

b)   Find the gradient of curve C at P.

(3 marks)

Hence or otherwise, find:

c)   (i)   the value of m.

(3 marks)

(ii)   the y-value at P.

(2 marks)

6   A steam train travels between Haverthwaite and Eskdale at a speed of x miles per hour and burns y units of coal, where y is given by: $2\sqrt{x} + \frac{8}{x}$, for $x > 2$.

a)   Find the speed that gives the minimum coal consumption.

(5 marks)

b)   Find $\frac{d^2y}{dx^2}$, and hence show that this speed gives the minimum coal consumption.

(2 marks)

c)   Calculate the minimum coal consumption.

(1 mark)

C1 Section 5 — Practice Questions

7   a)   Find $\dfrac{dy}{dx}$ for the curve $y = 6 + \dfrac{4x^3 - 15x^2 + 12x}{6}$.

(3 marks)

   b)   Hence, find the coordinates of the stationary points on the curve.

(5 marks)

   c)   Determine the nature of each stationary point.

(3 marks)

8   a)   Determine the coordinates of the stationary points for the curve $y = (\tfrac{1}{3}x - 1)(x^2 + 6x + 9)$.

(4 marks)

   b)   Find whether each of these points is a maximum or minimum.

(3 marks)

   c)   Sketch the curve of y.

(3 marks)

9   Ayesha is building a closed-back bookcase. She uses a total of 54 m² of wood (not including shelving) to make a bookcase that is x metres high, $\frac{x}{2}$ metres wide and d metres deep, as shown.

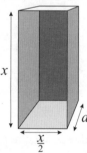

   a)   Show that the full capacity of the bookcase is given by: $V = 9x - \dfrac{x^3}{12}$.

(4 marks)

   b)   Find the value of x for which V is stationary.

(4 marks)

   c)   Show that this is a maximum point and hence calculate the maximum V.

(4 marks)

10   Function $f(x) = \tfrac{1}{2}x^4 - 54x$ has a single stationary point.

   a)   Find the coordinates of the stationary point.

(3 marks)

   b)   Determine the nature of the stationary point.

(2 marks)

   c)   State the range of values of x for which $f(x)$ is:

   (i)   increasing,

(1 mark)

   (ii)   decreasing.

(1 mark)

   d)   Sketch the curve for the function $f(x) = \tfrac{1}{2}x^4 - 54x$.

(2 marks)

General Certificate of Education
Advanced Subsidiary (AS) and Advanced Level

Core Mathematics C1 — Practice Exam One

Time Allowed: 1 hour 30 min

Calculators may **not** be used for this exam

There are 72 marks available for this paper.

1   a)   Write down the exact value of $36^{-\frac{1}{2}}$.

(2 marks)

   b)   Simplify $\dfrac{a^6 \times a^3}{\sqrt{a^4}} \div a^{\frac{1}{2}}$.

(3 marks)

2   Express $(5\sqrt{5} + 2\sqrt{3})^2$ in the form $a + b\sqrt{c}$, where a, b and c are integers to be found.

(4 marks)

3   Find $\dfrac{dy}{dx}$ for each of the following:

   a) $y = 3x^4 - 2x$

(2 marks)

   b) $y = (x^2 + 4)(x - 2)$

(3 marks)

4   Solve the following simultaneous equations:

$$y + x = 7 \quad \text{and} \quad y = x^2 + 3x - 5$$

(5 marks)

5   The line AB is part of the line with equation $y + 2x - 5 = 0$.
A is the point with coordinates $(1, 3)$ and B is the point with coordinates $(4, k)$.

   a)   Find the value of k.

(1 mark)

   b)   What is the equation of the line perpendicular to AB, that passes through A?

(4 marks)

6   a)   Solve the inequality $4x + 7 > 7x + 4$.

(2 marks)

   b)   Find the values of k, such that $(x - 5)(x - 3) > k$, for all possible values of x.

(3 marks)

7 Solve the equation $2x^{\frac{2}{3}} + 5x^{\frac{1}{3}} - 3 = 0$.

(5 marks)

8 The diagram shows a circle. A (2, 1) and B (0, –5) lie on the circle and AB is a diameter. C (4, –1) is also on the circle.

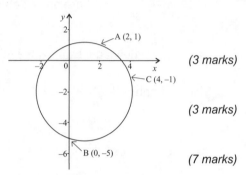

a) Find the centre and radius of the circle.

(3 marks)

b) Show that the equation of the circle can be written in the form:
$x^2 + y^2 - 2x + 4y - 5 = 0$

(3 marks)

c) The tangent at A and the normal at C cross at D. Find the coordinates of D.

(7 marks)

9 a) Find the coordinates of the point A, when A lies at the intersection of the lines l_1 and l_2, and when the equations of l_1 and l_2 respectively are $x - y + 1 = 0$ and $2x + y - 8 = 0$.

(3 marks)

b) The points B and C have coordinates (6, –4) and $\left(-\frac{4}{3}, -\frac{1}{3}\right)$ respectively, and D is the midpoint of AC.   Find the equation of the line BD in the form $ax + by + c = 0$, where a, b and c are integers.

(6 marks)

c) Show that the triangle ABD is a right-angled triangle.

(2 marks)

10 a) Express $x^2 - 6x + 5$ in the form $(x + a)^2 + b$.

(2 marks)

b) Factorise the expression $x^2 - 6x + 5$.

(2 marks)

c) Find the coordinates of the stationary point of the graph of $y = x^2 - 6x + 5$.

(3 marks)

d) Hence sketch the graph of $y = x^2 - 6x + 5$, clearly indicating where it cuts the axes.

(3 marks)

11 The equation $x^2 - 4x + (k - 1) = 0$, where k is a constant, has no real roots. Find the set of possible values of k.

(4 marks)

General Certificate of Education
Advanced Subsidiary (AS) and Advanced Level

Core Mathematics C1 — Practice Exam Two

Time Allowed: 1 hour 30 min

Calculators may **not** be used for this exam

There are 72 marks available for this paper.

1 a) Simplify $(\sqrt{3} + 1)(\sqrt{3} - 1)$.

(2 marks)

   b) Rationalise the denominator of the expression $\dfrac{\sqrt{3}}{\sqrt{3} + 1}$.

(3 marks)

2 a) Express $\dfrac{x^2 + 2x}{\sqrt{x}}$ in the form $x^m + 2x^n$, where m and n are constants to be found.

(2 marks)

   b) Find $\dfrac{dy}{dx}$ for $y = \dfrac{x^2 + 2x}{\sqrt{x}} + 3x^3 - x$ (where $x > 0$).

(4 marks)

3 Solve the equation $4x - 8x^{\frac{1}{2}} + 3 = 0$.

(5 marks)

4 a) Express $x^2 - 7x + 17$ in the form $(x - m)^2 + n$, where m and n are constants.
      Hence state the maximum value of $f(x) = \dfrac{1}{x^2 - 7x + 17}$.

(4 marks)

   b) Find the possible values of k if the equation $g(x) = 0$ is to have only one root,
      where $g(x)$ is given by $g(x) = 3x^2 + kx + 12$.

(3 marks)

5 The sides of a triangle ABC lie on lines given as follows:

   side AB lies on $y = 3$,   side BC lies on $2x - 3y - 21 = 0$,   side AC lies on $3x + 2y - 12 = 0$

   a) Find the coordinates of the vertices of the triangle.

(5 marks)

   b) Show that the triangle is right-angled.

(2 marks)

   The point D has coordinates $(3, d)$.

   c) If point D lies outside the triangle, but not on it, show that either $d > 3$ or $d < 1.5$.

(3 marks)

6 Given that the equation $3jx - jx^2 + 1 = 0$, where j is a constant, has no real roots,

    a) Show that $9j^2 + 4j < 0$

(3 marks)

    b) Hence find the set of possible values of j

(3 marks)

7 A curve has the equation $y = f(x)$, where $f(x) = x^3 - 3x + 2$.

    a) Find the coordinates of the stationary points of the curve.

(6 marks)

    b) Determine the nature of each of the stationary points.

(3 marks)

    c) For what values of x does $f(x)$ increase as x increases?

(2 marks)

8 The circle with equation $x^2 - 6x + y^2 - 4y = 0$ crosses the y-axis at the origin and the point A.

    a) Find the coordinates of A.

(2 marks)

    b) Rearrange the equation of the circle in the form: $(x - a)^2 + (y - b)^2 = c$.

(3 marks)

    c) Write down the radius and the coordinates of the centre of the circle.

(2 marks)

    d) Find the equation of the tangent to the circle at A.

(4 marks)

9 The diagram shows part of the graph with equation $y = x^3 - 2x^2 + 4$.

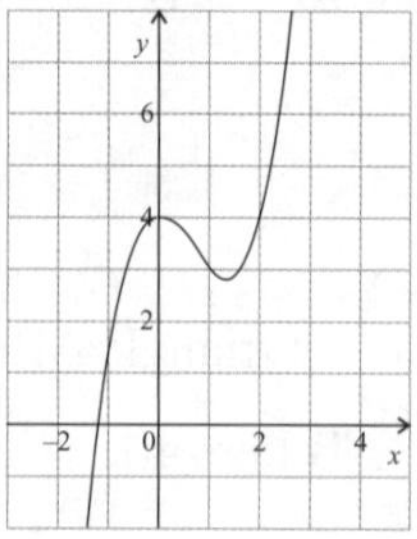

    a) Find the equation of the tangent at $x = 1$.

(3 marks)

    b) Find the equation of the normal to the curve at $x = 2$.

(3 marks)

    c) Find the distance between where the tangent and the normal cross the x-axis.

(2 marks)

    d) (i) The curve $y = x^3 - 2x^2 + 4$ is translated 3 units to the right.
           What is the equation of the curve after it has been translated?

(2 marks)

       (ii) The curve $y = x^3 - 2x^2 + 4$ is stretched by a factor of $+2$ along the y-axis.
            What is the equation of the curve after it has been translated?

(1 mark)

Factorising Cubics

Factorising a quadratic function is okay (and if you don't agree, go back and take another look at p11-12) — but you might also be asked to <u>factorise a cubic</u> (something with x^3 in it).
And that takes a bit more time — there are more steps, so there are more chances to make mistakes.

Factorising a cubic given *One Factor*

$$f(x) = 2x^3 + x^2 - 8x - 4$$

Factorising a cubic means exactly what it meant with a quadratic — putting brackets in.
When they ask you to factorise a cubic equation, they'll usually tell you one of the factors.

EXAMPLE Given that $(x+2)$ is a factor of $f(x) = 2x^3 + x^2 - 8x - 4$,
express $f(x)$ as the product of three linear factors.

① The first step is to find a quadratic factor. So write down
the factor you know, along with another set of brackets.

$$(x + 2)(\qquad) = 2x^3 + x^2 - 8x - 4$$

Put the x^2 bit in this new set of brackets.
These have to <u>multiply together</u> to give you this.

$$(x + 2)(2x^2 \qquad - 2) = 2x^3 + x^2 - 8x - 4$$

② Find the number for the second set of brackets.
These have to <u>multiply together</u> to give you this.

$$(x + 2)(2x^2 \qquad - 2) = 2x^3 + x^2 - 8x - 4$$

③ These multiplied give you $-2x$, but there's
$-8x$ in $f(x)$ — so you need an 'extra' $-6x$.
And that's what this $-3x$ is for.

$$(x + 2)(2x^2 - 3x - 2) = 2x^3 + x^2 - 8x - 4$$

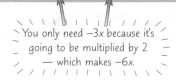
> You only need $-3x$ because it's
> going to be multiplied by 2
> — which makes $-6x$.

Factorising Cubics

1) **Write down the factor $(x-k)$.**

2) **Put in the x^2 term.**

3) **Put in the constant.**

4) **Put in the x term by comparing the number of x's on both sides.**

5) **Check there are the same number of x^2's on both sides.**

6) **Factorise the quadratic you've found — if that's possible.**

> If every term in the cubic contains an 'x'
> (i.e. $ax^3 + bx^2 + cx$) then just take out x
> as your first factor before factorising the
> remaining quadratic as usual.

④ Before you go any further, check that there
are the same number of x^2's on <u>both</u> sides.

$4x^2$ from here...

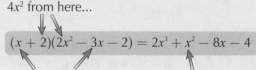
$$(x + 2)(2x^2 - 3x - 2) = 2x^3 + x^2 - 8x - 4$$

...and $-3x^2$ from here... ...add together to give this x^2.

If this is okay, factorise the quadratic into two linear factors.

$$(2x^2 - 3x - 2) = (2x + 1)(x - 2)$$

> If you wanted to solve a cubic, you'd do it
> exactly the same way — put it in the form
> $ax^3 + bx^2 + cx + d = 0$ and factorise.

<u>And so...</u> 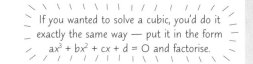 $2x^3 + x^2 - 8x - 4 = (x + 2)(2x + 1)(x - 2)$

I love the smell of fresh factorised cubics in the morning...

Factorising cubics is exactly the same as learning to unicycle... It's impossible at first. But when you finally manage it, it's really easy from then onwards and you'll never forget it. Probably. To tell the truth, I can't unicycle at all. So don't believe a word I say.

Algebraic Division

Algebraic division is one of those things that you have to learn when you do AS maths.
You'll probably never use it again once you've done your exam, but hey ho... such is life.

Do **Algebraic Division** by means of **Subtraction**

$$(2x^3 - 3x^2 - 3x + 7) \div (x - 2) = ?$$

The trick with this is to see how many times you can <u>subtract</u> $(x - 2)$ from $(2x^3 - 3x^2 - 3x + 7)$.
The idea is to keep <u>subtracting</u> lumps of $(x - 2)$ until you've got rid of all the <u>powers of x</u>.

Do the subtracting in **Stages**

At each stage, always try to get rid of the <u>highest</u> power of x.
Then start again with whatever you've got left.

① Start with $2x^3 - 3x^2 - 3x + 7$, and <u>subtract</u> $2x^2$ lots of $(x - 2)$ to get rid of the x^3 term.

$(2x^3 - 3x^2 - 3x + 7) - 2x^2(x - 2)$ $2x^3 \div x = 2x^2$
$(2x^3 - 3x^2 - 3x + 7) - 2x^3 + 4x^2$
$= x^2 - 3x + 7$ ← This is what's left — so now you have to get rid of the x^2 term.

② Now <u>start again</u> with $x^2 - 3x + 7$.
The highest power of x is the x^2 term.
So <u>subtract</u> x lots of $(x - 2)$ to get rid of that.

$(x^2 - 3x + 7) - x(x - 2)$
$(x^2 - 3x + 7) - x^2 + 2x$ Now start again with this — and get rid of the x term.
$= -x + 7$ ←

③ All that's left now is $-x + 7$.
Get rid of the $-x$ by <u>subtracting</u> -1 times $(x - 2)$.

$(-x + 7) - (-1(x - 2))$ There are no more powers of x to get rid of — so <u>stop here</u>.
$(-x + 7) + x - 2$
$= 5$ ←   The <u>remainder's</u> 5.

Interpreting the results...

Time to work out exactly what all that <u>meant</u>...

Started with: $2x^3 - 3x^2 - 3x + 7$

Subtracted: $2x^2(x - 2) + x(x - 2) - 1(x - 2)$

$= (x - 2)(2x^2 + x - 1)$

Remainder: $= 5$

So... $2x^3 - 3x^2 - 3x + 7 = (x - 2)(2x^2 + x - 1) + 5$

...or to put that another way...

$$\frac{2x^3 - 3x^2 - 3x + 7}{x - 2} = 2x^2 + x - 1 \text{ with remainder } 5.$$

$2x^2 + x - 1$ is called the <u>quotient</u>.

Algebraic Division

$$(ax^3 + bx^2 + cx + d) \div (x - k) = ?$$

1) <u>SUBTRACT</u> a multiple of $(x - k)$ to get rid of the highest power of x.

2) <u>REPEAT</u> step 1 until you've got rid of all the powers of x.

3) <u>WORK OUT</u> how many lumps of $(x - k)$, you've subtracted, and the <u>REMAINDER</u>.

Algebraic division is a beautiful thing that we should all cherish...

Revising algebraic division isn't the most enjoyable way to spend an afternoon, it's true, but it's <u>in the specification</u>, and so you need to be <u>comfortable</u> with it. It involves the same process you use when you're doing long division with numbers — so if you're having trouble following the above, do $4863 \div 7$ really slowly. What you're doing at each stage is subtracting multiples of 7, and you do this until you can't take any more 7s away, which is when you get your remainder.

The Remainder and Factor Theorems

The Remainder Theorem and the Factor Theorem are easy, and possibly quite useful.

The **Remainder Theorem** is an easy way to work out **Remainders**

> When you divide f(x) by ($x − a$), the remainder is f(a).

So in the example on the previous page, you could have worked out the remainder dead easily.

1) f(x) = $2x^3 − 3x^2 − 3x + 7$.
2) You're dividing by ($x − 2$), so $a = 2$.
3) So the remainder must be f(2) = (2 × 8) − (3 × 4) − (3 × 2) + 7 = 5.

Careful now... when you're dividing by something like ($x + 7$), a is negative — so here, a = −7.

If you want the remainder after dividing by something like (_ax − b_), there's an extension to the remainder theorem...

> When you divide f(x) by ($ax − b$), the remainder is f$\left(\dfrac{b}{a}\right)$.

EXAMPLE Find the remainder when you divide $2x^3 − 3x^2 − 3x + 7$ by $2x − 1$.

f(x) = $2x^3 − 3x^2 − 3x + 7$. You're dividing by $2x − 1$, so $a = 2$ and $b = 1$.

So the remainder must be: f$\left(\frac{1}{2}\right) = 2\left(\frac{1}{8}\right) − 3\left(\frac{1}{4}\right) − 3\left(\frac{1}{2}\right) + 7 = 5$

The **Factor Theorem** is just the Remainder Theorem with a **Zero Remainder**

If you get a remainder of zero when you divide f(x) by ($x − a$), then ($x − a$) must be a factor. That's the Factor Theorem.

> If f(x) is a polynomial, and f(a) = 0, then ($x − a$) is a factor of f(x).
> In other words: If you know the roots, you also know the factors — and vice versa.

EXAMPLE Show that ($2x + 1$) is a factor of f(x) = $2x^3 − 3x^2 + 4x + 3$.

The question's giving you a big hint here. Notice that $2x + 1 = 0$ when $x = −\frac{1}{2}$. So plug this value of x into f(x).
If you show that f($−\frac{1}{2}$)=0, then the factor theorem says that ($x + \frac{1}{2}$) is a factor — which means that
$2 × (x + \frac{1}{2}) = (2x + 1)$ is also a factor.

f(x) = $2x^3 − 3x^2 + 4x + 3$ and so f$\left(−\frac{1}{2}\right) = 2 × \left(−\frac{1}{8}\right) − 3 × \frac{1}{4} + 4 × \left(−\frac{1}{2}\right) + 3 = 0$

So, by the factor theorem, ($x + \frac{1}{2}$) is a factor of f(x), and so ($2x + 1$) is also a factor.

($x − 1$) is a Factor if the coefficients **Add Up To 0**

This works for all polynomials — no exceptions. It could save a fair whack of time in the exam.

EXAMPLE Factorise the polynomial f(x) = $6x^2 − 7x + 1$

The coefficients (6, −7 and 1) add up to 0. That means f(1) = 0, and so ($x − 1$) is a factor. Easy.

Then just factorise it like any quadratic to get this: f(x) = $6x^2 − 7x + 1 = (6x − 1)(x − 1)$

Factorising a **Cubic** given **No Factors**

If the question doesn't give you any factors, the best way to find a factor of a cubic is to guess — use trial and error.

First, add up the coefficients to check if ($x − 1$) is a factor.
If that doesn't work, keep trying small numbers (find f(−1), f(2), f(−2), f(3), f(−3) and so on) until you find a number that gives you zero when you put it in the cubic. Call that number k. ($x − k$) is a factor of the cubic.
Then finish factorising the cubic using the method on page 53.

C2 Section 1 — Practice Questions

What a start that was. One thing that's definitely true about that opening section is that it was <u>short</u>. It was 3 pages long, to be precise. That's about as short as it could be without being <u>really silly</u>. So stop complaining that you're hard done by and have a crack at <u>these questions</u>...

Warm-up Questions

1) Write the following functions f(x) in the form $f(x) = (x + 2)g(x) + $ remainder (where $g(x)$ is a quadratic):
   a) $f(x) = 3x^3 - 4x^2 - 5x - 6$,   b) $f(x) = x^3 + 2x^2 - 3x + 4$,   c) $f(x) = 2x^3 + 6x - 3$

2) Find the remainder when the following are divided by: (i) $(x + 1)$,   (ii) $(x - 1)$,   (iii) $(x - 2)$
   a) $f(x) = 6x^3 - x^2 - 3x - 12$,   b) $f(x) = x^4 + 2x^3 - x^2 + 3x + 4$,   c) $f(x) = x^5 + 2x^2 - 3$

3) Find the remainder when $f(x) = x^4 - 3x^3 + 7x^2 - 12x + 14$ is divided by:
   a) $x + 2$ b) $2x + 4$ c) $x - 3$ d) $2x - 6$

4) Which of the following are factors of $f(x) = x^5 - 4x^4 + 3x^3 + 2x^2 - 2$?
   a) $x - 1$ b) $x + 1$ c) $x - 2$ d) $2x - 2$

5) Find the values of c and d so that $2x^4 + 3x^3 + 5x^2 + cx + d$ is exactly divisible by $(x - 2)(x + 3)$.

There now, that wasn't so bad, was it? Now take a <u>deep breath</u> and have a go at some questions that are a bit more like the ones you may have to face <u>in the exam</u>.

Exam Questions

1   $f(x) = 2x^3 - 5x^2 - 4x + 3$

   a)   Find the remainder when $f(x)$ is divided by

      (i) $(x - 1)$

(2 marks)

      (ii) $(2x + 1)$

(2 marks)

   b)   Show using the factor theorem that $(x + 1)$ is a factor of $f(x)$.

(2 marks)

   c)   Factorise $f(x)$ completely.

(4 marks)

2   $f(x) = (4x^2 + 3x + 1)(x - p) + 5$, where p is a constant.

   a)   State the value of $f(p)$.

(1 mark)

   b)   Find the value of p, given that when $f(x)$ is divided by $(x + 1)$, the remainder is -1.

(2 marks)

   c)   Find the remainder when $f(x)$ is divided by $(x - 1)$.

(1 mark)

Sequences

A sequence is a list of numbers that follow a <u>certain pattern</u>. Sequences can be <u>finite</u> or <u>infinite</u> (infinity — oooh), and they're usually generated in one of two ways. And guess what? You have to know everything about them.

A *Sequence* can be defined by its nth *Term*

You almost definitely covered this stuff at GCSE, so <u>no excuses</u> for mucking it up.

The point of all this is to show how you can work out any <u>value</u> (<u>the nth term</u>) from its <u>position</u> in the sequence (<u>n</u>).

EXAMPLE   Find the nth term of the sequence 5, 8, 11, 14, 17, ...

1st	2nd	3rd	4th	5th
5	8	11	14	17

$$+3 \quad +3 \quad +3 \quad +3$$

Each term is <u>3 more</u> than the one before it. That means that you need to start by <u>multiplying n by 3</u>.

Take the first term (where $n = 1$). If you multiply n by 3, you still have to <u>add 2</u> to get 5.

The same goes for $n = 2$. To get 8 you need to multiply n by 3, then add 2.
Every term in the sequence is worked out exactly the same way.

So n^{th} term is $3n + 2$.

You can define a sequence by a *Recurrence Relation* too

Don't be put off by the fancy name — recurrence relations are pretty <u>easy</u> really.

> The main thing to remember is:
> a_k **just means the kth term of the sequence**

The <u>next term</u> in the sequence is a_{k+1}. You need to describe how to <u>work out</u> a_{k+1} if you're given a_k.

EXAMPLE   Find the recurrence relation of the sequence 5, 8, 11, 14, 17, ...

From the example above, you know that each term equals the one before it, plus 3.

This is written like this: $a_{k+1} = a_k + 3$

So, if k = 5, $a_k = a_5$ which stands for the 5th term, and $a_{k+1} = a_6$ which stands for the 6th term.

In everyday language, $a_{k+1} = a_k + 3$ means that the sixth term equals the fifth term plus 3.

<u>BUT</u> $a_{k+1} = a_k + 3$ on its own <u>isn't enough</u> to describe 5, 8, 11, 14, 17, ...

For example, the sequence 87, 90, 93, 96, 99, ... <u>also</u> has each term being 3 more than the one before.

The description needs to be more <u>specific</u>, so you've got to <u>give one term</u> in the sequence, as well as the recurrence relation. You almost always give the <u>first value</u>, a_1.

Putting all of this together gives 5, 8, 11, 14, 17, ... as $a_{k+1} = a_k + 3$, $a_1 = 5$.

Sequences

Some sequences involve **Multiplying**

You've done the easy 'adding' business. Now it gets really tough — <u>multiplying</u>. Are you sure you're ready for this...

EXAMPLE   A sequence is defined by $a_{k+1} = 2a_k - 1$, $a_2 = 5$. List the first five terms.

OK, you're told the second term, $a_2 = 5$.
Just plug that value into the equation, and carry on from there.

$$a_3 = 2 \times 5 - 1 = 9$$

From the equation $a_k = a_2$ so $a_{k+1} = a_3$

$$a_4 = 2 \times 9 - 1 = 17$$

Now use a_3 to find $a_{k+1} = a_4$ and so on...

$$a_5 = 2 \times 17 - 1 = 33$$

Now to find the first term, a_1:

$$a_2 = 2a_1 - 1$$
$$5 = 2a_1 - 1$$
$$2a_1 = 6$$
$$a_1 = 3$$

Just make $a_k = a_1$

So the first five terms of the sequence are $3, 5, 9, 17, 33$.

Some Sequences have a **Certain Number** of terms — others go on **Forever**

Some sequences are only defined for a <u>certain number</u> of terms.

It's the $1 \leq k \leq 20$ bit that tells you it's finite.

For example, $a_{k+1} = a_k + 3$, $a_1 = 1$, $1 \leq k \leq 20$

will be $1, 4, 7, 10, ..., 58$ and will contain 20 terms.

This is a finite sequence.

Other sequences <u>don't</u> have a specified number of terms and could go on <u>forever</u>.

For example, $u_{k+1} = u_k + 2$, $u_1 = 5$,

will be $5, 7, 9, 11, 13, ...$ and won't have a final term.

This is an infinite sequence.

While others are <u>periodic</u>, and just revisit the same values over and over again.

For example, $u_k = u_{k-3}$, $u_1 = 1$, $u_2 = 4$, $u_3 = 2$,

will be $1, 4, 2, 1, 4, 2, 1, 4, 2,...$

This is a periodic sequence with period 3.

Like maths teachers, sequences can go on and on and on and on...

If you know the formula for the nth term, you can work out any term using a single formula, so it's kind of easy. If you only know a recurrence relation, then you can only work out the <u>next</u> term. So if you want the 20th term, and you only know the first one, then you have to use the recurrence relation 19 times. (So it'd be quicker to work out a formula really.)

Arithmetic Progressions

Right, you've got basic sequences tucked under your belt now — time to step it up a notch (sounds painful).
When the terms of a sequence progress by <u>adding</u> a <u>fixed amount</u> each time, this is called an <u>arithmetic progression</u>.

It's all about *Finding* the nth *Term*

The <u>first term</u> of a sequence is given the symbol *a*. The <u>amount you add</u> each time is called the common difference,
or *d*. The <u>position of any term</u> in the sequence is called *n*.

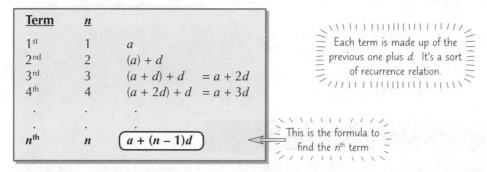

Term	$\underline{\textbf{n}}$	
1st	1	a
2nd	2	$(a) + d$
3rd	3	$(a + d) + d \quad = a + 2d$
4th	4	$(a + 2d) + d \quad = a + 3d$
.	.	.
.	.	.
$\textbf{n}^{th}$	n	$\boxed{a + (n - 1)d}$

Each term is made up of the previous one plus *d*. It's a sort of recurrence relation.

This is the formula to find the nth term

EXAMPLE Find the 20th term of the arithmetic progression 2, 5, 8, 11, … and find the formula for the nth term.

Here $a = 2$ and $d = 3$.

To get *d*, just find the difference between two terms next to each other — e.g. $11 - 8 = 3$

So 20th term $= a + (20 - 1)d$
$= 2 + 19 \times 3$
$= 59$

The <u>general term</u> is the $\underline{n^{th}}$ <u>term</u>, i.e. $a + (n - 1)d$
$= 2 + (n - 1)3$
$= 3n - 1$

A *Series* is when you *Add the Terms* to *Find the Total*

S_n is the total of the first n terms of the arithmetic progression:

$$\textbf{S}_n = \textbf{a} + (\textbf{a} + \textbf{d}) + (\textbf{a} + \textbf{2d}) + (\textbf{a} + \textbf{3d}) + \dots + (\textbf{a} + (\textbf{n} - \textbf{1})\textbf{d})$$

There's a really neat version of the same formula too:

$$\boxed{S_n = n \times \frac{(a + l)}{2}}$$

The *l* stands for the <u>last value</u> in the progression.
You work it out as $l = a + (n - 1)d$

Nobody likes formulas, so think of it as the <u>average</u> of the <u>first and last</u> terms multiplied by the <u>number of terms</u>.

EXAMPLE Find the sum of the series with first term 3, last term 87 and common difference 4.

Here you know *a*, *d* and *l*, but you don't know *n* yet.

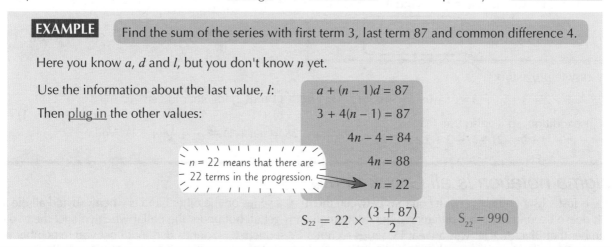

Use the information about the last value, *l*: $\quad a + (n - 1)d = 87$

Then <u>plug in</u> the other values: $\qquad\qquad 3 + 4(n - 1) = 87$

$\qquad\qquad\qquad\qquad\qquad\qquad\qquad\qquad 4n - 4 = 84$

$n = 22$ means that there are 22 terms in the progression.

$\qquad\qquad\qquad\qquad\qquad\qquad\qquad\qquad 4n = 88$

$\qquad\qquad\qquad\qquad\qquad\qquad\qquad\qquad\quad n = 22$

$$S_{22} = 22 \times \frac{(3 + 87)}{2} \qquad S_{22} = 990$$

Arithmetic Series and Sigma Notation

They **Won't** always give you the **Last Term**...

...but don't panic — there's a formula to use when the <u>last term is unknown</u>. But you knew I'd say that, didn't you?

You know $l = a + (n - 1)d$ and $S_n = n \times \dfrac{(a + l)}{2}$.

Plug l into S_n and rearrange to get the formula in the box:

$$S_n = \frac{n}{2}[2a + (n - 1)d]$$

EXAMPLE For the sequence –5, –2, 1, 4, 7, ... find the sum of the first 20 terms.

So $a = -5$ and $d = 3$.
The question says $n = 20$ too.

$$S_{20} = \frac{20}{2}[2 \times -5 + (20 - 1) \times 3]$$
$$= 10[-10 + 19 \times 3]$$
$$S_{20} = 470$$

There's **Another** way of **Writing Series**, too

So far, the letter S has been used for the sum. The Greeks did a lot of work on this — their capital letter for S is Σ or <u>sigma</u>. This is used today, together with the general term, to mean the <u>sum</u> of the series.

EXAMPLE Find $\displaystyle\sum_{n=1}^{15}(2n + 3)$

...and ending with $n = 15$

Starting with $n = 1$...

This means you have to find the sum of the <u>first 15 terms</u> of the series with nth term $2n + 3$.

The first term ($n = 1$) is 5, the second term ($n = 2$) is 7, the third is 9, ... and the last term ($n = 15$) is 33.

In other words, you need to find $5 + 7 + 9 + \ldots + 33$. This gives $a = 5$, $d = 2$, $n = 15$ and $l = 33$.

You know all of a, d, n and l, so you can use either formula:

$$S_n = n\frac{(a + l)}{2}$$
$$S_{15} = 15\frac{(5 + 33)}{2}$$
$$S_{15} = 15 \times 19$$
$$S_{15} = 285$$

It makes no difference which method you use.

$$S_n = \frac{n}{2}[2a + (n - 1)d]$$
$$S_{15} = \frac{15}{2}[2 \times 5 + 14 \times 2]$$
$$S_{15} = \frac{15}{2}[10 + 28]$$
$$S_{15} = 285$$

Use **Arithmetic Progressions** to add up the **First n Whole Numbers**

The <u>sum of the first n natural numbers</u> looks like this:

$$S_n = 1 + 2 + 3 + \ldots + (n - 2) + (n - 1) + n$$

So $a = 1$, $l = n$ and also $n = n$.
Now just plug those values into the formula:

Natural numbers are just positive whole numbers.

$$S_n = n \times \frac{(a + l)}{2} \implies \boxed{S_n = \frac{1}{2}n(n + 1)}$$

EXAMPLE

Add up all the whole numbers from 1 to 100.

Sounds pretty hard, but all you have to do is stick it into the formula:

$S_{100} = \frac{1}{2} \times 100 \times 101$. So $S_{100} = 5050$

It's pretty easy to <u>prove</u> this:

1) Say, $S_n = 1 + 2 + 3 + \ldots + (n - 2) + (n - 1) + n$ ①

2) ① is just addition, so it's also true that:
$S_n = n + (n - 1) + (n - 2) + \ldots + 3 + 2 + 1$ ②

3) Add ① and ② together to get:
$2S_n = (n + 1) + (n + 1) + (n + 1) + \ldots + (n + 1) + (n + 1) + (n + 1)$
$\Rightarrow 2S_n = n(n + 1) \Rightarrow S_n = \frac{1}{2}n(n + 1)$. Voilà.

This sigma notation is all Greek to me... (Ho ho ho)

A <u>sequence</u> is just a list of numbers (with commas between them) — a <u>series</u> on the other hand is when you add all the terms together. It doesn't sound like a big difference, but mathematicians get all hot under the collar when you get the two mixed up. Remember that Black<u>ADD</u>er was a great TV <u>series</u> — not a TV sequence. (Sounds daft, but I bet you remember it now.)

Geometric Progressions

You have a geometric progression when each term in a sequence is found by multiplying the previous term by a (constant) number. Let me explain...

Geometric Progressions Multiply by a Constant each time

Geometric progressions work like this: the next term in the sequence is obtained by multiplying the previous one by a constant value. Couldn't be easier.

$u_1 = a \qquad\qquad = a$

$u_2 = a \times r \qquad\quad = ar$

$u_3 = a \times r \times r \qquad = ar^2$

$u_4 = a \times r \times r \times r = ar^3$

The first term (u_1) is called 'a'.

The number you multiply by each time is called 'the common ratio', symbolised by 'r'.

Here's the formula describing any term in the geometric progression:

$$u_n = ar^{n-1}$$

EXAMPLE There is a chessboard with a 1p piece on the first square, 2p on the second square, 4p on the third, 8p on the fourth and so on until the board is full. Calculate how much money is on the board.

This is a geometric progression, where you get the next term in the sequence by multiplying the previous one by 2.

So $a = 1$ (because you start with 1p on the first square) and $r = 2$.

So $u_1 = 1$, $u_2 = 2$, $u_3 = 4$, $u_4 = 8$...

To be continued... (once we've gone over how to sum the terms of a geometric progression).

A Sequence becomes a Series when you Add the Terms

S_n stands for the sum of the first n terms of the geometric progression.
In the example above, you're told to work out S_{64} (because there are 64 squares on a chessboard).

To work out the formula for the sum of a G.P. you use two series and subtract.

For a G.P.:	$S_n = a + ar + ar^2 + ar^3 + ... + ar^{n-1}$
Multiplying by r gives:	$rS_n = ar + ar^2 + ar^3 + ... + ar^{n-2} + ar^{n-1} + ar^n$
Subtracting gives:	$S_n - rS_n = a - ar^n$
Factorising:	$(1-r)S_n = a(1-r^n) \implies \boxed{S_n = \dfrac{a(1-r^n)}{1-r}}$

If the series were subtracted the other way around you'd get

$$S_n = \frac{a(r^n - 1)}{r - 1}.$$

Both versions are correct.

So, back to the chessboard example:

$a = 1$, $r = 2$, $n = 64$ $\qquad S_{64} = \dfrac{1(1 - 2^{64})}{1 - 2}$

$$S_{64} = 1.84 \times 10^{19} \text{ pence or } £1.84 \times 10^{17}$$

The whole is more than the sum of the parts — hmm, not in maths, it ain't...

You really need to understand the difference between arithmetic and geometric progressions — it's not hard, but it needs to be fixed firmly in your head. There are only a few formulas for sequences and series (the nth term of a sequence, the sum of the first n terms of a series), and these are in the formula book they give you — but make sure you know how to use them.

Geometric Progressions

Geometric progressions can either Grow or Shrink

In the chessboard example, each term was <u>bigger</u> than the previous one: 1, 2, 4, 8, 16, …
You can create a series where each term is <u>smaller</u> than the previous one by using a <u>small value of r</u>.

EXAMPLE If $a = 20$ and $r = \frac{1}{5}$, write down the first five terms of the sequence and the 20th term.

$u_1 = 20$

Each term is the previous one multiplied by r.

$u_2 = 20 \times \frac{1}{5} = 4$

$u_3 = 4 \times \frac{1}{5} = 0.8$

$u_4 = 0.8 \times \frac{1}{5} = 0.16$

$u_5 = 0.16 \times \frac{1}{5} = 0.032$

$u_{20} = ar^{19}$
$= 20 \times \left(\frac{1}{5}\right)^{19}$
$= 1.048576 \times 10^{-12}$

The sequence is <u>tending towards zero</u>, but won't ever get there.

In general, for each term to be <u>smaller</u> than the one before, you need $|r| < 1$. ←
A sequence with $|r| < 1$ is called <u>convergent</u>, since the terms converge to a limit.
Any other sequence (like the chessboard example on page 61) is called <u>divergent</u>.

$|r|$ means the modulus (or size) of r, <u>ignoring the sign</u> of the number. So $|r| < 1$ means that $-1 < r < 1$.

A Convergent Series has a Sum to Infinity

In other words, if you just <u>kept</u> adding terms to a <u>convergent series</u>, you'd get <u>closer and closer</u> to a certain number, but you'd never actually reach it.

If $|r| < 1$ and n is very, very <u>big</u>, then r^n will be very, very <u>small</u> — or to put it technically, $r^n \to 0$. (Try working out $(\frac{1}{2})^{100}$ on your calculator if you don't believe me.)

This means $(1 - r^n)$ is really, really close to 1.

So, as $n \to \infty$, $S_n \to \dfrac{a}{1 - r}$.

It's easier to remember as $\boxed{S_\infty = \dfrac{a}{1 - r}}$

S_∞ just means 'sum to infinity'.

EXAMPLE If $a = 2$ and $r = \frac{1}{2}$, find the sum to infinity of the geometric series.

$u_1 = 2$ ⟹ $S_1 = 2$

$u_2 = 2 \times \frac{1}{2} = 1$ ⟹ $S_2 = 2 + 1 = 3$

These values are getting <u>smaller</u> each time.

$u_3 = 1 \times \frac{1}{2} = \frac{1}{2}$ ⟹ $S_3 = 2 + 1 + \frac{1}{2} = 3\frac{1}{2}$

$u_4 = \frac{1}{2} \times \frac{1}{2} = \frac{1}{4}$ ⟹ $S_4 = 2 + 1 + \frac{1}{2} + \frac{1}{4} = 3\frac{3}{4}$

$u_5 = \frac{1}{4} \times \frac{1}{2} = \frac{1}{8}$ ⟹ $S_5 = 2 + 1 + \frac{1}{2} + \frac{1}{4} + \frac{1}{8} = 3\frac{7}{8}$

$u_6 = \frac{1}{8} \times \frac{1}{2} = \frac{1}{16}$ ⟹ $S_6 = 2 + 1 + \frac{1}{2} + \frac{1}{4} + \frac{1}{8} + \frac{1}{16} = 3\frac{15}{16}$

These values are getting closer (<u>converging</u>) to 4.

So, the sum to infinity is 4.

You can show this <u>graphically</u>:

The line on the graph is getting <u>closer and closer</u> to 4, but it'll never actually get there.

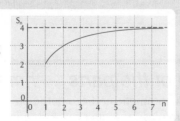

Of course, you could have saved yourself a lot of bother by using the <u>sum to infinity formula</u>:

$S_\infty = \dfrac{a}{1 - r} = \dfrac{2}{1 - \frac{1}{2}} = 4$

Geometric Progressions

A *Divergent* series *Doesn't* have a sum to infinity

EXAMPLE If $a = 2$ and $r = 2$, find the sum to infinity of the series.

$u_1 = 2$ $\Longrightarrow$ $S_1 = 2$
$u_2 = 2 \times 2 = 4$ $\Longrightarrow$ $S_2 = 2 + 4 = 6$
$u_3 = 4 \times 2 = 8$ $\Longrightarrow$ $S_3 = 2 + 4 + 8 = 14$
$u_4 = 8 \times 2 = 16$ $\Longrightarrow$ $S_4 = 2 + 4 + 8 + 16 = 30$
$u_5 = 16 \times 2 = 32$ $\Longrightarrow$ $S_5 = 2 + 4 + 8 + 16 + 32 = 62$

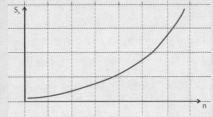

This is an <u>exponential</u> graph — see C2 Section 4.

As $n \to \infty$, $S_n \to \infty$ in a big way. So big, in fact, that
eventually you <u>can't work it out</u> — so don't bother.

There is <u>no sum to infinity</u> for a <u>divergent</u> series.

EXAMPLE When a baby is born, £3000 is invested in an account with a fixed interest rate of 4% per year.

a) What will the account be worth at the start of the seventh year?

b) What age will the child be, to the nearest year, when the account has doubled in value?

a) $u_1 = a = 3000$

$u_2 = 3000 + (4\% \text{ of } 3000)$ ← This is the interest.

$= 3000 + (0.04 \times 3000)$

$= 3000(1 + 0.04)$

$= 3000 \times 1.04$ ← So, r = 1.04

$u_3 = u_2 \times 1.04$

$= (3000 \times 1.04) \times 1.04$

$= 3000 \times (1.04)^2$

$u_4 = 3000 \times (1.04)^3$

I've missed out some steps here — check that you understand what's happened.

$\vdots$

$u_7 = 3000 \times (1.04)^6$

$= £3795.96$ (to the nearest penny)

b) You need to know when $u_n > 6000$ ← double the original value.
From part a) you can tell that $u_n = 3000 \times (1.04)^{n-1}$
So $3000 \times (1.04)^{n-1} > 6000$
$(1.04)^{n-1} > 2$

To complete this you need to use logs (see C2 Section 4):

$\log(1.04)^{n-1} > \log 2$

$(n - 1)\log(1.04) > \log 2$

$n - 1 > \dfrac{\log 2}{\log 1.04}$

$n - 1 > 17.67$

$n > 18.67$ (to 2 d.p.)

So u_{19} (the amount at the start of the 19th year) will be
more than double the original amount — plenty of
time to buy a Porsche for the 21st birthday.

So tell me — if my savings earn 4% per year, when will I be rich...

Now here's a funny thing — you can have a convergent geometric series if the common ratio is small enough.
I find this odd — that I can keep adding things to a sum forever, but the sum never gets really really big.

Sequence & Series Problems

Now that you've got your toolbox of formulas:

Arithmetic Progressions

$$u_n = a + (n-1)d$$

$$S_n = \frac{n}{2}[2a + (n-1)d]$$

Geometric Progressions

$$u_n = ar^{n-1}$$

$$S_n = \frac{a(1-r^n)}{1-r}$$

$$S_\infty = \frac{a}{1-r}$$

It's time to mix things up a bit and take on the big boys — some serious series problems...

*You might need to **Simultaneous Equations** to solve some problems...*

EXAMPLE The sum of the first five terms of an arithmetic progression is 5, and the sixth term is 13. Find the eighth term in the progression.

The question gives you a particular term and a sum of terms, so use the formulas $u_n = a + (n-1)d$ and $S_n = \frac{n}{2}[2a + (n-1)d]$.

Plugging the values given in the question gives: $u_6 = a + (6-1)d = 13$ and $S_5 = 5 = \frac{5}{2}[2a + (5-1)d]$

Which simplify to: $a + 5d = 13$, call this ①

$a + 2d = 1$, call this ②

Solve the <u>simultaneous equations</u>: ① − ② ⇒ $3d = 12$ ⇒ $d = 4$

$d = 4$ in ② ⇒ $a = 1 - 8 = -7$

Finally, use $a + (n-1)d$ to find the 8th term: $u_8 = a + (n-1)d = -7 + (7 \times 4) = 21$

*... and **Quadratic Equations** to solve others*

EXAMPLE The sum to infinity of a geometric series is –32. The second term of the progression is –8. Find the common ratio of the progression.

Use the formula for the nth term of a geometric progression: $u_n = ar^{n-1}$

and the sum to infinity of a geometric series: $S_\infty = \frac{a}{1-r}$

Plugging in the information from the question gives: $u_2 = ar = -8$, call this ①

$S_\infty = -32 = \frac{a}{1-r}$, call this ②

Rearrange ① into the form $a = -\frac{8}{r}$ in order to eliminate a from ②:

If you were trying to find a, then you would rearrange to eliminate r instead.

$$-32 = \frac{\left(\frac{-8}{r}\right)}{1-r}$$

$$-32(1-r) = \frac{(-8)}{r}$$

$$-32r + 32r^2 = -8$$

$$4r^2 - 4r + 1 = 0$$

$$(2r-1)^2 = 0$$

$$\Rightarrow 2r = 1, \quad r = \frac{1}{2}$$

This quadratic only has one root. If you get a quadratic with two roots, pick the one for which $|r| < 1$, as a series with a sum to infinity must be convergent.

At last – the series finalé...

Make sure you know which formulas apply to arithmetic and which to geometric progressions. You might have to use different combinations of them in the exam to get your simultaneous equations. Just look at what you are given in the question and what you are being asked to do, and use the corresponding formulas. That's all there is to it really.

Binomial Expansions

If you're feeling a bit stressed, just take a couple of minutes to relax before trying to get your head round this page — it's a bit of a stinker in places. Have a cup of tea and think about something else for a couple of minutes. Ready...

Writing **Binomial Expansions** is all about **Spotting Patterns**

Doing binomial expansions just involves <u>multiplying out</u> brackets. It would get nasty when you raise the brackets to <u>higher powers</u> — but once again I've got a <u>cunning plan</u>...

$$(1 + x)^0 = 1$$
$$(1 + x)^1 = 1 + x$$
$$(1 + x)^2 = 1 + 2x + x^2$$
$$(1 + x)^3 = 1 + 3x + 3x^2 + x^3$$
$$(1 + x)^4 = 1 + 4x + 6x^2 + 4x^3 + x^4$$

Anything to the power of O is 1.

$$(1 + x)^3 = (1 + x)(1 + x)^2$$
$$= (1 + x)(1 + 2x + x^2)$$
$$= 1 + 2x + x^2 + x + 2x^2 + x^3$$
$$= 1 + 3x + 3x^2 + x^3$$

A Frenchman named Pascal spotted the pattern in the coefficients and wrote them down in a <u>triangle</u>.
So it was called '<u>Pascal's Triangle</u>' (imaginative, eh?).
The pattern's easy — each number is the <u>sum</u> of the two above it.

So, the next line will be: **1 5 10 10 5 1**
giving $(1 + x)^5 = 1 + 5x + 10x^2 + 10x^3 + 5x^4 + x^5$.

```
              1
          1       1
        1    2      1
      1    3     3   + 1
    1    4     6    = 4   1
```

You **Don't** need to write out Pascal's Triangle for **Higher Powers**

There's a formula for the numbers in the triangle. The formula looks <u>horrible</u> (one of the worst in AS maths) so don't try to learn it letter by letter — look for the <u>patterns</u> in it instead. Here's an example:

> **EXAMPLE** Expand $(1 + x)^{20}$, giving the first four terms only.

So you can use this formula for any power, the power is called n. In this example $n = 20$.

$$(1 + x)^n = 1 + \frac{n}{1}x + \frac{n(n-1)}{1 \times 2}x^2 + \boxed{\frac{n(n-1)(n-2)}{1 \times 2 \times 3}x^3} + \ldots\ldots\ldots + x^n$$

Here's a closer look at the term in the black box:

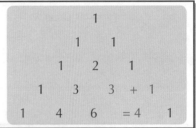

There are <u>three things</u> multiplied together on the top row. If n=20, this would be 20×19×18.

$$\frac{n(n-1)(n-2)}{1 \times 2 \times 3}x^3$$

<u>Start here</u>. The power of x is 3 and everything else here is based on 3.

There are <u>three integers</u> here multiplied together. 1×2×3 is written as 3! and called 3 <u>factorial</u>.

This means, if $n = 20$ and you were asked for '<u>the term in x^7</u>' you should write $\dfrac{20 \times 19 \times 18 \times 17 \times 16 \times 15 \times 14}{1 \times 2 \times 3 \times 4 \times 5 \times 6 \times 7}x^7$.

This can be <u>simplified</u> to $\dfrac{20!}{7!13!}x^7$

$20 \times 19 \times 18 \times 17 \times 16 \times 15 \times 14 = \dfrac{20!}{13!}$ because it's the numbers from 20 to 1 multiplied together, divided by the numbers from 13 to 1 multiplied together.

Believe it or not, there's an even <u>shorter</u> form: $\boxed{\dfrac{20!}{7!13!} \text{ is written as } {}^{20}C_7 \text{ or } \binom{20}{7}}$ ${}^nC_r = \binom{n}{r} = \dfrac{n!}{r!(n-r)!}$

Your calculator will probably have an nCr button for working this out. To calculate $\binom{20}{7}$ you'd put in 20 $\boxed{nCr}$ 7 =.

So, to finish the example, $(1 + x)^{20} = 1 + \dfrac{20}{1}x + \dfrac{20 \times 19}{1 \times 2}x^2 + \dfrac{20 \times 19 \times 18}{1 \times 2 \times 3}x^3 + \ldots = 1 + 20x + 190x^2 + 1140x^3 + \ldots$

Binomial Expansions

It's slightly more complicated when the **Coefficient** of x isn't 1

EXAMPLE   What is the term in x^5 in the expansion of $(1 - 3x)^{12}$?

The term in x^5 will be as follows:

$$\frac{12 \times 11 \times 10 \times 9 \times 8}{1 \times 2 \times 3 \times 4 \times 5}(-3x)^5$$

> Watch out — the –3 is included here with the x.

$$= \frac{12!}{5!7!}(-3)^5 x^5 = -\frac{12!}{5!7!} \times 3^5 x^5 = -192456 x^5$$

> Tip — the digits on the <u>bottom</u> of the fraction should always <u>add up</u> to the number on the <u>top</u>.

Note that $(-3)^{\text{even}}$ will always be <u>positive</u> and $(-3)^{\text{odd}}$ will always be <u>negative</u>.

Some **Binomials** contain **More Complicated Expressions**

The binomials so far have all had a <u>1</u> in the brackets — things get tricky when there's a <u>number other than 1</u>. Don't panic, though. The method is the same as before once you've done a bit of <u>factorising</u>.

EXAMPLE   What is the coefficient of x^4 in the expansion of $(2 + 5x)^7$?

Factorising $(2 + 5x)$ gives $2\left(1 + \frac{5}{2}x\right)$

So, $(2 + 5x)^7$ gives $2^7\left(1 + \frac{5}{2}x\right)^7$

> It's really easy to forget the first bit (here it's 2^7) — you've been warned...

$$(2 + 5x)^7 = 2^7\left(1 + \frac{5}{2}x\right)^7$$

$$= 2^7[1 + 7\left(\frac{5}{2}x\right) + \frac{7 \times 6}{1 \times 2}\left(\frac{5}{2}x\right)^2 + \frac{7 \times 6 \times 5}{1 \times 2 \times 3}\left(\frac{5}{2}x\right)^3 + \frac{7 \times 6 \times 5 \times 4}{1 \times 2 \times 3 \times 4}\left(\frac{5}{2}x\right)^4 + ...]$$

> Here's the one you want.

The coefficient of x^4 will be $2^7 \times \frac{7!}{4!3!}\left(\frac{5}{2}\right)^4 = 175000$

> Don't forget the 2^7.

So, there's <u>no need</u> to work out all of the terms.
In fact, you could have gone <u>directly</u> to the term in x^4 by using the method on page 65.

> Note: the question asked for the <u>coefficient of x^4</u> in the expansion, so <u>don't include any x's</u> in your answer. If you'd been asked for the <u>term in x^4</u> in the expansion, then you <u>should</u> have included the x^4 in your answer.
>
> <u>Always</u> read the question very carefully.

Binomial Expansions

Fed up of binomials yet? Good. Me neither.

Some *Binomials* are *More Complicated* still

Sometimes you'll see a binomial with a <u>power</u> of x inside the bracket, or even with <u>two brackets</u> together. Cripes.

EXAMPLE Expand $\left(1 + \frac{2}{x^2}\right)^4$.

This is the same method as the first example on the previous page, just, you know, worse.

The trick here is to break the problem down into stages.

First, expand $(1 + x)^4$, using the coefficients from Pascal's Triangle, but write $\left(\frac{2}{x^2}\right)$ in place of every x...

$$\left(1 + \frac{2}{x^2}\right)^4 = 1 + 4\left(\frac{2}{x^2}\right) + 6\left(\frac{2}{x^2}\right)^2 + 4\left(\frac{2}{x^2}\right)^3 + \left(\frac{2}{x^2}\right)^4$$

...then deal with the powers of x and tidy it up:

$$= 1 + 4\left(\frac{2}{x^2}\right) + 6\left(\frac{4}{x^4}\right) + 4\left(\frac{8}{x^6}\right) + \left(\frac{16}{x^8}\right) = 1 + \frac{8}{x^2} + \frac{24}{x^4} + \frac{32}{x^6} + \frac{16}{x^8}$$

EXAMPLE Find the coefficient of x^3 in the expansion of $(1 + x)(1 + 2x)^4$.

First, find the expansion of $(1 + 2x)^4$ using the method above:

$$(1 + 2x)^4 = 1 + 4(2x) + 6(2x)^2 + 4(2x)^3 + (2x)^4$$
$$= 1 + 8x + 24x^2 + 32x^3 + 16x^4$$

Then instead of multiplying the whole expansion by $(1 + x)$, just look at the bits which will multiply together to give a term with x^3 in, i.e.

$$(1 \times 32x^3) + (x \times 24x^2) = 32x^3 + 24x^3 = 56x^3$$

So the coefficient of x^3 in this expansion is 56.

Sometimes you'll just have to use the *Formula*

All of the binomials so far have been of the form $(c + dx)^n$, where c and d are constants. Things won't always be so nice though — you might be asked to expand something of the form $(a + b)^n$, where a and b could be <u>anything at all</u> (even functions of x). Fortunately, there's a <u>formula</u> to help you do it:

$$(a + b)^n = a^n + \binom{n}{1}a^{n-1}b + \binom{n}{2}a^{n-2}b^2 + \dots + \binom{n}{r}a^{n-r}b^r + \dots + b^n$$

Don't worry, you don't need to memorise this formula — you'll be given it in the exam.

I know, it's an absolute shocker, but it will make questions a lot easier if you can get your head around it. An example will help:

EXAMPLE Expand and simplify $\left(2x + \frac{1}{x}\right)^5$.

Comparing to the formula, $a = 2x$, $b = \frac{1}{x}$ and $n = 5$.
So use the formula with these values in place of a and b:

Remember
$$^nC_r = \binom{n}{r} = \frac{n!}{r!(n-r)!}$$

$$\left(2x + \frac{1}{x}\right)^5 = (2x)^5 + \binom{5}{1}(2x)^4\left(\frac{1}{x}\right) + \binom{5}{2}(2x)^3\left(\frac{1}{x}\right)^2 + \binom{5}{3}(2x)^2\left(\frac{1}{x}\right)^3 + \binom{5}{4}(2x)\left(\frac{1}{x}\right)^4 + \left(\frac{1}{x}\right)^5$$

$$= 32x^5 + 5(16x^4)\left(\frac{1}{x}\right) + 10(8x^3)\left(\frac{1}{x^2}\right) + 10(4x^2)\left(\frac{1}{x^3}\right) + 5(2x)\left(\frac{1}{x^4}\right) + \frac{1}{x^5}$$

$$= 32x^5 + 80x^3 + 80x + \frac{40}{x} + \frac{10}{x^3} + \frac{1}{x^5}$$

I never pay for food — I use the buy-no-meal formula...

That ^nC_r button is pretty bloomin' useful (but remember that it could be called something else on your calculator) — it saves a lot of button pressing and errors. Just make sure you put your numbers in the right way round. But that's all you need to know on binomial expansion, and on sequences and series in general — it wasn't that short, but it sure was sweet.

C2 Section 2 — Practice Questions

What's that I hear you cry? You want revision questions — and lots of them. Well it just so happens I've got a few here. With sequences and series, get a <u>clear idea</u> in your head before you start, or you could go in completely the <u>wrong direction</u>. That would be bad.

Warm-up Questions

1) Find the <u>nth term</u> for the following sequences:

   a) 2, 6, 10, 14, ...

   b) 0.2, 0.7, 1.2, 1.7, ...

   c) 21, 18, 15, 12, ...

   d) 76, 70, 64, 58, ...

2) Find the <u>sum</u> of the arithmetic series that <u>begins with</u> 5, 8, ... and <u>ends with</u> 65.

3) An arithmetic series has <u>first term</u> 7 and <u>5th term</u> 23.

   Find:　　a) the common difference,　b) the 15th term, and　　c) the sum of the first 10 terms.

4) Find $\sum_{n=1}^{10} (48 - 5n)$.

5) For the geometric progression 2, –6, 18, ..., find:

   a) the 10th term,

   b) the sum of the first 10 terms.

6) Find the sum of the first 12 terms of the following geometric series:

   a) 2 + 8 + 32 + ...

   b) 30 + 15 + 7.5 + ...

7) A geometric progression begins 2, 6, ...
   Which term of the geometric progression equals 1458?

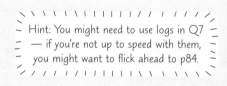
Hint: You might need to use logs in Q7 — if you're not up to speed with them, you might want to flick ahead to p84.

8) Find the coefficient of x^2 in the expansion of $(2 + 3x)^5$.

Exam Questions

1　A sequence is defined by the recurrence relation: $h_{n+1} = 2h_n + 2$ when $n \geq 1$.

   a)　Given that $h_1 = 5$, find the values of h_2, h_3, and h_4.

   (3 marks)

   b)　Calculate the value of $\sum_{r=3}^{6} h_r$.

   (3 marks)

C2 Section 2 — Practice Questions

More lovingly crafted questions, wrought from the finest numbers and quality equations for our valued customers...

2   A sequence $a_1, a_2, a_3,$ ... is defined by $a_1 = k$, $a_{n+1} = 3a_n + 11$, $n \geq 1$, where k is a constant.

     a)   Show that $a_4 = 27k + 143$.

(3 marks)

     b)   Find the value of k, given that $\sum_{r=1}^{4} a_r = 278$.

(3 marks)

3   Ned has 15 cuboidal pots that need filling with soil. Each pot is taller than the one before it. The different capacities of his 15 pots form an arithmetic sequence with first term (representing the smallest pot) a ml and the common difference d ml. The 7th pot is 580 ml and he will need a total of exactly 9525 ml of soil to fill all of them.

     Find the value of a and the value of d.

(7 marks)

4   The first term of an arithmetic sequence is 22 and the common difference is –1.1.

     a)   Find the value of the 31st term.

(2 marks)

     b)   If the kth term of the sequence is 0, find k.

(2 marks)

     c)   The sum to n terms of the sequence is S_n.
           Find the value of n at which S_n first becomes negative.

(4 marks)

5   David's personal trainer has given him a timetable to improve his upper-body strength, which gradually increases the amount of push-ups David does each day.
The timetable for the first four days is shown below:

Day:	Mon	Tue	Wed	Thur
Number of push-ups:	6	14	22	30

     a)   Find an expression, in terms of n, for the number of push-ups he will have to do on day n.

(3 marks)

     b)   David follows his exercise routine for 10 days. Calculate how many push-ups he has done in total over the 10 days.

(3 marks)

     His personal trainer recommends that David takes a break from his exercise routine when he has done a cumulative total of 2450 push-ups. Given that David completes his exercises on day k, but reaches the recommended limit part-way through day $(k + 1)$,

     c)   Show that k satisfies $(2k - 49)(k + 25) < 0$.

(3 marks)

     d)   Find the value of k.

(2 marks)

C2 Section 2 — Practice Questions

I like sequences, they're shiny and colourful and sparkly and... wait, what? ... Oh. Fiddlesticks.
Watch out for questions on this page that need logs — you can read up on them on p84.

6   Find the coefficients of x, x^2, x^3 and x^4 in the binomial expansion of $(4 + 3x)^{10}$.

(4 marks)

7   a)   Find the binomial expansion of $\left(\frac{1}{2x} + \frac{x}{2}\right)^3$. Simplify your answer.

(3 marks)

   b)   Hence find the coefficient of x in the expansion of $(2 + x^2)\left(\frac{1}{2x} + \frac{x}{2}\right)^3$.

(3 marks)

8   A geometric series has the first term 12 and is defined by: $u_{n+1} = 12 \times 1.3^n$.

   a)   Is the series convergent or divergent?

(1 mark)

   b)   Find the values of the 3rd and 10th terms.

(2 marks)

9   In a geometric series, $a = 20$ and $r = \frac{3}{4}$.

   Find values for the following, giving your answers to 3 significant figures where necessary:

   a)   The sum to infinity of the series

(2 marks)

   b) u_{15}

(2 marks)

   c)   The smallest value of n for which the sum of the first n terms is greater than 79.76.

(5 marks)

10   To raise money for charity, Alex, Chris and Heather were sponsored £1 for each kilometre they
    ran over a 10-day period. They receive sponsorship proportionally for partial kilometres completed.
    Alex ran 3 km every day.
    Chris ran 2 km on day 1 and on each subsequent day ran 20% further than the day before.
    Heather ran 1 km on day 1 and on each subsequent day, she ran 50% further than the previous day.

   a)   How far did Heather run on day 5, to the nearest 10 metres?

(2 marks)

   b)   Show that day 10 is the first day that Chris runs further than 10 km.

(3 marks)

   c)   Find the total amount raised by the end of the 10 days, to the nearest penny.

(4 marks)

11   Two different geometric series have the same second term and sum to infinity:

$$u_2 = 5 \text{ and } \sum_{n=1}^{\infty} u_n = 36.$$

   a)   Show that $36r^2 - 36r + 5 = 0$, where r represents the two possible ratios.

(4 marks)

   b)   Hence find the values of r, and the corresponding first terms, for both geometric series.

(4 marks)

Arc Length and Sector Area

Arc lengths and sector areas are easier than you'd think — once you've learnt two simple(ish) formulas.

Always work in **Radians** for **Arc Length** and **Sector Area Questions**

Remember — for arc length and sector area questions you've got to measure all the angles in <u>radians</u>.

The main thing is that you know how radians relate to <u>degrees</u>.
In short, 180 degrees = π radians. The table below shows you how to convert between the two units:

Converting angles	
<u>Radians to degrees:</u>	<u>Degrees to radians:</u>
Divide by π, multiply by 180.	Divide by 180, multiply by π.

Here's a table of some of the common angles you're going to need — in degrees and radians:

Degrees	0	30	45	60	90	120	180	270	360
Radians	0	$\dfrac{\pi}{6}$	$\dfrac{\pi}{4}$	$\dfrac{\pi}{3}$	$\dfrac{\pi}{2}$	$\dfrac{2\pi}{3}$	π	$\dfrac{3\pi}{2}$	2π

If you have <u>part of a circle</u> (like a section of pie chart), you can work out the <u>length of the curved side</u>, or the <u>area of the 'slice of pie'</u> — as long as you know the <u>angle</u> at the centre (θ) and the <u>length of the radius</u> (r). Read on...

You can find the **Length** of an **Arc** using a nice easy formula...

For a circle with a <u>radius of r</u>, where the angle θ is measured in <u>radians</u>, the <u>arc length of the sector S</u> is given by:

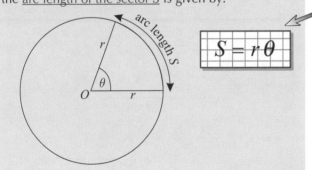

$$S = r\theta$$

If you put $\theta = 2\pi$ in this formula (and so make the sector equal to the whole circle), you get that the distance all the way round the outside of the circle is $S = 2\pi r$.

This is just the normal circumference formula.

...and the area of a **Sector** using a similar formula

For a circle with a <u>radius of r</u>, where the angle θ is measured in <u>radians</u>, you can work out A, the <u>area of the sector</u>, using:

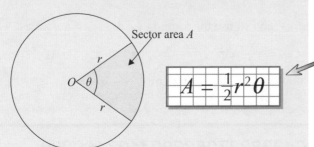

$$A = \tfrac{1}{2}r^2\theta$$

Again, if you put $\theta = 2\pi$ in the formula, you find that the area of the whole circle is $A = \tfrac{1}{2}r^2 \times 2\pi = \pi r^2$.

This is just the normal 'area of a circle' formula.

Arc Length and Sector Area

Questions on <u>trigonometry</u> quite often use the same angles — so it makes life easier if you know the sin, cos and tan of these commonly used angles. Or to put it another way, examiners expect you to know them — so learn them.

Draw Triangles to remember *sin*, *cos* and *tan* of the *Important Angles*

You should know the values of <u>sin</u>, <u>cos</u> and <u>tan</u> at 30°, 60° and 45°. But to help you remember, you can draw these two groovy triangles. It may seem a complicated way to learn a few numbers, but it does make it easier. Honest.

The idea is you draw the triangles below, putting in their angles and side lengths. Then you can use them to work out special trig values like <u>sin 45°</u> or <u>cos 60°</u> more accurately than any calculator (which only gives a few decimal places).

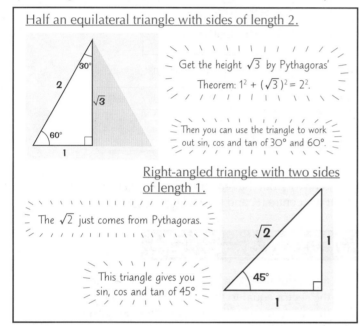

Half an equilateral triangle with sides of length 2.

Get the height $\sqrt{3}$ by Pythagoras' Theorem: $1^2 + (\sqrt{3})^2 = 2^2$.

Then you can use the triangle to work out sin, cos and tan of 30° and 60°.

Right-angled triangle with two sides of length 1.

The $\sqrt{2}$ just comes from Pythagoras.

This triangle gives you sin, cos and tan of 45°.

Remember: SOH CAH TOA...

$$\sin = \frac{\text{opp}}{\text{hyp}} \qquad \cos = \frac{\text{adj}}{\text{hyp}} \qquad \tan = \frac{\text{opp}}{\text{adj}}$$

Trig Values from Triangles

$$\sin 30° = \frac{1}{2} \qquad \sin 60° = \frac{\sqrt{3}}{2} \qquad \sin 45° = \frac{1}{\sqrt{2}}$$

$$\cos 30° = \frac{\sqrt{3}}{2} \qquad \cos 60° = \frac{1}{2} \qquad \cos 45° = \frac{1}{\sqrt{2}}$$

$$\tan 30° = \frac{1}{\sqrt{3}} \qquad \tan 60° = \sqrt{3} \qquad \tan 45° = 1$$

EXAMPLE Find the exact length L and area A in the diagram.

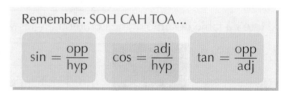

Right, first things first... it's an arc length and sector area, so you need the angle in radians.

$$45° = \frac{45 \times \pi}{180} = \frac{\pi}{4} \text{ radians}$$

Or you could just quote this if you've learnt the stuff on the previous page.

Now bung everything in your formulas:

$$L = r\theta = 20 \times \frac{\pi}{4} = 5\pi \text{ cm}$$

$$A = \frac{1}{2}r^2\theta = \frac{1}{2} \times 20^2 \times \frac{\pi}{4} = 50\pi \text{ cm}^2$$

EXAMPLE Find the area of the shaded part of the symbol.

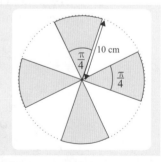

Instead, you could use the total angle of all the shaded sectors (π).

You need the area of the 'leaves' and so use the formula $\frac{1}{2}r^2\theta$.

Each leaf has area $\frac{1}{2} \times 10^2 \times \frac{\pi}{4} = \frac{25\pi}{2} \text{ cm}^2$

So the area of the whole symbol = $4 \times \frac{25\pi}{2} = 50\pi \text{ cm}^2$

π = *3.14159265358979323846264338327950288419716939...(Make sure you know it)*

It's worth repeating, just to make sure — those formulas for arc length and sector area only work if the angle is in <u>radians</u>.

The Trig Formulas You Need to Know

There are some more trig formulas you <u>need to know</u> for the exam.
So here they are — learn them or you're seriously stuffed. Worse than an aubergine.

The **Sine Rule** and **Cosine Rule** work for **Any** triangle

Remember, these three formulas work for <u>ANY</u> triangle, not just right-angled ones.

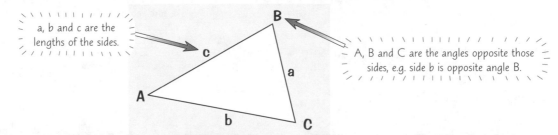

a, b and c are the lengths of the sides.

A, B and C are the angles opposite those sides, e.g. side b is opposite angle B.

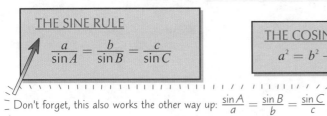

THE SINE RULE
$$\frac{a}{\sin A} = \frac{b}{\sin B} = \frac{c}{\sin C}$$

THE COSINE RULE
$$a^2 = b^2 + c^2 - 2bc\cos A$$

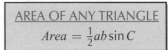

AREA OF ANY TRIANGLE
$$Area = \tfrac{1}{2}ab\sin C$$

Don't forget, this also works the other way up: $\frac{\sin A}{a} = \frac{\sin B}{b} = \frac{\sin C}{c}$

Sine Rule or **Cosine Rule** — which one is it...

To decide which of these two rules you need to use, look at what you <u>already</u> know about the triangle.

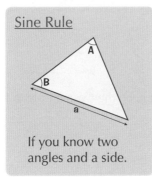

Sine Rule

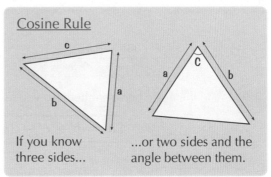

Cosine Rule

If you know two angles and a side.

If you know three sides...

...or two sides and the angle between them.

The **Best** has been saved till last...

These two identities are really important. You'll need them <u>loads</u>.

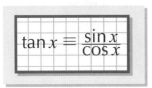
$$\tan x \equiv \frac{\sin x}{\cos x}$$

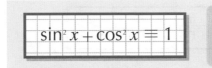
$$\sin^2 x + \cos^2 x \equiv 1$$

$$\Rightarrow \sin^2 x \equiv 1 - \cos^2 x$$
$$\cos^2 x \equiv 1 - \sin^2 x$$

Work out these two using $\sin^2 x + \cos^2 x \equiv 1$.

These two come up in exam questions <u>all the time</u>. Learn them.
Learnthemlearnthemlearnthemlearnthemlearnthemlear... okay, I'll stop now.

Tri angles — go on... you might like them.

Formulas and trigonometry go together even better than Richard and Judy. There are only a few of them on
this page, so please, just make sure you know them. If you haven't learnt them I will cry for you. I will sob.

Using the Sine and Cosine Rules

This page is about "solving" triangles, which just means finding all their <u>sides</u> and <u>angles</u> when you already know a few.

EXAMPLE   Solve $\triangle ABC$, in which A = 40°, a = 27 m, B = 73°. Then find the area.

Draw a quick sketch first — don't worry if it's not deadly accurate, though.

You're given 2 angles and a side, so you need the Sine Rule.

Make sure you put side a opposite angle A.

First of all, get the other angle: $\angle C = (180 - 40 - 73)^\circ = 67^\circ$

Then find the other sides, one at a time:

$$\frac{a}{\sin A} = \frac{b}{\sin B} \Rightarrow \frac{27}{\sin 40^\circ} = \frac{b}{\sin 73^\circ}$$
$$\Rightarrow b = \frac{\sin 73^\circ}{\sin 40^\circ} \times 27 = \underline{40.2\,\text{m}}$$

$$\frac{c}{\sin C} = \frac{a}{\sin A} \Rightarrow \frac{c}{\sin 67^\circ} = \frac{27}{\sin 40^\circ}$$
$$\Rightarrow c = \frac{\sin 67^\circ}{\sin 40^\circ} \times 27 = \underline{38.7\,\text{m}}$$

Now just use the formula to find its area.

$$\text{Area of } \triangle ABC = \tfrac{1}{2}ab\sin C$$
$$= \tfrac{1}{2} \times 27 \times 40.169 \times \sin 67^\circ$$
$$= \underline{499.2\,\text{m}^2}$$

Use a more accurate value for b here, rather than the rounded value 40.2.

EXAMPLE   Find X, Y and z.

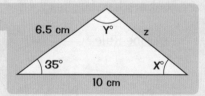

You've been given 2 sides and the angle between them, so you're first going to need the Cosine Rule to find side z.

$$a^2 = b^2 + c^2 - 2bc\cos A$$

$$z^2 = (6.5)^2 + 10^2 - 2(6.5)(10)\cos 35^\circ$$
$$\Rightarrow z^2 = 142.25 - 130\cos 35^\circ$$
$$\Rightarrow z^2 = 35.7602$$
$$\Rightarrow z = \underline{5.98\,\text{cm}}$$

In this case, angle A is 35°, and side a is actually z.

Now that you've got all the sides and one angle, you can use the Sine Rule to find the other two angles.

$$\frac{a}{\sin A} = \frac{b}{\sin B} = \frac{c}{\sin C}$$

Remember — if $\frac{a}{\sin A} = \frac{b}{\sin B}$ then $\frac{\sin A}{a} = \frac{\sin B}{b}$.

$$\frac{\sin X}{6.5} = \frac{\sin 35^\circ}{5.9800}$$
$$\Rightarrow \sin X = 0.6235$$
$$\Rightarrow X = \sin^{-1} 0.6235$$
$$\Rightarrow X = \underline{38.6^\circ}$$

$$\frac{\sin Y}{10} = \frac{\sin 35^\circ}{5.9800}$$
$$\Rightarrow \sin Y = 0.9592$$
$$\Rightarrow Y = \sin^{-1} 0.9592$$
$$\Rightarrow Y = 73.6^\circ \text{ or } \underline{106.4^\circ}$$

This is the answer you need. <u>Be careful</u>: your calculator only gives you values for $\sin^{-1}$ between −90° and 90°. See page 77.

Check your answers by adding up all the angles in the triangle. If they don't add up to 180°, you've gone wrong somewhere.

Graphs of Trig Functions

Before you leave this page, you should be able to close your eyes and picture these three graphs in your head, properly labelled and everything. If you can't, you need to learn them more. I'm not kidding.

sin x and cos x are always in the range –1 to 1

$\underline{\sin x}$ and $\underline{\cos x}$ are similar — they just bob up and down between –1 and 1.

sin x and cos x are both <u>periodic</u> (repeat themselves) with period 360°

$$\cos(x + 360°) = \cos x \qquad \sin(x + 360°) = \sin x$$

They bounce up and down from –1 to 1 — they can <u>never</u> have a value outside this range.

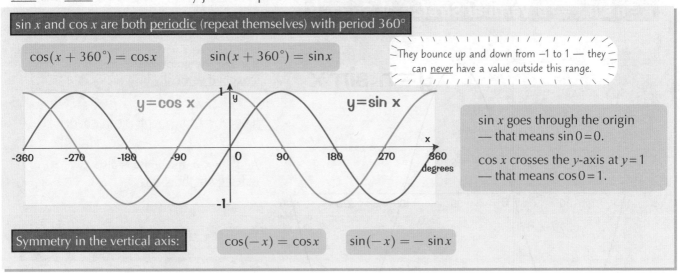

sin x goes through the origin — that means $\sin 0 = 0$.

cos x crosses the y-axis at $y = 1$ — that means $\cos 0 = 1$.

Symmetry in the vertical axis: $\cos(-x) = \cos x \qquad \sin(-x) = -\sin x$

tan x can be Any Value at all

tan x is different from sin x or cos x.
It doesn't go gently up and down between –1 and 1 — it goes between $-\infty$ and $+\infty$.

TAN X IS ALSO <u>PERIODIC</u> — BUT WITH PERIOD 180°

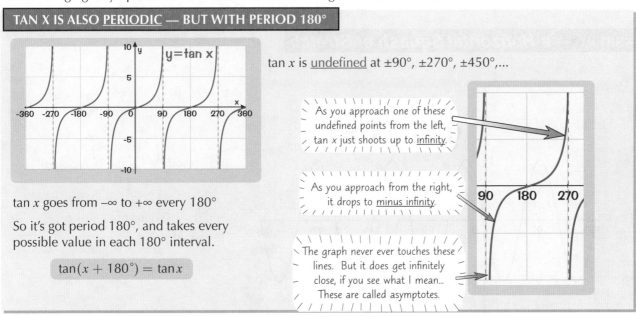

tan x is <u>undefined</u> at ±90°, ±270°, ±450°,...

As you approach one of these undefined points from the left, tan x just shoots up to <u>infinity</u>.

As you approach from the right, it drops to <u>minus infinity</u>.

The graph never ever touches these lines. But it does get infinitely close, if you see what I mean... These are called asymptotes.

tan x goes from $-\infty$ to $+\infty$ every 180°

So it's got period 180°, and takes every possible value in each 180° interval.

$$\tan(x + 180°) = \tan x$$

The easiest way to sketch any of these graphs is to plot the important points which happen every 90° (i.e. –180°, –90°, 0°, 90°, 180°, 270°, 360°...) and then just join the dots up.

Sin and cos can make your life worthwhile — give them a chance...

It's really really really really really important that you can draw the trig graphs on this page, and get all the labels right. Make sure you know what value sin, cos and tan have at the interesting points — i.e. 0°, 90°, 180°, 270°, 360°. It's easy to remember what the graphs look like, but you've got to know exactly <u>where</u> they're max, min, zero, etc.

Transformed Trig Graphs

Transformed trigonometric graphs look much the same as the bog-standard ones, just a little <u>different</u>.
There are two types of transformation you need to know about.

There are 2 types of **Stretched or Squashed Trig Graph**...

$y = n \sin x$ — a **Vertical Stretch** or **Squash**

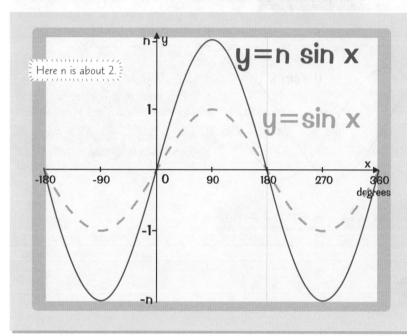

Here n is about 2.

$y = n \sin x$

$y = \sin x$

If $n > 1$, the graph of $y = \sin x$ is <u>stretched vertically</u> by a factor of n.

If $0 < n < 1$, the graph is <u>squashed</u>.

And if $n < 0$, the graph is also <u>reflected</u> in the <u>x-axis</u>.

$y = \sin nx$ — a **Horizontal Squash** or **Stretch**

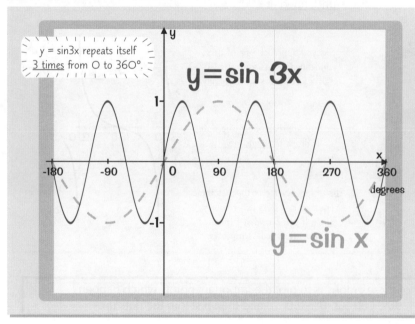

$y = \sin 3x$ repeats itself <u>3 times</u> from 0 to 360°.

$y = \sin 3x$

$y = \sin x$

If $n > 1$, the graph of $y = \sin x$ is <u>squashed horizontally</u> by a factor of n.

If $0 < n < 1$, the graph is <u>stretched</u>.

And if $n < 0$, the graph is also <u>reflected</u> in the <u>y-axis</u>.

Curling up on the sofa with 2cos x — that's my idea of cosiness ☺

One thing you've really got to be careful about is making sure you squash or stretch the graphs in the <u>right</u> direction.
In the two examples above, $n > 1$ means a <u>vertical stretch</u> but a <u>horizontal squash</u>.

Solving Trig Equations in a Given Interval

I used to really hate trig stuff like this. But once I'd got the hang of it, I just couldn't get enough. I stopped going out, lost interest in the opposite sex — the CAST method became my life. Learn it, but be careful. It's addictive.

There are **Two Ways** to find Solutions in an **Interval**...

EXAMPLE Solve $\cos x = \frac{1}{2}$ for $-360° \leq x \leq 720°$.

Like I said — there are two ways to solve this kind of question. Just use the one you prefer...

You can draw a **graph**...

Your calculator gives you a solution of 60°. Then you have to work out what the others will be.

The other solutions are 60° either side of the graph's peaks.

1) Draw the graph of $y = \cos x$ for the range you're interested in...

2) Get the first solution from your calculator and mark this on the graph,

3) Use the symmetry of the graph to work out what the other solutions are:

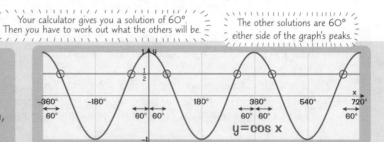

So the solutions are: $-300°, -60°, 60°, 300°, 420°$ and $660°$.

...or you can use the **CAST** diagram

CAST stands for COS, ALL, SIN, TAN — and the CAST diagram shows you where these functions are positive:

Between 90° and 180°, only SIN is positive.

Between 0 and 90°, ALL of sin, cos and tan are positive.

Between 180° and 270°, only TAN is positive.

Between 270° and 360°, only COS is positive.

This is positive — so you're only interested in where cos is positive.

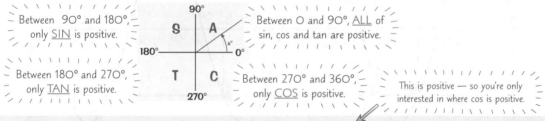

First, to find all the values of x between 0° and 360° where $\cos x = \frac{1}{2}$ — you do this:

Put the first solution onto the CAST diagram.	Find the other angles between 0° and 360° that might be solutions.	Ditch the ones that are the wrong sign.

The angle from your calculator goes anticlockwise from the x-axis (unless it's negative — then it would go clockwise into the 4th quadrant).

The other possible solutions come from making the same angle from the horizontal axis in the other 3 quadrants.

cos x = ½, which is positive. The CAST diagram tells you cos is positive in the 4th quadrant — but not the 2nd or 3rd — so ditch those two angles.

So you've got solutions 60° and 300° in the range 0° to 360°. But you need all the solutions in the range $-360°$ to 720°. Get these by repeatedly adding or subtracting 360° onto each until you go out of range:

$$x = 60° \Rightarrow \underline{(\text{adding } 360°)}\ x = 420°,\ 780°\ (\text{too big})$$

$$\text{and } \underline{(\text{subtracting } 360°)}\ x = -300°,\ -660°\ (\text{too small})$$

$$x = 300° \Rightarrow \underline{(\text{adding } 360°)}\ x = 660°,\ 1020°\ (\text{too big})$$

$$\text{and } \underline{(\text{subtracting } 360°)}\ x = -60°,\ -420°\ (\text{too small})$$

So the solutions are: $x = -300°, -60°, 60°, 300°, 420°$ and $660°$.

And I feel that love is dead, I'm loving angles instead...

Suppose the first solution you get is <u>negative</u>, let's say $-d°$, then you'd measure it <u>clockwise</u> on the CAST diagram. So it'd be $d°$ in the 4th quadrant. Then you'd work out the other 3 possible solutions in exactly the same way, rejecting the ones which weren't the right sign. Got that? No? Got that? No? Got that? Yes? Good!

Solving Trig Equations in a Given Interval

Sometimes it's a bit more complicated. But only a bit.

Sometimes you end up with *sin kx = number*

For these, it's definitely easier to draw the <u>graph</u> rather than use the CAST method —
that's one reason why being able to sketch trig graphs properly is so important.

EXAMPLE Solve: $\sin 3x = -\frac{1}{\sqrt{2}}$ for $0° \le x \le 360°$.

> You could get a question like this involving cos kx or
> tan kx instead — the method's the same as for sin,
> but make sure you're happy dealing with all three.

1) You've got $3x$ instead of x, which means the range you need to find solutions in is $0° \le 3x \le 1080°$.
   So draw the graph of $y = \sin x$ between $0°$ and $1080°$.

2) Use your calculator to find the first solution. You'll get $3x = -45°$ — but this is outside
   the range for $3x$, so use the pattern of the graph to find a solution in the range.
   As the sin curve repeats every $360°$, there'll be a solution at $360 - 45 = 315°$.

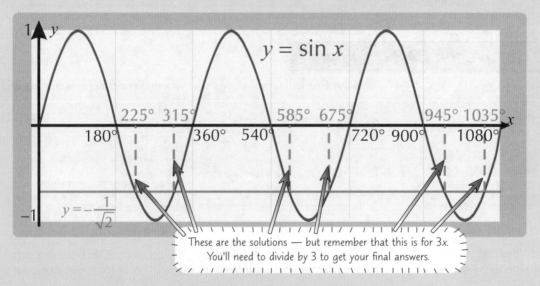

> These are the solutions — but remember that this is for 3x.
> You'll need to divide by 3 to get your final answers.

3) Now use your graph to find the other 5 solutions.
   You can see that there's another solution at $180 + 45 = 225°$.
   Then add on $360°$ and $720°$ to both $225°$ and $315°$ to get:

   $$3x = 225°, 315°, 585°, 675°, 945° \text{ and } 1035°.$$

   Divide by 3 to get the solutions for x:

   $$x = 75°, 105°, 195°, 225°, 315° \text{ and } 345°.$$

4) <u>Check</u> your answers by putting these values back into your calculator.

> It really is mega-important that you check these
> answers — it's dead easy to make a silly mistake.
> They should all be in the range $0° \le x \le 360°$.

Live a life of sin (and cos and tan)...

Yep, the example on this page is pretty fiddly. The most important bit is actually getting the sketch right for your new range.
If you don't, you're in big trouble. Then you've just got to carefully use the sketch to work out the other solutions.
It's tricky, but you'll feel better about yourself when you've got it mastered. Ah you will, you will, you will ...

Solving Trig Equations in a Given Interval

Now for something really exciting — trig identities. Mmm, well, maybe exciting was the wrong word. But they can be dead useful, so here goes...

For equations with *tan x* in, it often helps to use this...

$$\tan x \equiv \frac{\sin x}{\cos x}$$

This is a handy thing to know — and one the examiners love testing. Basically, if you've got a trig equation with a tan in it, together with a sin or a cos — chances are you'll be better off if you rewrite the tan using this formula.

EXAMPLE   Solve: $3\sin x - \tan x = 0$, for $0 \leq x \leq 2\pi$.

It's got sin and tan in it — so writing $\tan x$ as $\frac{\sin x}{\cos x}$ is probably a good move:

$$3\sin x - \tan x = 0$$
$$\Rightarrow 3\sin x - \frac{\sin x}{\cos x} = 0$$

Get rid of the $\cos x$ on the bottom by multiplying the whole equation by $\cos x$.

$$\Rightarrow 3\sin x \cos x - \sin x = 0$$

Now — there's a common factor of $\sin x$. Take that outside a bracket.

$$\Rightarrow \sin x (3\cos x - 1) = 0$$

And now you're almost there. You've got two things multiplying together to make zero. That means either one or both of them is equal to zero themselves.

$$\Rightarrow \sin x = 0 \quad \text{or} \quad 3\cos x - 1 = 0$$

$\sin x = 0$

The first solution is... $\sin 0 = 0$

Now find the other points where sin x is zero in the interval $0 \leq x \leq 2\pi$.
(Remember the sin graph is zero every π radians.)

$$\Rightarrow x = 0, \pi, 2\pi \text{ radians}$$

$3\cos x - 1 = 0$

CAST gives any solutions in the interval $0 \leq x \leq 2\pi$.

Rearrange... $\cos x = \frac{1}{3}$

So the first solution is...

$$\cos^{-1} \frac{1}{3} = 1.231$$

CAST (or the graph of $\cos x$) gives another solution in the 4th quadrant...

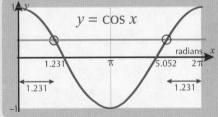

And the two solutions from this part are:

$$\Rightarrow x = 1.231, 5.052 \text{ radians}$$

So altogether you've got <u>five</u> possible solutions:

$$\Rightarrow x = 0, 1.231, \pi, 5.052, 2\pi \text{ radians}$$

Trigonometry is the root of all evil...

What a page — you don't have fun like that every day, do you? No, trig equations are where it's at. This is a really useful trick, though — and can turn a nightmare of an equation into a bit of a pussycat. <u>Rewriting</u> stuff using <u>different</u> formulas is always worth trying if it feels like you're getting stuck — even if you're not sure why when you're doing it. You might have a flash of inspiration when you see the new version.

Solving Trig Equations in a Given Interval

Another trig identity — and it's a good 'un — examiners love it. And it's not difficult either.

And if you have a *sin² x* or a *cos² x*, think of this straight away...

$$\sin^2 x + \cos^2 x \equiv 1 \implies \begin{array}{l} \sin^2 x \equiv 1 - \cos^2 x \\ \cos^2 x \equiv 1 - \sin^2 x \end{array}$$

Use this identity to get rid of a sin² or a cos² that's making things awkward...

EXAMPLE   Solve: $2\sin^2 x + 5\cos x = 4$, for $0° \leq x \leq 360°$.

You can't do much while the equation's got both sin's and cos's in it. So replace the sin²x bit with $1 - \cos^2 x$.

$$2(1 - \cos^2 x) + 5\cos x = 4$$

Multiply out the bracket and rearrange it so that you've got zero on one side — and you get a quadratic in cosx:

Now the only trig function is cos.

$$\Rightarrow 2 - 2\cos^2 x + 5\cos x = 4$$
$$\Rightarrow 2\cos^2 x - 5\cos x + 2 = 0$$

This is a quadratic in cosx. It's easier to factorise this if you make the substitution $y = \cos x$.

$$2y^2 - 5y + 2 = 0$$
$$\Rightarrow (2y - 1)(y - 2) = 0$$
$$\Rightarrow (2\cos x - 1)(\cos x - 2) = 0$$

$$2y^2 - 5y + 2 = (2y\ ?)(y\ ?)$$
$$= (2y - 1)(y - 2)$$

Now one of the brackets must be 0. So you get 2 equations as usual:

You've already done this example on page 77.

$$2\cos x - 1 = 0 \quad \text{or} \quad \cos x - 2 = 0$$

$$\cos x = \tfrac{1}{2} \Rightarrow x = 60° \quad \text{or} \quad x = 300° \quad \text{and} \quad \cos x = 2$$

This is a bit weird. cos x is always between −1 and 1. So you don't get any solutions from this bracket.

So at the end of all that, the only solutions you get are $x = 60°$ and $x = 300°$. How boring.

Use the **Trig Identities** to prove something is the **Same** as something else

Another use for these trig identities is proving that two things are the same.

EXAMPLE   Show that $\dfrac{\cos^2 \theta}{1 + \sin \theta} \equiv 1 - \sin \theta$

The identity sign ≡ means that this is true for all θ, rather than just certain values.

Prove things like this by playing about with one side of the equation until you get the other side.

Left-hand side: $\dfrac{\cos^2 \theta}{1 + \sin \theta}$

The only thing I can think of doing here is replacing $\cos^2 \theta$ with $1 - \sin^2 \theta$. (Which is good because it works.)

$$\equiv \dfrac{1 - \sin^2 \theta}{1 + \sin \theta}$$

The next trick is the hardest to spot. Look at the top — does that remind you of anything?

The top line is a difference of two squares:

$$\equiv \dfrac{(1 + \sin \theta)(1 - \sin \theta)}{1 + \sin \theta}$$

$$1 - a^2 = (1 + a)(1 - a)$$
$$\Rightarrow 1 - \sin^2 \theta = (1 + \sin \theta)(1 - \sin \theta)$$

$$\equiv 1 - \sin \theta, \text{ the right-hand side.}$$

Trig identities — the path to a brighter future...

That was a pretty miserable section. But it's over. These trig identities aren't exactly a barrel of laughs, but they are a definite source of marks — you can bet your last penny they'll be in the exam. That substitution trick to get rid of a sin² or a cos² and end up with a quadratic in sin x or cos x is a real examiners' favourite. Those identities can be a bit daunting, but it's always worth having a few tricks in the back of your mind — always look for things that factorise, or fractions that can be cancelled down, or ways to use those trig identities. Ah, it's all good clean fun.

C2 Section 3 — Practice Questions

I know, I know — that was a long section. And, rather predictably, it's followed by lots of <u>practice questions</u>. <u>Brace yourself</u> for the warm-up — this is going to be a <u>heavy session</u>...

Warm-up Questions

1) Write down the exact values of cos 30°, sin 30°, tan 30°, cos 45°, sin 45°, tan 45°, cos 60°, sin 60° and tan 60°.

2) Draw a triangle $\triangle XYZ$ with sides of length x, y and z.
Write down the Sine and Cosine Rules for this triangle. Write down an expression for its area.

3) What is tan x in terms of cos x and sin x? What is $\cos^2 x$ in terms of $\sin^2 x$?

4) Solve : a) $\triangle ABC$ in which A = 30°, C = 25°, b = 6 m, and find its area.
b) $\triangle PQR$ in which p = 3 km, q = 23 km, R = 10°. (answers to 2 d.p.)

5) My pet triangle Freda has sides of length 10, 20 and 25.
Find her angles (in degrees to 1 d.p.).

6) Sketch the graphs for sin x, cos x and tan x.
Make sure you label all the max/min/zero/undefined points.

7) Sketch the following graphs:
a) $y = \frac{1}{2}\cos x$ (for 0° $\leq x \leq$ 360°)   b) $y = \tan 3x$ (for 0° $\leq x \leq$ 180°)

8) a) Solve each of these equations for 0° $\leq \theta \leq$ 360°:
(i) $\sin \theta = -\frac{\sqrt{3}}{2}$ (ii) $\tan \theta = -1$ (iii) $\cos \theta = -\frac{1}{\sqrt{2}}$
b) Solve each of these equations for –180° $\leq \theta \leq$ 180° (giving your answer to 1 d.p.):
(i) $\cos 4\theta = -\frac{2}{3}$ (ii) $\tan\left(\frac{1}{2}\theta\right) = 500$

9) Find all the solutions to $6\sin^2 x = \cos x + 5$ in the range 0° $\leq x \leq$ 360° (answers to 1 d.p.).

10) Solve $3\tan x + 2\cos x = 0$ for –90° $\leq x \leq$ 90°

11) Simplify: $(\sin y + \cos y)^2 + (\cos y - \sin y)^2$

12) Show that $\dfrac{\sin^4 x + \sin^2 x \cos^2 x}{\cos^2 x - 1} \equiv -1$

Well after that vigorous warm-up you should be more than ready to tackle this <u>mental marathon</u> of exam-style questions. Take your time to work out <u>what each question wants</u> — if it looks impossible, there's probably a way of simplifying it somehow. A picture paints a thousand words, so <u>sketch it out</u> if you're totally confused.

Exam Questions

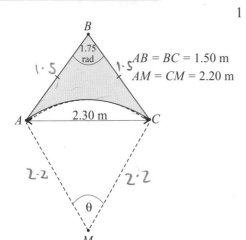

1   The shape ABC shown here is a concrete slab that forms part of a paved area around a circular pond.
The curve AC is an arc of a circle with centre M and radius 2.20 m.

AB = BC = 1.50 m
AM = CM = 2.20 m

Find, to 3 significant figures:

a) The size of angle θ in radians,
(2 marks)

b) The perimeter of the slab in m,
(3 marks)

c) The area of the slab in m².
(5 marks)

C2 Section 3 — Practice Questions

2   For an angle x, $3 \cos x = 2 \sin x$.

   a)   Find $\tan x$.

(2 marks)

   b)   Hence, or otherwise, find all the values of x, in the interval $0 \leq x \leq 360°$,
          for which $3 \cos x = 2 \sin x$, giving your answers to 1 d.p.

(2 marks)

3   A circle C is shown here.
     M is the centre of C, and J and K both lie on C.

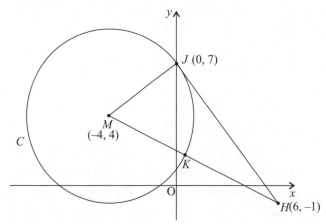

The line JH is a tangent to circle C at point J.

   a)   Show that angle $JMH = 1.1071$ radians to 4 d.p.

(4 marks)

   b)   Find the length of the shortest arc on C between J and K, giving your answer to 3 s.f.

(2 marks)

4   The diagram below shows the dimensions of a child's wooden toy. The toy is a prism with height 10 cm.
     Its cross-section is a sector of a circle with radius 20 cm and angle $\frac{\pi}{4}$ radians.

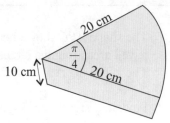

   a)   Show that the volume of the toy, $V = 500\pi$ cm³.

(3 marks)

   b)   Show that the surface area of the toy, $S = (150\pi + 400)$ cm².

(5 marks)

5   Solve, for $0 \leq x \leq 2\pi$: $\sin 2x = -\frac{1}{2}$

(6 marks)

C2 Section 3 — Practice Questions

6   a)   Sketch, for $0 \le x \le 180°$, the graph of $y = \sin 4x$.

(2 marks)

   b)   Solve, for $0 \le x \le 180°$, the equation: $\sin 4x = 0.5$,
        giving your answers in degrees.

(4 marks)

7   a)   Show that the equation:
$$2(1 - \cos x) = 3 \sin^2 x$$
        can be written as
$$3 \cos^2 x - 2 \cos x - 1 = 0$$

(2 marks)

   b)   Use this to solve the equation
$$2(1 - \cos x) = 3 \sin^2 x$$
        for $0 \le x \le 360°$, giving your answers to 1 d.p.

(6 marks)

8   The diagram shows the locations of two walkers, X and Y,
    after walking in different directions from the same start position.

    X walked due south for 150 m. Y walked 250 m on a bearing of 100°.

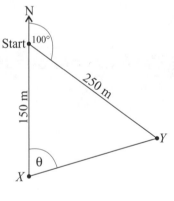

   a)   Calculate the distance between the two walkers,
        in m to the nearest m.

(2 marks)

   b)   Show that $\dfrac{\sin\theta}{\sin 80°} = 0.93$ to 2 decimal places.

(3 marks)

9   Find all the values of x, in the interval $0 \le x \le 2\pi$, for which:
$$2 - \sin x = 2 \cos^2 x$$
    giving your answers in terms of π.

(6 marks)

10 Solve the following equations, for $-\pi \le x \le \pi$:
   a) $(1 + 2 \cos x)(3 \tan^2 x - 1) = 0$

(6 marks)

   b) $\sqrt{2} \cos x = \dfrac{1}{\tan x}$

(4 marks)

Logs

Don't be put off by your parents or grandparents telling you that logs are hard. Logarithm is just a fancy word for power, and once you know how to use them you can solve all sorts of equations.

You need to be able to **Switch** between **Different Notations**

$$\log_a b = c \text{ means the same as } a^c = b$$

$$\text{That means that } \log_a a = 1 \text{ and } \log_a 1 = 0$$

The little number 'a' after 'log' is called the base. Logs can be to any base, but base 10 is the most common. The button marked 'log' on your calculator uses base 10.

EXAMPLE

Index notation: $10^2 = 100$ log notation: $\log_{10} 100 = 2$

The base goes here but it's usually left out if it's 10.

So the logarithm of 100 to the base 10 is 2, because 10 raised to the power of 2 is 100.

EXAMPLES

Write down the values of the following:

a) $\log_2 8$ b) $\log_9 3$ c) $\log_5 5$

a) 8 is 2 raised to the power of 3, so $2^3 = 8$ and $\log_2 8 = 3$

b) 3 is the square root of 9, or $9^{1/2} = 3$, so $\log_9 3 = \frac{1}{2}$

c) Anything to the power of 1 is itself, so $\log_5 5 = 1$

Write the following using log notation:

a) $5^3 = 125$ b) $3^0 = 1$

You just need to make sure you get things in the right place.

a) 3 is the power or logarithm that 5 (the base) is raised to to get 125, so $\log_5 125 = 3$

b) You'll need to remember this one: $\log_3 1 = 0$

The **Laws of Logarithms** are **Unbelievably Useful**

Whenever you have to deal with logs, you'll end up using the laws below. That means it's no bad idea to learn them by heart right now.

Laws of Logarithms

$$\log_a x + \log_a y = \log_a (xy)$$

$$\log_a x - \log_a y = \log_a \left(\frac{x}{y}\right)$$

$$\log_a x^k = k \log_a x$$

So $\log_a \frac{1}{x} = -\log_a x$

Use the **Laws** to **Manipulate Logs**

EXAMPLE

Write each expression in the form $\log_a n$, where n is a number.

a) $\log_a 5 + \log_a 4$ b) $2\log_a 6 - \log_a 9$

a) $\log_a x + \log_a y = \log_a (xy)$

You just have to multiply the numbers together:

$$\log_a 5 + \log_a 4 = \log_a (5 \times 4)$$
$$= \log_a 20$$

b) $\log_a x^k = k \log_a x$

$$2\log_a 6 = \log_a 6^2 = \log_a 36$$
$$\log_a 36 - \log_a 9 = \log_a (36 \div 9)$$
$$= \log_a 4$$

It's sometimes hard to see the wood for the trees — especially with logs...

Tricky, tricky, tricky... I think of $\log_a b$ as 'the power I have to raise a to if I want to end up with b' — that's all it is. And the log laws make a bit more sense if you think of 'log' as meaning 'power'. For example, you know that $2^a \times 2^b = 2^{a+b}$ — this just says that if you multiply the two numbers, you add the powers. Well, the first law of logs is saying the same thing. Any road, even if you don't really understand why they work, make sure you know the log laws like you know your own navel.

Exponentials and Logs

Okay, you've done the theory of logs. So now it's a bit of stuff about <u>exponentials</u> (the opposite of logs, kind of), and then it'll be time to get your calculator out for a bit of button pressing...

Graphs of a^x Never Reach Zero

All the graphs of $y = a^x$ (exponential graphs) where $a > 1$ have the <u>same basic shape</u>. The graphs for $a = 2$, $a = 3$ and $a = 4$ are shown on the right.

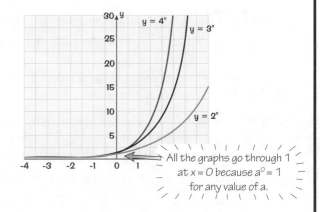

- All the a's are greater than 1 — so <u>y increases as x increases</u>.

- The <u>bigger</u> a is, the <u>quicker</u> the graphs increase.

- As x <u>decreases</u>, y <u>decreases</u> at a <u>smaller and smaller rate</u> — y will approach zero, but never actually get there.

All the graphs go through 1 at $x = 0$ because $a^0 = 1$ for any value of a.

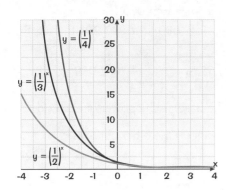

The graphs on the left are for $y = a^x$ where $a < 1$ (they're for $a = \frac{1}{2}$, $\frac{1}{3}$ and $\frac{1}{4}$).

- All the a's are less than 1 — meaning <u>y decreases as x increases</u>.

- As x <u>increases</u>, y <u>decreases</u> at a <u>smaller and smaller rate</u> — again, y will approach zero, but never actually get there.

*You can use **exponentials** and **logs** to **solve equations***

EXAMPLE 1) Solve $2^{4x} = 3$ to 3 significant figures.

You want x on its own, so take logs of both sides (by writing 'log' in front of both sides):

$$\log 2^{4x} = \log 3$$

Now use one of the laws of logs: $\log x^k = k \log x$:

$$4x \log 2 = \log 3$$

You can now divide both sides by '4 log 2' to get x on its own:

$$x = \frac{\log 3}{4 \log 2}$$

But $\frac{\log 3}{4 \log 2}$ is just a number you can find using a calculator:

$$x = 0.396 \text{ (to 3 s.f.)}$$

I don't know about you, but I enjoyed that more than the biggest, fastest rollercoaster. You want another? OK then...

EXAMPLE 2) Solve $7 \log_{10} x = 5$ to 3 significant figures.

You want x on its own, so begin by dividing both sides by 7:

$$\log_{10} x = \frac{5}{7}$$

You now need to take exponentials of both sides by doing '10 to the power of both sides' (since the log is to base 10):

$$10^{\log_{10} x} = 10^{\frac{5}{7}}$$

Logs and exponentials are inverse functions, so they cancel out:

$$x = 10^{\frac{5}{7}}$$

Again, $10^{\frac{5}{7}}$ is just a number you can find using a calculator:

$$x = 5.18 \text{ (to 3 s.f.)}$$

Exponentials and Logs

Use the **Calculator Log Button** Whenever You Can

EXAMPLE Use logarithms to solve the following for x, giving the answers to 4 s.f.

     a) $10^{3x} = 4000$ b) $7^x = 55$ c) $\log_2 x = 5$

You've got the magic buttons on your calculator, but you'd better <u>follow the instructions</u> and show that you know how to use the <u>log rules</u> covered earlier.

a) $10^{3x} = 4000$ — there's an 'unknown' in the power, so <u>take logs of both sides</u>.
(In theory, it doesn't matter what <u>base</u> you use, but your calculator has a '$\log_{10}$' button, so base 10 is usually a good idea. But whatever base you use, <u>use the same one for both sides</u>.)

So taking logs to base 10 of both sides of the above equation gives:
$$\log 10^{3x} = \log 4000$$
$$\text{i.e. } 3x \log 10 = \log 4000$$

Since $\log_{10} 10 = 1$ $\Longrightarrow$ i.e. $3x = \log 4000$, so $x = 1.201$ (to 4 sig. fig.)

b) $7^x = 55$. Again, take logs of both sides, and use the log rules: $x \log_{10} 7 = \log_{10} 55$, so $x = \dfrac{\log_{10} 55}{\log_{10} 7} = 2.059$

c) $\log_2 x = 5$ — to get rid of a log, you 'take exponentials', meaning you do '2 (the base) to the power of each side'.

Think of 'taking logs' and 'taking exponentials' as opposite processes — one cancels the other out:
$$2^{\log_2 x} = 2^5$$
$$\text{i.e. } x = 32$$

You might have to **Combine** the **Laws of Logs** to **Solve** equations

If the examiners are feeling particularly mean, they might make you use <u>more than one</u> law to solve an equation.

EXAMPLE Solve the equation $\log_3(2 - 3x) - 2\log_3 x = 2$.

First, combine the log terms into one term (you can do this because they both have the same base):
$$\log_3 \frac{2 - 3x}{x^2} = 2$$

Remember that $2\log x = \log x^2$.

Then take exponentials of both sides: $3^{\log_3 \frac{2-3x}{x^2}} = 3^2 \Rightarrow \dfrac{2 - 3x}{x^2} = 9$

Ignore the negative solution because you can't take logs of a negative number.

Finally, rearrange the equation and solve for x: $2 - 3x = 9x^2 \Rightarrow 0 = 9x^2 + 3x - 2$
$$\Rightarrow 0 = (3x - 1)(3x + 2)$$

So $x = \dfrac{1}{3}$.

Exponential Growth and **Decay** Applies to **Real-life** Problems

Logs can even be used to solve real-life problems.

EXAMPLE The radioactivity of a substance decays by 20 per cent over a year. The initial level of radioactivity is 400. Find the time taken for the radioactivity to fall to 200 (the half-life).

$R = 400 \times 0.8^T$ where R is the <u>level of radioactivity</u> at time T years.
We need $R = 200$, so solve $200 = 400 \times 0.8^T$

The 0.8 comes from $1 - 20\%$ decay.

$0.8^T = \dfrac{200}{400} = 0.5 \Rightarrow T \log 0.8 = \log 0.5 \Rightarrow T = \dfrac{\log 0.5}{\log 0.8} = 3.106$ years

If in doubt, take the log of something — that usually works...

The thing about exponential growth is that it's really useful, as it happens in real life all over the place. Money in a bank account earns interest at <u>a certain percentage per year</u>, and so the balance rises <u>exponentially</u> (if you don't spend or save anything). Likewise, if you got 20% cleverer for every week you studied, that would also be exponential... and impressive.

C2 Section 4 — Practice Questions

Logs and exponentials are <u>surprisingly useful</u> things. As well as being in your exam they pop up all over the place in real life — <u>savings</u>, <u>radioactive decay</u>, growth of <u>bacteria</u> — all logarithmic.
And now for something (marginally) different:

Warm-up Questions

1) Write down the values of the following:
   a) $\log_3 27$
   b) $\log_3 (1 \div 27)$
   c) $\log_3 18 - \log_3 2$

2) Simplify the following:
   a) $\log 3 + 2 \log 5$
   b) $\frac{1}{2} \log 36 - \log 3$
   c) $\log 2 - \frac{1}{4} \log 16$

3) Simplify $\log_b (x^2 - 1) - \log_b (x - 1)$

4) a) Copy and complete the table for the function $y = 4^x$:

x	–3	–2	–1	0	1	2	3
y							

   b) Using suitable scales, plot a graph of $y = 4^x$ for $-3 < x < 3$.
   c) Use the graph to solve the equation $4^x = 20$.

5) Solve these little jokers:
   a) $10^x = 240$
   b) $\log_{10} x = 5.3$
   c) $10^{2x+1} = 1500$
   d) $4^{(x-1)} = 200$

6) Find the smallest integer P such that $1.5^P > 1\,000\,000$.

Time for some practice at the <u>real thing</u>. On your marks... Get set... Go.

Exam Questions

1   a)   Write the following expressions in the form $\log_a n$, where n is an integer:
     (i) $\log_a 20 - 2 \log_a 2$

(3 marks)

     (ii) $\frac{1}{2} \log_a 16 + \frac{1}{3} \log_a 27$

(3 marks)

    b)   Find the value of:
     (i) $\log_2 64$

(1 mark)

     (ii) $2 \log_3 9$

(2 marks)

C2 Section 4 — Practice Questions

2   a)   Solve the equation

$$2^x = 9$$

giving your answer to 2 decimal places.

(3 marks)

       b)   Hence, or otherwise, solve the equation

$$2^{2x} - 13(2^x) + 36 = 0$$

giving each solution to an appropriate degree of accuracy.

(5 marks)

3   Solve the equation

$$\log_7 (y + 3) + \log_7 (2y + 1) = 1$$

where $y > 0$.

(5 marks)

4   a)   Solve the equation:

$$\log_3 x = -\frac{1}{2}$$

leaving your answer as an exact value.

(3 marks)

       b)   Find x, where

$$2 \log_3 x = -4$$

leaving your answer as an exact value.

(2 marks)

5   a)   Find x, if

$$6^{(3x + 2)} = 9$$

giving your answer to 3 significant figures.

(3 marks)

       b)   Find y, if

$$3^{(y^2 - 4)} = 7^{(y + 2)}$$

giving your answer to 3 significant figures.

(5 marks)

6   For the positive integers p and q,

$$\log_4 p - \log_4 q = \frac{1}{2}$$

    a)   Show that $p = 2q$.

(3 marks)

       b)   Solve the equation for p and q

$$\log_2 p + \log_2 q = 7$$

(5 marks)

Integration

Integration is the 'opposite' of differentiation — and so if you can differentiate, you can be pretty confident you'll be able to integrate too. There's just one extra thing you have to remember — the constant of integration...

You need the constant because there's **More Than One** right answer

When you integrate something, you're trying to find a function that returns to what you started with when you differentiate it. And when you add the constant of integration, you're just allowing for the fact that there's more than one possible function that does this...

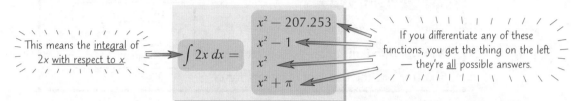

This means the integral of 2x with respect to x.

$$\int 2x\,dx = \begin{array}{l} x^2 - 207.253 \\ x^2 - 1 \\ x^2 \\ x^2 + \pi \end{array}$$

If you differentiate any of these functions, you get the thing on the left — they're all possible answers.

So the answer to this integral is actually...

$$\int 2x\,dx = x^2 + C$$

The 'C' just means 'any number'. This is the constant of integration.

You only need to add a constant of integration to indefinite integrals like these ones. Definite integrals are just integrals with limits (or little numbers) next to the integral sign.

Up the power by **One** — then **Divide** by it

The formula below tells you how to integrate any power of x (except x^{-1}).

This is an indefinite integral — it doesn't have any limits (numbers) next to the integral sign.

$$\int x^n\,dx = \frac{x^{n+1}}{n+1} + C$$

You can't do this to $\frac{1}{x} = x^{-1}$. When you increase the power by 1 (to get zero) and then divide by zero — you get big problems.

In a nutshell, this says:

To integrate a power of x: (i) Increase the power by one — then divide by it.

and (ii) Stick a constant on the end.

EXAMPLES Use the integration formula...

(1) For 'normal' powers,

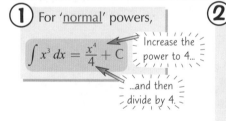

$$\int x^3\,dx = \frac{x^4}{4} + C$$

Increase the power to 4...

...and then divide by 4.

(2) For negative powers,

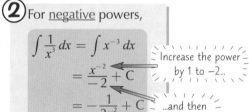

$$\int \frac{1}{x^3}\,dx = \int x^{-3}\,dx$$
$$= \frac{x^{-2}}{-2} + C$$
$$= -\frac{1}{2x^2} + C$$

Increase the power by 1 to –2...

...and then divide by –2.

(3) For fractional powers,

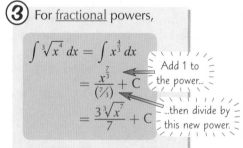

$$\int \sqrt[3]{x^4}\,dx = \int x^{\frac{4}{3}}\,dx$$
$$= \frac{x^{\frac{7}{3}}}{(7/3)} + C$$
$$= \frac{3\sqrt[3]{x^7}}{7} + C$$

Add 1 to the power...

...then divide by this new power.

(4) And for complicated looking stuff...

$$\int\left(3x^2 - \frac{2}{\sqrt{x}} + \frac{7}{x^2}\right)dx = \int\left(3x^2 - 2x^{-\frac{1}{2}} + 7x^{-2}\right)dx$$
$$= \frac{3x^3}{3} - \frac{2x^{\frac{1}{2}}}{(1/2)} + \frac{7x^{-1}}{-1} + C$$
$$= x^3 - 4\sqrt{x} - \frac{7}{x} + C$$

Do each of these bits separately.

CHECK YOUR ANSWERS:
You can check you've integrated properly by differentiating the answer — you should end up with the thing you started with.

Indefinite integrals — joy without limits...

This integration lark isn't so bad then — there's only a couple of things to remember and then you can do it no problem. But that constant of integration catches loads of people out — it's so easy to forget — and you'll definitely lose marks if you do forget it. You have been warned. Other than that, there's not much to it. Hurray.

Integration

By now, you're probably aware that maths isn't something you do unless you're a bit of a thrill-seeker. You know, sometimes they even ask you to find a curve with a certain derivative that goes through a certain point.

You sometimes need to find the Value of the Constant of Integration

When they tell you something else about the curve in addition to its derivative, you can work out the value of that constant of integration. Usually the something is the coordinates of one of the points the curve goes through.

Really Important Bit...

When you differentiate y, you get $\frac{dy}{dx}$.

And when you integrate $\frac{dy}{dx}$, you get y,

(if you ignore the constant of integration).

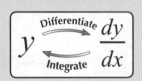

EXAMPLE The curve $f(x)$ goes through the point $(2, 8)$ and $f'(x) = 6x(x - 1)$.

Find $f(x)$.

$f'(x)$ is just another way of saying dy/dx. When you integrate $f'(x)$ you get $f(x)$ and when you differentiate $f(x)$ you get $f'(x)$.

You know the derivative $f'(x)$ and need to find the function $f(x)$ — so integrate.

Remember:
Even if you don't have any extra information about the curve — you still have to add a constant when you work out an integral without limits.

$$f'(x) = 6x(x - 1) = 6x^2 - 6x$$

So integrating both sides gives...

$$f(x) = \int (6x^2 - 6x)dx$$
$$\Rightarrow f(x) = \frac{6x^3}{3} - \frac{6x^2}{2} + C$$
$$\Rightarrow f(x) = 2x^3 - 3x^2 + C$$

Don't forget the constant of integration.

Check this is correct by differentiating it and making sure you get what you started with.

$$f(x) = 2x^3 - 3x^2 + C = 2x^3 - 3x^2 + Cx^0$$
$$f'(x) = 2(3x^2) - 3(2x^1) + C(0x^{-1})$$
$$f'(x) = 6x^2 - 6x$$

So this function's got the correct derivative — but you haven't finished yet.

You now need to find C — and you do this by using the fact that it goes through the point $(2, 8)$.

A constant always differentiates to zero.

$$f(x) = 2x^3 - 3x^2 + C$$

Putting $x = 2$ and $f(x) = 8$ in the above equation gives...

$$8 = (2 \times 2^3) - (3 \times 2^2) + C$$
$$\Rightarrow 8 = 16 - 12 + C$$
$$\Rightarrow C = 4$$

So the answer you need is this one:

$$f(x) = 2x^3 - 3x^2 + 4$$

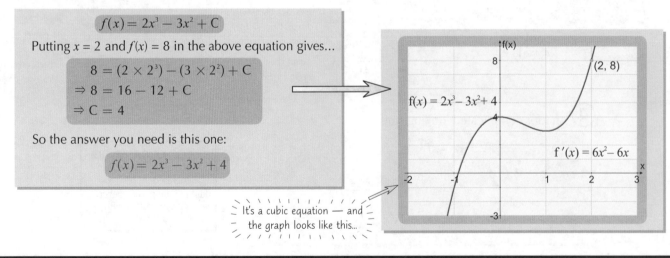

It's a cubic equation — and the graph looks like this...

Maths and alcohol don't mix — so never drink and derive...

That's another page under your belt and — go on, admit it — there was nothing too horrendous on it. If you can do the stuff from the previous page and then substitute some numbers into an equation, you can do everything from this page too. So if you think this is boring, you'd be right. But if you think it's much harder than the stuff before, you'd be wrong.

Integration

Some integrals have <u>limits</u> (i.e. little numbers) next to the integral sign. You integrate them in exactly the same way — but you <u>don't</u> need a constant of integration. Much easier. And scrummier and yummier too.

A *Definite Integral* finds the *Area Under a Curve*

This definite integral tells you the <u>area</u> between the graph of $y = x^3$ and the x-axis between $x = -2$ and $x = 2$:

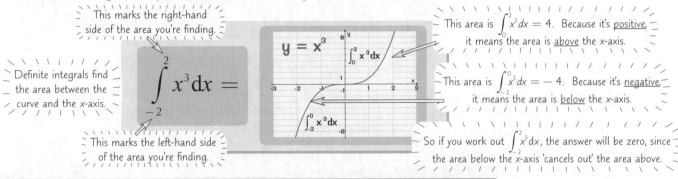

This marks the right-hand side of the area you're finding.

Definite integrals find the area between the curve and the x-axis.

This marks the left-hand side of the area you're finding.

$$\int_{-2}^{2} x^3 \, \mathrm{d}x =$$

This area is $\int_{0}^{2} x^3 dx = 4$. Because it's <u>positive</u>, it means the area is <u>above</u> the x-axis.

This area is $\int_{-2}^{0} x^3 dx = -4$. Because it's <u>negative</u>, it means the area is <u>below</u> the x-axis.

So if you work out $\int_{-2}^{2} x^3 dx$, the answer will be zero, since the area below the x-axis 'cancels out' the area above.

Do the integration in the same way — then use the *Limits*

Finding a definite integral isn't really any harder than an indefinite one — there's just an <u>extra</u> stage you have to do. After you've integrated the function you have to work out the value of this new function by sticking in the <u>limits</u>.

EXAMPLE

Evaluate $\int_{1}^{3} (x^2 + 2) \, dx$.

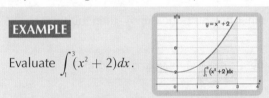

Find the integral in the normal way — then use the limits.

Put the integrated function in <u>square brackets</u> and rewrite the limits on the right-hand side.

$$\int_{1}^{3} (x^2 + 2) \, dx = \left[\frac{x^3}{3} + 2x \right]_{1}^{3}$$

$$= \left(\frac{3^3}{3} + 6 \right) - \left(\frac{1^3}{3} + 2 \right)$$

$$= 15 - \frac{7}{3} = \frac{38}{3}$$

$2 = 2x^0$ — so increase the power (to 1) and divide by 1 to get $2x$.

You don't need a constant of integration with a <u>definite</u> integral.

> **Definite Integrals**
> After you've integrated the function — put both the limits in and find the values. Then subtract what the bottom limit gave you from what the top limit gave you.

Integrate 'to *Infinity*' with the ∞ (infinity) sign

And you can integrate all the way to <u>infinity</u> as well. Just use the ∞ symbol as your upper limit. Or use $-\infty$ as your lower limit if you want to integrate to '<u>minus infinity</u>'.

EXAMPLE Find the area under the curve $y = \frac{15}{x^2} - \frac{30}{x^3}$ for $x \geq 2$.

For this, you need to integrate from $x = 2$ up to infinity (∞).

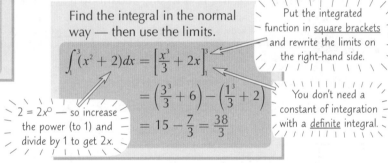

$$A = \int_{2}^{\infty} \left(\frac{15}{x^2} - \frac{30}{x^3} \right) dx = 15 \int_{2}^{\infty} (x^{-2} - 2x^{-3}) dx$$

Move <u>numbers</u> outside the integral sign or the square bracket as if you're <u>factorising</u> a normal bracket.

$$= 15 \left[\frac{x^{-1}}{-1} - \frac{2x^{-2}}{(-2)} \right]_{2}^{\infty}$$

$$= 15 \left[-\frac{1}{x} + \frac{1}{x^2} \right]_{2}^{\infty}$$

When you have to use the ∞ limit — remember: $\frac{1}{\infty} = \frac{1}{\infty^2} = \frac{1}{\infty^3} = 0$.

$$= 15 \left\{ (-0 + 0) - \left(-\frac{1}{2} + \frac{1}{4} \right) \right\} = 15 \times \frac{1}{4} = \frac{15}{4}$$

$y = \frac{15}{x^2} - \frac{30}{x^3}$

$y = \int_{0}^{\infty} \left(\frac{15}{x^2} - \frac{30}{x^3} \right) dx$

Curve continues forever in this direction. →

My hobbies? Well I'm really inte grating. Especially carrots.

It's still integration — but this time you're putting two numbers into an expression afterwards. So although this may not be the wild and crazy fun-packed time your teachers promised you when they were trying to persuade you to take AS maths, you've got to admit that a lot of this stuff is pretty similar — and if you can do one bit, you can use that to do quite a few other bits too. Maths is like that. But I admit it's probably not as much fun as a big banana-and-toffee cake.

The Trapezium Rule

Sometimes <u>integrals</u> can be just <u>too hard</u> to do using the normal methods — then you need to know other ways to solve them. That's where the <u>Trapezium Rule</u> comes in.

The *Trapezium Rule* is Used to Find the *Approximate Area* Under a Curve

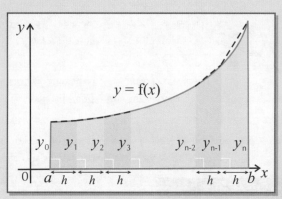

The area of each trapezium is $A = \frac{h}{2}(y_n + y_{n+1})$

The area represented by $\int_a^b y \, dx$ is approximately:

$$\int_a^b y \, dx \approx \frac{h}{2}[y_0 + 2(y_1 + y_2 + ... + y_{n-1}) + y_n]$$

where ***n*** is the number of strips or intervals and ***h*** is the width of each strip.

You can find the width of each strip using $h = \frac{(b-a)}{n}$

$y_0, y_1, y_2, ... , y_n$ are the heights of the sides of the trapeziums — you get these by putting the *x*-values into the curve.

So basically the formula for approximating $\int_a^b y \, dx$ works like this:

'Add the first and last heights $(y_0 + y_n)$ and add this to <u>twice</u> all the other heights added up — then multiply by $\frac{h}{2}$.'

EXAMPLE Find an approximate value for $\int_0^2 \sqrt{4 - x^2} \, dx$ using 4 strips. Give your answer to 4 s.f.

Start by working out the width of each strip: $h = \frac{(b-a)}{n} = \frac{(2-0)}{4} = 0.5$

This means the *x*-values are $x_0 = 0$, $x_1 = 0.5$, $x_2 = 1$, $x_3 = 1.5$ and $x_4 = 2$ (the question specifies 4 strips, so $n = 4$).

Set up a table and work out the *y*-values or heights using the equation in the integral.

x	$y = \sqrt{4 - x^2}$
$x_0 = 0$	$y_0 = \sqrt{4 - 0^2} = 2$
$x_1 = 0.5$	$y_1 = \sqrt{4 - 0.5^2} = \sqrt{3.75} = 1.936491673$
$x_2 = 1.0$	$y_2 = \sqrt{4 - 1.0^2} = \sqrt{3} = 1.732050808$
$x_3 = 1.5$	$y_3 = \sqrt{4 - 1.5^2} = \sqrt{1.75} = 1.322875656$
$x_4 = 2.0$	$y_4 = \sqrt{4 - 2.0^2} = 0$

Now put all the *y*-values into the formula with *h* and *n*:

$$\int_a^b y \, dx \approx \frac{0.5}{2}[2 + 2(1.9365 + 1.7321 + 1.3229) + 0]$$
$$\approx 0.25[2 + 2 \times 4.9915]$$
$$\approx 2.996 \text{ to 4 s.f.}$$

Watch out — if they ask you to work out a question with 5 *y*-values (or '<u>ordinates</u>') then this is the <u>same</u> as 4 strips. The *x*-values usually go up in <u>nice jumps</u> — if they don't then <u>check</u> your calculations carefully.

The Approximation might be an *Overestimate* or an *Underestimate*

It all depends on the shape of the curve...

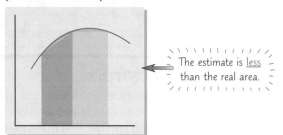

The estimate is <u>less</u> than the real area.

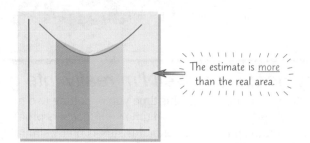

The estimate is <u>more</u> than the real area.

The Trapezium Rule

These are usually popular questions with examiners — as long as you're careful there are plenty of marks to be had.

The **Trapezium Rule** is in the **Formula Booklet**

...so don't try any heroics — always look it up and use it with these questions.

EXAMPLE   Use the trapezium rule with 7 ordinates to find an approximation to $\int_1^{2.2} 2\log_{10}x \, dx$

Remember, 7 ordinates means 6 strips — so $n = 6$.

Calculate the width of the strips: $h = \dfrac{(b-a)}{n} = \dfrac{(2.2-1)}{6} = 0.2$

Set up a table and work out the y-values using $y = 2\log_{10}x$: ⟶

x	$y = 2\log_{10}x$
$x_0 = 1.0$	$y_0 = 2\log_{10}1 = 0$
$x_1 = 1.2$	$y_1 = 2\log_{10}1.2 = 0.15836$
$x_2 = 1.4$	$y_2 = 0.29226$
$x_3 = 1.6$	$y_3 = 0.40824$
$x_4 = 1.8$	$y_4 = 0.51055$
$x_5 = 2.0$	$y_5 = 0.60206$
$x_6 = 2.2$	$y_6 = 0.68485$

$y_6 = 2\log_{10}b = 0.68485$

Putting all these values in the formula gives:

$$\int_a^b y \, dx \approx \frac{0.2}{2}[0 + 2(0.15836 + 0.29226 + 0.40824 + 0.51055 + 0.60206) + 0.68485]$$

$$\approx 0.1 \times [0.68485 + 2 \times 1.97147]$$

$$\approx 0.462779$$

$$\approx 0.463 \text{ to 3 d.p.}$$

EXAMPLE   Use the trapezium rule with 8 intervals to find an approximation to $\int_0^\pi \sin x \, dx$

Whenever you get a calculus question using trig functions, you have to use radians. You'll probably be given a limit with π in, which is a pretty good reminder.

There are 8 intervals, so $n = 8$.

Keep your x-values in terms of π.

Calculate the width of the strips: $h = \dfrac{(b-a)}{n} = \dfrac{(\pi-0)}{8} = \dfrac{\pi}{8}$

Set up a table and work out the y-values: ⟶

So, putting all this in the formula gives:

x	$y = \sin x$
$x_0 = 0$	$y_0 = \sin 0 = 0$
$x_1 = \dfrac{\pi}{8}$	$y_1 = 0.38268$
$x_2 = \dfrac{\pi}{4}$	$y_2 = 0.70711$
$x_3 = \dfrac{3\pi}{8}$	$y_3 = 0.92388$
$x_4 = \dfrac{\pi}{2}$	$y_4 = 1$
$x_5 = \dfrac{5\pi}{8}$	$y_5 = 0.92388$
$x_6 = \dfrac{3\pi}{4}$	$y_6 = 0.70711$
$x_7 = \dfrac{7\pi}{8}$	$y_7 = 0.38268$
$x_8 = \pi$	$y_8 = 0$

$$\int_a^b y \, dx \approx \frac{1}{2}\cdot\frac{\pi}{8}[0 + 2(0.383 + 0.707 + 0.924 + 1 + 0.924 + 0.707 + 0.383) + 0]$$

$$\approx \frac{\pi}{16} \times [2 \times 5.028]$$

$$\approx 1.97 \text{ to 3 s.f.}$$

These values are quicker to work-out if you know that the graph is symmetrical.

Maths rhyming slang #3: Dribble and drool — Trapezium rule...

Take your time with trapezium rule questions — it's so easy to make a mistake with all those numbers flying around. Make a nice table showing all your ordinates (careful — this is always one more than the number of strips). Then add up y_1 to y_{n-1} and multiply the answer by 2. Add on y_0 and y_n. Finally, multiply what you've got so far by the width of a strip and divide by 2. It's a good idea to write down what you get after each stage, by the way — then if you press the wrong button (easily done) you'll be able to pick up from where you went wrong. They're not hard — just fiddly.

Areas Between Curves

With a bit of thought, you can use integration to find all kinds of areas — even ones that look quite tricky at first. The best way to work out what to do is draw a <u>picture</u>. Then it'll seem easier. I promise you it will.

*Sometimes you have to **Add** integrals...*

This looks pretty hard — until you draw a picture and see what it's all about.

EXAMPLE Find the area enclosed by the curve $y = x^2$, the line $y = 2 - x$ and the x-axis.

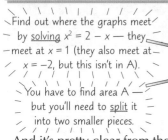
Find out where the graphs meet by <u>solving</u> $x^2 = 2 - x$ — they meet at $x = 1$ (they also meet at $x = -2$, but this isn't in A).

You have to find area A — but you'll need to <u>split</u> it into two smaller pieces.

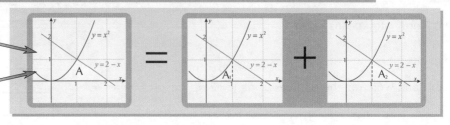

And it's pretty clear from the picture that you'll have to find the area in two lumps, A_1 and A_2.

The first area you need to find is A_1:

$$A_1 = \int_0^1 x^2\,dx$$
$$= \left[\frac{x^3}{3}\right]_0^1 = \left(\frac{1}{3} - 0\right) = \frac{1}{3}$$

The other area you need is A_2:

A_2 is just a triangle, with base length $2 - 1 = 1$ and height $= 1$. So the area of the triangle is $\frac{1}{2} \times b \times h = \frac{1}{2} \times 1 \times 1 = \frac{1}{2}$.

And the area the question actually asks for is $A_1 + A_2$. This is

$$A = A_1 + A_2$$
$$= \frac{1}{3} + \frac{1}{2} = \frac{5}{6}$$

You could also have integrated the line $y = 2 - x$ between $x = 1$ and $x = 2$, but finding the area of the triangle is easier.

*...sometimes you have to **Subtract** them*

Again, it's best to look at the <u>pictures</u> to work out exactly what you need to do.

EXAMPLE Find the area enclosed by the curves $y = x^2 + 1$ and $y = 9 - x^2$.

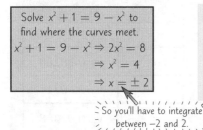
Solve $x^2 + 1 = 9 - x^2$ to find where the curves meet.
$x^2 + 1 = 9 - x^2 \Rightarrow 2x^2 = 8$
$\Rightarrow x^2 = 4$
$\Rightarrow x = \pm 2$

So you'll have to integrate between -2 and 2.

The area under the green curve A_1 is:

$$A_1 = \int_{-2}^{2}(9 - x^2)dx$$
$$= \left[9x - \frac{x^3}{3}\right]_{-2}^{2}$$
$$= \left(18 - \frac{2^3}{3}\right) - \left(-18 - \frac{(-2)^3}{3}\right)$$
$$= \left(18 - \frac{8}{3}\right) - \left(-18 - \left(\frac{-8}{3}\right)\right) = \frac{46}{3} - \left(-\frac{46}{3}\right) = \frac{92}{3}$$

The area under the red curve is:

$$A_2 = \int_{-2}^{2}(x^2 + 1)dx$$
$$= \left[\frac{x^3}{3} + x\right]_{-2}^{2}$$
$$= \left(\frac{2^3}{3} + 2\right) - \left(\frac{(-2)^3}{3} + (-2)\right)$$
$$= \left(\frac{8}{3} + 2\right) - \left(-\frac{8}{3} - 2\right) = \frac{28}{3}$$

And the area you need is the difference between these:

$$A = A_1 - A_2$$
$$= \frac{92}{3} - \frac{28}{3} = \frac{64}{3}$$

Instead of integrating before subtracting — you could try 'subtracting the curves', and then integrating. This last area A is also:

$$A = \int_{-2}^{2}\{(9 - x^2) - (x^2 + 1)\}\,dx$$

And so, our hero integrates the area between two curves, and saves the day...

That's the basic idea of finding the area enclosed by two curves and lines — draw a picture and then break the area down into <u>smaller, easier chunks</u>. And it's always a good idea to keep an eye out for anything <u>symmetrical</u> that could save you a bit of work. Questions like this aren't hard — but they can sometimes take a long time. Great.

C2 Section 5 — Practice Questions

Penguins evolved with a layer of blubber under their skin to keep them warm.
They should've saved themselves the effort and <u>done these questions</u> instead — mmm, toasty warm...

Warm-up Questions

1) <u>Integrate</u> these: a) $\int 10x^4 dx$,   b) $\int (3x + 5x^2)dx$,   c) $\int (x^2(3x + 2))dx$

2) Work out the <u>equation</u> of the curve that has <u>derivative</u> $\frac{dy}{dx} = 6x - 7$ and goes through the <u>point</u> (1, 0).

3) How can you tell whether an integral is a <u>definite</u> one or an <u>indefinite</u> one?
   (It's easy really — it just sounds difficult.)

4) Evaluate the following <u>definite integrals</u>:

   a) $\int_0^1 (4x^3 + 3x^2 + 2x + 1)dx$ b) $\int_1^2 \left(\frac{8}{x^5} + \frac{3}{\sqrt{x}}\right)dx$ c) $\int_1^6 \frac{3}{x^2}\, dx$.

5) Evaluate: a) $\int_{-3}^3 (9 - x^2)dx$ b) $\int_1^\infty \frac{3}{x^2}\, dx$.

   <u>Sketch the areas</u> represented by these integrals.

6) Find <u>area A</u> in the diagram below:

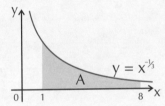

7) Use the <u>trapezium rule</u> with n intervals to estimate:

   a) $\int_0^3 (9 - x^2)^{\frac{1}{2}}dx$ with $n = 3$ b) $\int_{0.2}^{1.2} x^{x^2}dx$ with $n = 5$

8) Use integration to find the <u>yellow area</u> in each of these graphs:

   a)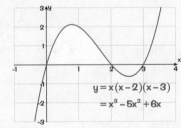

   b)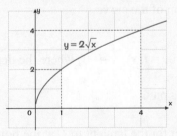

   c)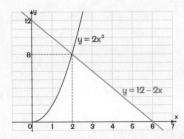

   d)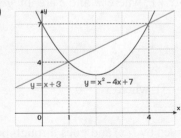

C2 Section 5 — Practice Questions

Exam Questions

1   Find $f(x)$ in each case below. Give each term in its simplest form.

   a) $f'(x) = x^{-\frac{1}{2}} + 4 - 5x^3$

(3 marks)

   b) $f'(x) = 2x + \dfrac{3}{x^2}$

(2 marks)

   c) $f'(x) = 6x^2 - \dfrac{1}{3\sqrt{x}}$

(2 marks)

2   a)   Show that $(5 + 2\sqrt{x})^2$ can be written in the form $a + b\sqrt{x} + cx$, stating the values of the constants a, b and c.

(3 marks)

   b)   Find $\int (5 + 2\sqrt{x})^2 dx$.

(3 marks)

3   The curve C has the equation $y = f(x)$, $x > 0$. $f'(x)$ is given as $2x + 5\sqrt{x} + \dfrac{6}{x^2}$.

   A point P on curve C has the coordinates $(3, 7)$.

   Find $f(x)$, giving your answer in its simplest form.

(6 marks)

4    $f'(x) = \dfrac{1}{\sqrt{36x}} - 2\left(\sqrt{\dfrac{1}{x^3}}\right)$ where $x > 0$.

   a)   Show that $f'(x) = Ax^{-\frac{1}{2}} - Bx^{-\frac{3}{2}}$ and give the values of A and B.

(3 marks)

   b)   The curve C is given by $y = f(x)$ and goes through point $P(1, 7)$.
        Find the equation of the curve.

(4 marks)

5   Curve C has equation $y = f(x)$, $x \neq 0$, where the derivative is given by $f'(x) = x^3 - \dfrac{2}{x^2}$.

   The point $P(1, 2)$ lies on C.

   a)   Find an equation for the tangent to C at the point P, giving your answer
        in the form $y = mx + c$, where m and c are integers.

(4 marks)

   b)   Find $f(x)$.

(5 marks)

6    $f'(x) = (x - 1)(3x - 1)$ where $x > 0$.

   a)   The curve C is given by $f(x)$ and goes through point $P(3, 10)$. Find $f(x)$.

(6 marks)

   b)   The equation for the normal to C at the point P can be written in the form $y = \dfrac{a - x}{b}$
        where a and b are integers. Find the values of a and b.

(4 marks)

C2 Section 5 — Practice Questions

7   Curve C, $y = (x-3)^2(x+1)$, is sketched on the diagram below:

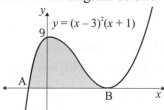

Calculate the shaded area between point A, where C intersects the
x-axis, and point B, where C touches the x-axis.

(8 marks)

8   Find the value of $\int_{2}^{7} (2x - 6x^2 + \sqrt{x})\,dx$. Give your answer to 4 d.p.

(5 marks)

9   a)   Using the trapezium rule with n intervals, estimate the values of:

(i) $\int_{2}^{8} \left(\sqrt{3x^3} + \dfrac{2}{\sqrt{x}}\right)dx$, $n = 3$

(4 marks)

(ii) $\int_{1}^{5} \left(\dfrac{x^3 - 2}{4}\right)dx$, $n = 4$

(4 marks)

b)   How could you change your application of the trapezium rule to get better approximations?

(1 mark)

10   Complete the table and hence use the trapezium rule with 6 ordinates to estimate $\int_{1.5}^{4} y\,dx$.

x	$x_0 = 1.5$	$x_1 =$	$x_2 =$	$x_3 =$	$x_4 = 3.5$	$x_5 = 4.0$
$y = 3x - \sqrt{2^x}$	$y_0 =$	$y_1 = 4$	$y_2 = 5.12156$	$y_3 =$	$y_4 =$	$y_5 = 8.0$

(7 marks)

11   The diagram below shows the curve $y = (x+1)(x-5)$.
Points J $(-1, 0)$ and K $(4, -5)$ lie on the curve.

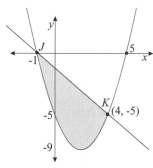

a)   Find the equation of the straight line joining J and K in the form $y = mx + c$.

(2 marks)

b)   Calculate $\int_{-1}^{4} (x+1)(x-5)\,dx$.

(5 marks)

c)   Find the area of the shaded region.

(4 marks)

...it is now.

General Certificate of Education
Advanced Subsidiary (AS) and Advanced Level

Core Mathematics C2 — Practice Exam One

Time Allowed: 1 hour 30 min

Graphical calculators may be used for this exam.

Give any non-exact numerical answers to an appropriate degree of accuracy.

There are 72 marks available for this paper.

1   a)   By sketching the graph of $y = \tan 2t$ for a suitable range of t, determine the number of solutions to the equation $\tan 2t = k$ in the range $0° \leq t < 360°$ where k is any number.

(3 marks)

     b)   Solve the equation $\sin 2t = \sqrt{2}\cos 2t$, giving all the solutions in the range $0° \leq t < 360°$.

(3 marks)

2   a)   Write down the value of $\log_3 3$.

(1 mark)

     b)   Given that $\log_a \chi = \log_a 4 + 3\log_a 2$, show that $\chi = 32$.

(2 marks)

$$K = 10j$$

3   The binomial expansion of $(j + kx)^6$ can written in the form $j^6[1 + ax + bx^2 + cx^3 + ...]$

     a)   Given that $c = 20\,000$, show that $jk = 10$ (where both j and k are positive integers).

(3 marks)

     b)   Given that $a = 37\,500$, find the values of j and k.

(4 marks)

     c)   Find b.

(2 marks)

4   The diagram shows the positions of three islands, A, B and C.

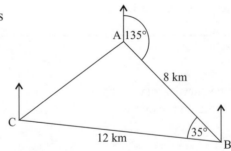

     a)   What is the bearing of C from B?

(2 marks)

     b)   What is the distance between A and C?

(2 marks)

     c)   Find the size of angle BAC, and hence find the bearing of A from C.

(4 marks)

5   a)   Sketch the curve $y = (x - 2)(x - 4)$ and the line $y = 2x - 4$ on the same set of axes, clearly marking the coordinates of the points of intersection.

(3 marks)

     b)   Evaluate the integral $\displaystyle\int_2^4 (x - 2)(x - 4)\,dx$.

(3 marks)

     c)   Hence, or otherwise, show that the total area enclosed by the curve $y = (x - 2)(x - 4)$ and the line $y = 2x - 4$ is $\dfrac{32}{3}$.

(4 marks)

6   The diagram below shows a sector of a circle of radius r cm and angle $120°$.
    The length of the arc of the sector is 40 cm.

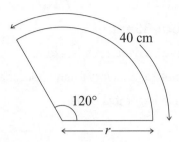

a)   Write $120°$ in radians.

(1 mark)

b)   Show that $r \approx 19.1$ cm.

(2 marks)

c)   Find the area of the sector to the nearest square centimetre.

(2 marks)

7   Calculate $\int (4x^3 + 6x + 3)\, dx$.

(3 marks)

8   For the series with second term –2 and common ratio –½, find:

a)   the 13th term,

(3 marks)

b)   the sum to infinity.

(3 marks)

9   a)   Rewrite the following equation in the form $f(x) = 0$,
         where $f(x)$ is of the form $f(x) = ax^3 + bx^2 + cx + d$:
         $$(x - 1)(x^2 + x + 1) = 2x^2 - 17$$

(2 marks)

b)   Show that $(x + 2)$ is a factor of $f(x)$.

(3 marks)

c)   Hence factorise $f(x)$ as the product of a linear factor and a quadratic factor.

(3 marks)

d)   By completing the square, or otherwise, show that $f(x)=0$ has only one root.

(2 marks)

e)   Divide the polynomial $x^3 - 2x^2 + 3x - 3$ by $(x - 1)$, showing both the quotient and remainder.

(4 marks)

10 The third term of an arithmetic progression is 9 and the seventh term is 33.

a)   Find the first term and the common difference.

(3 marks)

b)   Find S_{12}, the sum of the first 12 terms in the series.

(3 marks)

c)   Hence or otherwise find: $\sum_{1}^{12}(6n + 1)$

(2 marks)

General Certificate of Education
Advanced Subsidiary (AS) and Advanced Level

Core Mathematics C2 — Practice Exam Two

Time Allowed: 1 hour 30 min

Graphical calculators may be used for this exam.

Give any non-exact numerical answers to an appropriate degree of accuracy.

There are 72 marks available for this paper.

1 a) Sketch the graph of $y = \cos(3x)$ for x between $0°$ and $360°$.

(2 marks)

   b) Show that the equation $2\sin^2(3x) = 1 + \cos(3x)$ may be written as a quadratic in $\cos(3x)$.

(4 marks)

   c) Hence solve this equation, giving all values of x such that $0° \leq x \leq 360°$.

(4 marks)

2 a) Write down the first four terms in the expansion of $(1 + ax)^{10}$, $a > 0$.

(2 marks)

   b) Find the coefficient of x^2 in the expansion of $(2 + 3x)^5$.

(2 marks)

   c) If the coefficients of x^2 in both expansions are equal, find the value of a.

(2 marks)

3 The diagram shows the graph of $y = 2^{x^2}$.

   a) Use the trapezium rule with 4 intervals to find an estimate for the area of the region bounded by the axes, the curve and the line $x = 2$.

(4 marks)

   b) State whether the estimate in a) is an overestimate or an underestimate, giving a reason for your answer.

(2 marks)

4 A geometric series $u_1 + u_2 + ... + u_n$ has 3rd term $\frac{5}{2}$ and 6th term $\frac{5}{16}$.

   a) Find the common ratio and the first term of the series.
       Hence give the formula for the nth term of the series.

(4 marks)

   b) Find $\sum_{i=1}^{10} u_i$. Give your answer as a fraction in its simplest terms.

(3 marks)

   c) Show that the sum to infinity of the series is 20.

(2 marks)

5 a) Find the missing length a in the triangle.

(2 marks)

   b) Find the angles θ and ϕ.

(3 marks)

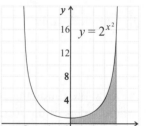

6   A new symmetrical mini-stage is to be built according to the design shown below.
    The design consists of a rectangle of length q metres and width $2r$ metres,
    two sectors of radius r and angle θ radians (shaded), and an isosceles triangle.

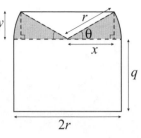

a) (i)   Show that distance x is given by $x = r\cos\theta$.

    (1 mark)

    (ii) Find a similar expression for distance y.

    (1 mark)

b) Find, in terms of r, q and θ, expressions for the perimeter P, and the area A, of the stage.

    (4 marks)

c) If the perimeter of the stage is to be 40 metres, and $\theta = \frac{\pi}{3}$,
    show that A is given approximately by $A = 40r - 3.614r^2$.

    (4 marks)

7   a) Find the remainder when the function $f(x) = x^3 - 6x^2 - x + 30$ is divided by:

    (i) $(x + 3)$

    (2 marks)

    (ii) $(4x - 1)$

    (2 marks)

b) Using the factor theorem, show that $(x - 3)$ is a factor of $f(x)$.

    (2 marks)

c) Factorise $f(x)$ completely.

    (4 marks)

8   a) Sketch the curve $y = \frac{1}{x^2}$ for $x > 0$.

    (1 mark)

b) Show that $\int_{1}^{\infty} \frac{1}{x^2}\, dx = 1$.

    (2 marks)

c) Find $f(x)$, where $y = f(x)$ is the equation of the tangent
    to the graph of $y = \frac{1}{x^2}$ at the point where $x = 1$.

    (2 marks)

d) Find $k < 1$ such that $\int_{0}^{k} f(x)\, dx = 1$, where $f(x)$ is the function found in part (c).

    Give your answer using surds.

    (3 marks)

9   An arithmetic series has first term a and common difference d. The value of the 12th term is 79, and the
    value of the 16th term is 103.

a) From the information given above, find two equations in terms of a and d, then solve them to
    find the values of a and d.

    (4 marks)

S_n is the sum of the first n terms of the series.

b) Find a simplified expression for S_n in terms of n, using your values of a and d from
    part a) above.

    (3 marks)

c) Calculate the value of S_{15}.

    (1 mark)

Histograms

Histograms are glorified bar charts. The main difference is that you plot the <u>frequency density</u> rather than the frequency. Frequency density is easy to find — you just divide the <u>frequency</u> by the <u>width of the corresponding class</u>.

Using frequency density means it's a column's <u>area</u> (and <u>not</u> its height) that represents the <u>frequency</u>.

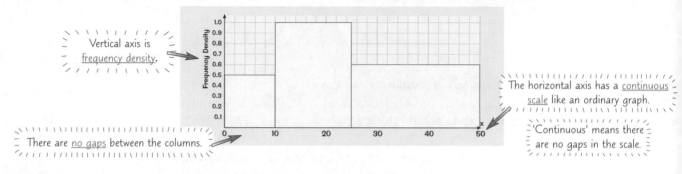

Vertical axis is <u>frequency density</u>.

There are <u>no gaps</u> between the columns.

The horizontal axis has a <u>continuous scale</u> like an ordinary graph.

'Continuous' means there are no gaps in the scale.

To Draw a **Histogram** it's best to Draw a **Table** First

Getting histograms right depends on finding the right <u>upper and lower boundaries</u> for each class.

EXAMPLE Draw a histogram to represent the data below showing the masses of parcels (given to the nearest 100 g).

Mass of parcel (to nearest 100 g)	100 - 200	300 - 400	500 - 700	800 - 1100
Number of parcels	100	250	600	50

First draw a table showing the <u>upper and lower class boundaries</u>, plus the <u>frequency density</u>:

<u>Smallest</u> mass of parcel that will go <u>in that class</u>.

<u>Biggest</u> mass that will go <u>in that class</u>.

= ucb − lcb

Mass of parcel	Lower class boundary (lcb)	Upper class boundary (ucb)	Class width	Frequency	Frequency density = frequency ÷ class width
100 - 200	50	250	200	100	0.5
300 - 400	250	450	200	250	1.25
500 - 700	450	750	300	600	2
800 - 1100	750	1150	400	50	0.125

= 250 ÷ 200

Look — no gaps between a ucb and the next lcb.

= 1150 − 750

Now you can draw the histogram.

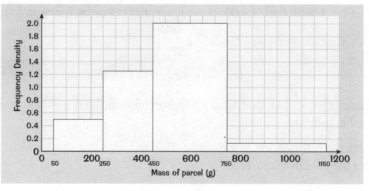

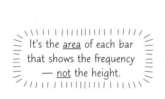

It's the <u>area</u> of each bar that shows the frequency — <u>not</u> the height.

Note: A class with a lower class boundary of 50 g and upper class boundary of 250 g can be written in different ways.

So you might see: "100 – 200 to nearest 100 g"
                      "$50 \leq \text{mass} < 250$"
                      "50–", followed by "250–" for the next class and so on.

They all mean the same — just make sure you know how to spot the lower and upper class boundaries.

Stem and Leaf Diagrams

Stem and Leaf Diagrams *look nothing like stems or leaves*

<u>Stem and leaf diagrams</u> are an easy way to represent your data.
They come in two flavours — plain and <u>back-to-back</u>.

EXAMPLE The lengths in metres of cars in a car park were measured to the nearest 10 cm.
Draw a stem and leaf diagram to show the following data: 2.9, 3.5, 4.0, 2.8, 4.1, 3.7, 3.1, 3.6, 3.8, 3.7

It's best to do a rough version first, and then put the 'leaves' in order afterwards.

It's a good idea to cross out the numbers
(in pencil) as you add them to your diagram.

My 'stems' are the numbers before the decimal point, and my 'leaves' are the numbers after.

```
2 | 9, 8
3 | 5, 7, 1, 6, 8, 7
4 | 0, 1
```

Put the digits after the
decimal point in order

```
2 | 8, 9
3 | 1, 5, 6, 7, 7, 8
4 | 0, 1
Key  2|9 means 2.9 m
```

Always give a key.

Digits after the decimal point — this row represents 4.0 m and 4.1 m.

EXAMPLE The heights of boys and girls in a year 11 class are given to the nearest cm
in the back-to-back stem and leaf diagram below. Write out the data in full.

First boy, 8|16|, has height 168 cm. The boys are read backwards.

First girl, |15|9, has height 159 cm.

Key 8|16|5 means
Boys 168 cm and girls 165 cm

Boys		Girls
	15	9
8	16	1, 5, 9
9, 8, 1	17	0, 2, 3, 5
5, 2	18	0
1	19	

<u>Boys</u>: 168, 171, 178, 179, 182, 185, 191

<u>Girls</u>: 159, 161, 165, 169, 170, 172, 173, 175, 180

EXAMPLE Construct a back-to-back stem and leaf diagram to represent the following data:
Boys' test marks: 34, 27, 15, 39, 20, 26, 32, 37, 19, 22
Girls' test marks: 21, 38, 37, 12, 27, 28, 39, 29, 25, 24, 31, 36

Boys		Girls
9, 5	1	2
2, 6, 0, 7	2	1, 7, 8, 9, 5, 4
7, 2, 9, 4	3	8, 7, 9, 1, 6

Put the digits in the
leaves in order

Boys		Girls
9, 5	1	2
7, 6, 2, 0	2	1, 4, 5, 7, 8, 9
9, 7, 4, 2	3	1, 6, 7, 8, 9

Key 0|2|1 means
Boys 20 and girls 21

The 'stems' represent 10, 20 and 30.

First things first: remember — there are lies, damned lies and statistics...

Histograms shouldn't cause too many problems — this is quite a friendly topic really. The main things to remember are to work out the <u>lower and upper boundaries</u> of each class <u>properly</u>, and then make sure you use <u>frequency density</u> (rather than just the frequency). Stem and leaf diagrams — hah, they're easy, I do them in my sleep. Make sure you can too.

Location: Mean, Median and Mode

The mean, median and mode are measures of <u>location</u> or <u>central tendency</u> (basically... where the <u>centre</u> of the data lies).

The **Definitions** are really GCSE stuff

You more than likely already know them. But if you don't, learn them now — you'll be needing them loads.

> **Mean** = $\bar{x} = \dfrac{\Sigma x}{n}$ or $\dfrac{\Sigma fx}{\Sigma f}$
>
> *The Σ (sigma) things just mean you add stuff up — so Σx means you add up all the values of x.*
>
> where each x is a <u>data value</u>, f is the <u>frequency</u> of each x-value (the number of times it occurs), and n is the <u>total number</u> of data values.
>
> **Median** = <u>middle</u> data value when all the data values are placed <u>in order of size</u>.
>
> **Mode** = <u>most frequently occurring</u> data value.

There are two ways to find the <u>median</u> (but they amount to the same thing):

<u>Either</u>: find the $\left(\dfrac{n+1}{2}\right)$th value in the ordered list. ◄————— *If ½(n+1) isn't a whole number, take the average of the terms either side.*

<u>Or</u>: (i) if $\dfrac{n}{2}$ is a <u>whole number</u> (i.e. n is <u>even</u>), then the median is the <u>average of this term and the one above</u>.

(ii) if $\dfrac{n}{2}$ is <u>not a whole number</u> (i.e. n is <u>odd</u>), just <u>round the number up</u> to find the position of the median.

EXAMPLE Find the mean, median and mode of the following list of data: 2, 3, 6, 2, 5, 9, 3, 8, 7, 2

Put in order first: 2, 2, 2, 3, 3, 5, 6, 7, 8, 9   **Mode = 2**

Mean = $\dfrac{2+2+2+3+3+5+6+7+8+9}{10}$ = **4.7**   **Median** = average of 5th and 6th values = **4**

Use a **Table** when there are a lot of **Numbers**

Number of letters	Number of houses
0	11
1	25
2	27
3	21
4	9
5	7

EXAMPLE The number of letters received one day in 100 houses was recorded. Find the mean, median and mode of the number of letters.

The first thing to do is make a <u>table</u> like this one:

Number of letters x	Number of houses f		fx
0	11	(11)	0
1	25	(36)	25
2	27	(63)	54
3	21		63
4	9		36
5	7		35
totals	100		213

Multiply x by f to get this column.

*The number of letters received by each house is a **discrete** quantity (e.g. 3 letters). There isn't a **continuous** set of possible values between getting 3 and 4 letters (e.g. 3.45 letters).*

Put the <u>cumulative frequency</u> (<u>running total</u>) in brackets — it's handy when you're finding the <u>median</u>. (But you can stop when you get past <u>halfway</u>.)

$\Sigma f = 100$ $\Sigma fx = 213$

① The <u>mean</u> is easy — just divide the <u>total</u> of the <u>fx-column</u> (sum of all the data values) by the total of the <u>f-column</u> (= n, the total number of data values).   **Mean** = $\dfrac{213}{100}$ = **2.13 letters**

② To find the <u>position</u> of the median, <u>add 1</u> to the total frequency (= $\Sigma f = n$) and then <u>divide by 2</u>. Here the median is in position: $(100 + 1) \div 2 = \underline{50.5}$.

So the median is <u>halfway between</u> the 50th and 51st data values.

Using your <u>running total</u> of f, you can see that the data values in positions 37 to 63 are all 2s. This means the data values at positions 50 and 51 are both 2 — so   **Median = 2 letters**

③ The <u>highest frequency</u> is for 2 letters — so   **Mode = 2 letters**

Location: Mean, Median and Mode

If the data's *Grouped* you'll have to *Estimate* the *Mean*

There are no precise readings here — each reading's been put into one of these groups.

If the data's grouped, you can only estimate the mean and median, and identify a modal class.

EXAMPLE The height of a number of trees was recorded. The data collected is shown in this table:

Height of tree to nearest m	0 - 5	6 - 10	11 - 15	16 - 20
Number of trees	26	17	11	6

Find an estimate of the mean height of the trees, and state the modal class.

To estimate the mean, you assume that every reading in a class takes the mid-class value (which you find by adding the lower class boundary to the upper class boundary and dividing by 2). It's best to make another table...

Height of tree to nearest m	Mid-class value x	Number of trees f	fx
0 - 5	2.75	26 (26)	71.5
6 - 10	8	17 (43)	136
11 - 15	13	11	143
16 - 20	18	6	108
	Totals	60 (= Σf)	458.5(= Σfx)

Lower class boundary (lcb) = 0.
Upper class boundary (ucb) = 5.5.
So the mid-class value = (0 + 5.5) ÷ 2 = 2.75.

Estimated mean = $\dfrac{458.5}{60}$ = **7.64 m**

The **modal class** is the class with the **highest frequency density**. In this example the modal class is **0 - 5 m**.

Linear Interpolation Means Assuming Values are *Evenly Spread*

When you have grouped data, you can only estimate the median. To do this, you use (linear) interpolation.

The median position in the above example is $(60 + 1) \div 2 = 30.5$, so the median is the 30.5th reading (halfway between the 30th and 31st). Your 'running total' tells you the median must be in the '6 - 10' class.

Now you have to assume that all the readings in this class are evenly spread.

There are 26 trees before class 6 - 10, so the 30.5th tree is the 4.5th value of this class.

Divide the class into 17 equally wide parts (as there are 17 readings) and assume there's a reading at the end of each part.

Width of class → $\frac{5}{17}$ $\frac{5}{17}$
Number of readings → 17

5.5 (= lcb) $5.5 + (1 \times \frac{5}{17})$ $5.5 + (2 \times \frac{5}{17})$ 10.5 (= ucb)

Then you want the '4.5th reading' (which is '4.5 × width of 1 part' along).

So the **estimated median** = lower class boundary + (4.5 × width of each 'part') = $5.5 + \left[4.5 \times \frac{5}{17}\right]$ = **6.8 m** (to 1 d.p.)

The Mean, Median and Mode are useful for *Different Kinds* of Data

These three different averages are useful for different kinds of data.

Mean:
- The mean's a good average because you use all your data in working it out.
- But it can be heavily affected by extreme values / outliers.
- And it can only be used with quantitative data (i.e. numbers).

See page 109 for more about outliers.

Median: The median is not affected by extreme values, so this is a good average to use when you have outliers.

Mode:
- The mode can be used even with non-numerical data.
- But some data sets can have more than one mode (and if every value in a data set occurs just once, then the mode isn't very helpful at all).

I can't deny it — these pages really are 'about average'...

If you have large amounts of grouped data ($n > 100$, say), it's usually okay to use the value in position $\frac{n}{2}$ (rather than $\frac{n+1}{2}$) as the median. With grouped data, you can only estimate the median anyway, and if you have a lot of data, that extra 'half a place' doesn't really make much difference. But if in any doubt, use the value in position $\frac{n+1}{2}$ — that'll always be okay.

Variation: Interquartile Range

'Variation' means how spread out your data is. There are different ways to measure it.

The Range is a Measure of Variation

The range is about the simplest measure of variation you could imagine.

> **Range** = highest value – lowest value

But the range is heavily affected by extreme values, so it isn't really the most useful way to measure variation.

Quartiles divide the data into Four

You've seen how the median divides a data set into two halves. Well, the quartiles divide the data into four parts — with 25% of the data less than the lower quartile, and 75% of the data less than the upper quartile.

There are various ways you can find the quartiles, and they sometimes give different results. But if you use the method below, you'll be fine.

① To find the lower quartile (Q_1), first work out $\frac{n}{4}$.

    (i)   if $\frac{n}{4}$ is a whole number, then the lower quartile is the average of this term and the one above.

    (ii) if $\frac{n}{4}$ is not a whole number, just round the number up to find the position of the lower quartile.

② To find the upper quartile (Q_3), first work out $\frac{3n}{4}$.

    (i)   if $\frac{3n}{4}$ is a whole number, then the upper quartile is the average of this term and the one above.

    (ii) if $\frac{3n}{4}$ is not a whole number, just round the number up to find the position of the upper quartile.

EXAMPLE   Find the median and quartiles of the following data: 2, 5, 3, 11, 6, 8, 3, 8, 1, 6, 2, 23, 9, 11, 18, 19, 22, 7.

First put the list in order: 1, 2, 2, 3, 3, 5, 6, 6, 7, 8, 8, 9, 11, 11, 18, 19, 22, 23

You need to find Q_1, Q_2 and Q_3, so work out $\frac{n}{4} = \frac{18}{4}$, $\frac{n}{2} = \frac{18}{2}$, and $\frac{3n}{4} = \frac{54}{4}$.

> *The median is also known as Q_2.*

1) $\frac{n}{4}$ is not a whole number (= 4.5), so round up and take the 5th term: $Q_1 = 3$

2) $\frac{n}{2}$ is a whole number (= 9), so find the average of the 9th and 10th terms: $Q_2 = \frac{7+8}{2} = 7.5$

3) $\frac{3n}{4}$ is not a whole number (= 13.5), so round up and take the 14th term: $Q_3 = 11$

If your data is grouped, you might need to use interpolation to find the quartiles. See page 105 for more info.

The Interquartile Range is Another Measure of Variation

> **Interquartile range (IQR)** = upper quartile (Q_3) – lower quartile (Q_1)

> *The IQR shows the range of the 'middle 50%' of the data.*

EXAMPLE   Find the interquartile range of the data in the previous example.

$Q_1 = 3$ and $Q_3 = 11$, so the   interquartile range = $Q_3 - Q_1 = 11 - 3 = 8$

Sing-a-long-a-stats — "Home, home on the interquartile range..."

Right then... the range and the interquartile range are both measures of how spread out your data is. The range is pretty crude, though — one freakily high or low value in your dataset and it can become completely misleading. The interquartile range is much better, and is easy to work out (easyish, anyway). Make sure all this is clear in your head before moving on.

Cumulative Frequency Graphs

Cumulative frequency means 'running total'. Cumulative frequency diagrams make medians and quartiles easy to find...

Use **Cumulative Frequency Graphs** to estimate the **Median** and **Quartiles**

EXAMPLE The ages of 200 students are shown. Draw a cumulative frequency graph and use it to estimate the median age, the interquartile range of ages, and how many students have already had their 18th birthday.

Age in completed years	11 - 12	13 - 14	15 - 16	17 - 18
Number of students	50	65	58	27

① First draw a table showing the <u>upper class boundaries</u> and the <u>cumulative frequency</u> (CF):

Age in completed years	Upper class boundary (ucb)	Number of students, f	Cumulative frequency (CF)
Under 11	11	0	0
11-12	13	50	50
13-14	15	65	115
15-16	17	58	173
17-18	19	27	200

The <u>first</u> reading in a <u>cumulative frequency</u> table <u>must</u> be <u>zero</u> — so add this <u>extra row</u> to show the number of students with age <u>less than 11</u> is O.

CF is the number of students with age <u>less than</u> the ucb — it's basically a <u>running total</u>.

The <u>last</u> number in the CF column should always be the <u>total number</u> of readings.

People say they're '18' right up until their 19th birthday — so the <u>ucb</u> of class 17-18 is <u>19</u>.

Next draw the <u>axes</u> — cumulative frequency <u>always</u> goes on the <u>vertical axis</u>. Here, age goes on the other axis. Then plot the <u>upper class boundaries</u> against the <u>cumulative frequencies</u>, and join the points.

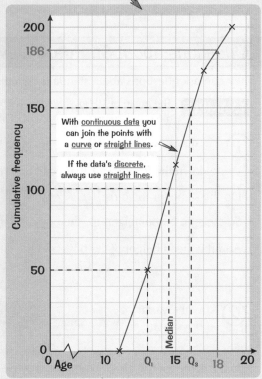

② To estimate the <u>median</u> from a graph, go to the <u>median position</u> on the vertical scale and read off the value from the horizontal axis.

Median position $= \frac{1}{2} \times 200 = 100$ so   Median $= \underline{14.5 \text{ years}}$

Because there are so many data values, and because you can only <u>estimate</u> the median (since your data values are in <u>groups</u>), you can say that the median is in position $\frac{n}{2}$ instead of $\frac{n+1}{2}$. And you can use a similar approximation for the position of the quartiles.

With <u>continuous data</u> you can join the points with a <u>curve</u> or <u>straight lines</u>.

If the data's <u>discrete</u>, always use <u>straight lines</u>.

Then you can estimate the <u>quartiles</u> in the same way. Find their positions first:

Q_1 position $= \frac{1}{4} \times 200 = 50$, and so the lower quartile, $Q_1 = \underline{13 \text{ years}}$

Q_3 position $= \frac{3}{4} \times 200 = 150$, and so the upper quartile, $Q_3 = \underline{16.2 \text{ years}}$

The <u>interquartile range</u> (IQR) $= Q_3 - Q_1$. It measures <u>variation</u>. The smaller it is the less variation the data has.

IQR $= Q_3 - Q_1 = 16.2 - 13 = \underline{3.2 \text{ years}}$

Always plot the <u>upper class boundary</u> of each class.

③ To estimate how many students have <u>not</u> yet had their 18th birthday, go up from 18 on the <u>horizontal axis</u>, and read off the number of students '<u>younger</u>' than 18 (= 186).

Then the number of students who are 'older' than 18 is just 200 – 186 = <u>14</u> (approximately).

I don't like those frequency tables — I've always wanted to live in a classless society...

Cumulative frequency sounds a bit scarier than running total — but if you remember they're the same thing, then that'll help. And remember to plot the points at the <u>upper class boundary</u> — this makes sense if you remember that a cumulative frequency graph shows how many data-values are <u>less than</u> the figure on the *x*-axis. The rest is more or less easyish.

Variation: Standard Deviation

Standard deviation and variance both measure how spread out the data is from the mean
— the bigger they are, the more spread out your readings are.

The **Formulas** look pretty **Tricky**

The formula is easier to use in these forms.

$$\text{Variance} = \frac{\sum(x - \bar{x})^2}{n} = \frac{\sum x^2}{n} - \bar{x}^2 \quad \text{or} \quad \text{Variance} = \frac{\sum fx^2}{\sum f} - \bar{x}^2$$

$$\text{Standard deviation} = \sqrt{\text{variance}}$$

The x-values are the data, $\bar{x}$ is the mean,
f is the frequency of each x, and n (or $\sum f$)
is the number of data values.

EXAMPLE Find the mean and standard deviation of the following numbers: 2, 3, 4, 4, 6, 11, 12

1) Find the <u>total</u> of the numbers first: $\sum x = 2 + 3 + 4 + 4 + 6 + 11 + 12 = 42$

2) Then the <u>mean</u> is easy: $\text{Mean} = \bar{x} = \frac{\sum x}{n} = \frac{42}{7} = 6$

3) Next find the <u>sum of the squares</u>: $\sum x^2 = 4 + 9 + 16 + 16 + 36 + 121 + 144 = 346$

4) Use this to find the <u>variance</u>: $\text{Variance} = \frac{\sum x^2}{n} - \bar{x}^2 = \frac{346}{7} - 6^2 = \frac{346 - 252}{7} = \frac{94}{7}$

5) And take the <u>square root</u> to find the standard deviation: $\text{Standard deviation} = \sqrt{\frac{94}{7}} = 3.66$ to 3 sig. fig.

Questions about **Standard Deviation** can look a bit **Weird**

They can ask questions about standard deviation in different ways. But you just need to use the same old formulas.

EXAMPLE The mean of 10 boys' heights is 180 cm, and the standard deviation is 10 cm. The mean for 9 girls is 165 cm, and the standard deviation is 8 cm. Find the mean and standard deviation of the whole group of 19 girls and boys.

(1) Let the boys' heights be x and the girls' heights be y.

Write down the formula for the mean and put the numbers in for the boys: $\bar{x} = \frac{\sum x}{n} \Rightarrow 180 = \frac{\sum x}{10} \Rightarrow \sum x = 1800$

Do the same for the girls: $165 = \frac{\sum y}{9} \Rightarrow \sum y = 1485$

So the sum of the heights for the <u>boys and the girls</u> $= \sum x + \sum y = 1800 + 1485 = 3285$

And the <u>mean height</u> of the boys and the girls is: $\frac{3285}{19} = \underline{172.9\text{ cm}}$ Round the fraction to 1 d.p. to give your answer. But if you need to use the mean in more calculations, use the <u>fraction</u> (or your <u>calculator's memory</u>) so you don't lose accuracy.

(2) Now the variance — boys first: $\text{Variance} = \frac{\sum x^2}{n} - \bar{x}^2 \Rightarrow 10^2 = \frac{\sum x^2}{10} - 180^2 \Rightarrow \sum x^2 = 10 \times (100 + 32\,400) = 325\,000$

Do the same for the girls: $\text{Variance} = \frac{\sum y^2}{n} - \bar{y}^2 \Rightarrow 8^2 = \frac{\sum y^2}{9} - 165^2 \Rightarrow \sum y^2 = 9 \times (64 + 27\,225) = 245\,601$

Okay, so the sum of the squares of the heights of the boys and the girls is: $\sum x^2 + \sum y^2 = 325\,000 + 245\,601 = 570\,601$

So for <u>all</u> the heights, the variance is: $\text{Variance} = \frac{570\,601}{19} - \left(\frac{3285}{19}\right)^2 = \underline{139.0\text{ cm}^2}$ Don't use the <u>rounded</u> mean (172.9) — you'll lose accuracy.

And finally the standard deviation of the boys and the girls is: $\text{standard deviation} = \sqrt{139.0} = \underline{11.8\text{ cm}}$

Phew.

People who enjoy this stuff are standard deviants...

The formula for the variance looks pretty scary, what with the x^2's and $\bar{x}$'s floating about. But it comes down to 'the mean of the squares minus the square of the mean'. That's how I remember it anyway — and my memory's rubbish.

Variation and Outliers

Use *Mid-Class Values* if your data's in a *Grouped Table*

With grouped data, assume every reading takes the mid-class value. Then use the frequencies to find $\sum fx$ and $\sum fx^2$.

EXAMPLE The heights of sunflowers in a garden were measured and recorded in the table below.
Estimate the mean height and the standard deviation.

Height of sunflower, h (cm)	$150 \leq h < 170$	$170 \leq h < 190$	$190 \leq h < 210$	$210 \leq h < 230$
Number of sunflowers	5	10	12	3

Draw up another table, and include columns for the mid-class values x, as well as fx and fx^2:

Height of sunflower (cm)	Mid-class value, x	x^2	f	fx	fx^2
$150 \leq h < 170$	160	25600	5	800	128000
$170 \leq h < 190$	180	32400	10	1800	324000
$190 \leq h < 210$	200	40000	12	2400	480000
$210 \leq h < 230$	220	48400	3	660	145200
		Totals	30 (= Σf)	5660 (= Σfx)	1077200 (= Σfx^2)

fx^2 means $f \times (x^2)$ — not $(fx)^2$.

Now you've got the totals in the table, you can calculate the mean and standard deviation:

$$\text{Mean} = \overline{x} = \frac{\sum fx}{\sum f} = \frac{5660}{30} = 189 \text{ cm to 3 sig. fig.}$$

$$\text{Variance} = \frac{\sum fx^2}{\sum f} - \overline{x}^2 = \frac{1\,077\,200}{30} - \left(\frac{5660}{30}\right)^2 = 312 \text{ to 3 sig. fig.}$$

$$\text{Standard deviation} = \sqrt{\text{variance}} = 17.7 \text{ cm to 3 sig. fig.}$$

Outliers can *Mess Up* some measures of *Central Tendency* and *Variation*

1) An outlier is a freak piece of data that lies a long way from the rest of the readings.
If your data includes outliers, that might affect how you choose to describe or display it.

2) Some measures are more affected by outliers than others. For example, the mean is much more likely to be affected by outliers than the median, so for data with outliers, the median is usually a better measure of central tendency.

> **EXAMPLE** Look at the following data set: 1, 2, 2, 3, 3, 5, 5, 5, 6, 7, 7, 7, 9, 9, 10, 10, 11, 12, 13, 85
>
> The data set has mean 10.6 and median 7.
> But that value of 85 is an outlier — it's much bigger than the other values.
> If we ignore the outlier, the mean of the other values is 6.68, and the median is still 7
> — the outlier has a big effect on the mean, but doesn't change the median at all.

3) Outliers can make the variance (and standard deviation) much larger than it would otherwise be — which means these freak pieces of data are having more influence than they deserve. If a data set contains outliers, then a better measure of variation is the interquartile range.

> Let's look at the variation of the data set above. The variance with the outlier is 302.94, and without the outlier it's 12.22 — that's a pretty massive difference. On the other hand, the IQR with the outlier included is 6 — without it, the IQR is 7.

4) You might also need to think about outliers when you're deciding which sort of graph to use to display your data.

> The box-and-whisker plot (see p111) for the data set above would have a really long 'whisker' on the right hand side. You couldn't tell from that whether the values above Q_3 are evenly spread, or if there's an outlier. But you could draw a histogram with a really short, wide bar on the right — this wouldn't tell you for sure that there was just one outlier, but it would make it clearer there aren't many values near the top of the range.

'Outlier' is the name I give to something that my theory can't explain...

Measures of location (or central tendency) and variation should capture the essential characteristics of a data set in just one or two numbers. So don't choose a measure that's heavily affected by freaky, far-flung outliers — it won't be much good.

Coding

Coding can make the Numbers much Easier

Coding means doing something to <u>every reading</u> (like <u>adding</u> or <u>multiplying</u> by a number) to make life easier.

Finding the mean of 1001, 1002 and 1006 looks hard(ish). But take 1000 off each number and finding the mean of what's left (1, 2 and 6) is much easier — it's <u>3</u>. So the mean of the original numbers must be <u>1003</u>. That's coding.

You usually change your original variable, x, to an easier one to work with, y (so here, if $x = 1001$, then $y = 1$).

Write down a formula connecting the two variables: e.g. $y = \dfrac{x - b}{a}$. ← You can add/subtract a number, and multiply/divide by one as well — it all depends on what will make life easiest.

Then $\overline{y} = \dfrac{\overline{x} - b}{a}$ where $\overline{x}$ and $\overline{y}$ are the means of variables x and y.

Note that if you don't multiply or divide your readings by anything (i.e. if a = 1), then the standard deviation isn't changed.

Also **standard deviation of y's $= \dfrac{\text{standard deviation of } x\text{'s}}{a}$**

EXAMPLE   Find the mean and standard deviation of: 1 000 020, 1 000 040, 1 000 010 and 1 000 050.

The obvious thing to do is subtract a million from every reading to leave 20, 40, 10 and 50.
Then make life even simpler by dividing by 10 — giving 2, 4, 1 and 5.

① So use the coding: $y = \dfrac{x - 1 000 000}{10}$. Then $\overline{y} = \dfrac{\overline{x} - 1 000 000}{10}$ and s.d. of $y = \dfrac{\text{s.d. of } x}{10}$. · s.d. = 'standard deviation'

② Find the mean and standard deviation of the y values: $\overline{y} = \dfrac{2 + 4 + 1 + 5}{4} = \underline{3}$

$$\text{s.d. of } y = \sqrt{\dfrac{2^2 + 4^2 + 1^2 + 5^2}{4} - 3^2}$$
$$= \sqrt{\dfrac{46}{4} - 9} = \sqrt{2.5} = \underline{1.58} \text{ to 3 sig. fig.}$$

③ Then use the formulas to find the mean and standard deviation of the original values:

$$\overline{x} = 10\overline{y} + 1 000 000 = (10 \times 3) + 1 000 000 = \underline{1 000 030}$$
$$\text{s.d. of } x = 10 \times \text{s.d. of } y = 10 \times 1.58 = \underline{15.8}$$

And so variance of the x's = (s.d. of x's)^2 = (10 × s.d. of y's)^2 = $\underline{10^2}$ × (s.d. of y's)^2 = $\underline{10^2}$ × variance of the y's.

You can use coding with Summarised Data

This kind of question looks tricky at first — but use the same old formulas and it's a piece of cake.

EXAMPLE   A set of 10 numbers (x-values) can be summarised as shown: Find the mean and standard deviation of the numbers. $\sum(x - 10) = 15$ and $\sum(x - 10)^2 = 100$

① Okay, the obvious first thing to try is: $y = x - 10 \Longrightarrow$ That means: $\sum y = 15$ and $\sum y^2 = 100$

② Work out $\overline{y}$ and the standard deviation of the y's using the normal formulas: $\overline{y} = \dfrac{\sum y}{n} = \dfrac{15}{10} = 1.5$

$$\text{Variance of } y = \dfrac{\sum y^2}{n} - \overline{y}^2 = \dfrac{100}{10} - 1.5^2 = 10 - 2.25 = 7.75$$
$$\text{so standard deviation of } y = \sqrt{7.75} = 2.78 \text{ to 3 sig. fig.}$$

③ Then finding the mean and standard deviation of the x-values is easy: $\overline{x} = \overline{y} + 10 = 1.5 + 10 = \underline{11.5}$

The s.d. of x is the same as the s.d. of y since you've only subtracted 10 from every number. → s.d. of x = s.d. of y = $\underline{2.78}$ to 3 sig. fig.

I thought coding would be a little more... well, James Bond...

Coding data isn't hard — the only tricky thing can be to work out <u>how</u> best to code it, although there will usually be some pretty hefty clues in the question if you care to look. But remember that adding/subtracting a number from every reading won't change the variation (the variance or standard deviation), but multiplying/dividing readings by something will.

Comparing Distributions

To compare data sets, you need to know <u>how to use</u> all the formulas <u>and</u> what the results <u>tell you</u>.

Box-and-Whisker Plots are a Visual Summary of a Distribution

<u>Box-and-whisker plots</u> show the median and quartiles in an easy-to-look-at kind of way. They look like this:

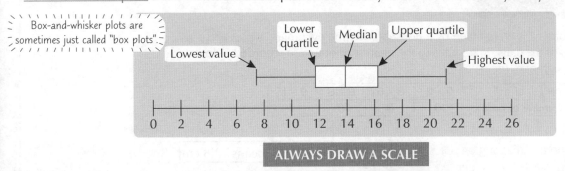

Box-and-whisker plots are sometimes just called "box plots".

Lowest value | Lower quartile | Median | Upper quartile | Highest value

ALWAYS DRAW A SCALE

Use Location and Variation to Compare Distributions

EXAMPLE

This table summarises the marks obtained in Maths 'calculator' and 'non-calculator' papers. Compare the location and variation of the distributions.

Calculator Paper		Non-calculator paper
28	Minimum	12
78	Maximum	82
40	Lower quartile, Q_1	35
58	Median, Q_2	42
70	Upper quartile, Q_3	56
55	Mean	46.1
21.2	Standard deviation	17.8

<u>Location:</u> The <u>mean</u>, the <u>median</u> and the <u>quartiles</u> are all higher for the calculator paper. This means that scores were <u>generally higher</u> on the calculator paper.

Although the maximum mark on the non-calculator paper was higher than the maximum mark on the calculator paper, this doesn't say anything about the results <u>generally</u>.

<u>Variation:</u> The <u>interquartile range</u> (IQR) for the calculator paper is $Q_3 - Q_1 = 70 - 40 = 30$.
The <u>interquartile range</u> (IQR) for the non-calculator paper is $Q_3 - Q_1 = 56 - 35 = 21$.
The <u>range</u> for the calculator paper is $78 - 28 = 50$.
The <u>range</u> for the non-calculator paper is $82 - 12 = 70$.

The <u>IQR</u> and the <u>standard deviation</u> are both <u>bigger</u> for the calculator paper, so it looks like the scores on the calculator paper are <u>more spread out</u> than for the non-calculator paper.
Although the <u>range</u> is bigger for the non-calculator paper, this might not be a reliable guide to the variation since the data may well contain outliers.

EXAMPLE Compare the distributions represented by the box-and-whisker plots below.

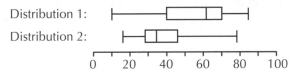

Distribution 1:
Distribution 2:

<u>Location:</u> The <u>median</u> and the <u>quartiles</u> are higher for Distribution 1, showing that these data values are <u>generally higher</u> than for Distribution 2.

<u>Variation:</u> The <u>interquartile range</u> (IQR) and the <u>range</u> for Distribution 1 are bigger, showing that the values are more varied for Distribution 1 than for Distribution 2.

That's the end of the Data section — hurrah for that...

On exam day, you could be asked to compare two distributions. Just work out any measures of <u>location</u> and <u>variation</u> you can. Then say which distribution has a <u>higher value</u> for each measure, and <u>what it means</u> — e.g. a higher variance means the values are <u>more spread out</u>, while a higher mean means the scores are <u>generally higher</u>. And so on.

S1 Section 1 — Practice Questions

It's important to make sure you know this stuff like the back of your hand — but unlike the back of your hand you won't have this book in the exam. So here are some practice questions to help you remember it all. We'll start off gently...

Warm-up Questions

1) Twenty phone calls were made by a householder one evening.
   The lengths of the calls (in minutes to the nearest minute) are recorded below.
   Draw a histogram of the data.

Length of call	0 - 2	3 - 5	6 - 8	9 - 15
Number of calls	10	6	3	1

2) The stem and leaf diagram on
   the right represents the lengths
   (in cm) of 15 bananas.
   Write down the original data as a list.

   ```
   12 | 8          Key  12|8 means 12.8 cm
   13 | 2, 5
   14 | 3, 3, 6, 8
   15 | 2, 9
   16 | 1, 1, 2, 3
   17 | 0, 2
   ```

3) Calculate the mean, median and mode of the data in this table. $\Longrightarrow$

x	0	1	2	3	4
f	5	4	4	2	1

4) The speeds of 60 cars travelling in a 40 mph speed limit area were measured to the nearest mph.
   The data is summarised in the table.
   Estimate the mean and median,
   and state the modal class.

Speed (mph)	30 - 34	35 - 39	40 - 44	45 - 50
Frequency	12	37	9	2

5) Find the median and quartiles of the data below, and draw a box and whisker diagram.
   Amount of pocket money (in £) received per week by twenty 15-year-olds:
   10, 5, 20, 50, 5, 1, 6, 5, 15, 20, 5, 7, 5, 10, 12, 4, 8, 6, 7, 30.

6) Draw a cumulative frequency diagram of the data given in the table.
   Use your diagram to estimate the median and interquartile range.

Distance walked (km)	0 - 2	2 - 4	4 - 6	6 - 8
Number of walkers	10	5	3	2

7) Find the mean and standard deviation of the following numbers: 11, 12, 14, 17, 21, 23, 27.

8) The scores in an IQ test for 50 people
   are recorded in the table.

Score	100 - 106	107 - 113	114 - 120	121 - 127	128 - 134
Frequency	6	11	22	9	2

   Estimate the mean and variance of the distribution.

9) For a set of data, $n = 100$, $\sum(x - 20) = 125$, and $\sum(x - 20)^2 = 221$.
   Find the mean and standard deviation of x.

10) The time taken (to the nearest minute) for a commuter to travel to work on 20 consecutive work days is
    recorded in the table. Use coding to estimate the mean and standard deviation of the times.

Time to nearest minute	30 - 33	34 - 37	38 - 41	42 - 45
Frequency	3	6	7	4

S1 Section 1 — Practice Questions

Well wasn't that lovely. I bet you're now ready and raring to test yourself with some proper exam-style questions. Here are some I made earlier, lucky you.

Exam Questions

1. A group of 19 people played a game. The scores, x, that the people achieved are summarised by:
    $$\sum(x - 30) = 228 \text{ and } \sum(x - 30)^2 = 3040$$

    a) Calculate the mean and the standard deviation of the 19 scores.

    (3 marks)

    b) Show that $\sum x = 798$ and $\sum x^2 = 33\,820$.

    (3 marks)

    c) Another student played the game. Her score was 32.
        Find the new mean and standard deviation of all 20 scores.

    (4 marks)

2. Two workers iron clothes. Each irons 10 items, and records the time it takes for each, to the nearest minute:

    Worker A: 3 5 2 7 10 4 5 5 4 12
    Worker B: 3 4 8 6 7 8 9 10 11 9

    a) For worker A's times. Find:
        (i) the median

    (1 mark)

        (ii) the lower and upper quartiles

    (2 marks)

    b) On graph paper, draw two box-and-whisker plots representing the workers' times (i.e. one box-and-whisker plot for each worker). Both box-and-whisker plots should be drawn using the same scale.

    (6 marks)

    c) Make one statement comparing the two sets of data.

    (1 mark)

    d) Which worker would be better to employ? Give a reason for your answer.

    (1 mark)

3. In a supermarket two types of chocolate drops were compared.
    The weights, a grams, of 20 chocolate drops of brand A are summarised by:
    $$\Sigma a = 60.3\,\text{g} \qquad \Sigma a^2 = 219\,\text{g}^2$$

    The mean weight of 30 chocolate drops of brand B was 2.95 g, and the standard deviation was 1 g.

    a) Find the mean weight of a brand A chocolate drop.

    (1 mark)

    b) Find the standard deviation of the weight of the brand A chocolate drops.

    (3 marks)

    c) Compare brands A and B.

    (2 marks)

    d) Find the standard deviation of the weight of all 50 chocolate drops.

    (4 marks)

S1 Section 1 — Practice Questions

Despair not, valiant mathematician, for the end is nigh. Just a few more questions, then you can have a nap and a biscuit.

Exam Questions

4   The table shows the number of hits received by people at a paint ball party.

No. of Hits	12	13	14	15	16	17	18	19	20	21	22	23	24	25
Frequency	2	4	6	7	6	4	4	2	1	1	0	0	0	1

a)   Find the median and mode number of hits.

(3 marks)

b)   Suggest why the median might be a better measure of location for this data than the mean.

(1 mark)

c)   Sketch a box-and-whisker plot of the distribution.

(1 mark)

d)   How would the shape of the distribution be affected if the value of 25 was removed?

(1 mark)

5   The profits of 100 businesses are given in the table.

Profit, £x million.	Number of businesses
$4.5 \leqslant x < 5.0$	24
$5.0 \leqslant x < 5.5$	26
$5.5 \leqslant x < 6.0$	21
$6.0 \leqslant x < 6.5$	19
$6.5 \leqslant x < 8.0$	10

a)   Represent the data in a histogram.

(3 marks)

b)   Comment on the distribution of the profits of the businesses.

(2 marks)

6   The stem and leaf diagram shows the test marks for 30 male students and 16 female students.

```
    Male students          Female students
           8, 3, 3  │ 4 │
     8, 7, 7, 5, 3, 2  │ 5 │ 5, 6, 7
9, 7, 6, 6, 5, 5, 2, 2, 1, 1, 0  │ 6 │ 1, 2, 3, 3, 4, 5, 6, 7, 9
  9, 9, 8, 5, 4, 3, 1, 0, 0  │ 7 │ 2, 4, 8, 9
```

Key 5|6|2 means Male student test mark 65 and Female student test mark 62

a)   Find the median test mark of the male students.

(1 mark)

b)   Compare the distribution of the male and female marks.

(2 marks)

7   The histogram shows the nose-to-tail lengths of 50 lions in a game reserve.

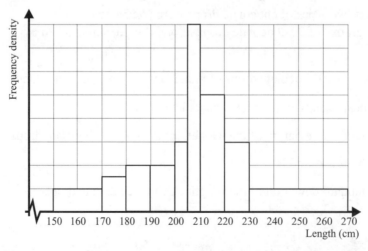

Use the histogram to find the number of lions who measured over 220 cm from nose to tail.

(5 marks)

Random Events and Venn Diagrams

Random events happen <u>by chance</u>. <u>Probability</u> is a measure of how likely they are. It can be a chancy business.

A Random Event has **Various Outcomes**

1) In a <u>trial</u> (or experiment) the things that can happen are called <u>outcomes</u> (so if I time how long it takes to eat my dinner, 63 seconds is a possible outcome).

2) <u>Events</u> are 'groups' of one or more outcomes (so an event might be 'it takes me less than a minute to eat my dinner every day one week').

3) When all outcomes are <u>equally likely</u>, you can work out the <u>probability</u> of an event by <u>counting</u> the outcomes:

$$P(\text{event}) = \frac{\text{Number of outcomes where event happens}}{\text{Total number of possible outcomes}}$$

> **EXAMPLE**   Suppose I've got a bag with 15 balls in — 5 red, 6 blue and 4 green.
>
> If I take a ball out without looking, then any ball is equally likely — there are 15 possible outcomes.
> Of these 15 outcomes, 5 are red, 6 are blue and 4 are green. And so...
>
> $$P(\text{red ball}) = \frac{5}{15} = \frac{1}{3} \qquad P(\text{blue ball}) = \frac{6}{15} = \frac{2}{5} \qquad P(\text{red or green ball}) = \frac{9}{15} = \frac{3}{5}$$
>
> If I then do <u>90 trials</u> (i.e. I pick a ball out 90 times, replacing the ball each time), then I would <u>expect</u> to pick:
>
> a red ball $\frac{1}{3} \times 90 = 30$ times   a blue ball $\frac{2}{5} \times 90 = 36$ times   either a red or a green ball $\frac{3}{5} \times 90 = 54$ times

You can also use <u>relative frequencies</u> to assign probabilities — you use the results of trials you've <u>already carried out</u>.

$$P(\text{event}) = \frac{\text{Number of trials where event happened}}{\text{Total number of trials carried out}}$$

The **Sample Space** is the Set of **All Possible Outcomes**

Drawing the sample space (called S) helps you count the outcomes you're interested in.

> **EXAMPLE**   The classic probability machine is a dice. If you roll it twice, you can record all the possible outcomes in a 6 × 6 table (a possible diagram of the sample space).
>
> There are 36 outcomes in total. You can find probabilities by counting the ones you're interested in (and using the above formula). For example:
>
> (i) The probability of an odd number and then a '1'. There are 3 outcomes that make up this event, so the probability is: $\frac{3}{36} = \frac{1}{12}$
>
> (ii) The probability of the total being 7. There are 6 outcomes that correspond to this event, giving a probability of: $\frac{6}{36} = \frac{1}{6}$

Venn Diagrams show which **Outcomes** correspond to which **Events**

Say you've got 2 events, A and B — a Venn diagram can show which outcomes satisfy event A, which satisfy B, which satisfy both, and which satisfy neither.

(i) All outcomes satisfying event A go in one part of the diagram, and all outcomes satisfying event B go in another bit.

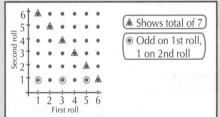

(ii) If they satisfy '<u>both A and B</u>', they go in the dark green middle bit, written $A \cap B$ (and called the <u>intersection</u> of A and B).

(iii) The whole of the green area is written $A \cup B$ — it means 'either A or B' (and is called the <u>union</u> of A and B).

Again, you can work out probabilities of events by counting outcomes and using the formula above.
You can also get a nice formula linking $P(A \cap B)$ and $P(A \cup B)$.

$$P(A \cup B) = P(A) + P(B) - P(A \cap B)$$

If you just add up the outcomes in A and B, you end up counting $A \cap B$ twice — that's why you have to subtract it.

> **EXAMPLE**   If you roll a dice, event A could be 'I get an even number', and B 'I get a number bigger than 4'. The Venn diagram would be:
>
> $$P(A) = \frac{3}{6} = \frac{1}{2} \qquad P(B) = \frac{2}{6} = \frac{1}{3} \qquad P(A \cap B) = \frac{1}{6} \qquad P(A \cup B) = \frac{4}{6} = \frac{2}{3}$$

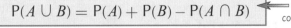

Here, I've just counted outcomes — but I could have used the formula.

Random Events and Venn Diagrams

You can also use Venn diagrams to show probabilities...

EXAMPLE A survey was carried out to find what pets people like.

The probability they like dogs is 0.6. The probability they like cats is 0.5. The probability they like gerbils is 0.4.
The probability they like dogs and cats is 0.4. The probability they like cats and gerbils is 0.1, and the probability they like gerbils and dogs is 0.2. Finally, the probability they like all three kinds of animal is 0.1.
You can draw all this in a Venn diagram. (Here I've used C for 'likes cats', D for 'likes dogs' and G for 'likes gerbils'.)

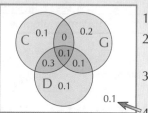

1) Stick in the middle one first — 'likes all 3 animals' (i.e. $C \cap D \cap G$).

2) Then do the 'likes 2 animals' probabilities by taking 0.1 from each of the given 'likes 2 animals' probabilities. (If they like 3 animals, they'll also be in the 'likes 2 animals' bits.)

3) Then do the 'likes 1 kind of animal' probabilities, by making sure the total probability in each circle adds up to the probability in the question.

4) Finally, subtract all the probabilities so far from 1 to find 'likes none of these animals'.

① From the Venn diagram, the probability that someone likes either dogs or cats is 0.7.

② The probability that someone likes gerbils but not dogs is 0.2.

③ You can work out the probability that a dog-lover <u>also</u> like cats by ignoring everything outside the 'dogs' circle.

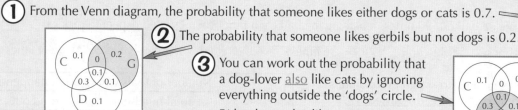

P(dog-lover also like cats)
$$= \frac{0.3 + 0.1}{0.3 + 0.1 + 0.1 + 0.1} = \frac{2}{3}$$

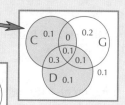

The **Complement** of 'Event A' is **'Not Event A'**

An event A will either happen or not happen. The event 'A doesn't happen' is called the <u>complement</u> of A (or <u>A'</u>).
On a Venn diagram, it would look like this (because $A \cup A' = S$, the sample space):
At least one of A and A' has to happen, so...

$$P(A) + P(A') = 1 \quad \text{or} \quad P(A') = 1 - P(A)$$

EXAMPLE A teacher keeps socks loose in a box. One morning, he picks out a sock. He calculates that the probability of then picking out a matching sock is 0.56. What is the probability of him not picking a matching sock?

Call event A 'picks a matching sock'. Then A' is 'doesn't pick a matching sock'. Now A and A' are <u>complementary</u> events (and P(A) = 0.56), so $P(A) + P(A') = 1$, and therefore $P(A') = 1 - 0.56 = 0.44$

Mutually Exclusive Events Have **No Overlap**

If two events can't both happen at the same time (i.e. P(A ∩ B) = 0) they're called <u>mutually exclusive</u> (or just 'exclusive').
If A and B are exclusive, then the probability of A <u>or</u> B is: P(A ∪ B) = P(A) + P(B). ← Use the formula from page 115, but put P(A ∩ B) = 0.
More generally,

For *n* <u>exclusive</u> events (i.e. only one of them can happen at a time):
$$P(A_1 \cup A_2 \cup ... \cup A_n) = P(A_1) + P(A_2) + ... + P(A_n)$$

EXAMPLE Find the probability that a card pulled at random from a standard pack of cards (no jokers) is <u>either</u> a picture card (a Jack, Queen or King) <u>or</u> the 7, 8 or 9 of clubs.

Call <u>event A</u> — 'I get a picture card', and <u>event B</u> — 'I get the 7, 8 or 9 of clubs'.
Events A and B are <u>mutually exclusive</u> — they can't both happen. Also, $P(A) = \frac{12}{52} = \frac{3}{13}$ and $P(B) = \frac{3}{52}$.
So the probability of either A or B is: $P(A \cup B) = P(A) + P(B) = \frac{12}{52} + \frac{3}{52} = \frac{15}{52}$

Two heads are better than one — though only half as likely using two coins...

I must admit — I kind of like these pages. This stuff isn't too hard, and it's really useful for answering loads of questions.
And one other good thing is that Venn diagrams look, well, nice somehow. But more importantly, when you're filling one in, the thing to remember is that you usually need to 'start from the inside and work out'.

Tree Diagrams

Tree diagrams — they blossom from a tiny question-acorn into a beautiful tree of possibility. Inspiring <u>and</u> useful.

Tree Diagrams *Show Probabilities for* **Two or More** *Events*

Each 'chunk' of a tree diagram is a trial, and each branch of that chunk is a possible outcome.
Multiplying probabilities along the branches gives you the probability of a <u>series</u> of outcomes.

EXAMPLE If Susan plays tennis one day, the probability that she'll play the next day is 0.2.
If she doesn't play tennis, the probability that she'll play the next day is 0.6.
She plays tennis on Monday. What is the probability she plays tennis:

  (i)   on both the Tuesday and Wednesday of that week?
  (ii) on the Wednesday of the same week?

Let T mean 'plays tennis' (and then T' means 'doesn't play tennis').

(i) Then the probability that she plays on Tuesday
<u>and</u> Wednesday is $P(T \text{ and } T) = 0.2 \times 0.2 = \underline{0.04}$
(<u>multiply</u> probabilities since you need a <u>series</u> of
outcomes — T and then T).

(ii) Now you're interested in <u>either</u> P(T and T) <u>or</u>
P(T' and T). To find the probability of one event <u>or</u>
another happening, you have to <u>add</u> probabilities:
$P(\text{plays on Wednesday}) = 0.04 + 0.48 = \underline{0.52}$.

Notice that these add up to 1.

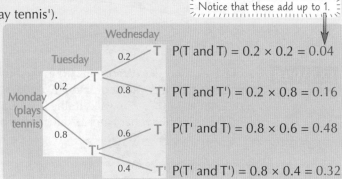

$P(T \text{ and } T) = 0.2 \times 0.2 = 0.04$

$P(T \text{ and } T') = 0.2 \times 0.8 = 0.16$

$P(T' \text{ and } T) = 0.8 \times 0.6 = 0.48$

$P(T' \text{ and } T') = 0.8 \times 0.4 = 0.32$

Sometimes a Branch is **Missing**

EXAMPLE A box of biscuits contains 5 chocolate biscuits
and 1 lemon biscuit. George takes out 3 biscuits
at random, one at a time, and eats them.

a) Find the probability that he eats 3 chocolate biscuits.

b) Find the probability that the last biscuit is chocolate.

Let C mean 'picks a chocolate biscuit' and L mean 'picks the lemon biscuit'.

*After the lemon biscuit there are only chocolate biscuits left,
so the tree diagram doesn't 'branch' after an 'L'.*

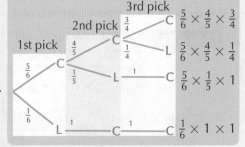

a) Three chocolate biscuits is shown by only one 'path' along the branches.

$$P(C \text{ and } C \text{ and } C) = \tfrac{5}{6} \times \tfrac{4}{5} \times \tfrac{3}{4} = \tfrac{60}{120} = \tfrac{1}{2}$$

b) The third biscuit being chocolate is shown by 3 'paths' along the branches — so you can add up the probabilities:

$$P(\text{third biscuit is chocolate}) = \left(\tfrac{5}{6} \times \tfrac{4}{5} \times \tfrac{3}{4}\right) + \left(\tfrac{5}{6} \times \tfrac{1}{5} \times 1\right) + \left(\tfrac{1}{6} \times 1 \times 1\right) = \tfrac{1}{2} + \tfrac{1}{6} + \tfrac{1}{6} = \tfrac{5}{6}$$

There's a quicker way to do this, since there's only one outcome where the chocolate <u>isn't</u> picked last:

$$P(\text{third biscuit is } \underline{\text{not}} \text{ chocolate}) = \tfrac{5}{6} \times \tfrac{4}{5} \times \tfrac{1}{4} = \tfrac{1}{6}, \text{ so } P(\text{third biscuit is chocolate}) = 1 - \tfrac{1}{6} = \tfrac{5}{6}$$

*Working out the probability of the <u>complement</u> of
the event you're interested in is sometimes easier.*

Sampling **with replacement** *— the probabilities stay the same*

In the above example, each time George takes a biscuit he eats it before taking the next one (i.e. he doesn't replace it) — this is <u>sampling without replacement</u>. Suppose instead that each time he takes a biscuit he puts it back in the box before taking the next one — this is <u>sampling with replacement</u>. All this means is that the probability of choosing a particular item <u>remains the same</u> for each pick.

So part a) above becomes:

$$P(C \text{ and } C \text{ and } C) = \tfrac{5}{6} \times \tfrac{5}{6} \times \tfrac{5}{6} = \tfrac{125}{216} > \tfrac{1}{2}$$

So the probability that George picks 3 chocolate biscuits is slightly greater when sampling is done <u>with replacement</u>. This makes sense because now there are, on average, more chocolate biscuits available for his 2nd and 3rd picks, so he is more likely to choose one.

Conditional Probability

After the first set of branches, tree diagrams actually show <u>conditional probabilities</u>. Read on...

P(B|A) means **Probability of B**, given that **A has Already Happened**

Conditional probability means the probability of something, given that something else has already happened.
For example, P(B|A) means the probability of B, given that A has already happened. Back to tree diagrams...

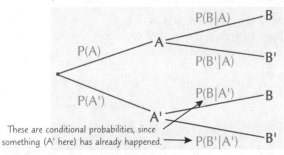

These are conditional probabilities, since something (A' here) has already happened.

If you multiply probabilities along the branches, you get:

i.e. P(A and B) ⟹ $$P(A \cap B) = P(A) \times P(B \mid A)$$

You can rewrite this as:

$$P(B \mid A) = \frac{P(A \cap B)}{P(A)}$$

EXAMPLE Horace either walks (W) or runs (R) to the bus stop. If he walks he catches (C) the bus with a probability of 0.3. If he runs he catches it with a probability of 0.7. He walks to the bus stop with a probability of 0.4. Find the probability that Horace catches the bus.

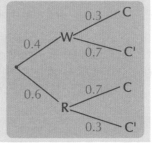

P(C) = P(C ∩ W) + P(C ∩ R)

= P(W) P(C|W) + P(R) P(C|R)

= (0.4 × 0.3) + (0.6 × 0.7) = 0.12 + 0.42 = <u>0.54</u>

This is easier to follow if you match each part of this working to the probabilities in the tree diagram.

If **B is Conditional** on A then **A is Conditional** on B

If B depends on A then A depends on B — and it doesn't matter which event happens first.

EXAMPLE Horace turns up at school either late (L) or on time (L'). He is then either shouted at (S) or not (S'). The probability that he turns up late is 0.4. If he turns up late the probability that he is shouted at is 0.7. If he turns up on time the probability that he is shouted at is 0.2.

If you hear Horace being shouted at, what is the probability that he turned up late?

1) The probability you want is P(L|S).
   Get this the right way round — he's <u>already</u> being shouted at.

2) Use the conditional probability formula: $P(L \mid S) = \frac{P(L \cap S)}{P(S)}$

3) The best way to find P(L ∩ S) and P(S) is with a tree diagram.
   Be careful with questions like this — the information in the question tells you what you need to know to draw the tree diagram with L (or L') considered first.
   But you need P(L|S) — where S is considered first. So don't just rush in.

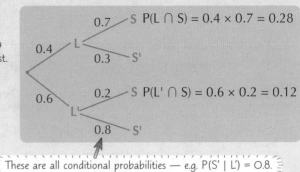

   P(L ∩ S) = 0.4 × 0.7 = 0.28
   P(S) = P(L ∩ S) + P(L' ∩ S) = 0.28 + 0.12 = 0.40

4) Put these in your conditional probability formula to get:

   $P(L \mid S) = \frac{0.28}{0.4} = 0.7$

   These are all conditional probabilities — e.g. P(S' | L') = 0.8.

There's a **Formula** for Working this Out — but it's **Easier** to Use the **Tree Diagram**

This formula will be on the formula sheet in your exam.

$$P(A \mid B) = \frac{P(A \cap B)}{P(B)} = \frac{P(B \mid A)P(A)}{P(B \mid A)P(A) + P(B \mid A')P(A')}$$

This is basically the same working as with the tree diagram above.

Here, this gives:

$$P(L \mid S) = \frac{P(L \cap S)}{P(S)} = \frac{P(S \mid L)P(L)}{P(S \mid L)P(L) + P(S \mid L')P(L')} = \frac{0.7 \times 0.4}{(0.7 \times 0.4) + (0.2 \times 0.6)} = \frac{0.28}{0.4} = 0.7$$

Independent Events

Independent Events *Have* **No Effect** *on Each Other*

If the probability of B happening doesn't depend on whether or not A has happened, then A and B are <u>independent</u>.

1) If A and B are independent, $P(A \mid B) = P(A)$.

2) If you put this in the conditional probability formula, you get: $P(A \mid B) = P(A) = \dfrac{P(A \cap B)}{P(B)}$

Or, to put that another way:

> For independent events: $P(A \cap B) = P(A)P(B)$

EXAMPLE V and W are independent events, where $P(V) = 0.2$ and $P(W) = 0.6$.
     a) Find $P(V \cap W)$.   b) Find $P(V \cup W)$.

a) Just put the numbers into the formula for independent events: $P(V \cap W) = P(V)P(W) = 0.2 \times 0.6 = 0.12$

b) Using the formula on page 115: $P(V \cup W) = P(V) + P(W) - P(V \cap W) = 0.2 + 0.6 - 0.12 = 0.68$

Sometimes you'll be asked if two events are independent or not. Here's how you work it out...

EXAMPLE You are exposed to two infectious diseases — one after the other. The probability you catch the first (A) is 0.25, the probability you catch the second (B) is 0.5, and the probability you catch both of them is 0.2. Are catching the two diseases independent events?

You need to compare $P(A \mid B)$ and $P(A)$ — if they're different, the events <u>aren't independent</u>.

$$P(A \mid B) = \frac{P(A \cap B)}{P(B)} = \frac{0.2}{0.5} = 0.4 \qquad P(A) = 0.25 \qquad P(A \mid B) \text{ and } P(A) \text{ are different, so they're } \underline{\text{not independent}}.$$

Take Your Time with **Tough** *Probability Questions*

EXAMPLE A and B are two events, with $P(A) = 0.4$, $P(B \mid A) = 0.25$, and $P(A' \cap B) = 0.2$.
    a) Find: (i) $P(A \cap B)$,   (ii) $P(A')$,   (iii) $P(B' \mid A)$,   (iv) $P(B \mid A')$,   (v) $P(B)$,   (vi) $P(A \mid B)$.
    b) Say whether or not A and B are independent.

a) i) $P(B \mid A) = \dfrac{P(A \cap B)}{P(A)} = 0.25$, so $P(A \cap B) = 0.25 \times P(A) = 0.25 \times 0.4 = 0.1$

$P(A' \cap B)$

ii) $P(A') = 1 - P(A) = 1 - 0.4 = 0.6$

> A Venn diagram sometimes makes it easier to see what's going on. Fill it in as you find anything out.

iii) $P(B' \mid A) = 1 - P(B \mid A) = 1 - 0.25 = 0.75$

> Since $P(B' \mid A) + P(B \mid A) = 1$.

iv) $P(B \mid A') = \dfrac{P(B \cap A')}{P(A')} = \dfrac{0.2}{0.6} = \dfrac{1}{3}$

> $P(B \cap A') = P(A' \cap B)$

> From (i) $P(A \cap B) = 0.1$, so you know this must be 0.3.

v) $P(B) = P(B \mid A)P(A) + P(B \mid A')P(A') = (0.25 \times 0.4) + \left(\dfrac{1}{3} \times 0.6\right) = 0.3$

> Or use the Venn diagram.

vi) $P(A \mid B) = \dfrac{P(A \cap B)}{P(B)} = \dfrac{0.1}{0.3} = \dfrac{1}{3}$

> Or you could say that $P(A \cap B) = 0.1$, while $P(A)P(B) = 0.4 \times 0.3 = 0.12$ — they're different, which shows A and B are not independent.

A Venn diagram showing two overlapping circles A and B, with A region 0.3, overlap 0.1, B region 0.2, and outside 0.4.

b) If $P(B \mid A) = P(B)$, then A and B are independent.
But $P(B \mid A) = 0.25$, while $P(B) = 0.3$, so A and B are <u>not</u> independent.

Statisticians say: P(Having cake $\cap$ Eating it) = 0...

Probability questions can be tough. For tricky questions like the last one, try drawing a Venn diagram or a tree diagram, even if the question doesn't tell you to — they're really useful for getting your head round things and understanding what on earth is going on. And don't forget the tests for independent events — you're likely to get asked a question on those.

Arrangements and Selections

This page is a bit of a gentle introduction to this topic — it's basically about counting things.

n Different Objects can be Arranged in *n!* Different Ways...

There are $n!$ ("*n* factorial") ways of arranging *n* different objects, where $n! = n \times (n-1) \times (n-2) \times ... \times 3 \times 2 \times 1$.

> **EXAMPLE** In how many ways can 4 different ornaments be arranged on a shelf?
>
> You have 4 choices for the first ornament, 3 choices for the second ornament, 2 choices for the third ornament, and 1 choice for the last ornament.
>
> So there are $4! = 4 \times 3 \times 2 \times 1 = 24$ arrangements.

...but *Divide by r!* if *r* of These Objects are the *Same*

If *r* of your *n* objects are identical, then the total number of possible arrangements is $n! \div r!$.

> **EXAMPLE** In how many different ways can 5 objects be arranged in a line if 2 of those objects are identical?
>
> Imagine those 2 identical objects were different.
> Then there would be $5! = 120$ possible arrangements.
>
> But because those 2 objects are actually identical, you can always swap them round without making a different arrangement.
> $2! = 2 \times 1 = 2.$
>
> So there are really only $120 \div 2 = 60$ different ways to arrange the objects.

Arrangement Questions are about *Counting Choices*

Some arrangement questions are a bit more complicated.
For example, you might have more than one group of identical objects.

> **EXAMPLE** In how many ways can the letters of the word STEEPLES be arranged?
>
> Start by pretending the various S's and E's are different. Then there would be 8 choices for the first letter, 7 for the second, and so on. This would give $8! = 40\ 320$ arrangements.
>
> But in fact, you can swap those two S's around without getting a different arrangement, so divide by 2!.
> And you can swap the three E's about too, so divide by 3!. This means there are $\dfrac{8!}{2! \times 3!} = 3360$ arrangements.

Some questions will put restrictions on the order you can arrange the objects in.

> **EXAMPLE** Alice, Bernie, Camilla and Dave are going to sit on a 4-person bench, but Dave doesn't want to sit next to Bernie. How many acceptable arrangements are there?
>
> First, you need to choose someone for the first seat — but there are two cases:
> Either: (i) Dave or Bernie is in this first position, Or: (ii) Alice or Camilla is in this first position.
>
> (i) Choose Dave or Bernie for position 1 (= 2 choices). Then there are also 2 choices for who sits in the next seat (i.e. Alice or Camilla). Now there are no more restrictions — you have 2 choices for Position 3 and 1 choice for Position 4 — giving $2 \times 2 \times 2 \times 1 = 8$ arrangements.
> *Otherwise they'll be together in the last two places.*
>
> (ii) Choose Alice or Camilla for position 1 (= 2 choices). The next person must then be Dave or Bernie (= 2 choices). The next person must be either Alice or Camilla (whoever isn't in position 1) — so you have only 1 choice. And you also have only 1 choice for Position 4. This means there are $2 \times 2 \times 1 \times 1 = 4$ arrangements.
>
> This gives a grand total of $8 + 4 = 12$ possible arrangements altogether.

You can use your fingers and toes for counting up to 5! ÷ 3!...

Hopefully that didn't seem too bad. But statistics (like maths generally) is one of those subjects where everything builds on what you've just learnt. So you need to commit all this to memory, and (preferably) understand why it's true too.

Arrangements and Selections

<u>Choices</u>. That's what this page is all about. Bear that in mind when I tell you that you <u>must</u> read all this <u>very carefully</u>.

In a **Permutation**, the **Order Matters**

First of all, you need to know that a <u>permutation</u> is an arrangement of things where the <u>order matters</u>.
So AB and BA are <u>different permutations</u> of the letters A and B, for example.

> **EXAMPLE** How many 3-digit permutations using the numbers 0-9 are there, if each digit can only appear once?
>
> You have <u>10 choices</u> for the first digit, <u>9 choices</u> for the second digit, and <u>8 choices</u> for the third digit.
> So there are $10 \times 9 \times 8 = \underline{720}$ different permutations.
> This is just $\dfrac{10 \times 9 \times 8 \times 7 \times ... \times 1}{7 \times 6 \times ... \times 1} = \dfrac{10!}{7!} = \dfrac{10!}{(10-3)!}$.

Always count the 'choices' you have at each point.

> ### Permutations
> When choosing r objects from n, the number of possible <u>permutations</u> is: $^nP_r = \dfrac{n!}{(n-r)!}$

Most calculators have a button for finding ^nP_r

In a **Combination**, the **Order Doesn't Matter**

In a <u>combination</u>, the <u>order</u> of things <u>isn't important</u>. So AB and BA are actually the <u>same combination</u> of A and B.

> **EXAMPLE** How many 3-digit combinations using the numbers 0-9 are there, if each digit can only appear once?
>
> From the example above, there are 720 <u>permutations</u> with 3 digits. But think of the permutation 123 —
> this is the <u>same combination</u> as 321. In fact, it's the same combination as <u>any</u> rearrangement of the digits
> 1, 2 and 3 (and there are 3! = 3 × 2 × 1 = 6 permutations (or arrangements) of the digits 1, 2 and 3).
> So the number of <u>combinations</u> of 3 digits must be $720 \div 6 = \underline{120}$. This is $\dfrac{10!}{7!3!} = \dfrac{10!}{(10-3)! \times 3!}$.

> ### Combinations
> When choosing r objects from n, the number of possible <u>combinations</u> is: $^nC_r = \dbinom{n}{r} = \dfrac{n!}{(n-r)!r!}$

Your calculator will have a button for finding ^nC_r too.

Use **Binomial Coefficients** if There are **Only Two Types** of Object

The values of ^nC_r for any particular values of r and n are called <u>binomial coefficients</u>.
They're useful for arrangement questions with <u>two different types</u> of object.

> **EXAMPLE** a) In how many different ways can n objects of two types be arranged if r are of the first type?
> b) How many ways are there to select 11 players from a squad of 16?
>
> a) If the objects were all <u>different</u>, there would be $n!$ ways to arrange them. But r of the objects are of the
> same type and could be <u>swapped around</u>, so divide by $r!$. Since there are only <u>two types</u>, the other $(n-r)$
> could also be <u>swapped around</u> — so divide by $(n-r)!$. This means there are $\dfrac{n!}{r!(n-r)!}$ arrangements.
>
> b) This is basically a 'combinations' problem. Imagine the 16 players are lined up — then you could
> 'pick' or 'not pick' players by giving each of them a sign marked with a tick or a cross.
> So just find the number of ways to arrange 11 ticks and 5 crosses — this is $\dbinom{16}{11} = \dfrac{16!}{11!5!} = 4368$.

In the Exam, you'll have no choice but to answer a question on this topic...

You must learn all this business about permutations and combinations. Once you've done that, you can calculate how
many tickets you'd need to buy to be certain of winning the lottery jackpot. Quite a few, I'm guessing.

Arrangements and Selections

Now you know all about arrangements, permutations and combinations, here's the fun bit.
And by 'the fun bit', I mean 'the bit where you use them in probability questions'.

Probability Questions Introduce Restrictions

Probability questions involving arrangements, combinations and permutations are pretty straightforward.
They involve random events, so you can use the formula from p115 — you just need to decide the best way
to calculate the number of possible outcomes and the number that match your event.

EXAMPLE Pete is on an all-fruit diet, and is going to eat an apple, an orange, a banana, a peach
and a pear for his lunch. He eats them one at a time, and selects which one to eat next
at random. What is the probability that Pete eats the apple first and the banana last?

The <u>total</u> number of <u>possible arrangements</u> of the 5 pieces of fruit is $5! = 120$.

Now we need to find how many of those have the <u>apple first</u> and the <u>banana last</u>.
As the first and last positions are <u>fixed</u>, that means we're looking for the number
of ways of arranging the orange, peach and pear in the 2nd, 3rd and 4th places.

So the number of arrangements with the apple first and the banana last is $3! = 6$.

So   P(apple first and banana last) $= \frac{6}{120} = \frac{1}{20}$

EXAMPLE Emma has 10 cards marked with the digits 0-9.
She picks 4 cards at random without replacing them.
What is the probability that she only picks odd numbers?

To find the probability, we need to <u>divide</u> the number of possible selections that are
<u>all odd</u> by the <u>total number</u> of possible selections.

The order the cards are picked <u>doesn't matter</u>, so this is a <u>combination</u> question.

The total number of possible combinations of 4 cards from 10 is $^{10}C_4 = \frac{10!}{4!6!} = 210$.

If all the numbers are odd, then there are only <u>5 cards</u> she could pick.

The number of possible combinations of 4 cards from 5 is $^{5}C_4 = \frac{5!}{1!4!} = 5$.

So   P(picking only odd numbers) $= \frac{5}{210} = \frac{1}{42}$.

EXAMPLE Four letters are picked at random without replacement from the letters
A-H and displayed in the order they are chosen. What is the probability
that the letters ABCD are displayed in alphabetical order?

The <u>order</u> in which the letters are picked matters here, so we need
to find the number of <u>permutations</u> of 4 letters from 8. This is:

$\frac{8!}{4!} = \underline{1680}$

There's only <u>1 permutation</u> with ABCD in alphabetical order,

so   P(ABCD displayed in order) $= \frac{1}{1680}$

> You'd get the same answer if you did this with a tree diagram:
> P(A with 1st pick) $= \frac{1}{8}$, P(B with 2nd pick) $= \frac{1}{7}$, and so on,
> so P(ABCD displayed in order) $= \frac{1}{8} \times \frac{1}{7} \times \frac{1}{6} \times \frac{1}{5} = \frac{1}{1680}$

Mind your Ps and Cs...

You might see Hollywood actors or famous rock stars mixing up combinations and permutations and think it's a cool thing
to do. But it's not — nobody will be impressed if you do it. Seriously, I know I only said it a page ago, but it's important to
learn the difference between them — there's a really good chance they'll come up on your S1 exam.

S1 Section 2 — Practice Questions

Gosh. A whole page of warm-up questions. By the time you've finished these, you'll be warmer than a wolf in woollen mittens. Oh, and you'll probably be <u>awesome at probability questions</u> too.

Warm-up Questions

1) A standard dice and a coin are thrown and the outcomes recorded.
   If a head is thrown, the score on the dice is doubled.
   If a tail is thrown, 4 is added to the score on the dice.

   a) Represent this by means of a sample space diagram.

   b) What is the probability that you score more than 5?

   c) If you throw a tail, what is the probability that you get an even score?

2) Half the students in a sixth-form college eat sausages for dinner and 20% eat chips.
   10% of those who eat chips also eat sausages. By use of a Venn diagram or otherwise, find:

   a) the percentage of students who eat both chips and sausages,

   b) the percentage of students who eat chips but not sausages,

   c) the percentage of students who eat either chips or sausages but not both.

3) Arabella rolls two standard dice and adds the two results together.

   a) What is the probability that she scores a prime number?

   b) What is the probability that she scores a square number?

   c) What is the probability that she scores a number that is
      either a prime number or a square number?

4) In a school orchestra (made up of pupils in either the upper or lower school),
   40% of the musicians are boys. Of the boys, 30% are in the upper school.
   Of the girls in the orchestra, 50% are in the upper school.

   a) Draw a tree diagram to show the various probabilities.

   b) Find the probability that a musician chosen at random is in the upper school.

5) Albert eats a limited choice of lunch. He eats either chicken or beef
   for his main course, and either chocolate pudding or ice cream for dessert.
   The probability that he eats chicken is 1/3, the probability that he eats
   ice cream given that he has chicken is 2/5, and the probability that he
   has ice cream given that he has beef is 3/4.
   a) Find the probability he has either chicken or ice cream — but not both.
   b) Find the probability that he eats ice cream.
   c) Find the probability that he had chicken given that you see him eating ice cream.

6) How many arrangements of the letters in the word STATISTICS are there?

7) Three married couples are about to sit on the 6 back seats of a coach.
   a) How many different arrangements of the 6 people are possible?
   b) In how many of these is Mr Brown sitting next to his wife?
   c) What is the probability that, from a randomly chosen arrangement,
      Mr Brown is not sitting next to his wife?

S1 Section 2 — Practice Questions

Boop. Boop. Boop. Exam simulation has begun. Repeat, exam simulation has begun. Please ensure your safety goggles are firmly attached. Emergency exits can be found on the right- and left-hand sides of the page.

Exam Questions

1   A school is picking its team for a maths quiz. A team of 6 is chosen at random from a group of 10 volunteers. 4 of the volunteers are boys and 6 are girls.

   a)   How many different teams could be chosen?

   (1 mark)

   b)   Find the probability that the team chosen consists of 3 boys and 3 girls.

   (3 marks)

   At the quiz, the team sits in a row. The team has one captain and one vice captain.

   c)   What is the probability that the captain and vice captain sit next to each other?

   (3 marks)

2   A jar contains counters of 3 different colours. There are 3 red counters, 4 white counters and 5 green counters. Two random counters are removed from the jar one at a time. Once removed, the colour of the counter is noted. The first counter is not replaced before the second one is drawn.

   a)   Draw a tree diagram to show the probabilities of the various outcomes.

   (3 marks)

   b)   Find the probability that the second counter is green.

   (2 marks)

   c)   Find the probability that both the counters are red.

   (2 marks)

   d)   Find the probability that the two counters are not both the same colour.

   (3 marks)

3   Event J and Event K are independent events, where $P(J) = 0.7$ and $P(K) = 0.1$.

   a)   Find:

   (i) $P(J \cap K)$,

   (1 mark)

   (ii) $P(J \cup K)$.

   (2 marks)

   b)   If L is the event that neither J or K occurs, find $P(L|K')$.

   (3 marks)

4   For a particular biased dice, the event 'throw a 6' is called event B. $P(B) = 0.2$. This biased dice and a fair dice are rolled together. Find the probability that:

   a)   the biased dice doesn't show a 6,

   (1 mark)

   b)   at least one of the dice shows a 6,

   (2 marks)

   c)   exactly one of the dice shows a 6, given that at least one of them shows a 6.

   (3 marks)

Probability Distributions

This stuff isn't hard — but it can seem a bit weird at times.

Getting your head round this **Basic Stuff** will help a bit

This first bit isn't particularly interesting. But understanding the difference between X and x (bear with me) might make the later stuff a bit less confusing. Might.

1) X (upper case) is just the <u>name</u> of a <u>random variable</u>. So X could be 'score on a dice' — it's <u>just a name</u>.

2) A <u>random variable</u> doesn't have a <u>fixed</u> value. Like with a dice score — the value on any 'roll' is all down to chance.

3) x (lower case) is a <u>particular value</u> that X can take. So for one roll of a dice, x could be 1, 2, 3, 4, 5 or 6.

4) <u>Discrete</u> random variables only have a <u>certain number</u> of possible values. Often these values are whole numbers, but they don't have to be. Usually there are only a few possible values (e.g. the possible scores with one roll of a dice).

5) A <u>probability distribution</u> is a <u>table showing the possible values</u> of x, plus the <u>probability</u> for each one.

6) A <u>probability function</u> is a formula that generates the probabilities for different values of x.

All the Probabilities **Add up to 1**

For a discrete random variable X:

$$\sum_{\text{all } x} P(X = x) = 1$$

This says that if you add up the probabilities of all the possible values of X, you get 1.

EXAMPLE The random variable X has probability function $P(X = x) = kx$ for $x = 1, 2, 3$. Find the value of k.

So X has three possible values ($x = 1, 2$ and 3), and the probability of each is kx (where you need to find k).

It's easier to understand with a table:

x	1	2	3
$P(X = x)$	$k \times 1 = k$	$k \times 2 = 2k$	$k \times 3 = 3k$

Now just use the formula: $\sum_{\text{all } x} P(X = x) = 1$ Here, this means: $\quad k + 2k + 3k = 6k = 1$

i.e. $k = \dfrac{1}{6}$

Piece of cake.

EXAMPLE The discrete random variable X has the probability distribution shown below.

x	0	1	2	3	4
$P(X = x)$	0.1	0.2	0.3	0.2	a

Find: (i) the value of a,   (ii) $P(X > 2)$ (iii) $P(2 \leq X < 4)$.

(i) Use the formula $\sum_{\text{all } x} P(X = x) = 1$ again.

From the table: $0.1 + 0.2 + 0.3 + 0.2 + a = 1$
$0.8 + a = 1$
$\underline{a = 0.2}$

(ii) This is asking you to find the probability that 'X is greater than 2'.
So you need to add up the probabilities for $x = 3$ and $x = 4$.

$P(X > 2) = P(X = 3) + P(X = 4) = 0.2 + 0.2 = \underline{0.4}$

(iii) This is asking for the probability that 'X is greater than or equal to 2, but less than 4'.
Easy — just add up the probabilities again.

Careful with the inequality signs — you need to include $x = 2$ but not $x = 4$.

$P(2 \leq X < 4) = P(X = 2) + P(X = 3) = 0.3 + 0.2 = \underline{0.5}$

Probability Distributions

EXAMPLE An unbiased six-sided dice has faces marked 1, 1, 1, 2, 2, 3.
The dice is rolled twice. Let X be the random variable "sum of the two scores on the dice".
Show that $P(X = 4) = \frac{5}{18}$. Find the probability distribution of X.

① Make a table showing the 36 possible outcomes.
You can see from the table that 10 of these have the outcome $X = 4$

... so $P(X = 4) = \frac{10}{36} = \frac{5}{18}$

Score on roll 1

+	1	1	1	2	2	3
1	2	2	2	3	3	4
1	2	2	2	3	3	4
1	2	2	2	3	3	4
2	3	3	3	4	4	5
2	3	3	3	4	4	5
3	4	4	4	5	5	6

Score on roll 2

Don't forget to change the fractions into their simplest form.

② Use the table to work out the probabilities for the other outcomes and then fill in a table summarising the probability distribution. So...

... $\frac{9}{36}$ of the outcomes are a score of 2

... $\frac{12}{36}$ of the outcomes are a score of 3

... $\frac{4}{36}$ of the outcomes are a score of 5

... $\frac{1}{36}$ of the outcomes are a score of 6

x	2	3	4	5	6
$P(X = x)$	$\frac{1}{4}$	$\frac{1}{3}$	$\frac{5}{18}$	$\frac{1}{9}$	$\frac{1}{36}$

Do Complicated questions Bit by bit

EXAMPLE A game involves rolling two fair dice. If the sum of the scores is greater than 10 then the player wins 50p.
If the sum is between 8 and 10 (inclusive) then they win 20p. Otherwise they get nothing.
If X is the random variable "amount player wins", find the probability distribution of X.

There are 3 possible values for X (0, 20 and 50) and you need the probability of each.
To work these out, you need the probability of getting various totals on the dice.

① You need to know $P(8 \leq \text{score} \leq 10)$ — the probability that the score is between 8 and 10 inclusive
(i.e. including 8 and 10) and $P(11 \leq \text{score} \leq 12)$ — the probability that the score is greater than 10.

This means working out: $P(\text{score} = 8)$, $P(\text{score} = 9)$, $P(\text{score} = 10)$, $P(\text{score} = 11)$ and $P(\text{score} = 12)$. Use a table...

②

Score on dice 1

+	1	2	3	4	5	6
1	2	3	4	5	6	7
2	3	4	5	6	7	8
3	4	5	6	7	8	9
4	5	6	7	8	9	10
5	6	7	8	9	10	11
6	7	8	9	10	11	12

Score on dice 2

There are 36 possible outcomes...

...5 of these have a total of 8 — so the probability of scoring 8 is $\frac{5}{36}$

...4 have a total of 9 — so the probability of scoring 9 is $\frac{4}{36}$

...the probability of scoring 10 is $\frac{3}{36}$

...the probability of scoring 11 is $\frac{2}{36}$

...the probability of scoring 12 is $\frac{1}{36}$

③ To find the probabilities you need, you just add the right bits together:

$P(X = 20p) = P(8 \leq \text{score} \leq 10) = \frac{5}{36} + \frac{4}{36} + \frac{3}{36} = \frac{12}{36} = \frac{1}{3}$ $P(X = 50p) = P(11 \leq \text{score} \leq 12) = \frac{2}{36} + \frac{1}{36} = \frac{3}{36} = \frac{1}{12}$

To find $P(X = 0)$ just take the total of the two probabilities above from 1 (since $X = 0$ is the only other possibility).

$P(X = 0) = 1 - \left[\frac{12}{36} + \frac{3}{36}\right] = 1 - \frac{15}{36} = \frac{21}{36} = \frac{7}{12}$

④ Now just stick all this info in a table (and check that the probabilities all add up to 1):

x	0	20	50
$P(X = x)$	$\frac{7}{12}$	$\frac{1}{3}$	$\frac{1}{12}$

Useful quotes: All you need in life is ignorance and confidence, then success is sure[*]...

I said earlier that the 'counting the outcomes' approach was useful — well there you go. And if you remember how to do that, then you can work out a probability distribution. And if you can work out one of those, then you can often begin to unravel even fairly daunting-looking questions. But most of all, REMEMBER THAT ALL THE PROBABILITIES ADD UP TO 1.

Expected Values, Mean and Variance

This is all about the mean and variance of <u>random variables</u> — <u>not</u> a load of data. It's a tricky concept, but bear with it.

Discrete Random Variables *have an* 'Expected Value' *or* 'Mean'

You can work out the <u>expected value</u> (or 'mean') <u>E(X)</u> for a discrete <u>random variable</u> X.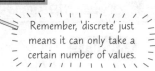
E(X) is a kind of 'theoretical mean' — it's what you'd <u>expect</u> the mean of X to be if you took <u>loads</u> of readings. <u>In practice</u>, the mean of your results is unlikely to match the theoretical mean <u>exactly</u>, but it should be pretty near.

Remember, 'discrete' just means it can only take a certain number of values.

If the possible values of X are x_1, x_2, x_3,... then the expected value of X is:

$$\text{Mean} = \text{Expected Value, } E(X) = \sum x_i P(X = x_i) = \sum x_i p_i \qquad p_i = P(X = x_i)$$

EXAMPLE The probability distribution of X, the number of daughters in a family of 3 children, is shown in the table. Find the expected number of daughters.

x_i	0	1	2	3
p_i	$\frac{1}{8}$	$\frac{3}{8}$	$\frac{3}{8}$	$\frac{1}{8}$

$$\text{Mean} = \sum x_i p_i = \left[0 \times \tfrac{1}{8}\right] + \left[1 \times \tfrac{3}{8}\right] + \left[2 \times \tfrac{3}{8}\right] + \left[3 \times \tfrac{1}{8}\right] = 0 + \tfrac{3}{8} + \tfrac{6}{8} + \tfrac{3}{8} = \tfrac{12}{8} = 1.5$$

So the <u>expected</u> number of daughters is 1.5 — which sounds a bit weird.
But all it means is that if you check a <u>large number</u> of 3-child families, the <u>mean</u> will be close to 1.5.

The Variance *measures how* Spread Out *the distribution is*

You can also find the <u>variance</u> of a random variable. It's the 'expected variance' of a <u>large number</u> of readings.

$$\text{Var}(X) = E(X^2) - [E(X)]^2 = \sum x_i^2 p_i - \left[\sum x_i p_i\right]^2$$

This formula needs $E(X^2) = \sum x_i^2 p_i$ — take each possible value of x, square it, multiply it by its probability and then add up all the results.

EXAMPLE Work out the variance for the '3 daughters' example above:

First work out $E(X^2)$: $E(X^2) = \sum x_i^2 p_i = \left[0^2 \times \tfrac{1}{8}\right] + \left[1^2 \times \tfrac{3}{8}\right] + \left[2^2 \times \tfrac{3}{8}\right] + \left[3^2 \times \tfrac{1}{8}\right]$

$$= 0 + \tfrac{3}{8} + \tfrac{12}{8} + \tfrac{9}{8} = \tfrac{24}{8} = 3$$

The <u>standard deviation</u> (s.d.) of a random variable is the <u>square root</u> of its variance: s.d. = $\sqrt{\text{Var}(X)}$

Now you take away the mean squared: $\text{Var}(X) = E(X^2) - [E(X)]^2 = 3 - 1.5^2 = 3 - 2.25 = \underline{0.75}$

EXAMPLE X has the probability function $P(X = x) = k(x + 1)$ for x = 0, 1, 2, 3, 4.
Find the mean and variance of X.

① First you need to find k — work out all the probabilities and make sure they add up to 1.

$P(X = 0) = k \times (0 + 1) = k$. Similarly, $P(X = 1) = 2k$, $P(X = 2) = 3k$, $P(X = 3) = 4k$, $P(X = 4) = 5k$.

So $k + 2k + 3k + 4k + 5k = 1$, i.e. $15k = 1$, and so $k = \dfrac{1}{15}$

Now you can work out p_1, p_2, p_3... where $p_1 = P(X = 1)$ etc.

② Now use the formulas — find the mean E(X) first:

$$E(X) = \sum x_i p_i = \left[0 \times \tfrac{1}{15}\right] + \left[1 \times \tfrac{2}{15}\right] + \left[2 \times \tfrac{3}{15}\right] + \left[3 \times \tfrac{4}{15}\right] + \left[4 \times \tfrac{5}{15}\right] = \tfrac{40}{15} = \tfrac{8}{3}$$

For the variance you need $E(X^2)$:

$$E(X^2) = \sum x_i^2 p_i = \left[0^2 \times \tfrac{1}{15}\right] + \left[1^2 \times \tfrac{2}{15}\right] + \left[2^2 \times \tfrac{3}{15}\right] + \left[3^2 \times \tfrac{4}{15}\right] + \left[4^2 \times \tfrac{5}{15}\right] = \tfrac{130}{15} = \tfrac{26}{3}$$

And finally: $\text{Var}(X) = E(X^2) - [E(X)]^2 = \tfrac{26}{3} - \left[\tfrac{8}{3}\right]^2 = \tfrac{14}{9}$

The Geometric Distribution

When you think of the <u>geometric distribution</u>, think "fail, fail,..., fail, succeed!"
So it's a bit like England at the Football World Cup, only the geometric distribution ends in a success.

The Geometric Distribution Models "The Number of Trials Before a Success"

EXAMPLE I'm rolling a fair dice. Find the probability that I first roll a six:
a) on the 4th throw,
b) on the nth throw.

a) If the first 'six' occurs on the 4th throw, then the first 3 throws must all have landed on 'not a six'.

So $P(\text{first 'six' on 4th throw}) = \left(\frac{5}{6}\right)^3 \times \frac{1}{6} = \frac{125}{1296}$ ← This is the probability of needing 4 trials for the first success.

b) If the first 'six' occurs on the nth throw, then the first $(n-1)$ throws must all have landed on 'not a six'.

So $P(\text{first 'six' on } n\text{th throw}) = \left(\frac{5}{6}\right)^{n-1} \times \frac{1}{6}$ ← This is the probability of needing n trials for the first success.

Learn the **Conditions** for a **Geometric** Probability Distribution

Geometric Distribution Geo(p)

A random variable X follows a <u>Geometric Distribution</u> as long as these conditions are satisfied:

1) There is a sequence of <u>independent</u> trials with only <u>two possible outcomes</u> ('success' and 'failure').

2) There is a <u>constant probability</u> (p) of success at each trial.

3) X is the <u>number of trials before the first success occurs</u> (including the 'successful' trial).

In this case $\mathbf{P(X = x) = p(1 - p)^{x-1}}$ for $x = 1, 2, 3...$ ← Random variables following a geometric distribution have an infinite number of possible values.

You can write $X \sim \mathbf{Geo}(p)$. The expected value is given by $\mathbf{E(X) = \dfrac{1}{p}}$.

Make Sure You Understand these **Geometric Distribution** Examples

EXAMPLE X is a discrete random variable, and $X \sim \text{Geo}(0.4)$.
a) Find: (i) $P(X = 7)$, (ii) $P(X > 3)$, (iii) $E(X)$.

b) Show that $P(X \text{ is a multiple of } 2) = \dfrac{q}{1 + q}$, where $q = 1 - p$.

a) (i) $P(X = 7) = 0.4 \times 0.6^6 = 0.019$ (to 3 d.p.)

(ii) $P(X > 3) = 1 - P(X \leq 3) = 1 - (P(X = 1) + P(X = 2) + P(X = 3)) = 1 - (0.4 + 0.4 \times 0.6 + 0.4 \times 0.6^2) = 0.216$

(iii) $E(X) = \dfrac{1}{p} = \dfrac{1}{0.4} = 2.5$

b) $P(X \text{ is a multiple of } 2) = P(X = 2) + P(X = 4) + P(X = 6) + ...$
$= (1 - p)p + (1 - p)^3 p + (1 - p)^5 p + ...$
$= (1 - p)p\{1 + (1 - p)^2 + (1 - p)^4 + ...\}$
$= (1 - p)p \times \dfrac{1}{1 - (1 - p)^2}$
$= (1 - p)p \times \dfrac{1}{p(2 - p)} = \dfrac{1 - p}{2 - p} = \dfrac{q}{1 + q}$

Factorise by taking $(1 - p)p$ outside the big brackets.

The thing in the big brackets is just the sum to infinity of a geometric series (p65). So you can write the sum using the formula: $S_\infty = \dfrac{a}{1 - r}$. Here the ratio ($r$) is $(1 - p)^2$.

Geometry means "measuring the earth" — so why is this a "geometric distribution"...

There's nothing too horrendous about the geometric distribution really. If you didn't follow the sum to infinity stuff, head back to the Core 2 bit of this book and check it out — it's a cracking read. Make sure you learn the conditions for the geometric distribution — they won't always tell you if you're dealing with a geometric distribution in the exam.

The Binomial Probability Function

This page involves counting the number of <u>different arrangements</u> of things — and it uses <u>binomial coefficients</u> to do it. If you need a reminder about either of those topics, look back to pages 120-121.

Use **Binomial Coefficients** to Count Arrangements of 'Successes' and 'Failures'

A while ago, you learnt that if p = P(something happens), then $1 - p$ = P(that thing doesn't happen). You'll need that fact now.

> **EXAMPLE** I toss a fair coin 5 times. Find the probability of:
> a) 0 heads, b) 1 head, c) 2 heads.

On n tosses, with r heads and $(n - r)$ tails, there are ^nC_r or $\binom{n}{r}$ ways to arrange them (see p.121). This is the <u>binomial coefficient</u>.

First, note that each coin toss is <u>independent</u> of the others. That means you can <u>multiply</u> individual probabilities together.

a) P(0 heads) = P(tails) × P(tails) × P(tails) × P(tails) × P(tails) = 0.5^5 = 0.03125

P(tails) = P(heads) = 0.5.

b) P(1 head) = P(heads) × P(tails) × P(tails) × P(tails) × P(tails)
   + P(tails) × P(heads) × P(tails) × P(tails) × P(tails)
   + P(tails) × P(tails) × P(heads) × P(tails) × P(tails)
   + P(tails) × P(tails) × P(tails) × P(heads) × P(tails)
   + P(tails) × P(tails) × P(tails) × P(tails) × P(heads)

These are the $\binom{5}{1}$ = 5 ways to arrange 1 head and 4 tails.

So P(1 head) = $0.5 \times (0.5)^4 \times \binom{5}{1} = 0.03125 \times \frac{5!}{1!4!} = 0.15625$

= P(heads) × [P(tails)]⁴ × ways to arrange 1 head and 4 tails.

c) P(2 heads) = [P(heads)]² × [P(tails)]³ × ways to arrange 2 heads and 3 tails = $(0.5)^2 \times (0.5)^3 \times \binom{5}{2} = 0.3125$

The **Binomial Probability Function** gives P(r successes out of n trials)

The previous example really just shows why this thing in a box must be true.

Binomial Probability Function

$$P(r \text{ successes in } n \text{ trials}) = \binom{n}{r} \times [P(\text{success})]^r \times [P(\text{failure})]^{n-r}$$

This is the <u>probability function</u> for a <u>binomial distribution</u> — see next page for more info.

> **EXAMPLE** I roll a fair dice 5 times. Find the probability of rolling: a) 2 sixes, b) 3 sixes, c) 4 numbers less than 3.

Again, note that each roll of a dice is <u>independent</u> of the other rolls.

a) For this part, call "roll a 6" a success, and "roll anything other than a 6" a failure.

Then P(roll 2 sixes) = $\binom{5}{2} \times \left(\frac{1}{6}\right)^2 \times \left(\frac{5}{6}\right)^3 = \frac{5!}{2!3!} \times \frac{1}{36} \times \frac{125}{216} = 0.161$ (to 3 d.p.).

b) Again, call "roll a 6" a success, and "roll anything other than a 6" a failure.

Then P(roll 3 sixes) = $\binom{5}{3} \times \left(\frac{1}{6}\right)^3 \times \left(\frac{5}{6}\right)^2 = \frac{5!}{3!2!} \times \frac{1}{216} \times \frac{25}{36} = 0.032$ (to 3 d.p.).

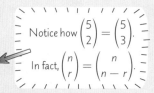

Notice how $\binom{5}{2} = \binom{5}{3}$. In fact, $\binom{n}{r} = \binom{n}{n-r}$.

c) This time, success means "roll a 1 or a 2", while failure is now "roll a 3, 4, 5 or 6".

Then P(roll 4 numbers less than 3) = $\binom{5}{4} \times \left(\frac{1}{3}\right)^4 \times \left(\frac{2}{3}\right) = \frac{5!}{4!1!} \times \frac{1}{81} \times \frac{2}{3} = 0.041$ (to 3 d.p.).

Let this formula for success go to your head — and then keep it there...

This page is all about finding the probabilities of <u>different numbers</u> of successes in n trials. Now then... if you carry out n trials, there are $n + 1$ possibilities for the number of successes (0, 1, 2, ..., n). This 'family' of possible results along with their probabilities is sounding suspiciously like a <u>probability distribution</u>. Oh rats... I've given away what's on the next page.

The Binomial Distribution

I know you're having so much fun learning all about random variables... well, there's more to come. This page is about discrete random variables following a binomial distribution (whose probability function you saw on p129).

There are 5 Conditions for a Binomial Distribution

Binomial Distribution: B(n, p)

A random variable X follows a Binomial Distribution as long as these 5 conditions are satisfied:

1) There is a fixed number (n) of trials.
2) Each trial involves either "success" or "failure".
3) All the trials are independent.
4) The probability of "success" (p) is the same in each trial.
5) The variable is the total number of successes in the n trials.

Binomial random variables are discrete, since they only take values 0, 1, 2... n.

n and p are the two parameters of the binomial distribution. (Or n is sometimes called the 'index'.)

In this case, $P(X = x) = \binom{n}{x} \times p^x \times (1 - p)^{n-x}$ for $x = 0, 1, 2,..., n$, and you can write $X \sim \mathbf{B}(\mathbf{n, p})$.

EXAMPLE: Which of the random variables described below would follow a binomial distribution? For those that do, state the distribution's parameters.

a) **The number of faulty items (T) produced in a factory per day, if the probability of each item being faulty is 0.01 and there are 10 000 items produced every day.**
Binomial — there's a fixed number (10 000) of trials with two possible results ('faulty' or 'not faulty'), a constant probability of 'success', and T is the total number of 'faulty' items.
So (as long as faulty items occur independently) $T \sim B(10\ 000, 0.01)$.

b) **The number of red cards (R) drawn from a standard 52-card deck in 10 picks, not replacing the cards each time.**
Not binomial, since the probability of 'success' changes each time (as I'm not replacing the cards).

c) **The number of red cards (R) drawn from a standard 52-card deck in 10 picks, replacing the cards each time.**
Binomial — there's a fixed number (10) of independent trials with two possible results ('red' or 'black/not red'), a constant probability of success (I'm replacing the cards), and R is the number of red cards drawn. $R \sim B(10, 0.5)$.

d) **The number of times (T) I have to toss a coin before I get heads.**
Not binomial, since the number of trials isn't fixed.

e) **The number of left-handed people (L) in a sample of 500 randomly chosen people, if the fraction of left-handed people in the population as a whole is 0.13.**
Binomial — there's a fixed number (500) of independent trials with two possible results ('left-handed' or 'not left-handed'), a constant probability of success (0.13), and L is the number of left-handers. $L \sim B(500, 0.13)$.

EXAMPLE: When I toss a grape in the air and try to catch it in my mouth, my probability of success is always 0.8. The number of grapes I catch in 10 throws is described by the discrete random variable X.
    a) How is X distributed? Name the type of distribution, and give the values of any parameters.
    b) Find the probability of me catching at least 9 grapes.

a) There's a fixed number (10) of independent trials with two possible results ('catch' and 'not catch'), a constant probability of success (0.8), and X is the total number of catches.
Therefore X follows a binomial distribution, $X \sim B(10, 0.8)$.

b) P(at least 9 catches) $= P(9 \text{ catches}) + P(10 \text{ catches})$
$$= \left\{\binom{10}{9} \times 0.8^9 \times 0.2^1\right\} + \left\{\binom{10}{10} \times 0.8^{10} \times 0.2^0\right\}$$
$$= 0.268435... + 0.107374... = 0.376 \text{ (to 3 d.p.)}.$$

Binomial distributions come with 5 strings attached...

There's a big, boring box at the top of the page with a list of 5 conditions in — and you do need to know it, unfortunately. There's only one way to learn it — keep trying to write down the 5 conditions until you can do it in your sleep.

Using Binomial Tables

Your life is just about to be made a whole lot _easier_. So smile sweetly and admit that statistics isn't _all_ bad.

Look up Probabilities in **Binomial Tables**

EXAMPLE I have an unfair coin. When I toss this coin, the probability of getting heads is 0.35.
Find the probability that it will land on heads fewer than 3 times when I toss it 12 times in total.

If the random variable X represents the number of heads I get in 12 tosses, then $X \sim B(12, 0.35)$.
You need to find $P(X \leq 2)$.

① You _could_ work this out 'manually'...

$$P(0 \text{ heads}) + P(1 \text{ head}) + P(2 \text{ heads}) = \left\{\binom{12}{0} \times 0.35^0 \times 0.65^{12}\right\} + \left\{\binom{12}{1} \times 0.35^1 \times 0.65^{11}\right\} + \left\{\binom{12}{2} \times 0.35^2 \times 0.65^{10}\right\}$$

$$= 0.0057 + 0.0368 + 0.1088 = 0.1513$$

② But it's much quicker to use tables of the binomial cumulative distribution function (c.d.f.).
The c.d.f. of a distribution is a function that gives the probability that X will be
less than or equal to a particular value. So the tables show $P(X \leq x)$, for $X \sim B(n, p)$.

- First find the table for the _correct values of n and p_. Then the table gives you a value for $P(X \leq x)$.
- Here: $n = 12$ and $p = 0.35$.

n = 12																					
p	0.05	0.1	0.15	1/6	0.2	0.25	0.3	1/3	0.35	0.4	0.45	0.5	0.55	0.6	0.65	2/3	0.7	0.75	0.8	5/6	0.85	0.9	0.95
x = 0	0.5404	0.2824	0.1422	0.1122	0.0687	0.0317	0.0138	0.0077	0.0057	0.0022	0.0008	0.0002	0.0001	0.0000	0.0000	0.0000	0.0000	0.0000	0.0000	0.0000	0.0000	0.0000	0.0000
1	0.8816	0.6590	0.4435	0.3813	0.2749	0.1584	0.0850	0.0540	0.0424	0.0196	0.0083	0.0032	0.0011	0.0003	0.0001	0.0000	0.0000	0.0000	0.0000	0.0000	0.0000	0.0000	0.0000
2	0.9804	0.8891	0.7358	0.6774	0.5583	0.3907	0.2528	0.1811	0.1513	0.0834	0.0421	0.0193	0.0079	0.0028	0.0008	0.0005	0.0002	0.0000	0.0000	0.0000	0.0000	0.0000	0.0000
3	0.9978	0.9744	0.9078	0.8748	0.7946	0.6488	0.4925	0.3931	0.3467	0.2253	0.1345	0.0730	0.0356	0.0153	0.0056	0.0039	0.0017	0.0004	0.0001	0.0000	0.0000	0.0000	0.0000
4	0.9998	0.9957	0.9761	0.9636	0.9274	0.8424	0.7237	0.6315	0.5833	0.4382	0.3044	0.1938	0.1117	0.0573	0.0255	0.0188	0.0095	0.0028	0.0006	0.0002	0.0001	0.0000	0.0000
5	1.0000	0.9995	0.9954	0.9921	0.9806	0.9456	0.8822	0.8223	0.7873	0.6652	0.5269	0.3872	0.2607	0.1582	0.0846	0.0664	0.0386	0.0143	0.0039	0.0013	0.0007	0.0001	0.0000
6	1.0000	0.9999	0.9993	0.9987	0.9961	0.9857	0.9614	0.9336	0.9154	0.8418	0.7393	0.6128	0.4731	0.3348	0.2127	0.1777	0.1178	0.0544	0.0194	0.0079	0.0046	0.0005	0.0000
7	1.0000	1.0000	0.9999	0.9998	0.9994	0.9972	0.9905	0.9812	0.9745	0.9427	0.8883	0.8062	0.6956	0.5618	0.4167	0.3685	0.2763	0.1576	0.0726	0.0364	0.0239	0.0043	0.0002
8	1.0000	1.0000	1.0000	1.0000	0.9999	0.9996	0.9983	0.9961	0.9944	0.9847	0.9644	0.9270	0.8655	0.7747	0.6533	0.6069	0.5075	0.3512	0.2054	0.1252	0.0922	0.0256	0.0022
9	1.0000	1.0000	1.0000	1.0000	1.0000	1.0000	0.9998	0.9995	0.9992	0.9972	0.9921	0.9807	0.9579	0.9166	0.8487	0.8189	0.7472	0.6093	0.4417	0.3226	0.2642	0.1109	0.0196
10	1.0000	1.0000	1.0000	1.0000	1.0000	1.0000	1.0000	1.0000	0.9999	0.9997	0.9989	0.9968	0.9917	0.9804	0.9576	0.9460	0.9150	0.8416	0.7251	0.6187	0.5565	0.3410	0.1184
11	1.0000	1.0000	1.0000	1.0000	1.0000	1.0000	1.0000	1.0000	1.0000	1.0000	0.9999	0.9998	0.9992	0.9978	0.9943	0.9923	0.9862	0.9683	0.9313	0.8878	0.8578	0.7176	0.4596
12	1.0000	1.0000	1.0000	1.0000	1.0000	1.0000	1.0000	1.0000	1.0000	1.0000	1.0000	1.0000	1.0000	1.0000	1.0000	1.0000	1.0000	1.0000	1.0000	1.0000	1.0000	1.0000	1.0000

- You need $P(X \leq 2)$.
- The table tells you this is 0.1513.

See p150 for more binomial tables.

Practise using those **Binomial Tables**

Binomial tables can be a bit _awkward_. Make sure you know how to find out what you want to know.

EXAMPLE I have a different unfair coin. When I toss this coin, the probability of getting tails is 0.6.
The random variable X represents the number of tails in 12 tosses, so $X \sim B(12, 0.6)$.

If I toss this coin 12 times, use the table above to find the probability that:

a) it will land on tails at least 9 times,
b) it will land on heads exactly 9 times,
c) it will land on heads at least 6 times,
d) it will land on tails more than 3 but fewer than 6 times.

a) $P(X \geq 9) = 1 - P(X < 9) = 1 - P(X \leq 8) = 1 - 0.7747 = 0.2253$
1) P(event happens) = 1 − P(event doesn't happen),
2) P(X < 9) = P(X ≤ 8), as X takes whole number values.

b) This means exactly 3 tails.
$P(X = 3) = P(X \leq 3) - P(X \leq 2) = 0.0153 - 0.0028 = 0.0125$
Use P(A or B) = P(A) + P(B) with the mutually exclusive events "X ≤ 2 " and "X = 3" to get P(X ≤ 3) = P(X ≤ 2) + P(X = 3).
Or you can think of it as "subtracting P(X ≤ 2) from P(X ≤ 3) leaves just P(X = 3)".

c) At least 6 heads means 6 or fewer tails. $P(X \leq 6) = 0.3348$

d) $P(3 < X < 6) = P(X \leq 5) - P(X \leq 3) = 0.1582 - 0.0153 = 0.1429$

Statistical tables are the original labour-saving device...

...as long as you know what you're doing. Careful, though — it's easy to trip yourself up. Basically, as long as you can find the right value of n and p in a table, you can use those tables to work out _anything_ you might need. So hurrah for tables.

Mean and Variance of B(n, p)

You know from page 127 what the <u>mean</u> (or <u>expected value</u>) and <u>variance</u> of a random variable are. And you also know what the <u>binomial distribution</u> is. Put those things together, and you get this page.

For a Binomial Distribution: **Mean = np**

This formula will be in your formula booklet, but it's worth committing to memory anyway.

Mean of a Binomial Distribution

If $X \sim$ B(n, p), then:

Mean (or Expected Value) = μ = E(X) = np

> Greek letters (e.g. μ) often show something based purely on <u>theory</u> rather than <u>experimental results</u>.

Remember... the expected value is the value you'd expect the random variable to take <u>on average</u> if you took loads and loads of readings. It's a "<u>theoretical mean</u>" — the mean of experimental results is unlikely to match it <u>exactly</u>.

EXAMPLE If $X \sim$ B(20, 0.2), what is E(X)?

Just use the formula: E(X) = np = 20 × 0.2 = 4

EXAMPLE What's the expected number of sixes when I roll a fair dice 30 times? Interpret your answer.

If the random variable X represents the number of sixes in 30 rolls, then $X \sim$ B(30, $\frac{1}{6}$).

So the expected value of X is E(X) = $30 \times \frac{1}{6} = 5$

If I were to repeatedly throw the dice 30 times, and find the <u>average</u> number of sixes in each set of 30 throws, then I would expect it to end up pretty close to 5. And the more sets of 30 throws I did, the closer to 5 I'd expect the average to be.

Notice that the probability of getting <u>exactly</u> 5 sixes on my next set of 30 throws = $\binom{30}{5} \times \left(\frac{1}{6}\right)^5 \times \left(\frac{5}{6}\right)^{25} = 0.192$
So I'm much more likely <u>not</u> to get exactly 5 sixes (= 1 − 0.192 = 0.808).
This is why it only makes sense to talk about the mean as a "<u>long-term average</u>", and <u>not</u> as "what I expect to happen next".

For a Binomial Distribution: **Variance = npq**

Variance of a Binomial Distribution

If $X \sim$ B(n, p), then:

Variance = Var(X) = σ^2 = $np(1 - p)$ = npq

Standard Deviation = σ = $\sqrt{np(1 - p)}$ = $\sqrt{npq}$

> For a binomial distribution, P(success) is usually called p, and P(failure) is sometimes called q (= 1 − p).

EXAMPLE If $X \sim$ B(20, 0.2), what is Var(X)?

Just use the formula: Var(X) = $np(1 - p)$ = 20 × 0.2 × 0.8 = 3.2

EXAMPLE If $X \sim$ B(25, 0.2), find: a) P($X \le \mu$), b) P($X \le \mu - \sigma$), c) P($X \le \mu - 2\sigma$)

E(X) = μ = 25 × 0.2 = 5, and Var(X) = σ^2 = 25 × 0.2 × (1 − 0.2) = 4, which gives $\sigma = 2$.

So, using tables (for n = 25 and p = 0.2): a) P($X \le \mu$) = P($X \le 5$) = 0.6167

See page 150.

b) P($X \le \mu - \sigma$) = P($X \le 3$) = 0.2340

c) P($X \le \mu - 2\sigma$) = P($X \le 1$) = 0.0274

For B(n, p) — the variance is always less than the mean...

Nothing too fancy there really. A couple of easy-to-remember formulas, and some stuff about how to interpret these figures which you've seen before anyway. So learn the formulas, put the kettle on, and have a cup of tea while the going's good.

Binomial Distribution Problems

That's everything you need to know about binomial distributions (for now).
So it's time to put it all together and have a look at the kind of thing you might get asked in the exam.

EXAMPLE 1: Selling Double Glazing

A double-glazing salesman is handing out leaflets in a busy shopping centre. He knows that the probability of each passing person taking a leaflet is always 0.3. During a randomly chosen one-minute interval, 30 people passed him.
a)   Suggest a suitable model to describe the number of people (X) who take a leaflet.
b)   What is the probability that more than 10 people take a leaflet?
c)   How many people would the salesman expect to take a leaflet?
d)   Find the variance and standard deviation of X.

a)   During this one-minute interval, there's a fixed number (30) of independent trials with two possible results ("take a leaflet" and "do not take a leaflet"), a constant probability of success (0.3), and X is the total number of people taking leaflets. So $X \sim B(30, 0.3)$.

b) $P(X > 10) = 1 - P(X \le 10) = 1 - 0.7304 = 0.2696$ *Use binomial tables for this — see p150.*

c)   The number of people the salesman could expect to take a leaflet is $E(X) = np = 30 \times 0.3 = 9$

d)   Variance $= np(1-p) = 30 \times 0.3 \times (1 - 0.3) = 6.3$ Standard deviation $= \sqrt{6.3} = 2.51$ (to 2 d.p.)

EXAMPLE 2: Multiple-Choice Guessing

A student has to take a 25-question multiple-choice exam, where each question has five possible answers, of which only one is correct. He believes he can pass the exam by guessing answers at random.
a)   How many questions could the student be expected to guess correctly?
b)   If the pass mark is 10, what is the probability that the student will pass the exam?
c)   The examiner decides to set the pass mark so that it is at least 3 standard deviations above the expected number of correct guesses. What should the minimum pass mark be?

Let X be the number of correct guesses over the 25 questions. Then $X \sim B(25, 0.2)$.   *Define your random variable first, and say how it will be distributed.*

a) $E(X) = np = 25 \times 0.2 = 5$

b) $P(X \ge 10) = 1 - P(X < 10) = 1 - P(X \le 9) = 1 - 0.9827 = 0.0173$

c) $Var(X) = np(1-p) = 25 \times 0.2 \times 0.8 = 4$ — so the standard deviation $= \sqrt{4} = 2$.
So the pass mark needs to be at least $5 + (3 \times 2) = 11$.

EXAMPLE 3: An Unfair Coin

I am spinning a coin that I know is three times as likely to land on heads as it is on tails.
a)   What is the probability that it lands on tails for the first time on the third spin?
b)   What is the probability that in 10 spins, it lands on heads at least 7 times?   *Careful... this doesn't need you to use one of the binomial formulas (it's a geometric distribution).*

You know that $P(heads) = 3 \times P(tails)$, and that $P(heads) + P(tails) = 1$.
This means that $P(heads) = 0.75$ and $P(tails) = 0.25$.

a)   P(lands on tails for the first time on the third spin) $= 0.75 \times 0.75 \times 0.25 = 0.141$ (to 3 d.p.).

b)   If X represents the number of heads in 10 spins, then $X \sim B(10, 0.75)$.

$P(X \ge 7) = 1 - P(X < 7) = 1 - P(X \le 6) = 1 - 0.2241 = 0.7759$

Proof that you shouldn't send a monkey to take your multi-choice exams...

You can see now how useful a working knowledge of statistics is. Ever since you first started using CGP books, I've been banging on about how hard it is to pass an exam without revising. Well, now you can prove I was correct using a bit of knowledge and binomial tables. Yup... statistics can help out with some of those tricky situations you face in life.

S1 Section 3 — Practice Questions

Probability distribution, probability function... <u>fancy-looking names</u> for things that are actually quite straightforward...ish. Have a go at these to make sure you know who's who in the <u>glitzy world of discrete random variables</u>.

Warm-up Questions

1) The probability distribution of Y is:

y	0	1	2	3
P($Y = y$)	0.5	k	k	$3k$

   a) Find the value of k.   b) Find P($Y < 2$).

2) A discrete random variable X has the probability distribution shown in the table, where k is a constant.

x_i	1	2	3	4
p_i	$\frac{1}{6}$	$\frac{1}{2}$	k	$\frac{5}{24}$

   a) Find k.   b) Find E(X) and show that Var(X) = 63/64.

3) A discrete random variable X has the probability distribution shown in the table.

x_i	1	2	3	4	5	6
p_i	0.1	0.2	0.25	0.2	0.1	0.15

   a) Find E(X).   b) Find Var(X).

4) $X \sim$ Geo(0.1). Find the probability that it takes 15 attempts to record a 'success'. What is E(X)?

5) What is the probability of the following?
   a) Getting <u>exactly</u> 5 heads when you spin a fair coin 10 times.
   b) Getting <u>exactly</u> 9 heads when you spin a fair coin 10 times.

6) Which of the following would follow a binomial distribution? Explain your answers.
   a) The number of prime numbers you throw in 30 throws of a standard dice.
   b) The number of people in a particular class at a school who get 'heads' when they flip a coin.
   c) The number of aces in a 7-card hand dealt from a standard deck of 52 cards.
   d) The number of shots I have to take before I score from the free-throw line in basketball.

7) What is the probability of the following?
   a) Getting <u>at least</u> 5 heads when you spin a fair coin 10 times.
   b) Getting <u>at least</u> 9 heads when you spin a fair coin 10 times.

8) If $X \sim$ B(14, 0.27), find: a) P($X = 4$)   b) P($X < 2$)   c) P($5 < X \le 8$)

9) If $X \sim$ B(25, 0.15) and $Y \sim$ B(16, 0.65) find:
   a) P($X \le 3$)   b) P($X \le 7$)   c) P($X \le 15$)
   d) P($Y \le 3$)   e) P($Y \le 7$)   f) P($Y \le 16$)

10) Find the required probability for each of the following binomial distributions.
   a) P($X \le 15$) if $X \sim$ B(20, 0.4)   b) P($X < 4$) if $X \sim$ B(18, 0.15)
   c) P($X > 7$) if $X \sim$ B(25, 0.45)   d) P($X \ge 10$) if $X \sim$ B(12, 0.8)
   e) P($X = 20$) if $X \sim$ B(30, 0.7)   f) P($X = 7$) if $X \sim$ B(10, 0.75)

11) Find the mean and variance of the following random variables.
   a) $X \sim$ B(20, 0.4)   b) $X \sim$ B(40, 0.15)   c) $X \sim$ B(25, 0.45)
   d) $X \sim$ B(50, 0.8)   e) $X \sim$ B(30, 0.7)   f) $X \sim$ B(45, 0.012)

S1 Section 3 — Practice Questions

There's nothing I enjoy more than pretending I'm <u>in an exam</u>. An eerie silence, sweaty palms, having to be escorted to the toilet by a responsible adult... and all these <u>lovely maths questions</u> too. Just like the real thing.

Exam Questions

1   A discrete random variable X has the probability function:

$$P(X = x) = ax \text{ for } x = 1, 2, 3, \text{ where } a \text{ is a constant.}$$

   a)   Show $a = \frac{1}{6}$.

(1 mark)

   b)   Find E(X).

(2 marks)

   c)   If Var(X) = $\frac{5}{9}$ find E(X^2).

(2 marks)

2   In a game a player tosses three fair coins.
    If three heads occur then the player gets 20p; if two heads occur then the player gets 10p.
    For any other outcome, the player gets nothing.

   a)   If X is the random variable 'amount received', tabulate the probability distribution of X.

(4 marks)

The player pays 10p to play one game.

   b)   Use the probability distribution to find the probability that the player wins
        (i.e. gets more money than they pay to play) in one game.

(2 marks)

3   a)   The random variable X follows the binomial distribution B(12, 0.6). Find:

      (i)   P($X < 8$),

(1 mark)

      (ii)   P($X = 5$),

(2 marks)

      (iii) P($3 < X \le 7$).

(3 marks)

   b)   If $Y \sim$ B(11, 0.8), find:

      (i)   P($Y = 4$),

(2 marks)

      (ii)   E(Y),

(1 mark)

      (iii) Var(Y).

(1 mark)

S1 Section 3 — Practice Questions

4 A game involves throwing 2 dice and gaining a double to start.

a) Find the mean number of throws needed to start the game.

(2 marks)

b) Calculate (to 3 significant figures) the probability that it takes:

(i) 4 throws to start,

(2 marks)

(ii) at least 3 throws to start.

(3 marks)

5 The probability of an apple containing a maggot is 0.15.

a) Find the probability that in a random sample of 20 apples there are:

(i) fewer than 6 apples containing maggots,

(2 marks)

(ii) more than 2 apples containing maggots,

(2 marks)

(iii) exactly 7 apples containing maggots.

(2 marks)

b) These apples are sold in crates of 20. Ed buys 3 crates.
Find the probability that more than 1 crate contains more than 2 apples with maggots.

(3 marks)

6 Simon tries to solve the crossword puzzle in his newspaper every day for two weeks.
He either succeeds in solving the puzzle, or he fails to solve it.

a) Simon believes that this situation can be modelled by a random variable following a binomial distribution.

(i) State two conditions needed for a binomial distribution to arise here.

(2 marks)

(ii) State which quantity would follow a binomial distribution (assuming the above conditions are satisfied).

(1 mark)

b) Simon believes a random variable X follows the distribution B(18, p).
If P($X = 4$) = P($X = 5$), find p.

(5 marks)

Correlation

Correlation is all about how closely two quantities are <u>linked</u>. And it can involve a fairly hefty formula.

Draw a **Scatter Diagram** to see **Patterns** in Data

Sometimes variables are measured in <u>pairs</u> — maybe because you want to find out <u>how closely</u> they're <u>linked</u>.
These pairs of variables might be things like: — '<u>my age</u>' and '<u>length of my feet</u>', or
                                         — '<u>temperature</u>' and '<u>number of accidents on a stretch of road</u>'.

You can plot readings from a pair of variables on a <u>scatter diagram</u> — this'll tell you something about the data.

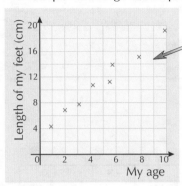

The variables 'my age' and 'length of my feet'
seem linked — all the points lie <u>close</u> to a <u>line</u>.
As I got older, my feet got bigger and bigger
(though I stopped measuring when I was 10).

It's a lot harder to see any connection between the
variables 'temperature' and 'number of accidents'
— the data seems <u>scattered</u> pretty much everywhere.

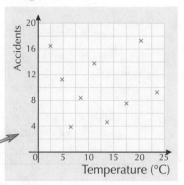

Correlation is a measure of **How Closely** variables are **Linked**

1) Sometimes, as one variable gets <u>bigger</u>, the other one also gets <u>bigger</u> — then the scatter diagram
might look like the one on the right. Here, a line of best fit would have a <u>positive gradient</u>.
The two variables are <u>positively correlated</u> (or there's a <u>positive correlation</u> between them).

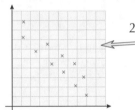

2) But if one variable gets <u>smaller</u> as the other one gets <u>bigger</u>,
then the scatter diagram might look like this one — and the
line of best fit would have a <u>negative gradient</u>.
The two variables are <u>negatively correlated</u> (or there's a
<u>negative correlation</u> between them).

3) And if the two variables <u>aren't</u> linked at all, you'd expect a <u>random</u>
scattering of points — it's hard to say where the line of best fit would be.
The variables <u>aren't correlated</u> (or there's <u>no correlation</u>).

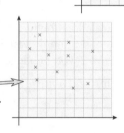

The **Product-Moment Correlation Coefficient (r)** measures Correlation

1) The <u>Product-Moment Correlation Coefficient</u> (<u>PMCC</u>, or <u>r</u>, for short) measures how close
to a <u>straight line</u> the points on a scatter graph lie.

2) The PMCC is always <u>between +1 and –1</u>.
If all your points lie <u>exactly</u> on a <u>straight line</u> with a <u>positive gradient</u> (perfect positive correlation), <u>r = +1</u>.
If all your points lie <u>exactly</u> on a <u>straight line</u> with a <u>negative gradient</u> (perfect negative correlation), <u>r = –1</u>.
(In reality, you'd never expect to get a PMCC of +1 or –1 — your scatter graph points might lie <u>pretty close</u> to a
straight line, but it's unlikely they'd all be <u>on</u> it.)

3) If $r = 0$ (or more likely, <u>pretty close</u> to 0), that would mean the variables <u>aren't correlated</u>.

4) The formula for the PMCC is a <u>real stinker</u>. But some calculators can work it out if you type in the pairs of readings,
which makes life easier. Otherwise, just take it nice and slow.

This is the easiest one to use, but
it's still a bit hefty. Fortunately,
it'll be on your formula sheet.

$$r = \frac{S_{xy}}{\sqrt{S_{xx}S_{yy}}} = \frac{\sum[x-\bar{x}][y-\bar{y}]}{\sqrt{(\sum[x-\bar{x}]^2)(\sum[y-\bar{y}]^2)}} = \frac{\sum xy - \frac{[\sum x][\sum y]}{n}}{\sqrt{(\sum x^2 - \frac{[\sum x]^2}{n})(\sum y^2 - \frac{[\sum y]^2}{n})}}$$

See pages 139-140 for
more about S_{xy}, S_{xx} and S_{yy}.

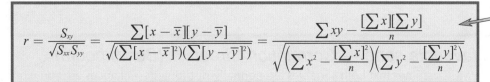

Correlation

Don't rush questions on correlation. In fact, take your time and draw yourself a nice table.

EXAMPLE Illustrate the following data with a scatter diagram, and find the product-moment correlation coefficient (r) between the variables x and y.

If $p = 4x - 3$ and $q = 9y + 17$, what is the PMCC between p and q?

x	1.6	2.0	2.1	2.1	2.5	2.8	2.9	3.3	3.4	3.8	4.1	4.4
y	11.4	11.8	11.5	12.2	12.5	12.0	12.9	13.4	12.8	13.4	14.2	14.3

1) The scatter diagram's the easy bit — just plot the points.

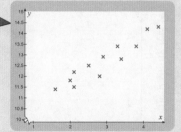

Now for the correlation coefficient. From the scatter diagram, the points lie pretty close to a straight line with a positive gradient — so if the correlation coefficient doesn't come out pretty close to +1, we'd need to worry...

2) There are 12 pairs of readings, so $n = 12$. That bit's easy — now you have to work out a load of sums. It's best to add a few extra rows to your table...

x	1.6	2	2.1	2.1	2.5	2.8	2.9	3.3	3.4	3.8	4.1	4.4	$35 = \Sigma x$
y	11.4	11.8	11.5	12.2	12.5	12	12.9	13.4	12.8	13.4	14.2	14.3	$152.4 = \Sigma y$
x^2	2.56	4	4.41	4.41	6.25	7.84	8.41	10.89	11.56	14.44	16.81	19.36	$110.94 = \Sigma x^2$
y^2	129.96	139.24	132.25	148.84	156.25	144	166.41	179.56	163.84	179.56	201.64	204.49	$1946.04 = \Sigma y^2$
xy	18.24	23.6	24.15	25.62	31.25	33.6	37.41	44.22	43.52	50.92	58.22	62.92	$453.67 = \Sigma xy$

Stick all these in the formula to get:
$$r = \frac{\left[453.67 - \dfrac{35 \times 152.4}{12}\right]}{\sqrt{\left[110.94 - \dfrac{35^2}{12}\right] \times \left[1946.04 - \dfrac{152.4^2}{12}\right]}} = \frac{9.17}{\sqrt{8.857 \times 10.56}} = \underline{0.948}$$
(to 3 s.f.)

This is pretty close to 1, so there's a strong positive correlation between x and y.

3) Correlation coefficients aren't affected by linear transformations — you can multiply variables by a number, and add a number to them, and you won't change the PMCC between them.

So if p and q are given by $p = 4x - 3$ and $q = 9y + 17$, then the PMCC between p and q is also $\underline{0.948}$.

Don't make **Sweeping Statements** using Statistics

1) A high correlation coefficient doesn't necessarily mean that one factor causes the other.

EXAMPLE The number of televisions sold in Japan and the number of cars sold in America may well be correlated, but that doesn't mean that high TV sales in Japan cause high car sales in the US.

2) The PMCC is only a measure of a linear relationship between two variables (i.e. how close they'd be to a straight line if you plotted a scatter diagram).

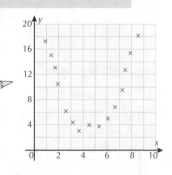

EXAMPLE In the diagram on the right, the PMCC would be pretty low, but the two variables definitely look linked. It looks like the points lie on a parabola (the shape of an x^2 curve) — not a straight line.

What's a statistician's favourite soap — Correlation Street... (Boom boom)

It's worth remembering that the PMCC assumes that both variables are normally distributed — chances are you won't get asked a question about that, but there's always the possibility that you might, so learn it.

Linear Regression

Linear regression is just fancy stats-speak for 'finding lines of best fit'. Not so scary now, eh...

Decide which is the **Independent Variable** and which is the **Dependent**

EXAMPLE   The data below shows the load on a lorry, x (in tonnes), and the fuel efficiency, y (in km per litre).

x	5.1	5.6	5.9	6.3	6.8	7.4	7.8	8.5	9.1	9.8
y	9.6	9.5	8.6	8.0	7.8	6.8	6.7	6	5.4	5.4

1) The variable along the x-axis is the explanatory or independent variable — it's the variable you can control, or the one that you think is affecting the other. The variable 'load' goes along the x-axis here.

2) The variable up the y-axis is the response or dependent variable — it's the variable you think is being affected. In this example, this is the fuel efficiency.

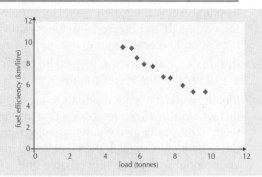

The **Regression Line** (Line of Best Fit) is in the form **y = a + bx**

To find the line of best fit for the above data you need to work out some sums.
Then it's quite easy to work out the equation of the line. If your line of best fit is $y = a + bx$, this is what you do...

(1) First work out these four sums — a table is probably the best way: $\sum x$, $\sum y$, $\sum x^2$, $\sum xy$.

x	5.1	5.6	5.9	6.3	6.8	7.4	7.8	8.5	9.1	9.8	$72.3 = \sum x$
y	9.6	9.5	8.6	8	7.8	6.8	6.7	6	5.4	5.4	$73.8 = \sum y$
x^2	26.01	31.36	34.81	39.69	46.24	54.76	60.84	72.25	82.81	96.04	$544.81 = \sum x^2$
xy	48.96	53.2	50.74	50.4	53.04	50.32	52.26	51	49.14	52.92	$511.98 = \sum xy$

(2) Then work out S_{xy}, given by: $S_{xy} = \sum(x - \overline{x})(y - \overline{y}) = \sum xy - \dfrac{(\sum x)(\sum y)}{n}$

and S_{xx}, given by: $S_{xx} = \sum(x - \overline{x})^2 = \sum x^2 - \dfrac{(\sum x)^2}{n}$

These are the same as the terms used to work out the PMCC (see p.137).

(3) The gradient (b) of your regression line is given by: $b = \dfrac{S_{xy}}{S_{xx}}$

(4) And the intercept (a) is given by: $a = \overline{y} - b\overline{x}$.

(5) Then the regression line is just: $y = a + bx$.

Loads of calculators will work out regression lines for you — but you still need to know this method, since they might give you just the sums from Step 1.

EXAMPLE   Find the equation of the regression line of y on x for the data above. ⟵ The 'regression line of y on x' means that x is the independent variable, and y is the dependent variable.

1) Work out the sums: $\sum x = 72.3$, $\sum y = 73.8$, $\sum x^2 = 544.81$, $\sum xy = 511.98$.

2) Then work out S_{xy} and S_{xx}: $S_{xy} = 511.98 - \dfrac{72.3 \times 73.8}{10} = -21.594$, $S_{xx} = 544.81 - \dfrac{72.3^2}{10} = 22.081$

3) So the gradient of the regression line is: $b = \dfrac{-21.594}{22.081} = -0.978$ (to 3 sig. fig.)   Remember: $\overline{x} = \dfrac{\sum x}{n}$

4) And the intercept is: $a = \dfrac{\sum y}{n} - b\dfrac{\sum x}{n} = \dfrac{73.8}{10} - (-0.978) \times \dfrac{72.3}{10} = 14.451 = 14.5$ (to 3 sig. fig.)

5) This all means that your regression line is: $y = 14.5 - 0.978x$ The regression line always goes through the point $(\overline{x}, \overline{y})$.

This tells you: (i) for every extra tonne carried, you'd expect the lorry's fuel efficiency to fall by 0.978 km per litre, and (ii) with no load ($x = 0$), you'd expect the lorry to do 14.5 km per litre of fuel. ⟵ Assuming the trend continues down to $x = 0$.

Linear Regression

Residuals — the difference between *Practice* and *Theory*

A <u>residual</u> is the <u>difference</u> between an <u>observed y-value</u> and the y-value <u>predicted</u> by the regression line.

> Residual = Observed y-value – Estimated y-value

1) Residuals show the <u>experimental error</u> between the y-value that's <u>observed</u> and the y-value your regression line says it <u>should</u> be.

2) Residuals are shown by a <u>vertical line</u> from the actual point to the regression line.

3) Ideally, you'd like your residuals to be <u>small</u> — this would show your regression line fits the data well. If they're <u>large</u> (i.e. a <u>high percentage</u> of the dependent variable), then that could mean your model <u>won't</u> be a very <u>reliable</u> one.

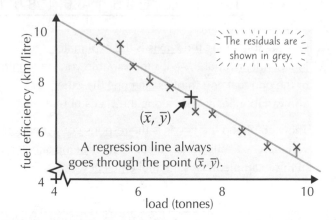

The residuals are shown in grey.

$(\bar{x}, \bar{y})$

A regression line always goes through the point $(\bar{x}, \bar{y})$.

EXAMPLE For the fuel efficiency example on the last page, calculate the residuals for: (i) $x = 5.6$, (ii) $x = 7.4$.

(i) When $x = 5.6$, the residual = $9.5 - (-0.978 \times 5.6 + 14.451) = \underline{0.526}$ (to 3 sig. fig.)

(ii) When $x = 7.4$, the residual = $6.8 - (-0.978 \times 7.4 + 14.451) = \underline{-0.414}$ (to 3 sig. fig.)

A <u>positive residual</u> means the regression line is <u>too low</u> for that value of x.
A <u>negative residual</u> means the regression line is <u>too high</u>.

> This kind of regression is called <u>Least Squares Regression</u>, because you're finding the equation of the line which <u>minimises the sum of the squares of the residuals</u> (i.e. $\sum e_k^2$ is as small as possible, where the e_k are the residuals).

You can also Find the **Regression Line of x on y**

The formulas on the previous page give you the 'regression line of y on x', which you use when x is the <u>independent</u> variable and y the <u>dependent</u> variable. But if y is actually the <u>independent</u> variable, then you need the 'regression line of x on y'.

1) In that case, your regression line will be $x = c + dy$,
   where: $d = \dfrac{S_{xy}}{S_{yy}}$ and $c = \bar{x} - d\bar{y}$.

2) And your <u>residuals</u> will look like this:

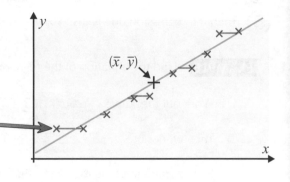

$(\bar{x}, \bar{y})$

> You <u>can't</u> just rearrange the regression line of y on x to get the regression line of x on y. You <u>must</u> work it out from scratch.

I predicted I'd win a million on the lottery — but the residual turned out to be large...

Residuals are errors in the dependent variable — not the independent variable. The regression equations on the previous page will be in your formula booklet, so you don't need to learn them, but practise <u>using</u> and <u>interpreting</u> them.

More About Regression and Correlation

Use Regression Lines With Care

You can use your regression line to <u>predict</u> values of the dependent variable.
But it's best <u>not</u> to do this for values of the independent variable <u>outside</u> the <u>range</u> of your original table of values.

> **EXAMPLE** Use your regression equation from p139 to estimate the value of y when: (i) $x = 7.6$, (ii) $x = 12.6$
>
> (i) When $x = 7.6$, $y = -0.978 \times 7.6 + 14.5 = \underline{7.1}$ (to 2 sig. fig.). This should be a pretty <u>reliable</u> guess, since $x = 7.6$ falls in the range of x we <u>already have readings for</u> — this is called <u>interpolation</u>.
>
> (ii) When $x = 12.6$, $y = -0.978 \times 12.6 + 14.5 = \underline{2.2}$ (to 2 sig. fig.). This may well be <u>unreliable</u> since $x = 12.6$ is <u>bigger than the biggest x-value we already have</u> — this is called <u>extrapolation</u>.

<u>Outliers</u> can also be a problem — they can have a <u>big</u> effect on the regression line's equation, and drag it <u>far away</u> from the rest of the data values. Here, the <u>circled</u> data value is an outlier.

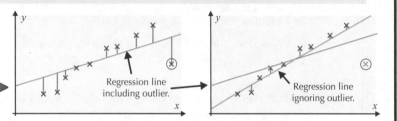

Regression line including outlier.

Regression line ignoring outlier.

Spearman's Rank Correlation Coefficient (SRCC or r_s) works with Ranks

You can use the <u>SRCC</u> (or r_s, for short) when your data is a set of <u>ranks</u>. (Ranks are the <u>positions</u> of the values when you put them <u>in order</u> — e.g. from biggest to smallest, or from best to worst, etc.)

> **EXAMPLE** At a dog show, two judges put 8 labradors (A-H) in the following orders, from best to worst. Calculate the SRCC between the sets of ranks.
>
> | Position | 1st | 2nd | 3rd | 4th | 5th | 6th | 7th | 8th |
> |---|---|---|---|---|---|---|---|---|
> | Judge 1: | B | C | E | A | D | F | G | H |
> | Judge 2: | C | B | E | D | F | A | G | H |
>
> First, make a table of the <u>ranks</u> of the 8 labradors — i.e. for each dog, write down <u>where it came</u> in the show.
>
> | Dog | A | B | C | D | E | F | G | H |
> |---|---|---|---|---|---|---|---|---|
> | Rank from Judge 1: | 4 | 1 | 2 | 5 | 3 | 6 | 7 | 8 |
> | Rank from Judge 2: | 6 | 2 | 1 | 4 | 3 | 5 | 7 | 8 |
>
> Now for each dog, work out the <u>difference</u> (d) between the ranks from the two judges — you can <u>ignore</u> minus signs.
>
> | Dog | A | B | C | D | E | F | G | H |
> |---|---|---|---|---|---|---|---|---|
> | d | 2 | 1 | 1 | 1 | 0 | 1 | 0 | 0 |
>
> Take a deep breath, and add <u>another row</u> to your table — this time for $\underline{d^2}$:
>
> | Dog | A | B | C | D | E | F | G | H | Total = Σd^2 |
> |---|---|---|---|---|---|---|---|---|---|
> | d^2 | 4 | 1 | 1 | 1 | 0 | 1 | 0 | 0 | 8 |
>
> Then the SRCC is:
>
> $$r_s = 1 - \frac{6\sum d^2}{n(n^2 - 1)}$$
>
> This formula is given on the formula sheet.
>
> You can ignore minus signs when you work out d, since only d^2 is used to work out the SRCC.
>
> So here, $r_s = 1 - \dfrac{6 \times 8}{8 \times (8^2 - 1)} = 1 - \dfrac{48}{504} = 0.905$ (to 3 sig. fig.).
>
> Interpret r_s in the same way as you'd interpret the PMCC (see p137).
>
> — this is close to +1, so the judges ranked the dogs in a <u>pretty similar</u> way.

99% of all statisticians make sweeping statements...

Be careful with that extrapolation business — it's like me saying that because I grew at an average rate of 10 cm a year for the first few years of my life, by the time I'm 50 I should be 5 metres tall. (There's still time, but I can't see that happening.)

S1 Section 4 — Practice Questions

That was a short section, but chock-full of <u>fiddly terms</u> and <u>hefty equations</u>. The only way to learn all those details is by using them — so stretch your maths muscles and take a jog around this obstacle course of <u>practice questions</u>.

Warm-up Questions

1) The table below shows the results of some measurements concerning alcoholic cocktails. Here, x = total volume in ml, and y = percentage alcohol concentration by volume.

x	90	100	100	150	160	200	240	250	290	300
y	40	35	25	30	25	25	20	25	15	7

   a) Draw a scatter diagram representing this information.

   b) Calculate the product-moment correlation coefficient (PMCC) of these values.

   c) What does the PMCC tell you about these results?

2) For each pair of variables below, state which would be the dependent variable and which would be the independent variable.

   a) • the annual number of volleyball-related injuries
      • the annual number of sunny days

   b) • the annual number of rainy days
      • the annual number of Monopoly-related injuries

   c) • a person's disposable income
      • a person's spending on luxuries

   d) • the number of trips to the loo per day
      • the number of cups of tea drunk per day

   e) • the number of festival tickets sold
      • the number of pairs of Wellington boots bought

3) The radius in mm, x, and the weight in grams, y, of 10 randomly selected blueberry pancakes are given in the table below.

x	48.0	51.0	52.0	54.5	55.1	53.6	50.0	52.6	49.4	51.2
y	100	105	108	120	125	118	100	115	98	110

   a) Find: (i) $S_{xx} = \sum x^2 - \dfrac{(\sum x)^2}{n}$,   (ii) $S_{xy} = \sum xy - \dfrac{(\sum x)(\sum y)}{n}$

   The regression line of y on x has equation $y = a + bx$.

   b) Find b, the gradient of the regression line.

   c) Find a, the intercept of the regression line on the y-axis.

   d) Write down the equation of the regression line of y on x.

   e) Use your regression line to estimate the weight of a blueberry pancake of radius 60 mm.

   f) Comment on the reliability of your estimate, giving a reason for your answer.

4) These are the marks obtained by 10 pupils in their Physics and English exams. Calculate Spearman's rank correlation coefficient.

Physics	54	34	23	57	56	58	13	65	69	52
English	16	73	89	83	23	81	56	62	61	37

S1 Section 4 — Practice Questions

<u>Land ahoy</u>, ye lily-livered yellow-bellies.
Just a quick heave-ho through these exam questions, then <u>drop anchor</u> and <u>row ashore</u>. Yaarrr, freedom...

Exam Questions

1   Values of two variables x and y are recorded in the table below.

x	1	2	3	4	5	6	7	8
y	0.50	0.70	0.10	0.82	0.50	0.36	0.16	0.80

a)   Represent this data on a scatter diagram.

(2 marks)

b)   Calculate the product-moment correlation coefficient (PMCC) between the two variables.

(4 marks)

c)   What does this value of the PMCC tell you about these variables?

(1 mark)

2   The following times (in seconds) were taken by eight different runners to complete distances of 20 metres and 60 metres.

Runner	A	B	C	D	E	F	G	H
20-metre time (x)	3.39	3.20	3.09	3.32	3.33	3.27	3.44	3.08
60-metre time (y)	8.78	7.73	8.28	8.25	8.91	8.59	8.90	8.05

a)   Plot a scatter diagram to represent the data.

(2 marks)

b)   Find the equation of the regression line of y on x, and plot it on your scatter diagram.

(8 marks)

c)   Use the equation of the regression line to estimate the value of y when:
(i) $x = 3.15$,   (ii) $x = 3.88$.
Comment on the reliability of your estimates.

(4 marks)

d)   Find the residuals for:
(i) $x = 3.32$ (ii) $x = 3.27$.
Illustrate them on your scatter diagram.

(4 marks)

3   A journalist at British Biking Monthly recorded the distance in miles, x, cycled by 20 different cyclists in the morning and the number of calories, y, eaten at lunch. The following summary statistics were provided:
$$S_{xx} = 310\,880 \qquad S_{yy} = 788.95 \qquad S_{xy} = 12\,666$$

a)   Use these values to calculate the product-moment correlation coefficient.

(2 marks)

b)   Give an interpretation of your answer to part a).

(1 mark)

A Swedish cycling magazine calculated the product-moment correlation coefficient of the data after converting the distances to km.

c)   State the value of the product-moment correlation coefficient in this case.

(1 mark)

4   The equation of the line of regression for a set of data is $y = 211.599 + 9.602x$.

a)   Use the equation of the regression line to estimate the value of y when:
(i) $x = 12.5$ (ii) $x = 14.7$.

(2 marks)

b)   Calculate the residuals if the respective observed y-values were $y = 332.5$ and $y = 352.1$.

(2 marks)

General Certificate of Education
Advanced Subsidiary (AS) and Advanced Level

Statistics S1 — Practice Exam One

Time Allowed: 1 hour 30 min

Graphical calculators may be used for this exam.

Unless told otherwise, give any non-exact numerical answers to 3 significant figures.

Statistical tables can be found on page 150.
Values used from these tables must be quoted in full.

There are 72 marks available for this paper.

1   The heights of giraffes in a game reserve were measured.
     This data is summarised in the box-and-whisker plot below.

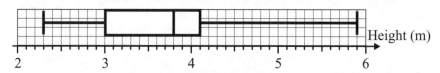

    a)   What height do only 25% of the giraffes exceed?

(1 mark)

The heights of giraffes living in a zoo in the same country range from 2.8 m to 5.8 m.
The quartiles of their heights are 3.4 m, 4.1 m, and 5.2 m.

    b)   Draw a box-and-whisker plot below to represent the heights of the giraffes in the zoo.

(4 marks)

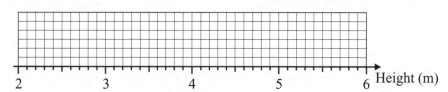

    c)   Compare the heights of these two groups of giraffes.

(4 marks)

2   Rebecca is making a fruit cake. The recipe tells her to use equal measures of any 4 different types of dried
     fruit. She goes out to buy ingredients and finds that the supermarket sells 8 different types of dried fruit.

    a)   How many distinct selections of 4 different types of dried fruit could Rebecca buy?

(2 marks)

Two of the 8 types of dried fruit available are raisins and sultanas.
Rebecca decides she wants to use one of these, but not both.

    b)   If Rebecca selects her 4 types of dried fruit at random, find the probability that her selection includes:

        (i)   both raisins and sultanas,

(2 marks)

        (ii)   either raisins or sultanas, but not both.

(3 marks)

3. The probability distribution for the cash prizes, x pence, offered by a gambling machine is as follows:

x	0	10	20	50	100
$P(X=x)$	$\frac{7}{20}$	$\frac{1}{5}$	$\frac{3}{20}$	$\frac{3}{20}$	p

    a)   Write down the value of p.

(2 marks)

    b)   Find $E(X)$ and $Var(X)$.

(4 marks)

    c)   The owner of the machine charges 30p per game. Comment on this cost.

(2 marks)

    d)   Comment on whether the above distribution is really likely to be used in gambling machines.

(2 marks)

4. An average of 5% of chocolate bars made by a particular manufacturer contain a 'golden ticket'.
A student buys 5 chocolate bars every week for 6 weeks.
The number of golden tickets he finds is represented by the random variable X.

    a)   State two necessary conditions for X to follow the binomial distribution $B(30, 0.05)$.

(2 marks)

    b)   Assuming that $X \sim B(30, 0.05)$, find:

         (i) $P(X > 1)$,

(2 marks)

         (ii) $P(3 < X < 7)$,

(3 marks)

         (iii) $E(X)$.

(1 mark)

    c)   One student buys a chocolate bar every day until she finds a golden ticket.
If W denotes the number of bars she buys, up to and including the
first one containing a golden ticket, find $P(W = 6)$.

(3 marks)

5. Six pairs of dancers, denoted A to F, are competing in a televised dancing competition.
The table below shows the rankings of their performances according
to the expert judges and the public telephone vote.

Position	1	2	3	4	5	6
Judges	C	A	F	E	D	B
Public	A	F	B	C	D	E

Calculate Spearman's rank correlation coefficient, r_s, for the two sets of rankings.

(5 marks)

6   Of 30 drivers interviewed, 9 have been involved in a car crash at some time.
    Of those who have been involved in a crash, 5 wear glasses. The probability of wearing glasses,
    given that the driver has not been involved in a car crash, is $\frac{1}{3}$.

    a)   Represent this information in a tree diagram, giving all probabilities as fractions
         in their simplest form.

         (3 marks)

    b)   What is the probability that a person chosen at random wears glasses?

         (3 marks)

    c)   What is the probability that a glasses wearer has been a crash victim?

         (3 marks)

7   A group of 10 friends play a round of minigolf.
    Their total score $(\sum x)$ is 500 and $\sum x^2 = 25\ 622$.

    a)   Find the mean, μ, and the standard deviation, σ, for this data.

         (3 marks)

    b)   Another friend wants to incorporate his score of 50. Without further calculation and
         giving reasons, explain the effect of adding this score on:

         (i)   the mean,

               (2 marks)

         (ii) the standard deviation.

               (2 marks)

8   A teacher collects the following data showing students' marks in an examination (y) and the amount of
    revision undertaken in hours (x).

x	12	10	9	5	14	11	12	6
y	88	72	65	59	92	75	80	69

    ($\Sigma x = 79$, $\Sigma y = 600$, $\Sigma x^2 = 847$, $\Sigma y^2 = 45\ 884$ and $\Sigma xy = 6143$.)

    a)   Calculate S_{xx}, S_{yy} and S_{xy}.

         (3 marks)

    b)   Calculate the product-moment correlation coefficient for y and x.

         (2 marks)

    c)   Which of y and x is the independent variable? Explain your answer.

         (2 marks)

    d)   The teacher believes she can fit a linear regression line $y = a + bx$ to the data.
         Give one reason to support her conclusion.

         (1 mark)

    e)   Find the equation of the regression line of y on x in the form $y = a + bx$.

         (4 marks)

    f)   The teacher must estimate the examination mark of a student who did not take the examination.
         The teacher knows this student to have done 4 hours of revision.

         Estimate the likely mark for this student.

         (1 mark)

    g)   Comment on the reliability of your estimate in f).

         (1 mark)

General Certificate of Education
Advanced Subsidiary (AS) and Advanced Level

Statistics S1 — Practice Exam Two

Time Allowed: 1 hour 30 min

Graphical calculators may be used for this exam.

Unless told otherwise, give any non-exact numerical answers to 3 significant figures.

Statistical tables can be found on page 150.
Values used from these tables must be quoted in full.

There are 72 marks available for this paper.

---

1   A box of chocolates contains 20 chocolates, all of which are either hard or soft centred.
Some of the chocolates contain nuts. 13 chocolates have hard centres, of which 6 contain nuts.
There are 10 nutty chocolates in total.

   a)   A chocolate is selected at random. Find the probability of:

      (i)   it having a soft centre.

(1 mark)

      (ii)   it having a hard centre, given that it contains a nut.

(2 marks)

   b)   If 3 chocolates are selected at random without replacement, find the probability that
      exactly one has a hard centre.

(3 marks)

2   The discrete random variable X has the probability distribution shown below:

x	1	2	3	4	5	6
$P(X = x)$	$\frac{1}{12}$	$\frac{1}{6}$	$\frac{1}{4}$	$\frac{1}{4}$	$\frac{1}{6}$	$\frac{1}{12}$

   a)   Find $P(X \le 3)$.

(2 marks)

   b)   Show that $E(X) = 3.5$.

(2 marks)

   c)   Find $Var(X)$.

(3 marks)

3   Rob is carrying out an experiment in which he tosses a biased coin 9 times.
The probability of the coin landing on heads on each toss is p, and the expected number of heads is 3.

   a)   Find the value of p.

(2 marks)

   b)   Find the probability of the coin landing on heads exactly 4 times in the experiment.

(3 marks)

4   The following table shows a set of bivariate data.

x	0.3	0.6	0.9	1.2	1.5
y	3	8	11	k	20

(You may use the following: $\Sigma x = 4.5$, $\Sigma y = 42 + k$, $\Sigma xy = 45.6 + 1.2k$, $\Sigma x^2 = 4.95$, $\Sigma y^2 = 594 + k^2$, $n = 5$)

a)   The value of Spearman's rank correlation coefficient for this data is 1.
     Without any further calculation, what does this tell you about the value of k?
     Give a reason for your answer.

(2 marks)

b)   Given that $S_{xy} = 12$, find:

   (i)   the value of k,

(2 marks)

   (ii)   the value of r, the product moment correlation coefficient.

(3 marks)

5   For a particular flight, an airline has 5 spare seats available in first class.
    There is a list of 9 passengers who are eligible to be upgraded to first class.
    The 5 available seats will be randomly allocated to 5 passengers from this list.

a)   In how many ways can the 5 seats be filled?

(2 marks)

b)   Amy and Sam are both on the list of passengers who could be upgraded.
     What is the probability that at least one of them gets upgraded?

(3 marks)

c)   Only two of the spare seats are next to each other.
     Given that Amy and Sam both get upgraded, what is the probability that they sit together?

(3 marks)

6   The sales figures of a gift shop for a 12-week period are shown below.

Week	1	2	3	4	5	6	7	8	9	10	11	12
Sales (£'000s), x	5.5	4.2	5.8	9.1	3.8	4.6	6.4	6.2	4.9	5.9	6.0	4.1

(You may use $\Sigma x = 66.5$, and $\Sigma x^2 = 390.97$.)

a)   Find the mean and variance of the weekly sales.

(4 marks)

b)   Find the median and quartiles of the sales data.

(3 marks)

Sales figures (in £'000s) of another gift shop in a neighbouring town for the same period were analysed. The mean of the weekly sales was 5.48, the variance was 0.726, the median was 5.6 and the interquartile range was 1.5.

c)   Compare the central tendency and variation of the sales data for the two shops.

(2 marks)

d)   Suggest why the median is sometimes a better measure of central tendency than the mean.

(1 mark)

7   S is a discrete random variable. If $S \sim \text{Geo}(0.4)$, find:

a) $P(S = 3)$,

(2 marks)

b) $P(S < 4)$,

(3 marks)

c) $E(S)$.

(2 marks)

8   A construction company measures the length, y metres, of a cable when put under different amounts of tension (x, measured in kilonewtons, kN). The results of its tests are shown below.

x (kN)	1	2	3	5	8	10	15	20
y (metres)	3.05	3.1	3.13	3.15	3.27	3.4	3.5	3.6

a) Draw a scatter graph to show these results.

(2 marks)

b) Calculate S_{xx} and S_{xy}.
    (You may use $\Sigma x^2 = 828$ and $\Sigma xy = 219.05$.)

(2 marks)

An engineer believes a linear regression line of the form $y = a + bx$ could be found to accurately describe the results.

c) Find the equation of this regression line.

(4 marks)

d) Explain what your values of a and b represent.

(2 marks)

e) Use your regression line to predict the length of the cable when put under a tension of 30 kilonewtons.

(2 marks)

f) Comment on the reliability of the estimate in e).

(1 mark)

9   Each student in a class has a standard pack of 52 cards, where each pack is made up of the same number of red and black cards and contains 12 picture cards in total.

a) One student picks 3 cards at random from her pack, without replacing the selected cards before the next pick. The random variable X represents the number of picture cards picked.
    Explain why X does not follow a binomial distribution.

(1 mark)

b) Another student chooses 3 cards at random, but replaces each of the selected cards before the next pick. The random variable Y represents the number of picture cards picked. Calculate:

    (i)   the probability that the student chooses exactly two picture cards,

(2 marks)

    (ii) the mean of Y,

(1 mark)

    (ii) the variance of Y.

(1 mark)

c) All 20 students in the group now choose 4 cards at random from their pack, replacing their selected cards each time. The random variable Q represents the number of students that choose exactly 3 red cards. Find the probability that Q is at least 2 but no greater than 8.

(4 marks)

Cumulative binomial probabilities

n = 5

p	0.05	0.1	0.15	1/6	0.2	0.25	0.3	1/3	0.35	0.4	0.45	0.5	0.55	0.6	0.65	2/3	0.7	0.75	0.8	5/6	0.85	0.9	0.95
x = 0	0.7738	0.5905	0.4437	0.4019	0.3277	0.2373	0.1681	0.1317	0.1160	0.0778	0.0503	0.0313	0.0185	0.0102	0.0053	0.0041	0.0024	0.0010	0.0003	0.0001	0.0001	0.0000	0.0000
1	0.9774	0.9185	0.8352	0.8038	0.7373	0.6328	0.5282	0.4609	0.4284	0.3370	0.2562	0.1875	0.1312	0.0870	0.0540	0.0453	0.0308	0.0156	0.0067	0.0033	0.0022	0.0005	0.0000
2	0.9988	0.9914	0.9734	0.9645	0.9421	0.8965	0.8369	0.7901	0.7648	0.6826	0.5931	0.5000	0.4069	0.3174	0.2352	0.2099	0.1631	0.1035	0.0579	0.0355	0.0266	0.0086	0.0012
3	1.0000	0.9995	0.9978	0.9967	0.9933	0.9844	0.9692	0.9547	0.9460	0.9130	0.8688	0.8125	0.7438	0.6630	0.5716	0.5391	0.4718	0.3672	0.2627	0.1962	0.1648	0.0815	0.0226
4	1.0000	1.0000	0.9999	0.9999	0.9997	0.9990	0.9976	0.9959	0.9947	0.9898	0.9815	0.9688	0.9497	0.9222	0.8840	0.8683	0.8319	0.7627	0.6723	0.5981	0.5563	0.4095	0.2262
5	1.0000	1.0000	1.0000	1.0000	1.0000	1.0000	1.0000	1.0000	1.0000	1.0000	1.0000	1.0000	1.0000	1.0000	1.0000	1.0000	1.0000	1.0000	1.0000	1.0000	1.0000	1.0000	1.0000

n = 6

p	0.05	0.1	0.15	1/6	0.2	0.25	0.3	1/3	0.35	0.4	0.45	0.5	0.55	0.6	0.65	2/3	0.7	0.75	0.8	5/6	0.85	0.9	0.95
x = 0	0.7351	0.5314	0.3771	0.3349	0.2621	0.1780	0.1176	0.0878	0.0754	0.0467	0.0277	0.0156	0.0083	0.0041	0.0018	0.0014	0.0007	0.0002	0.0001	0.0000	0.0000	0.0000	0.0000
1	0.9672	0.8857	0.7765	0.7368	0.6554	0.5339	0.4202	0.3512	0.3191	0.2333	0.1636	0.1094	0.0692	0.0410	0.0223	0.0178	0.0109	0.0046	0.0016	0.0007	0.0004	0.0001	0.0000
2	0.9978	0.9842	0.9527	0.9377	0.9011	0.8306	0.7443	0.6804	0.6471	0.5443	0.4415	0.3438	0.2553	0.1792	0.1174	0.1001	0.0705	0.0376	0.0170	0.0087	0.0059	0.0013	0.0001
3	0.9999	0.9987	0.9941	0.9913	0.9830	0.9624	0.9295	0.8999	0.8826	0.8208	0.7447	0.6563	0.5585	0.4557	0.3529	0.3196	0.2557	0.1694	0.0989	0.0623	0.0473	0.0159	0.0022
4	1.0000	0.9999	0.9996	0.9993	0.9984	0.9954	0.9891	0.9822	0.9777	0.9590	0.9308	0.8906	0.8364	0.7667	0.6809	0.6488	0.5798	0.4661	0.3446	0.2632	0.2235	0.1143	0.0328
5	1.0000	1.0000	1.0000	1.0000	0.9999	0.9998	0.9993	0.9986	0.9982	0.9959	0.9917	0.9844	0.9723	0.9533	0.9246	0.9122	0.8824	0.8220	0.7379	0.6651	0.6229	0.4686	0.2649
6	1.0000	1.0000	1.0000	1.0000	1.0000	1.0000	1.0000	1.0000	1.0000	1.0000	1.0000	1.0000	1.0000	1.0000	1.0000	1.0000	1.0000	1.0000	1.0000	1.0000	1.0000	1.0000	1.0000

n = 7

p	0.05	0.1	0.15	1/6	0.2	0.25	0.3	1/3	0.35	0.4	0.45	0.5	0.55	0.6	0.65	2/3	0.7	0.75	0.8	5/6	0.85	0.9	0.95
x = 0	0.6983	0.4783	0.3206	0.2791	0.2097	0.1335	0.0824	0.0585	0.0490	0.0280	0.0152	0.0078	0.0037	0.0016	0.0006	0.0005	0.0002	0.0001	0.0000	0.0000	0.0000	0.0000	0.0000
1	0.9556	0.8503	0.7166	0.6698	0.5767	0.4449	0.3294	0.2634	0.2338	0.1586	0.1024	0.0625	0.0357	0.0188	0.0090	0.0069	0.0038	0.0013	0.0004	0.0001	0.0001	0.0000	0.0000
2	0.9962	0.9743	0.9262	0.9042	0.8520	0.7564	0.6471	0.5706	0.5323	0.4199	0.3164	0.2266	0.1529	0.0963	0.0556	0.0453	0.0288	0.0129	0.0047	0.0020	0.0012	0.0002	0.0000
3	0.9998	0.9973	0.9879	0.9824	0.9667	0.9294	0.8740	0.8267	0.8002	0.7102	0.6083	0.5000	0.3917	0.2898	0.1998	0.1733	0.1260	0.0706	0.0333	0.0176	0.0121	0.0027	0.0002
4	1.0000	0.9998	0.9988	0.9980	0.9953	0.9871	0.9712	0.9547	0.9444	0.9037	0.8471	0.7734	0.6836	0.5801	0.4677	0.4294	0.3529	0.2436	0.1480	0.0958	0.0738	0.0257	0.0038
5	1.0000	1.0000	0.9999	0.9999	0.9996	0.9987	0.9962	0.9931	0.9910	0.9812	0.9643	0.9375	0.8976	0.8414	0.7662	0.7366	0.6706	0.5551	0.4233	0.3302	0.2834	0.1497	0.0444
6	1.0000	1.0000	1.0000	1.0000	1.0000	0.9999	0.9998	0.9995	0.9994	0.9984	0.9963	0.9922	0.9848	0.9720	0.9510	0.9415	0.9176	0.8665	0.7903	0.7209	0.6794	0.5217	0.3017
7	1.0000	1.0000	1.0000	1.0000	1.0000	1.0000	1.0000	1.0000	1.0000	1.0000	1.0000	1.0000	1.0000	1.0000	1.0000	1.0000	1.0000	1.0000	1.0000	1.0000	1.0000	1.0000	1.0000

n = 8

p	0.05	0.1	0.15	1/6	0.2	0.25	0.3	1/3	0.35	0.4	0.45	0.5	0.55	0.6	0.65	2/3	0.7	0.75	0.8	5/6	0.85	0.9	0.95
x = 0	0.6634	0.4305	0.2725	0.2326	0.1678	0.1001	0.0576	0.0390	0.0319	0.0168	0.0084	0.0039	0.0017	0.0007	0.0002	0.0002	0.0001	0.0000	0.0000	0.0000	0.0000	0.0000	0.0000
1	0.9428	0.8131	0.6572	0.6047	0.5033	0.3671	0.2553	0.1951	0.1691	0.1064	0.0632	0.0352	0.0181	0.0085	0.0036	0.0026	0.0013	0.0004	0.0001	0.0000	0.0000	0.0000	0.0000
2	0.9942	0.9619	0.8948	0.8652	0.7969	0.6785	0.5518	0.4682	0.4278	0.3154	0.2201	0.1445	0.0885	0.0498	0.0253	0.0197	0.0113	0.0042	0.0012	0.0004	0.0002	0.0000	0.0000
3	0.9996	0.9950	0.9786	0.9693	0.9437	0.8862	0.8059	0.7414	0.7064	0.5941	0.4770	0.3633	0.2604	0.1737	0.1061	0.0879	0.0580	0.0273	0.0104	0.0046	0.0029	0.0004	0.0000
4	1.0000	0.9996	0.9971	0.9954	0.9896	0.9727	0.9420	0.9121	0.8939	0.8263	0.7396	0.6367	0.5230	0.4059	0.2936	0.2586	0.1941	0.1138	0.0563	0.0307	0.0214	0.0050	0.0004
5	1.0000	1.0000	0.9998	0.9996	0.9988	0.9958	0.9887	0.9803	0.9747	0.9502	0.9115	0.8555	0.7799	0.6846	0.5722	0.5318	0.4482	0.3215	0.2031	0.1348	0.1052	0.0381	0.0058
6	1.0000	1.0000	1.0000	1.0000	0.9999	0.9996	0.9987	0.9974	0.9964	0.9915	0.9819	0.9648	0.9368	0.8936	0.8309	0.8049	0.7447	0.6329	0.4967	0.3953	0.3428	0.1869	0.0572
7	1.0000	1.0000	1.0000	1.0000	1.0000	1.0000	0.9999	0.9998	0.9998	0.9993	0.9983	0.9961	0.9916	0.9832	0.9681	0.9610	0.9424	0.8999	0.8322	0.7674	0.7275	0.5695	0.3366
8	1.0000	1.0000	1.0000	1.0000	1.0000	1.0000	1.0000	1.0000	1.0000	1.0000	1.0000	1.0000	1.0000	1.0000	1.0000	1.0000	1.0000	1.0000	1.0000	1.0000	1.0000	1.0000	1.0000

Cumulative binomial probabilities (continued)

n = 9

p \ x	0.05	0.1	0.15	1/6	0.2	0.25	0.3	1/3	0.35	0.4	0.45	0.5	0.55	0.6	0.65	2/3	0.7	0.75	0.8	5/6	0.85	0.9	0.95
x=0	0.6302	0.3874	0.2316	0.1938	0.1342	0.0751	0.0404	0.0260	0.0207	0.0101	0.0046	0.0020	0.0008	0.0003	0.0001	0.0001	0.0000	0.0000	0.0000	0.0000	0.0000	0.0000	0.0000
1	0.9288	0.7748	0.5995	0.5427	0.4362	0.3003	0.1960	0.1431	0.1211	0.0705	0.0385	0.0195	0.0091	0.0038	0.0014	0.0010	0.0004	0.0001	0.0000	0.0000	0.0000	0.0000	0.0000
2	0.9916	0.9470	0.8591	0.8217	0.7382	0.6007	0.4628	0.3772	0.3373	0.2318	0.1495	0.0898	0.0498	0.0250	0.0112	0.0083	0.0043	0.0013	0.0003	0.0001	0.0000	0.0000	0.0000
3	0.9994	0.9917	0.9661	0.9520	0.9144	0.8343	0.7297	0.6503	0.6089	0.4826	0.3614	0.2539	0.1658	0.0994	0.0536	0.0424	0.0253	0.0100	0.0031	0.0011	0.0006	0.0001	0.0000
4	1.0000	0.9991	0.9944	0.9910	0.9804	0.9511	0.9012	0.8552	0.8283	0.7334	0.6214	0.5000	0.3786	0.2666	0.1717	0.1448	0.0988	0.0489	0.0196	0.0090	0.0056	0.0009	0.0000
5	1.0000	0.9999	0.9994	0.9989	0.9969	0.9900	0.9747	0.9576	0.9464	0.9006	0.8342	0.7461	0.6386	0.5174	0.3911	0.3497	0.2703	0.1657	0.0856	0.0480	0.0339	0.0083	0.0006
6	1.0000	1.0000	1.0000	0.9999	0.9997	0.9987	0.9957	0.9917	0.9888	0.9750	0.9502	0.9102	0.8505	0.7682	0.6627	0.6228	0.5372	0.3993	0.2618	0.1783	0.1409	0.0530	0.0084
7	1.0000	1.0000	1.0000	1.0000	1.0000	0.9999	0.9996	0.9990	0.9986	0.9962	0.9909	0.9805	0.9615	0.9295	0.8789	0.8569	0.8040	0.6997	0.5638	0.4573	0.4005	0.2252	0.0712
8	1.0000	1.0000	1.0000	1.0000	1.0000	1.0000	1.0000	0.9999	0.9999	0.9997	0.9992	0.9980	0.9954	0.9899	0.9793	0.9740	0.9596	0.9249	0.8658	0.8062	0.7684	0.6126	0.3698
9	1.0000	1.0000	1.0000	1.0000	1.0000	1.0000	1.0000	1.0000	1.0000	1.0000	1.0000	1.0000	1.0000	1.0000	1.0000	1.0000	1.0000	1.0000	1.0000	1.0000	1.0000	1.0000	1.0000

n = 10

p \ x	0.05	0.1	0.15	1/6	0.2	0.25	0.3	1/3	0.35	0.4	0.45	0.5	0.55	0.6	0.65	2/3	0.7	0.75	0.8	5/6	0.85	0.9	0.95
x=0	0.5987	0.3487	0.1969	0.1615	0.1074	0.0563	0.0282	0.0173	0.0135	0.0060	0.0025	0.0010	0.0003	0.0001	0.0000	0.0000	0.0000	0.0000	0.0000	0.0000	0.0000	0.0000	0.0000
1	0.9139	0.7361	0.5443	0.4845	0.3758	0.2440	0.1493	0.1040	0.0860	0.0464	0.0233	0.0107	0.0045	0.0017	0.0005	0.0004	0.0001	0.0000	0.0000	0.0000	0.0000	0.0000	0.0000
2	0.9885	0.9298	0.8202	0.7752	0.6778	0.5256	0.3828	0.2991	0.2616	0.1673	0.0996	0.0547	0.0274	0.0123	0.0048	0.0034	0.0016	0.0004	0.0001	0.0000	0.0000	0.0000	0.0000
3	0.9990	0.9872	0.9500	0.9303	0.8791	0.7759	0.6496	0.5593	0.5138	0.3823	0.2660	0.1719	0.1020	0.0548	0.0260	0.0197	0.0106	0.0035	0.0009	0.0003	0.0001	0.0000	0.0000
4	0.9999	0.9984	0.9901	0.9845	0.9672	0.9219	0.8497	0.7869	0.7515	0.6331	0.5044	0.3770	0.2616	0.1662	0.0949	0.0766	0.0473	0.0197	0.0064	0.0024	0.0014	0.0001	0.0000
5	1.0000	0.9999	0.9986	0.9976	0.9936	0.9803	0.9527	0.9234	0.9051	0.8338	0.7384	0.6230	0.4956	0.3669	0.2485	0.2131	0.1503	0.0781	0.0328	0.0155	0.0099	0.0016	0.0001
6	1.0000	1.0000	0.9999	0.9997	0.9991	0.9965	0.9894	0.9803	0.9740	0.9452	0.8980	0.8281	0.7340	0.6177	0.4862	0.4407	0.3504	0.2241	0.1209	0.0697	0.0500	0.0128	0.0010
7	1.0000	1.0000	1.0000	1.0000	0.9999	0.9996	0.9984	0.9966	0.9952	0.9877	0.9726	0.9453	0.9004	0.8327	0.7384	0.7009	0.6172	0.4744	0.3222	0.2248	0.1798	0.0702	0.0115
8	1.0000	1.0000	1.0000	1.0000	1.0000	1.0000	0.9999	0.9996	0.9995	0.9983	0.9955	0.9893	0.9767	0.9536	0.9140	0.8960	0.8507	0.7560	0.6242	0.5155	0.4557	0.2639	0.0861
9	1.0000	1.0000	1.0000	1.0000	1.0000	1.0000	1.0000	1.0000	1.0000	0.9999	0.9997	0.9990	0.9975	0.9940	0.9865	0.9827	0.9718	0.9437	0.8926	0.8385	0.8031	0.6513	0.4013
10	1.0000	1.0000	1.0000	1.0000	1.0000	1.0000	1.0000	1.0000	1.0000	1.0000	1.0000	1.0000	1.0000	1.0000	1.0000	1.0000	1.0000	1.0000	1.0000	1.0000	1.0000	1.0000	1.0000

n = 12

p \ x	0.05	0.1	0.15	1/6	0.2	0.25	0.3	1/3	0.35	0.4	0.45	0.5	0.55	0.6	0.65	2/3	0.7	0.75	0.8	5/6	0.85	0.9	0.95
x=0	0.5404	0.2824	0.1422	0.1122	0.0687	0.0317	0.0138	0.0077	0.0057	0.0022	0.0008	0.0002	0.0001	0.0000	0.0000	0.0000	0.0000	0.0000	0.0000	0.0000	0.0000	0.0000	0.0000
1	0.8816	0.6590	0.4435	0.3813	0.2749	0.1584	0.0850	0.0540	0.0424	0.0196	0.0083	0.0032	0.0011	0.0003	0.0001	0.0000	0.0000	0.0000	0.0000	0.0000	0.0000	0.0000	0.0000
2	0.9804	0.8891	0.7358	0.6774	0.5583	0.3907	0.2528	0.1811	0.1513	0.0834	0.0421	0.0193	0.0079	0.0028	0.0008	0.0005	0.0002	0.0000	0.0000	0.0000	0.0000	0.0000	0.0000
3	0.9978	0.9744	0.9078	0.8748	0.7946	0.6488	0.4925	0.3931	0.3467	0.2253	0.1345	0.0730	0.0356	0.0153	0.0056	0.0039	0.0017	0.0004	0.0001	0.0000	0.0000	0.0000	0.0000
4	0.9998	0.9957	0.9761	0.9636	0.9274	0.8424	0.7237	0.6315	0.5833	0.4382	0.3044	0.1938	0.1117	0.0573	0.0255	0.0188	0.0095	0.0028	0.0006	0.0002	0.0001	0.0000	0.0000
5	1.0000	0.9995	0.9954	0.9921	0.9806	0.9456	0.8822	0.8223	0.7873	0.6652	0.5269	0.3872	0.2607	0.1582	0.0846	0.0664	0.0386	0.0143	0.0039	0.0013	0.0007	0.0001	0.0000
6	1.0000	0.9999	0.9993	0.9987	0.9961	0.9857	0.9614	0.9336	0.9154	0.8418	0.7393	0.6128	0.4731	0.3348	0.2127	0.1777	0.1178	0.0544	0.0194	0.0079	0.0046	0.0005	0.0000
7	1.0000	1.0000	0.9999	0.9998	0.9994	0.9972	0.9905	0.9812	0.9745	0.9427	0.8883	0.8062	0.6956	0.5618	0.4167	0.3685	0.2763	0.1576	0.0726	0.0364	0.0239	0.0043	0.0002
8	1.0000	1.0000	1.0000	1.0000	0.9999	0.9996	0.9983	0.9961	0.9944	0.9847	0.9644	0.9270	0.8655	0.7747	0.6533	0.6069	0.5075	0.3512	0.2054	0.1252	0.0922	0.0256	0.0022
9	1.0000	1.0000	1.0000	1.0000	1.0000	1.0000	0.9998	0.9995	0.9992	0.9972	0.9921	0.9807	0.9579	0.9166	0.8487	0.8189	0.7472	0.6093	0.4417	0.3226	0.2642	0.1109	0.0196
10	1.0000	1.0000	1.0000	1.0000	1.0000	1.0000	1.0000	1.0000	0.9999	0.9997	0.9989	0.9968	0.9917	0.9804	0.9576	0.9460	0.9150	0.8416	0.7251	0.6187	0.5565	0.3410	0.1184
11	1.0000	1.0000	1.0000	1.0000	1.0000	1.0000	1.0000	1.0000	1.0000	1.0000	0.9999	0.9998	0.9992	0.9978	0.9943	0.9923	0.9862	0.9683	0.9313	0.8878	0.8578	0.7176	0.4596
12	1.0000	1.0000	1.0000	1.0000	1.0000	1.0000	1.0000	1.0000	1.0000	1.0000	1.0000	1.0000	1.0000	1.0000	1.0000	1.0000	1.0000	1.0000	1.0000	1.0000	1.0000	1.0000	1.0000

Cumulative binomial probabilities (continued)

n = 14

x \ p	0.05	0.1	0.15	1/6	0.2	0.25	0.3	1/3	0.35	0.4	0.45	0.5	0.55	0.6	0.65	2/3	0.7	0.75	0.8	5/6	0.85	0.9	0.95
0	0.4877	0.2288	0.1028	0.0779	0.0440	0.0178	0.0068	0.0034	0.0024	0.0008	0.0002	0.0001	0.0000	0.0000	0.0000	0.0000	0.0000	0.0000	0.0000	0.0000	0.0000	0.0000	0.0000
1	0.8470	0.5846	0.3567	0.2960	0.1979	0.1010	0.0475	0.0274	0.0205	0.0081	0.0029	0.0009	0.0003	0.0001	0.0000	0.0000	0.0000	0.0000	0.0000	0.0000	0.0000	0.0000	0.0000
2	0.9699	0.8416	0.6479	0.5795	0.4481	0.2811	0.1608	0.1053	0.0839	0.0398	0.0170	0.0065	0.0022	0.0006	0.0001	0.0001	0.0000	0.0000	0.0000	0.0000	0.0000	0.0000	0.0000
3	0.9958	0.9559	0.8535	0.8063	0.6982	0.5213	0.3552	0.2612	0.2205	0.1243	0.0632	0.0287	0.0114	0.0039	0.0011	0.0007	0.0002	0.0000	0.0000	0.0000	0.0000	0.0000	0.0000
4	0.9996	0.9908	0.9533	0.9310	0.8702	0.7415	0.5842	0.4755	0.4227	0.2793	0.1672	0.0898	0.0426	0.0175	0.0060	0.0040	0.0017	0.0003	0.0000	0.0000	0.0000	0.0000	0.0000
5	1.0000	0.9985	0.9885	0.9809	0.9561	0.8883	0.7805	0.6898	0.6405	0.4859	0.3373	0.2120	0.1189	0.0583	0.0243	0.0174	0.0083	0.0022	0.0004	0.0001	0.0000	0.0000	0.0000
6	1.0000	0.9998	0.9978	0.9959	0.9884	0.9617	0.9067	0.8505	0.8164	0.6925	0.5461	0.3953	0.2586	0.1501	0.0753	0.0576	0.0315	0.0103	0.0024	0.0007	0.0003	0.0000	0.0000
7	1.0000	1.0000	0.9997	0.9993	0.9976	0.9897	0.9685	0.9424	0.9247	0.8499	0.7414	0.6047	0.4539	0.3075	0.1836	0.1495	0.0933	0.0383	0.0116	0.0041	0.0022	0.0002	0.0000
8	1.0000	1.0000	1.0000	0.9999	0.9996	0.9978	0.9917	0.9826	0.9757	0.9417	0.8811	0.7880	0.6627	0.5141	0.3595	0.3102	0.2195	0.1117	0.0439	0.0191	0.0115	0.0015	0.0000
9	1.0000	1.0000	1.0000	1.0000	1.0000	0.9997	0.9983	0.9960	0.9940	0.9825	0.9574	0.9102	0.8328	0.7207	0.5773	0.5245	0.4158	0.2585	0.1298	0.0690	0.0467	0.0092	0.0004
10	1.0000	1.0000	1.0000	1.0000	1.0000	1.0000	0.9998	0.9993	0.9989	0.9961	0.9886	0.9713	0.9368	0.8757	0.7795	0.7388	0.6448	0.4787	0.3018	0.1937	0.1465	0.0441	0.0042
11	1.0000	1.0000	1.0000	1.0000	1.0000	1.0000	1.0000	0.9999	0.9999	0.9994	0.9978	0.9935	0.9830	0.9602	0.9161	0.8947	0.8392	0.7189	0.5519	0.4205	0.3521	0.1584	0.0301
12	1.0000	1.0000	1.0000	1.0000	1.0000	1.0000	1.0000	1.0000	1.0000	0.9999	0.9997	0.9991	0.9971	0.9919	0.9795	0.9726	0.9525	0.8990	0.8021	0.7040	0.6433	0.4154	0.1530
13	1.0000	1.0000	1.0000	1.0000	1.0000	1.0000	1.0000	1.0000	1.0000	1.0000	1.0000	0.9999	0.9998	0.9992	0.9976	0.9966	0.9932	0.9822	0.9560	0.9221	0.8972	0.7712	0.5123
14	1.0000	1.0000	1.0000	1.0000	1.0000	1.0000	1.0000	1.0000	1.0000	1.0000	1.0000	1.0000	1.0000	1.0000	1.0000	1.0000	1.0000	1.0000	1.0000	1.0000	1.0000	1.0000	1.0000

n = 16

x \ p	0.05	0.1	0.15	1/6	0.2	0.25	0.3	1/3	0.35	0.4	0.45	0.5	0.55	0.6	0.65	2/3	0.7	0.75	0.8	5/6	0.85	0.9	0.95
0	0.4401	0.1853	0.0743	0.0541	0.0281	0.0100	0.0033	0.0015	0.0010	0.0003	0.0001	0.0000	0.0000	0.0000	0.0000	0.0000	0.0000	0.0000	0.0000	0.0000	0.0000	0.0000	0.0000
1	0.8108	0.5147	0.2839	0.2272	0.1407	0.0635	0.0261	0.0137	0.0098	0.0033	0.0010	0.0003	0.0001	0.0000	0.0000	0.0000	0.0000	0.0000	0.0000	0.0000	0.0000	0.0000	0.0000
2	0.9571	0.7892	0.5614	0.4868	0.3518	0.1971	0.0994	0.0594	0.0451	0.0183	0.0066	0.0021	0.0006	0.0001	0.0000	0.0001	0.0000	0.0000	0.0000	0.0000	0.0000	0.0000	0.0000
3	0.9930	0.9316	0.7899	0.7291	0.5981	0.4050	0.2459	0.1659	0.1339	0.0651	0.0281	0.0106	0.0035	0.0009	0.0002	0.0001	0.0000	0.0000	0.0000	0.0000	0.0000	0.0000	0.0000
4	0.9991	0.9830	0.9209	0.8866	0.7982	0.6302	0.4499	0.3391	0.2892	0.1666	0.0853	0.0384	0.0149	0.0049	0.0013	0.0008	0.0003	0.0000	0.0000	0.0000	0.0000	0.0000	0.0000
5	0.9999	0.9967	0.9765	0.9622	0.9183	0.8103	0.6598	0.5469	0.4900	0.3288	0.1976	0.1051	0.0486	0.0191	0.0062	0.0040	0.0016	0.0003	0.0000	0.0000	0.0000	0.0000	0.0000
6	1.0000	0.9995	0.9944	0.9899	0.9733	0.9204	0.8247	0.7374	0.6881	0.5272	0.3660	0.2272	0.1241	0.0583	0.0229	0.0159	0.0071	0.0016	0.0002	0.0000	0.0000	0.0000	0.0000
7	1.0000	0.9999	0.9989	0.9979	0.9930	0.9729	0.9256	0.8735	0.8406	0.7161	0.5629	0.4018	0.2559	0.1423	0.0671	0.0500	0.0257	0.0075	0.0015	0.0004	0.0002	0.0000	0.0000
8	1.0000	1.0000	0.9998	0.9996	0.9985	0.9925	0.9743	0.9500	0.9329	0.8577	0.7441	0.5982	0.4371	0.2839	0.1594	0.1265	0.0744	0.0271	0.0070	0.0021	0.0011	0.0001	0.0000
9	1.0000	1.0000	1.0000	1.0000	0.9998	0.9984	0.9929	0.9841	0.9771	0.9417	0.8759	0.7728	0.6340	0.4728	0.3119	0.2626	0.1753	0.0796	0.0267	0.0101	0.0056	0.0005	0.0000
10	1.0000	1.0000	1.0000	1.0000	1.0000	0.9997	0.9984	0.9960	0.9938	0.9809	0.9514	0.8949	0.8024	0.6712	0.5100	0.4531	0.3402	0.1897	0.0817	0.0378	0.0235	0.0033	0.0001
11	1.0000	1.0000	1.0000	1.0000	1.0000	1.0000	0.9997	0.9992	0.9987	0.9951	0.9851	0.9616	0.9147	0.8334	0.7108	0.6609	0.5501	0.3698	0.2018	0.1134	0.0791	0.0170	0.0009
12	1.0000	1.0000	1.0000	1.0000	1.0000	1.0000	1.0000	0.9999	0.9998	0.9991	0.9965	0.9894	0.9719	0.9349	0.8661	0.8341	0.7541	0.5950	0.4019	0.2709	0.2101	0.0684	0.0070
13	1.0000	1.0000	1.0000	1.0000	1.0000	1.0000	1.0000	1.0000	1.0000	0.9999	0.9994	0.9979	0.9934	0.9817	0.9549	0.9406	0.9006	0.8029	0.6482	0.5132	0.4386	0.2108	0.0429
14	1.0000	1.0000	1.0000	1.0000	1.0000	1.0000	1.0000	1.0000	1.0000	1.0000	0.9999	0.9997	0.9990	0.9967	0.9902	0.9863	0.9739	0.9365	0.8593	0.7728	0.7161	0.4853	0.1892
15	1.0000	1.0000	1.0000	1.0000	1.0000	1.0000	1.0000	1.0000	1.0000	1.0000	1.0000	1.0000	0.9999	0.9997	0.9990	0.9985	0.9967	0.9900	0.9719	0.9459	0.9257	0.8147	0.5599
16	1.0000	1.0000	1.0000	1.0000	1.0000	1.0000	1.0000	1.0000	1.0000	1.0000	1.0000	1.0000	1.0000	1.0000	1.0000	1.0000	1.0000	1.0000	1.0000	1.0000	1.0000	1.0000	1.0000

OCR S1 — STATISTICAL TABLES

Cumulative binomial probabilities (continued)

n = 18

x \ p	0.05	0.1	0.15	1/6	0.2	0.25	0.3	1/3	0.35	0.4	0.45	0.5	0.55	0.6	0.65	2/3	0.7	0.75	0.8	5/6	0.85	0.9	0.95
0	0.3972	0.1501	0.0536	0.0376	0.0180	0.0056	0.0016	0.0007	0.0004	0.0001	0.0000	0.0000	0.0000	0.0000	0.0000	0.0000	0.0000	0.0000	0.0000	0.0000	0.0000	0.0000	0.0000
1	0.7735	0.4503	0.2241	0.1728	0.0991	0.0395	0.0142	0.0068	0.0046	0.0013	0.0003	0.0001	0.0000	0.0000	0.0000	0.0000	0.0000	0.0000	0.0000	0.0000	0.0000	0.0000	0.0000
2	0.9419	0.7338	0.4797	0.4027	0.2713	0.1353	0.0600	0.0326	0.0236	0.0082	0.0025	0.0007	0.0001	0.0000	0.0000	0.0000	0.0000	0.0000	0.0000	0.0000	0.0000	0.0000	0.0000
3	0.9891	0.9018	0.7202	0.6479	0.5010	0.3057	0.1646	0.1017	0.0783	0.0328	0.0120	0.0038	0.0010	0.0002	0.0000	0.0000	0.0000	0.0000	0.0000	0.0000	0.0000	0.0000	0.0000
4	0.9985	0.9718	0.8794	0.8318	0.7164	0.5187	0.3327	0.2311	0.1886	0.0942	0.0411	0.0154	0.0049	0.0013	0.0003	0.0001	0.0000	0.0000	0.0000	0.0000	0.0000	0.0000	0.0000
5	0.9998	0.9936	0.9581	0.9347	0.8671	0.7175	0.5344	0.4122	0.3550	0.2088	0.1077	0.0481	0.0183	0.0058	0.0014	0.0009	0.0003	0.0000	0.0000	0.0000	0.0000	0.0000	0.0000
6	1.0000	0.9988	0.9882	0.9794	0.9487	0.8610	0.7217	0.6085	0.5491	0.3743	0.2258	0.1189	0.0537	0.0203	0.0062	0.0039	0.0014	0.0002	0.0000	0.0000	0.0000	0.0000	0.0000
7	1.0000	0.9998	0.9973	0.9947	0.9837	0.9431	0.8593	0.7767	0.7283	0.5634	0.3915	0.2403	0.1280	0.0576	0.0212	0.0144	0.0061	0.0012	0.0002	0.0000	0.0000	0.0000	0.0000
8	1.0000	1.0000	0.9995	0.9989	0.9957	0.9807	0.9404	0.8924	0.8609	0.7368	0.5778	0.4073	0.2527	0.1347	0.0597	0.0433	0.0210	0.0054	0.0009	0.0002	0.0001	0.0000	0.0000
9	1.0000	1.0000	0.9999	0.9998	0.9991	0.9946	0.9790	0.9567	0.9403	0.8653	0.7473	0.5927	0.4222	0.2632	0.1391	0.1076	0.0596	0.0193	0.0043	0.0011	0.0005	0.0000	0.0000
10	1.0000	1.0000	1.0000	1.0000	0.9998	0.9988	0.9939	0.9856	0.9788	0.9424	0.8720	0.7597	0.6085	0.4366	0.2717	0.2233	0.1407	0.0569	0.0163	0.0053	0.0027	0.0002	0.0000
11	1.0000	1.0000	1.0000	1.0000	1.0000	0.9998	0.9986	0.9961	0.9938	0.9797	0.9463	0.8811	0.7742	0.6257	0.4509	0.3915	0.2783	0.1390	0.0513	0.0206	0.0118	0.0012	0.0000
12	1.0000	1.0000	1.0000	1.0000	1.0000	1.0000	0.9997	0.9991	0.9986	0.9942	0.9817	0.9519	0.8923	0.7912	0.6450	0.5878	0.4656	0.2825	0.1329	0.0653	0.0419	0.0064	0.0002
13	1.0000	1.0000	1.0000	1.0000	1.0000	1.0000	1.0000	0.9999	0.9997	0.9987	0.9951	0.9846	0.9589	0.9058	0.8114	0.7689	0.6673	0.4813	0.2836	0.1682	0.1206	0.0282	0.0015
14	1.0000	1.0000	1.0000	1.0000	1.0000	1.0000	1.0000	1.0000	1.0000	0.9998	0.9990	0.9962	0.9880	0.9672	0.9217	0.8983	0.8354	0.6943	0.4990	0.3521	0.2798	0.0982	0.0109
15	1.0000	1.0000	1.0000	1.0000	1.0000	1.0000	1.0000	1.0000	1.0000	1.0000	0.9999	0.9993	0.9975	0.9918	0.9764	0.9674	0.9400	0.8647	0.7287	0.5973	0.5203	0.2662	0.0581
16	1.0000	1.0000	1.0000	1.0000	1.0000	1.0000	1.0000	1.0000	1.0000	1.0000	1.0000	0.9999	0.9997	0.9987	0.9954	0.9932	0.9858	0.9605	0.9009	0.8272	0.7759	0.5497	0.2265
17	1.0000	1.0000	1.0000	1.0000	1.0000	1.0000	1.0000	1.0000	1.0000	1.0000	1.0000	1.0000	1.0000	0.9999	0.9996	0.9993	0.9984	0.9944	0.9820	0.9624	0.9464	0.8499	0.6028
18	1.0000	1.0000	1.0000	1.0000	1.0000	1.0000	1.0000	1.0000	1.0000	1.0000	1.0000	1.0000	1.0000	1.0000	1.0000	1.0000	1.0000	1.0000	1.0000	1.0000	1.0000	1.0000	1.0000

n = 20

x \ p	0.05	0.1	0.15	1/6	0.2	0.25	0.3	1/3	0.35	0.4	0.45	0.5	0.55	0.6	0.65	2/3	0.7	0.75	0.8	5/6	0.85	0.9	0.95
0	0.3585	0.1216	0.0388	0.0261	0.0115	0.0032	0.0008	0.0003	0.0002	0.0000	0.0000	0.0000	0.0000	0.0000	0.0000	0.0000	0.0000	0.0000	0.0000	0.0000	0.0000	0.0000	0.0000
1	0.7358	0.3917	0.1756	0.1304	0.0692	0.0243	0.0076	0.0033	0.0021	0.0005	0.0001	0.0000	0.0000	0.0000	0.0000	0.0000	0.0000	0.0000	0.0000	0.0000	0.0000	0.0000	0.0000
2	0.9245	0.6769	0.4049	0.3287	0.2061	0.0913	0.0355	0.0176	0.0121	0.0036	0.0009	0.0002	0.0000	0.0000	0.0000	0.0000	0.0000	0.0000	0.0000	0.0000	0.0000	0.0000	0.0000
3	0.9841	0.8670	0.6477	0.5665	0.4114	0.2252	0.1071	0.0604	0.0444	0.0160	0.0049	0.0013	0.0003	0.0000	0.0000	0.0000	0.0000	0.0000	0.0000	0.0000	0.0000	0.0000	0.0000
4	0.9974	0.9568	0.8298	0.7687	0.6296	0.4148	0.2375	0.1515	0.1182	0.0510	0.0189	0.0059	0.0015	0.0003	0.0000	0.0000	0.0000	0.0000	0.0000	0.0000	0.0000	0.0000	0.0000
5	0.9997	0.9887	0.9327	0.8982	0.8042	0.6172	0.4164	0.2972	0.2454	0.1256	0.0553	0.0207	0.0064	0.0016	0.0003	0.0002	0.0000	0.0000	0.0000	0.0000	0.0000	0.0000	0.0000
6	1.0000	0.9976	0.9781	0.9629	0.9133	0.7858	0.6080	0.4793	0.4166	0.2500	0.1299	0.0577	0.0214	0.0065	0.0015	0.0009	0.0003	0.0000	0.0000	0.0000	0.0000	0.0000	0.0000
7	1.0000	0.9996	0.9941	0.9887	0.9679	0.8982	0.7723	0.6615	0.6010	0.4159	0.2520	0.1316	0.0580	0.0210	0.0060	0.0037	0.0013	0.0002	0.0000	0.0000	0.0000	0.0000	0.0000
8	1.0000	0.9999	0.9987	0.9972	0.9900	0.9591	0.8867	0.8095	0.7624	0.5956	0.4143	0.2517	0.1308	0.0565	0.0196	0.0130	0.0051	0.0009	0.0001	0.0000	0.0000	0.0000	0.0000
9	1.0000	1.0000	0.9998	0.9994	0.9974	0.9861	0.9520	0.9081	0.8782	0.7553	0.5914	0.4119	0.2493	0.1275	0.0532	0.0376	0.0171	0.0039	0.0006	0.0001	0.0000	0.0000	0.0000
10	1.0000	1.0000	1.0000	0.9999	0.9994	0.9961	0.9829	0.9624	0.9468	0.8725	0.7507	0.5881	0.4086	0.2447	0.1218	0.0919	0.0480	0.0139	0.0026	0.0006	0.0002	0.0000	0.0000
11	1.0000	1.0000	1.0000	1.0000	0.9999	0.9991	0.9949	0.9870	0.9804	0.9435	0.8692	0.7483	0.5857	0.4044	0.2376	0.1905	0.1133	0.0409	0.0100	0.0028	0.0013	0.0001	0.0000
12	1.0000	1.0000	1.0000	1.0000	1.0000	0.9998	0.9987	0.9963	0.9940	0.9790	0.9420	0.8684	0.7480	0.5841	0.3990	0.3385	0.2277	0.1018	0.0321	0.0113	0.0059	0.0004	0.0000
13	1.0000	1.0000	1.0000	1.0000	1.0000	1.0000	0.9997	0.9991	0.9985	0.9935	0.9786	0.9423	0.8701	0.7500	0.5834	0.5207	0.3920	0.2142	0.0867	0.0371	0.0219	0.0024	0.0000
14	1.0000	1.0000	1.0000	1.0000	1.0000	1.0000	1.0000	0.9998	0.9997	0.9984	0.9936	0.9793	0.9447	0.8744	0.7546	0.7028	0.5836	0.3828	0.1958	0.1018	0.0673	0.0113	0.0003
15	1.0000	1.0000	1.0000	1.0000	1.0000	1.0000	1.0000	1.0000	1.0000	0.9997	0.9985	0.9941	0.9811	0.9490	0.8818	0.8485	0.7625	0.5852	0.3704	0.2313	0.1702	0.0432	0.0026
16	1.0000	1.0000	1.0000	1.0000	1.0000	1.0000	1.0000	1.0000	1.0000	1.0000	0.9997	0.9987	0.9951	0.9840	0.9556	0.9396	0.8929	0.7748	0.5886	0.4335	0.3523	0.1330	0.0159
17	1.0000	1.0000	1.0000	1.0000	1.0000	1.0000	1.0000	1.0000	1.0000	1.0000	1.0000	0.9998	0.9991	0.9964	0.9879	0.9824	0.9645	0.9087	0.7939	0.6713	0.5951	0.3231	0.0755
18	1.0000	1.0000	1.0000	1.0000	1.0000	1.0000	1.0000	1.0000	1.0000	1.0000	1.0000	1.0000	0.9999	0.9995	0.9979	0.9967	0.9924	0.9757	0.9308	0.8696	0.8244	0.6083	0.2642
19	1.0000	1.0000	1.0000	1.0000	1.0000	1.0000	1.0000	1.0000	1.0000	1.0000	1.0000	1.0000	1.0000	1.0000	0.9998	0.9997	0.9992	0.9968	0.9885	0.9739	0.9612	0.8784	0.6415
20	1.0000	1.0000	1.0000	1.0000	1.0000	1.0000	1.0000	1.0000	1.0000	1.0000	1.0000	1.0000	1.0000	1.0000	1.0000	1.0000	1.0000	1.0000	1.0000	1.0000	1.0000	1.0000	1.0000

Cumulative binomial probabilities (continued)

n = 25 x \ p	0.05	0.1	0.15	1/6	0.2	0.25	0.3	1/3	0.35	0.4	0.45	0.5	0.55	0.6	0.65	2/3	0.7	0.75	0.8	5/6	0.85	0.9	0.95
0	0.2774	0.0718	0.0172	0.0105	0.0038	0.0008	0.0001	0.0000	0.0000	0.0000	0.0000	0.0000	0.0000	0.0000	0.0000	0.0000	0.0000	0.0000	0.0000	0.0000	0.0000	0.0000	0.0000
1	0.6424	0.2712	0.0931	0.0629	0.0274	0.0070	0.0016	0.0005	0.0003	0.0001	0.0000	0.0000	0.0000	0.0000	0.0000	0.0000	0.0000	0.0000	0.0000	0.0000	0.0000	0.0000	0.0000
2	0.8729	0.5371	0.2537	0.1887	0.0982	0.0321	0.0090	0.0035	0.0021	0.0004	0.0001	0.0000	0.0000	0.0000	0.0000	0.0000	0.0000	0.0000	0.0000	0.0000	0.0000	0.0000	0.0000
3	0.9659	0.7636	0.4711	0.3816	0.2340	0.0962	0.0332	0.0149	0.0097	0.0024	0.0005	0.0001	0.0001	0.0000	0.0000	0.0000	0.0000	0.0000	0.0000	0.0000	0.0000	0.0000	0.0000
4	0.9928	0.9020	0.6821	0.5937	0.4207	0.2137	0.0905	0.0462	0.0320	0.0095	0.0023	0.0005	0.0004	0.0001	0.0000	0.0000	0.0000	0.0000	0.0000	0.0000	0.0000	0.0000	0.0000
5	0.9988	0.9666	0.8385	0.7720	0.6167	0.3783	0.1935	0.1120	0.0826	0.0294	0.0086	0.0020	0.0016	0.0003	0.0000	0.0000	0.0000	0.0000	0.0000	0.0000	0.0000	0.0000	0.0000
6	0.9998	0.9905	0.9305	0.8908	0.7800	0.5611	0.3407	0.2215	0.1734	0.0736	0.0258	0.0073	0.0058	0.0012	0.0002	0.0001	0.0000	0.0000	0.0000	0.0000	0.0000	0.0000	0.0000
7	1.0000	0.9977	0.9745	0.9553	0.8909	0.7265	0.5118	0.3703	0.3061	0.1536	0.0639	0.0216	0.0174	0.0043	0.0008	0.0004	0.0001	0.0000	0.0000	0.0000	0.0000	0.0000	0.0000
8	1.0000	0.9995	0.9920	0.9843	0.9532	0.8506	0.6769	0.5376	0.4668	0.2735	0.1340	0.0539	0.0440	0.0132	0.0029	0.0016	0.0005	0.0000	0.0000	0.0000	0.0000	0.0000	0.0000
9	1.0000	0.9999	0.9979	0.9953	0.9827	0.9287	0.8106	0.6956	0.6303	0.4246	0.2424	0.1148	0.0960	0.0344	0.0093	0.0056	0.0018	0.0002	0.0000	0.0000	0.0000	0.0000	0.0000
10	1.0000	1.0000	0.9995	0.9988	0.9944	0.9703	0.9022	0.8220	0.7712	0.5858	0.3843	0.2122	0.1827	0.0778	0.0255	0.0164	0.0060	0.0009	0.0001	0.0000	0.0000	0.0000	0.0000
11	1.0000	1.0000	0.9999	0.9997	0.9985	0.9893	0.9558	0.9082	0.8746	0.7323	0.5426	0.3450	0.3063	0.1538	0.0604	0.0415	0.0175	0.0034	0.0001	0.0000	0.0000	0.0000	0.0000
12	1.0000	1.0000	1.0000	0.9999	0.9996	0.9966	0.9825	0.9585	0.9396	0.8462	0.6937	0.5000	0.4574	0.2677	0.1254	0.0918	0.0442	0.0107	0.0004	0.0001	0.0000	0.0000	0.0000
13	1.0000	1.0000	1.0000	1.0000	0.9999	0.9991	0.9940	0.9836	0.9745	0.9222	0.8173	0.6550	0.6157	0.4142	0.2288	0.1780	0.0978	0.0297	0.0015	0.0003	0.0001	0.0000	0.0000
14	1.0000	1.0000	1.0000	1.0000	1.0000	0.9998	0.9982	0.9944	0.9907	0.9656	0.9040	0.7878	0.7576	0.5754	0.3697	0.3044	0.1894	0.0713	0.0056	0.0012	0.0005	0.0000	0.0000
15	1.0000	1.0000	1.0000	1.0000	1.0000	1.0000	0.9995	0.9984	0.9971	0.9868	0.9560	0.8852	0.8660	0.7265	0.5332	0.4624	0.3231	0.1494	0.0173	0.0047	0.0021	0.0001	0.0000
16	1.0000	1.0000	1.0000	1.0000	1.0000	1.0000	0.9999	0.9996	0.9992	0.9957	0.9826	0.9461	0.9361	0.8464	0.6939	0.6297	0.4882	0.2735	0.0468	0.0157	0.0080	0.0005	0.0000
17	1.0000	1.0000	1.0000	1.0000	1.0000	1.0000	1.0000	0.9999	0.9998	0.9988	0.9942	0.9784	0.9742	0.9264	0.8266	0.7785	0.6593	0.4389	0.1091	0.0447	0.0255	0.0023	0.0000
18	1.0000	1.0000	1.0000	1.0000	1.0000	1.0000	1.0000	1.0000	1.0000	0.9997	0.9984	0.9927	0.9914	0.9706	0.9174	0.8880	0.8065	0.6217	0.2200	0.1092	0.0695	0.0095	0.0002
19	1.0000	1.0000	1.0000	1.0000	1.0000	1.0000	1.0000	1.0000	1.0000	0.9999	0.9996	0.9980	0.9977	0.9905	0.9680	0.9538	0.9095	0.7863	0.3833	0.2280	0.1615	0.0334	0.0012
20	1.0000	1.0000	1.0000	1.0000	1.0000	1.0000	1.0000	1.0000	1.0000	1.0000	0.9999	0.9995	0.9995	0.9976	0.9903	0.9851	0.9668	0.9038	0.5793	0.4063	0.3179	0.0980	0.0072
21	1.0000	1.0000	1.0000	1.0000	1.0000	1.0000	1.0000	1.0000	1.0000	1.0000	1.0000	0.9999	0.9999	0.9996	0.9979	0.9965	0.9910	0.9679	0.7660	0.6184	0.5289	0.2364	0.0341
22	1.0000	1.0000	1.0000	1.0000	1.0000	1.0000	1.0000	1.0000	1.0000	1.0000	1.0000	1.0000	1.0000	0.9999	0.9997	0.9995	0.9984	0.9930	0.9018	0.8113	0.7463	0.4629	0.1271
23	1.0000	1.0000	1.0000	1.0000	1.0000	1.0000	1.0000	1.0000	1.0000	1.0000	1.0000	1.0000	1.0000	1.0000	1.0000	1.0000	0.9999	0.9992	0.9726	0.9371	0.9069	0.7288	0.3576
24	1.0000	1.0000	1.0000	1.0000	1.0000	1.0000	1.0000	1.0000	1.0000	1.0000	1.0000	1.0000	1.0000	1.0000	1.0000	1.0000	1.0000	1.0000	0.9962	0.9895	0.9828	0.9282	0.7226
25	1.0000	1.0000	1.0000	1.0000	1.0000	1.0000	1.0000	1.0000	1.0000	1.0000	1.0000	1.0000	1.0000	1.0000	1.0000	1.0000	1.0000	1.0000	1.0000	1.0000	1.0000	1.0000	1.0000

OCR S1 — STATISTICAL TABLES

Cumulative binomial probabilities (continued)

n = 30

x \ p	0.05	0.1	0.15	1/6	0.2	0.25	0.3	1/3	0.35	0.4	0.45	0.5	0.55	0.6	0.65	2/3	0.7	0.75	0.8	5/6	0.85	0.9	0.95
0	0.2146	0.0424	0.0076	0.0042	0.0012	0.0002	0.0000	0.0000	0.0000	0.0000	0.0000	0.0000	0.0000	0.0000	0.0000	0.0000	0.0000	0.0000	0.0000	0.0000	0.0000	0.0000	0.0000
1	0.5535	0.1837	0.0480	0.0295	0.0105	0.0020	0.0003	0.0001	0.0000	0.0000	0.0000	0.0000	0.0000	0.0000	0.0000	0.0000	0.0000	0.0000	0.0000	0.0000	0.0000	0.0000	0.0000
2	0.8122	0.4114	0.1514	0.1028	0.0442	0.0106	0.0021	0.0007	0.0003	0.0000	0.0000	0.0000	0.0000	0.0000	0.0000	0.0000	0.0000	0.0000	0.0000	0.0000	0.0000	0.0000	0.0000
3	0.9392	0.6474	0.3217	0.2396	0.1227	0.0374	0.0093	0.0033	0.0019	0.0003	0.0000	0.0000	0.0000	0.0000	0.0000	0.0000	0.0000	0.0000	0.0000	0.0000	0.0000	0.0000	0.0000
4	0.9844	0.8245	0.5245	0.4243	0.2552	0.0979	0.0302	0.0122	0.0075	0.0015	0.0002	0.0000	0.0000	0.0000	0.0000	0.0000	0.0000	0.0000	0.0000	0.0000	0.0000	0.0000	0.0000
5	0.9967	0.9268	0.7106	0.6164	0.4275	0.2026	0.0766	0.0355	0.0233	0.0057	0.0011	0.0002	0.0000	0.0000	0.0000	0.0000	0.0000	0.0000	0.0000	0.0000	0.0000	0.0000	0.0000
6	0.9994	0.9742	0.8474	0.7765	0.6070	0.3481	0.1595	0.0838	0.0586	0.0172	0.0040	0.0007	0.0001	0.0000	0.0000	0.0000	0.0000	0.0000	0.0000	0.0000	0.0000	0.0000	0.0000
7	0.9999	0.9922	0.9302	0.8863	0.7608	0.5143	0.2814	0.1668	0.1238	0.0435	0.0121	0.0026	0.0004	0.0000	0.0000	0.0000	0.0000	0.0000	0.0000	0.0000	0.0000	0.0000	0.0000
8	1.0000	0.9980	0.9722	0.9494	0.8713	0.6736	0.4315	0.2860	0.2247	0.0940	0.0312	0.0081	0.0016	0.0002	0.0000	0.0000	0.0000	0.0000	0.0000	0.0000	0.0000	0.0000	0.0000
9	1.0000	0.9995	0.9903	0.9803	0.9389	0.8034	0.5888	0.4317	0.3575	0.1763	0.0694	0.0214	0.0050	0.0009	0.0001	0.0000	0.0000	0.0000	0.0000	0.0000	0.0000	0.0000	0.0000
10	1.0000	0.9999	0.9971	0.9933	0.9744	0.8943	0.7304	0.5848	0.5078	0.2915	0.1350	0.0494	0.0138	0.0029	0.0004	0.0002	0.0002	0.0000	0.0000	0.0000	0.0000	0.0000	0.0000
11	1.0000	1.0000	0.9992	0.9980	0.9905	0.9493	0.8407	0.7239	0.6548	0.4311	0.2327	0.1002	0.0334	0.0083	0.0014	0.0007	0.0006	0.0000	0.0000	0.0000	0.0000	0.0000	0.0000
12	1.0000	1.0000	0.9998	0.9995	0.9969	0.9784	0.9155	0.8340	0.7802	0.5785	0.3592	0.1808	0.0714	0.0212	0.0045	0.0025	0.0021	0.0001	0.0000	0.0000	0.0000	0.0000	0.0000
13	1.0000	1.0000	1.0000	0.9999	0.9991	0.9918	0.9599	0.9102	0.8737	0.7145	0.5025	0.2923	0.1356	0.0481	0.0124	0.0072	0.0064	0.0002	0.0000	0.0000	0.0000	0.0000	0.0000
14	1.0000	1.0000	1.0000	1.0000	0.9998	0.9973	0.9831	0.9565	0.9348	0.8246	0.6448	0.4278	0.2309	0.0971	0.0301	0.0188	0.0169	0.0008	0.0001	0.0000	0.0000	0.0000	0.0000
15	1.0000	1.0000	1.0000	1.0000	0.9999	0.9992	0.9936	0.9812	0.9699	0.9029	0.7691	0.5722	0.3552	0.1754	0.0652	0.0435	0.0401	0.0027	0.0002	0.0000	0.0000	0.0000	0.0000
16	1.0000	1.0000	1.0000	1.0000	1.0000	0.9998	0.9979	0.9928	0.9876	0.9519	0.8644	0.7077	0.4975	0.2855	0.1263	0.0898	0.0845	0.0082	0.0009	0.0001	0.0000	0.0000	0.0000
17	1.0000	1.0000	1.0000	1.0000	1.0000	0.9999	0.9994	0.9975	0.9955	0.9788	0.9286	0.8192	0.6408	0.4215	0.2198	0.1660	0.1593	0.0216	0.0031	0.0005	0.0002	0.0000	0.0000
18	1.0000	1.0000	1.0000	1.0000	1.0000	1.0000	0.9998	0.9993	0.9986	0.9917	0.9666	0.8998	0.7673	0.5689	0.3452	0.2761	0.2696	0.0507	0.0095	0.0020	0.0008	0.0000	0.0000
19	1.0000	1.0000	1.0000	1.0000	1.0000	1.0000	1.0000	0.9998	0.9996	0.9971	0.9862	0.9506	0.8650	0.7085	0.4922	0.4152	0.4112	0.1057	0.0256	0.0067	0.0029	0.0001	0.0000
20	1.0000	1.0000	1.0000	1.0000	1.0000	1.0000	1.0000	1.0000	0.9999	0.9991	0.9950	0.9786	0.9306	0.8237	0.6425	0.5683	0.5685	0.1966	0.0611	0.0197	0.0097	0.0005	0.0000
21	1.0000	1.0000	1.0000	1.0000	1.0000	1.0000	1.0000	1.0000	1.0000	0.9998	0.9984	0.9919	0.9688	0.9060	0.7753	0.7140	0.7186	0.3264	0.1287	0.0506	0.0278	0.0020	0.0000
22	1.0000	1.0000	1.0000	1.0000	1.0000	1.0000	1.0000	1.0000	1.0000	1.0000	0.9996	0.9974	0.9879	0.9565	0.8762	0.8332	0.8405	0.4857	0.2392	0.1137	0.0698	0.0078	0.0001
23	1.0000	1.0000	1.0000	1.0000	1.0000	1.0000	1.0000	1.0000	1.0000	1.0000	0.9999	0.9993	0.9960	0.9828	0.9414	0.9162	0.9234	0.6519	0.3930	0.2235	0.1526	0.0258	0.0006
24	1.0000	1.0000	1.0000	1.0000	1.0000	1.0000	1.0000	1.0000	1.0000	1.0000	1.0000	0.9998	0.9989	0.9943	0.9767	0.9645	0.9698	0.7974	0.5725	0.3836	0.2894	0.0732	0.0033
25	1.0000	1.0000	1.0000	1.0000	1.0000	1.0000	1.0000	1.0000	1.0000	1.0000	1.0000	1.0000	0.9998	0.9985	0.9925	0.9878	0.9907	0.9021	0.7448	0.5757	0.4755	0.1755	0.0156
26	1.0000	1.0000	1.0000	1.0000	1.0000	1.0000	1.0000	1.0000	1.0000	1.0000	1.0000	1.0000	1.0000	0.9997	0.9981	0.9967	0.9979	0.9626	0.8773	0.7604	0.6783	0.3526	0.0608
27	1.0000	1.0000	1.0000	1.0000	1.0000	1.0000	1.0000	1.0000	1.0000	1.0000	1.0000	1.0000	1.0000	1.0000	0.9997	0.9993	0.9997	0.9894	0.9558	0.8972	0.8486	0.5886	0.1878
28	1.0000	1.0000	1.0000	1.0000	1.0000	1.0000	1.0000	1.0000	1.0000	1.0000	1.0000	1.0000	1.0000	1.0000	1.0000	0.9999	1.0000	0.9980	0.9895	0.9705	0.9520	0.8163	0.4465
29	1.0000	1.0000	1.0000	1.0000	1.0000	1.0000	1.0000	1.0000	1.0000	1.0000	1.0000	1.0000	1.0000	1.0000	1.0000	1.0000	1.0000	0.9998	0.9988	0.9958	0.9924	0.9576	0.7854
30	1.0000	1.0000	1.0000	1.0000	1.0000	1.0000	1.0000	1.0000	1.0000	1.0000	1.0000	1.0000	1.0000	1.0000	1.0000	1.0000	1.0000	1.0000	1.0000	1.0000	1.0000	1.0000	1.0000

Vectors

'Vector' might sound like a really dull Bond villain, but... well, it's not. Vectors have both size (or <u>magnitude</u>) and <u>direction</u>. If a measurement just has size but not direction, it's called a <u>scalar</u>.

Vectors *have* **Magnitude** *and* **Direction** — **Scalars** *only have* **Magnitude**

<u>Vectors</u>: velocity, displacement, acceleration, force. E.g. a train heading due east at 16 ms^{-1}.

<u>Scalars</u>: speed, distance. E.g. a car travelling at 4 ms^{-1}.

A really important thing to remember is that an object's speed and velocity <u>aren't always the same</u>:

> **EXAMPLE**   A runner sprints 100 m along a track at a speed of 8 ms^{-1} and then she jogs back 50 m at 4 ms^{-1}.

<u>Average Speed</u>

Speed = Distance ÷ Time

The runner takes (100 ÷ 8) + (50 ÷ 4) = 25 s to travel **150 m**.

So the average speed is 150 ÷ 25 = 6 ms^{-1}

<u>Average Velocity</u>

Velocity = Change in displacement ÷ Time

In total, the runner ends up **50 m** away from her start point and it takes 25 s.

So the average velocity is 50 ÷ 25 = 2 ms^{-1} in the direction of the sprint.

She jogged back 50 m after she jogged forward 100 m.

The **Length** *of the* **Arrow** *shows the* **Magnitude** *of a Vector*

You can draw vectors as arrows where the <u>length</u> shows the <u>magnitude</u>:

① A vector acting due east with magnitude 16

② A vector acting due west with magnitude 8

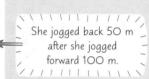

The arrow is half the size since the vector has half the magnitude.

You can add vectors together by drawing the arrows <u>nose to tail</u>.
The single vector that goes from the start to the end of the vectors is called the <u>resultant</u> vector.

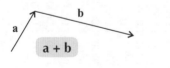

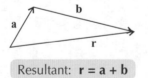

Resultant: **r = a + b**

a + b = b + a

> You can also <u>multiply</u> a vector by a <u>scalar</u> (just a number): the <u>length changes</u> but the <u>direction stays the same</u>.

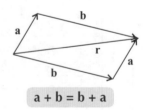

So Vector, you expect me to talk?...

...No Mr Bond, I expect you to die — Ak ak ak!
Oh, what fun we have. Anyway, you need to make sure you take the time to get your head around this page before you move on — vectors are well important and pop up all the way through M1. If you do think you're ready, then let's crack on...

Vectors

Resolving means writing a vector as Component Vectors

1) Splitting a vector up into different <u>components</u> means you can work things out <u>one component at a time</u>.

2) When <u>adding</u> vectors to get a <u>resultant vector</u>, it's easier to <u>add</u> the <u>horizontal</u> and <u>vertical</u> components <u>separately</u>.

3) You <u>split</u> the vector into components first — this is <u>resolving</u>, and it's <u>well useful</u>.

4) You can use <u>trig</u> and <u>Pythagoras</u> to change a vector into <u>component form</u>.

EXAMPLE

a) The vector **a** has magnitude a and acts at an angle of 30° to the horizontal. Find the horizontal and vertical components of **a**.

First, draw a diagram and make a right-angle triangle:

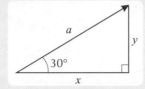

Using trigonometry, we can find x and y:

$\cos 30° = \frac{x}{a}$ so $x = a\cos 30°$

$\sin 30° = \frac{y}{a}$ so $y = a\sin 30°$

---

b) Two vectors act at the point O. One vector has magnitude 5 and acts in the direction of the positive x-axis. The other has magnitude 4 and acts in the direction of the positive y-axis. The resultant vector **a** has magnitude a and makes an angle of $\alpha°$ with the horizontal. Find a and α.

Use Pythagoras to work out a:

$a^2 = 5^2 + 4^2 = 41$

so $a = \sqrt{41} = 6.40$ (3 s.f.)

And trigonometry to work out α:

$\tan \alpha = \frac{4}{5}$ so $\alpha = \tan^{-1}\left(\frac{4}{5}\right) = 38.7°$ (3 s.f.)

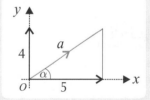

Simple eh?

EXAMPLE

Three vectors **A**, **B** and **C** have magnitudes 100, 75 and 125 and act at bearings of 025°, 140° and 215° respectively from a point O. Find the magnitude and direction of the resultant vector, **r**.

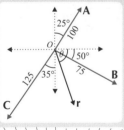

Resolve <u>Horizontally</u>, taking 'right' as positive:

$100\sin 25° + 75\cos 50° - 125\sin 35° = 18.77$ (4 s.f.)

Resolve <u>Vertically</u>, taking 'up' as positive:

$100\cos 25° - 75\sin 50° - 125\cos 35° = -69.22$ (4 s.f.)

> Resolving and adding components like this gives you the components of the resultant vector.

Using Pythagoras, magnitude of **r** $= \sqrt{18.77^2 + (-69.22)^2} = 71.7$ (3 s.f.)

Direction $\theta = \tan^{-1}\left(\frac{69.22}{18.77}\right) = 74.8°$ (3 s.f.) $\Rightarrow$ Bearing is $90° + 74.8° = 164.8°$

So **r** has magnitude 71.7 (3 s.f.) and acts at a bearing of 165° (3 s.f.)

> Remember that bearings are always measured <u>clockwise</u> starting from <u>north</u>.

You can Resolve in any two Perpendicular Directions — not just x and y

EXAMPLE

The magnitudes and directions of four vectors are shown below. Find the magnitude and direction of the resultant vector.

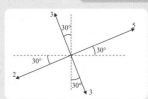

Resolving in ⟍ direction: $3 - 3 = 0$

Resolving in ⟋ direction: $5 - 2 = 3$

> The two vectors of magnitude 3 are acting in opposite directions, so you take one away from the other — balancing them out.

So the resultant vector has magnitude 3 and acts in the direction of the vector with magnitude 5.

Forces and Modelling

Vector questions talk about forces all the time in M1, so you need to understand what each type of force is.
Then you can use that information to create a model to work from.

Hint: 'modelling' in maths doesn't have anything to do with plastic aeroplane kits... or catwalks.

Types *of forces*

WEIGHT (*W*)

Due to the particle's mass, <u>m</u> and the force of gravity, g: $W = mg$ — weight always acts <u>downwards</u>.

$W = mg$

THE NORMAL REACTION (*R* OR *N*)

The reaction from a surface. Reaction is always at <u>90° to the surface</u>.

R
W

TENSION (*T*)

Force in a taut rope, wire or string.

T
w

FRICTION (*F*)

Due to the <u>roughness</u> between a body and a surface. Always acts <u>against</u> motion, or likely motion.

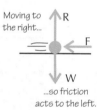

Moving to the right...
R
F
W
...so friction acts to the left.

THRUST

<u>Force in a rod</u> (e.g. the pole of an open umbrella).

Talk *the Talk*

Maths questions in M1 use a lot of words that you already know, but here they're used
to mean something very <u>precise</u>. Learn these definitions so you don't get caught out:

<u>Particle</u>	the body is a point so its dimensions don't matter	<u>Rigid</u>	the body does not bend
<u>Light</u>	the body has no mass	<u>Thin</u>	the body has no thickness
<u>Static</u>	not moving	<u>Equilibrium</u>	nothing's moving
<u>Rough</u>	the surface will oppose motion with friction / drag	<u>Plane</u>	a flat surface
<u>Beam or Rod</u>	a long, straight body (e.g. a broom handle)	<u>Inextensible</u>	the body can't be stretched
<u>Uniform</u>	the mass is evenly spread out throughout the body	<u>Smooth</u>	the surface doesn't have friction / drag opposing motion
<u>Non-uniform</u>	the mass is unevenly spread out		

Mathematical Modelling

You'll have to make lots of assumptions in M1. Doing this is called
'<u>modelling</u>', and you do it to make a sticky real-life situation <u>simpler</u>.

EXAMPLE   **The ice hockey player**

You might have to assume:

- no friction between the skates and the ice
- no drag (air resistance)
- the skater generates a constant forward force S
- the skater is very small (a point mass)
- there is only one point of contact with the ice
- the weight acts downwards

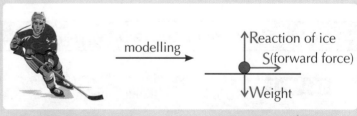

modelling →

Reaction of ice
S(forward force)
Weight

Tom Horton —
coffee shop owner

Tom as a **point
mass** with forces

The simplified model you end up with can then be used as your vector diagram.

Forces and Modelling

Modelling is a Cycle

Having created a model you can later <u>improve</u> it by making more (or fewer) <u>assumptions</u>.
Solve the problem using the initial assumptions, <u>compare</u> it to real life, <u>evaluate</u> the model and then
use that information to <u>change</u> the assumptions. Then keep going until you're <u>satisfied</u> with the model.

Always start by drawing a Simple Diagram of the Model

Here are a couple of old chestnuts that often turn up in M1 exams in one form or another.

EXAMPLE

The book on a table

A book is put flat on a table. One end of the table is slowly lifted and the angle to the horizontal is measured when the book starts to slide. What assumptions might you make?

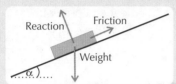

<u>Assumptions:</u>
The book is <u>rigid</u>, so it doesn't bend or open.
The book is a <u>particle</u>, so its dimensions don't matter.
There's <u>no</u> wind or other <u>external forces</u> involved.

EXAMPLE

The pulley

Two particles are connected by a string that passes over a fixed peg. The particles are released from rest. Draw a model of the forces. What assumptions have you made?

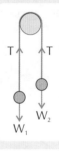

<u>Assumptions:</u>
The peg is <u>smooth</u>, so there's no friction.
The string is <u>light</u>, so its mass can be ignored.
The string is <u>inextensible</u>, so it doesn't stretch.
The tension in the string is <u>the same</u> either side of the pulley.

EXAMPLE

The sledge

A sledge is being steadily pulled by a small child on horizontal snow. Draw a force diagram for a model of the sledge. List your assumptions.

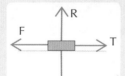

> It's quicker and easier to use just the first letter of the force in your diagram, e.g. *F* = friction.

<u>Assumptions:</u>
Friction is <u>too big</u> to be ignored (i.e. it's not ice).
The string is <u>horizontal</u> (it's a small child).
The sledge is a <u>small particle</u> (so its size doesn't matter).

EXAMPLE

The mass on a string

A ball is held by two strings, A and B, at angles α and β to the vertical. Draw a diagram to model this scenario. State your assumptions.

<u>Assumptions:</u>
The ball is modelled as a <u>particle</u> (its dimensions don't matter).
The strings are <u>light</u> (their mass can be ignored).
The strings are <u>inextensible</u> (they can't stretch).

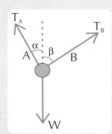

I used to be a model when I was younger, but then I fell apart...

Make sure you're completely familiar with the different forces and all the jargon that gets bandied about in mechanics.
Keep your models as simple as possible — that will make answering the questions as simple as possible too.

Forces are Vectors

Forces have direction and magnitude, which makes them vectors — this means that all the stuff you learnt about vectors you'll need here. To help you out, we've given you some more vector examples all about forces...

Forces have **Components**

You've done a fair amount of <u>trigonometry</u> already, so this should be as straightforward as watching dry paint.

EXAMPLE A particle is acted on by a force of 15 N at 30° above the horizontal. Find the <u>horizontal</u> and <u>vertical components</u> of the force.

A bit of trigonometry is all that's required:

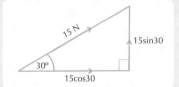

Horizontal component:
$15 \cos 30° = 12.990... = 13.0$ N (3 s.f.)

Vertical component:
$15 \sin 30° = 7.5$ N

Add Forces **Nose to Tail** to get the **Resultant**

The important bit when you're drawing a diagram to find the resultant is to make sure the <u>arrows</u> are the <u>right way round</u>. Repeat after me: nose to tail, nose to tail, nose to tail.

EXAMPLE A second horizontal force of 20 N to the right is also applied to the particle in the example above. Find the resultant of these forces.

You need to put the arrows nose to tail:

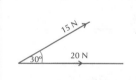 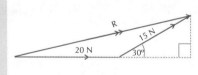 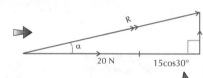

The 15 N force has been split into horizontal and vertical components.

Using Pythagoras and trigonometry:

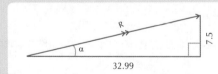

$R = \sqrt{32.99^2 + 7.5^2} = 33.8$ N (3 s.f.)

$\alpha = \tan^{-1}\left(\dfrac{7.5}{32.99}\right) = 12.8°$ (3 s.f.) above the horizontal.

EXAMPLE Find the magnitude and direction of the resultant of the forces shown acting on the particle.

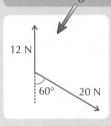 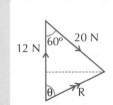 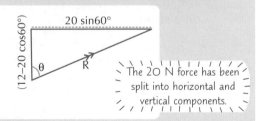

The 20 N force has been split into horizontal and vertical components.

Hint: you could also use the cosine rule here to get R.

$R = \sqrt{(12 - 20\cos 60°)^2 + (20\sin 60°)^2} = 17.4$ N (3 s.f.)

$\theta = \tan^{-1}\left(\dfrac{20\sin 60°}{12 - 20\cos 60°}\right) = 83.4°$ (3 s.f.) to the vertical.

If a particle is released it will move in the direction of the resultant.

Forces are Vectors

Resolving *more than Two Forces*

A question could involve <u>more than two forces</u>. You still work it out the <u>same</u> though — <u>resolve, resolve, resolve</u>...

EXAMPLE
Three forces of magnitudes 9 N, 12 N and 13 N act on a particle *P* in the directions shown in the diagram.
Find the magnitude and direction of the resultant of the three forces.

One of the forces is already aligned with the *y*-axis, so it makes sense to start by resolving the other forces relative to this.

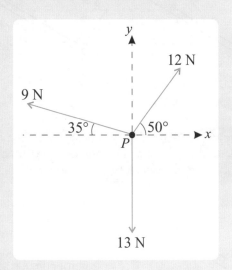

Along the *y*-axis:
Sum of components = $9\sin 35° + 12\sin 50° - 13$
= **1.355 N** (4 s.f.)

Along the *x*-axis:
Sum of components = $12\cos 50° - 9\cos 35°$
= **0.3411 N** (4 s.f.)

Magnitude of resultant = $\sqrt{1.355^2 + 0.3411^2}$
= **1.40 N** (3 s.f.)

Direction of resultant:
$\theta = \tan^{-1}\dfrac{1.355}{0.3411} = 75.9°$ above the positive *x*-axis.

Particles in *Equilibrium Don't Move*

Forces acting on a particle in <u>equilibrium</u> add up to zero force. That means when you draw all the arrows nose to tail, you finish up where you started. That's why diagrams showing equilibrium are called '<u>triangles of forces</u>'.

EXAMPLE
Two perpendicular forces of magnitude 20 N act on a particle. A third force, P, acts at 45° to the horizontal, as shown. Given that the particle is in equilibrium, find the magnitude of P.

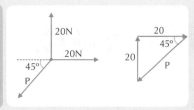

$P\cos 45° = 20$

$P = 28.3\,\text{N}$ (3 s.f.)

EXAMPLE
A force of 50 N acts on a particle at an angle of 20° to the vertical, as shown. Find the magnitude of the two other forces, T and S, if the particle is in equilibrium.

$S = 50\sin 70° = 47.0\,\text{N}$ (3 s.f.)
$T = 50\cos 70° = 17.1\,\text{N}$ (3 s.f.)

EXAMPLE
Three forces act upon a particle. A force of magnitude 85 N acts horizontally, the force Q acts vertically, and the force P acts at 55° to the horizontal, as shown. The particle is in equilibrium. Find the magnitude of P and Q.

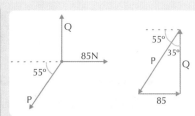

$\sin 35° = \dfrac{85}{P}$ so $P = 148\,\text{N}$ (3 s.f.)

$\tan 35° = \dfrac{85}{Q}$ so $Q = 121\,\text{N}$ (3 s.f.)

Forces are Vectors

*An **Inclined Plane** is a **Sloping Surface***

EXAMPLE A particle of mass 0.1 kg is held at rest on a rough plane inclined at 20° to the horizontal by a friction force acting up the plane. Find the magnitude of this friction force and the normal reaction. ($g = 9.8$ ms^{-2}.)

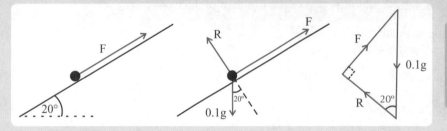

$F = 0.1g\sin 20°$
$= 0.335$ N (3 s.f.)

$R = 0.1g\cos 20°$
$= 0.921$ N (3 s.f.)

EXAMPLE A sledge of weight 1000 N is being held on a rough plane inclined at an angle of 35° to the horizontal by a force of 700 N acting parallel to the slope. Find the normal contact force N and the frictional force F acting on the sledge.

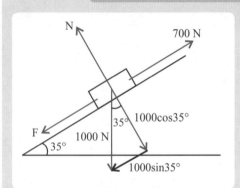

All the forces, except the weight, involved here act either <u>parallel</u> or <u>perpendicular</u> to the <u>slope</u> so it makes sense to resolve in these directions.

<u>Perpendicular</u> to the slope:

$N - 1000\cos 35° = 0$

So $N = 1000\cos 35°$

$= 819$ N (3 s.f.)

<u>Parallel</u> to the slope:

$700 - 1000\sin 35° - F = 0$

So $F = 700 - 1000\sin 35°$

$= 126$ N (3 s.f.)

Masses** on Strings **Produce Tension

EXAMPLE A mass of 12 kg is held by two light, inextensible strings, P and Q, acting at 40° and 20° to the vertical, as shown. Find T_P and T_Q, the tension in each string. Take $g = 9.8$ ms^{-2}.

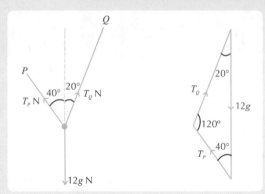

Sine rule:

$$\frac{T_P}{\sin 20°} = \frac{12g}{\sin 120°}$$

So $T_P = 46.4$ N

$$\frac{T_Q}{\sin 40°} = \frac{12g}{\sin 120°}$$

So $T_Q = 87.3$ N

Always look out for <u>sine rule</u> triangles in your polygons of forces.

Cliché #27 — "The more things change, the more they stay the same"...

As it makes their lives easier, examiners always stick the <u>same</u> kinds of questions into M1 exams. So, no need to panic — just keep practising the questions and then there'll be no surprises when it comes to the exam. Simple.

Friction

Friction tries to prevent motion, but don't let it prevent you getting marks in the exam — revise this page and it won't.

Friction Tries to **Prevent Motion**

Push hard enough and a particle will move, even though there's friction opposing the motion. A <u>friction force</u>, <u>F</u>, has a <u>maximum value</u>. This depends on the <u>roughness</u> of the surface and the value of the <u>normal reaction</u> from the surface.

$$F \leq \mu R \quad \text{OR} \quad F \leq \mu N$$

(where R and N both stand for normal reaction)

μ has no units.
μ is pronounced as 'mu'.

μ is called the "<u>coefficient of friction</u>". The <u>rougher</u> the surface, the <u>bigger</u> μ gets.

EXAMPLE

What range of values can a friction force take in resisting a horizontal force P acting on a particle Q, of mass 12 kg, resting on a rough horizontal plane which has a coefficient of friction of 0.4? (Take $g = 9.8$ ms^{-2}.)

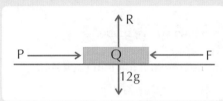

Resolving vertically: $R = 12g$

Use formula from above: $F \leq \mu R$

$F \leq 0.4(12g)$

$F \leq 47.0$ N (3 s.f.)

So friction can take any value between 0 and 47.04 N, depending on how large P is.

If $P \leq 47.04$ N then Q remains in equilibrium. If P = 47.04 N then Q is <u>on the point of sliding</u> — i.e. friction is at its <u>limit</u>. If P > 47.04 then Q will start to move.

Limiting Friction is When Friction is at **Maximum** $(F = \mu R)$

EXAMPLE

A particle of mass 6 kg is placed on a rough horizontal plane which has a coefficient of friction of 0.3. A horizontal force Q is applied to the particle. Describe what happens if Q is: a) 16 N   b) 20 N
Take $g = 9.8$ ms^{-2}

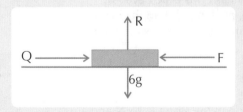

Resolving vertically: $R = 6g$

Using formula above: $F \leq \mu R$
$F \leq 0.3(6g)$
$F \leq 17.6$ N (3 s.f.)

a) Since Q < 17.64 it <u>won't move</u>.

b) Since Q > 17.64 it'll <u>start moving</u>. No probs.

EXAMPLE

A particle of mass 4 kg at rest on a rough horizontal plane is acted on by a force of 30 N, applied at an angle of 20° to the horizontal. Given that the particle is on the point of moving, find the coefficient of friction. Take $g = 9.8$ ms^{-2}.

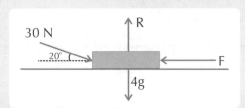

Resolving horizontally: $F = 30\cos20°$
Resolving vertically: $R = 4g + 30\sin20°$
The particle's about to move, so friction is at its limit:

$F = \mu R \Rightarrow 30\cos20° = \mu(4g + 30\sin20°)$

$$\mu = \frac{30\cos20}{4g + 30\sin20} = 0.570 \text{ (3 s.f.)}$$

Sometimes friction really rubs me up the wrong way...

Friction can be a right nuisance, but without it we'd just slide all over the place, which would be worse (I imagine).

M1 Section 1 — Practice Questions

Time to resolve the force applied to your revision along the question axis... That didn't sound as good as I hoped. Still, at least you can distract yourself from my terrible sense of humour with these excellent practice questions.

Warm-up Questions

Take $g = 9.8$ ms^{-2} in each of these questions.

1) Find the average velocity of a cyclist who cycles at 15 kmh^{-1} north for 15 minutes and then cycles south at 10 kmh^{-1} for 45 minutes.

2) The following items are dropped from a height of 2 m onto a cushion:

   a) a full 330 ml drinks can   b) an empty drinks can   c) a table tennis ball

   The time each takes to fall is measured.
   Draw a model of each situation and list any assumptions which you've made.

3) A car is travelling at 25 mph along a straight level road.
   Draw a model of the situation and list any assumptions which you've made.

4) Find the magnitudes and directions to the horizontal of the resultant force in each situation.

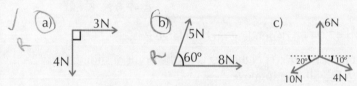

5) A mass of m kg is suspended by two light wires A and B, with angles 60° and 30° to the vertical respectively, as shown. The tension in A is 20 N. Find:

   a) the tension in wire B,

   b) the value of m.

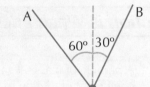

6) 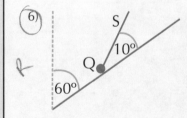 A particle, Q, of mass m kg, is in equilibrium on a smooth plane which makes an angle of 60° to the vertical. This is achieved by an attached string S, with tension 70 N, angled at 10° to the plane, as shown. Draw a force diagram and find both the mass of Q and the reaction on it from the surface.

7) A toy train of weight 25 N is pulled up a slope of 20°. The tension in the string is 25 N and a frictional force of 5 N acts on the train. Find the normal contact force and the resultant force acting on the train.

8) a) Describe the motion of a mass of 12 kg pushed by a force of 50 N parallel to the rough horizontal plane on which the mass is placed. The plane has coefficient of friction $\mu = \frac{1}{2}$.

   b) What minimum force would be needed to move the mass in part a)?

M1 Section 1 — Practice Questions

Now you can apply your vector and statics knowledge to some exam questions so that when you take the real thing there'll be no need for your pen to remain at equilibrium.

Exam Questions

Take $g = 9.8 \text{ ms}^{-2}$ in each of these questions.

1

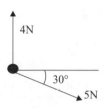

The diagram shows two forces acting on a particle.

Find the magnitude and direction of the resultant force.

(4 marks)

2   A box of mass 39 kg is at rest on a rough horizontal surface. The box is pushed with a force of 140 N from an angle of 20° above the horizontal. The box remains stationary.

    a)   Draw a diagram to show the four forces acting on the box.

(2 marks)

    b)   Calculate the magnitude of the normal reaction force and the frictional force on the box.

(4 marks)

3   A force of magnitude 7 N acts horizontally on a particle. Another force, of magnitude 4 N, acts on the particle at an angle of 30° to the horizontal force. The resultant of the two forces has a magnitude R at an angle α above the horizontal.

    Find:

    a)   the force R,

(4 marks)

    b)   the angle α.

(2 marks)

4

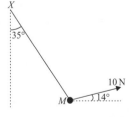

A particle, M, is attached to the end of a light, inextensible rod fixed at point X. A force of magnitude 10 N is applied to M at 14° to the horizontal. M is held in equilibrium at an angle of 35° as shown in the diagram. Find the mass of M.

(4 marks)

M1 Section 1 — Practice Questions

Another page of questions to practise on here, so keep on truckin' (remembering that "truckin'" is a vector quantity with both magnitude *and* direction). The normal reaction to that joke is a sigh... on with the questions.

5   Three forces of magnitudes 15 N, 12 N and W act on a particle as shown.
    Given that the particle is in equilibrium, find:

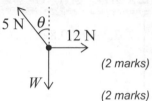

   a)   the value of θ,
                                                                          (2 marks)

   b)   the force W.
                                                                          (2 marks)

   The force W is now removed.

   c)   State the magnitude and direction of the resultant of the two remaining forces.
                                                                          (2 marks)

6   A sledge is held at rest on a smooth slope which makes an angle of 25° with the horizontal.
    The rope holding the sledge is at an angle of 20° above the slope. The normal reaction acting on
    the sledge due to contact with the surface is 80 N.
    Find:

   a)   The tension, T, in the rope.
                                                                          (3 marks)

   b)   The weight of the sledge.
                                                                          (2 marks)

7   A particle of mass m kg is held in equilibrium by two light inextensible strings.
    One string is attached at an angle of 50° to the horizontal, as shown, and has tension T N.
    The other string is horizontal and has tension 58 N. Find:

   a)   the magnitude of T.
                                                                          (3 marks)

   b)   the mass, m, of the particle.
                                                                          (3 marks)

8   A 2 kg ring threaded on a rough horizontal rod is pulled by a rope having tension S and
    attached at 40° to the horizontal, as shown. The coefficient of friction between the rod and
    the ring is $\frac{3}{10}$. Given that the ring is about to slide, find the magnitude of S.

                                                                          (4 marks)

Constant Acceleration Equations

Welcome to the technicolour world of kinematics. Fashions may change, but there will <u>always</u> be M1 questions that involve objects travelling in a <u>straight line</u>. It's just a case of picking the right equations to solve the problem.

There are **Five Constant Acceleration Equations**

Examiners call these "<u>uvast</u>" questions (pronounced ewe-vast, like a large sheep) because of the five variables involved:

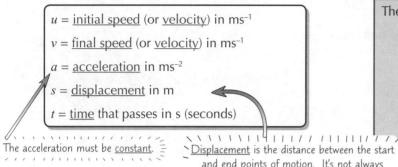

u = <u>initial speed</u> (or <u>velocity</u>) in ms^{-1}

v = <u>final speed</u> (or <u>velocity</u>) in ms^{-1}

a = <u>acceleration</u> in ms^{-2}

s = <u>displacement</u> in m

t = <u>time</u> that passes in s (seconds)

The constant acceleration equations are:
$$v = u + at$$
$$s = ut + \tfrac{1}{2}at^2$$
$$s = \tfrac{1}{2}(u + v)t$$
$$v^2 = u^2 + 2as$$
$$s = vt - \tfrac{1}{2}at^2$$

The acceleration must be <u>constant</u>.

<u>Displacement</u> is the distance between the start and end points of motion. It's not always the same as the <u>total distance</u> travelled.

Speed and distance are <u>scalar</u> quantities. Acceleration, velocity and displacement are <u>vector</u> quantities. See p. 156.

None of those equations are in the formula book, so you're going to have to <u>learn them</u>. Questions will usually give you <u>three variables</u> — your job is to choose the equation that will find you a missing <u>fourth variable</u>.

EXAMPLE

A jet ski travels in a straight line along a river. It passes under two bridges 200 m apart and is observed to be travelling at 5 ms^{-1} under the first bridge and at 9 ms^{-1} under the second bridge. Calculate its acceleration (assuming it is constant).

List the variables ("<u>uvast</u>"):

$u = 5$

$v = 9$ — You have to work out a.

$a = a$

$s = 200$ — You're not told about the time taken.

$t = t$

Choose the equation with u, v, s and a in it: $\quad v^2 = u^2 + 2as$

Check you're using the right <u>units</u> — m, s, ms^{-1} and ms^{-2}.

<u>Substitute</u> values: $\quad 9^2 = 5^2 + (2 \times a \times 200)$

<u>Simplify</u>: $\quad 81 = 25 + 400a$

<u>Rearrange</u>: $\quad 400a = 81 - 25 = 56$

Then <u>solve</u>: $\quad a = \dfrac{56}{400} = 0.14\,\text{ms}^{-2}$

---

*Motion under Gravity just means taking **a = g**...*

Don't be put off by questions involving objects <u>moving freely under gravity</u> — they're just telling you the <u>acceleration is g</u>.

Use the value of g given on the front of the paper or in the question. If you don't, you risk losing a mark because your answer won't match the examiners' answer.

EXAMPLE

A pebble is dropped into a well 18 m deep and moves freely under gravity until it hits the bottom. Calculate the time it takes to reach the bottom. (Take $g = 9.8$ ms^{-2}.)

First, list the variables:

$u = 0$ — Because the pebble was <u>dropped</u>, not thrown.

$v = v$

$a = 9.8$ — $a = g = 9.8$ ms^{-2}, because it's falling freely.

$s = 18$

$t = t$

You need the equation with u, a, s and t in it: $\quad s = ut + \tfrac{1}{2}at^2$

Substitute values: $\quad 18 = (0 \times t) + (\tfrac{1}{2} \times 9.8 \times t^2)$

Simplify: $\quad 18 = 4.9t^2$

Rearrange to give t^2: $\quad t^2 = \dfrac{18}{4.9} = 3.67...$

Solve by square-rooting: $\quad t = \sqrt{3.67...} = 1.92$ s

Watch out for tricky questions like this — at first it <u>looks like</u> they've only given you <u>one variable</u>. You have to spot that the pebble was <u>dropped</u> (so it started with no velocity) and that it's <u>moving freely under gravity</u>.

Constant Acceleration Equations

...or a = –g

EXAMPLE

A ball is projected vertically upwards at 3 ms⁻¹ from a point 1.5 m above the ground. How long does it take to reach its maximum height? How fast will the ball be travelling when it hits the ground? (Take g = 9.8 ms⁻².)

First, list the variables, taking up as the positive direction:

$u = 3$

$v = 0$ ← *When projected objects reach the top of their motion, they stop momentarily.*

$a = -9.8$ ← *Because g always acts downwards and up was taken as positive, a is negative.*

$s = s$

$t = ?$

s is negative as the ground is below the point of projection.

Use the equation with u, v, a and t in it:

Substitute values:

Simplify:

Rearrange and solve to find t:

$v = u + at$

$0 = 3 + (-9.8 \times t)$

$0 = 3 - 9.8t$

$t = \dfrac{3}{9.8} = 0.306$ s (3 s.f.)

To find the speed of the ball when it hits the ground consider the complete path of the ball.

$s = -1.5$ as it's the displacement from the ball's original position, not total distance travelled.

Using $v^2 = u^2 + 2as$ where $u = 3$, $v = ?$, $a = -9.8$, $s = -1.5$:

$v^2 = u^2 + 2as = 3^2 + 2(-9.8 \times -1.5) = 38.4$, so $v = \sqrt{38.4} = 6.20$ ms⁻¹ (to 3 s.f.)

Sometimes there's More Than One Object Moving at the Same Time

For these questions, t is often the same (or connected as in this example) because time ticks along for both objects at the same rate. The distance travelled might also be connected.

EXAMPLE

A car, A, travelling along a straight road at a constant 30 ms⁻¹ passes point R at $t = 0$. Exactly 2 seconds later, a second car, B, travelling at 25 ms⁻¹, moves in the same direction from point R. Car B accelerates at a constant 2 ms⁻². Show that the two cars are level when $t^2 - 9t - 46 = 0$, where t is the time taken by car A.

For each car, there are different "uvast" equations, so you write separate lists and separate equations.

CAR A

Constant speed so $a_A = 0$

$u_A = 30$ $v_A = 30$

$a_A = 0$ $s_A = s$

$t_A = t$

CAR B

$u_B = 25$ $v_B = v$

$a_B = 2$ $s_B = s$

$t_B = (t - 2)$

s is the same for both cars because they're level.

B starts moving 2 seconds after A passes point R.

The two cars are level, so choose an equation with s in it:

$s = ut + \frac{1}{2}at^2$

Substitute values: $s = 30t + (\frac{1}{2} \times 0 \times t^2)$

Simplify: $s = 30t$

Use the same equation for car B: $s = ut + \frac{1}{2}at^2$

Substitute values: $s = 25(t - 2) + (\frac{1}{2} \times 2 \times (t - 2)^2)$

Simplify: $s = 25t - 50 + (t - 2)(t - 2)$

$s = 25t - 50 + (t^2 - 4t + 4)$

$s = t^2 + 21t - 46$

The distance travelled by both cars is equal, so put the expressions for s equal to each other:

$30t = t^2 + 21t - 46$

$t^2 - 9t - 46 = 0$

That's the result you were asked to find.

Constant acceleration questions involve modelling assumptions (simplifications to real life so you can use the equations):

1) The object is a particle — this just means it's very small and so isn't affected by air resistance as cars or stones would be in real life.

2) Acceleration is constant — without it, the equations couldn't be used.

As Socrates once said, "The unexamined life is not worth living"... *but what did he know...*

Make sure you: 1) Make a list of the uvast variables EVERY time you get one of these questions.

2) Look out for "hidden" values — e.g. "particle initially at rest..." means $u = 0$.

3) Choose and solve the equation that goes with the variables you've got.

Motion Graphs

You can use <u>displacement-time</u> (t, x), <u>velocity-time</u> (t, v) and <u>acceleration-time</u> (t, a) graphs to represent all sorts of motion.

Displacement-time Graphs: Height = Displacement and Gradient = Velocity

The <u>steeper</u> the line, the <u>greater</u> the velocity. A <u>horizontal</u> line has a <u>zero gradient</u>, so that means the object isn't moving.

EXAMPLE   A cyclist's journey is shown on this (t, x) graph. Describe the motion.

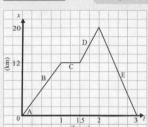

A: Starts from rest (when $t = 0$, $x = 0$)

B: Travels 12 km in 1 hour at a velocity of 12 kmh^{-1}

C: Rests for ½ hour ($v = 0$)

D: Cycles 8 km in ½ hour at a velocity of 16 kmh^{-1}

E: Returns to starting position, cycling 20 km in 1 hour at a velocity of –20 kmh^{-1} (i.e. 20 kmh^{-1} in the opposite direction)

EXAMPLE   A girl jogs 2 km in 15 minutes and a boy runs 1.5 km in 6 min, rests for 1 min then walks the last 0.5 km in 8 min. Show the two journeys on a (t, x) graph.

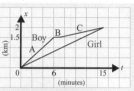

Girl: constant velocity, so there's just one straight line for her journey from (0, 0) to (15, 2)

Boy: three parts to the journey, so there are three straight lines: A - run, B - rest, C - walk

Velocity-time Graphs: Area = Displacement and Gradient = Acceleration

The <u>area</u> under the graph can be calculated by <u>splitting</u> the area into rectangles, triangles or trapeziums. Work out the areas <u>separately</u>, then <u>add</u> them all up at the end.

EXAMPLE   A train journey is shown on the (t, v) graph on the right. Find the distance travelled and the rate of deceleration as the train comes to a stop.

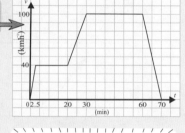

The time is given in minutes and the velocity as kilometres per hour, so divide the time in minutes by 60 to get the time in hours.

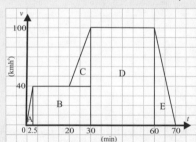

Area of A: $(2.5 \div 60 \times 40) \div 2 = 0.833...$

Area of B: $27.5 \div 60 \times 40 = 18.33...$

Area of C: $(10 \div 60 \times 60) \div 2 = 5$

Area of D: $30 \div 60 \times 100 = 50$

Area of E: $(10 \div 60 \times 100) \div 2 = 8.33...$

Total area = 82.5 so distance is 82.5 km

> You could get a <u>curved</u> (t, v) graph. This means that the acceleration isn't constant. There's more about variable acceleration on p. 171-2.

The gradient of the graph at the end of the journey is -100 kmh$^{-1} \div (10 \div 60)$ hours $= -600$ kmh^{-2}
So the train decelerates at 600 kmh^{-2}.

EXAMPLE   The (t, v) graph on the right shows the motion of a man walking his dog in a straight line over a 6 minute time period. Find:
a) the total distance the man walks during the 6 minutes,
b) the man's displacement from his starting point after 6 minutes.

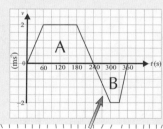

a) The <u>total distance</u> can be found by <u>adding</u> the areas of A and B. Using the same method as above:

Area of A = $[(60 \times 2) \div 2] + [120 \times 2] + [(60 \times 2) \div 2] = 360$

Area of B = $[(60 \times 2) \div 2] + [30 \times 2] + [(30 \times 2) \div 2] = 150$

So the total distance travelled is $360 + 150 = 510$ m.

> When the graph goes below the t-axis, the velocity is <u>negative</u>. This means the motion is in the <u>opposite</u> <u>direction</u> to when the graph is above the t-axis.

b) The man's <u>displacement</u> can be found by <u>subtracting</u> B from A:

Displacement = $360 - 150 = 210$ m.

> The area of B is the distance the man walks <u>back</u> <u>towards</u> his original position, so his final displacement will be <u>less</u> than the total distance walked.

Motion Graphs

Graphs can be used to **Solve Complicated Problems**

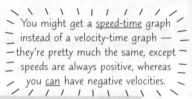
You might get a speed-time graph instead of a velocity-time graph — they're pretty much the same, except speeds are always positive, whereas you can have negative velocities.

As well as working out distance, velocity and acceleration from graphs, you can also solve more complicated problems. These might involve working out information not shown directly on the graph.

EXAMPLE

A jogger and a cyclist set off at the same time. The jogger runs with a constant velocity. The cyclist accelerates uniformly from rest, reaching a velocity of 5 ms⁻¹ after 6 s and then continues at this velocity. The cyclist overtakes the jogger after 15 s.

Draw a graph of the motion and find the velocity of the jogger.

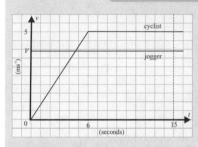

Call the velocity of the jogger V.

After 15 s the distance each has travelled is the same, so you can work out the area under the two graphs to get the distances:

Jogger: Area = distance = $15V$

Cyclist: Area = distance = $(6 \times 5) \div 2 + (9 \times 5) = 60$

area of triangle + area of rectangle

So $15V = 60$
$V = 4$ ms⁻¹

EXAMPLE

A man throws a pebble vertically upwards from ground level with a speed of u ms⁻¹. The pebble takes 2.6 s to return to ground level and reaches a maximum height of 9.4 m.

Draw a graph of the motion and find the value of u.

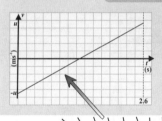 **OR**

Using $s = \frac{1}{2}(u + v)t$ until pebble reaches maximum height, where $v = 0$ ms⁻¹:

$9.4 = \frac{1}{2}(u + 0)1.3$

so $u = \frac{9.4}{0.65} = 14.5$ ms⁻¹

The pebble reaches maximum height in half the time it takes to fall to the floor.

The pebble's velocity is negative for half of its motion. As you can choose up or down to be the positive direction, there are two possible graphs that describe the motion. The graph on the left takes 'down' as positive, while the one on the right takes 'up' as positive.

EXAMPLE

A bus is travelling at V ms⁻¹. When it reaches point A it accelerates uniformly for 4 s, reaching a speed of 21 ms⁻¹ as it passes point B. At point B, the driver brakes uniformly until the bus comes to a halt 7 s later. The rate of deceleration is twice the rate of acceleration.

Draw a speed-time graph of the motion and find the value of V.

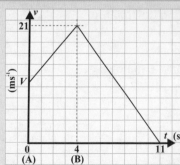

To find the deceleration use $a = \frac{(v - u)}{t}$:

$a = \frac{(0 - 21)}{7} = -3$ ms⁻²

Just $v = u + at$ rearranged.

Rate of deceleration is twice the rate of acceleration, so rate of acceleration = 1.5 ms⁻².

Finding V using $u = v - at$:

$V = 21 - (1.5 \times 4)$

So, $V = 15$ ms⁻¹

Random tongue-twister #1 — I wish to wash my Irish wristwatch...

If a picture can tell a thousand words then a graph can tell... um... a thousand and one. Make sure you know what type of graph you're using and learn what the gradient and the area under each type of graph tells you.

Displacement, Velocity and Acceleration

The "uvast" equations are all well and good when you've got a particle with constant acceleration. But when the acceleration of a particle varies with time, you need a few new tricks up your sleeve...

Differentiate to find Velocity and Acceleration from Displacement...

If you've got a particle moving in a straight line with acceleration that varies with time, you need to use calculus to find equations to describe the motion. (See p. 39 and p. 89 for a reminder about calculus.)

1) To find an equation for velocity, differentiate the equation for displacement with respect to time.

2) To find an equation for acceleration, differentiate the equation for velocity with respect to time. (Or differentiate the equation for displacement with respect to time twice.)

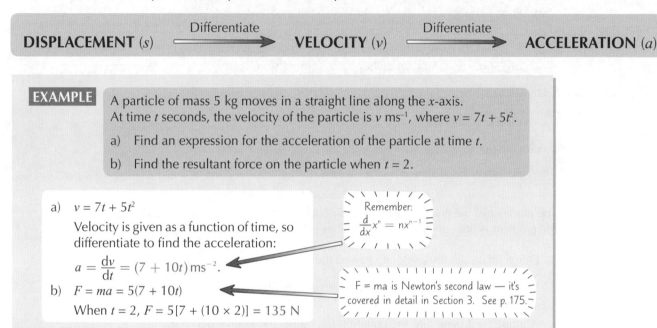

DISPLACEMENT (s) $\xrightarrow{\text{Differentiate}}$ **VELOCITY** (v) $\xrightarrow{\text{Differentiate}}$ **ACCELERATION** (a)

EXAMPLE A particle of mass 5 kg moves in a straight line along the x-axis.
At time t seconds, the velocity of the particle is v ms^{-1}, where $v = 7t + 5t^2$.

a) Find an expression for the acceleration of the particle at time t.

b) Find the resultant force on the particle when $t = 2$.

a) $v = 7t + 5t^2$

Velocity is given as a function of time, so differentiate to find the acceleration:

$a = \dfrac{\mathrm{d}v}{\mathrm{d}t} = (7 + 10t)\,\mathrm{ms}^{-2}.$

Remember: $\dfrac{d}{dx}x^n = nx^{n-1}$

b) $F = ma = 5(7 + 10t)$

When $t = 2$, $F = 5[7 + (10 \times 2)] = 135$ N

F = ma is Newton's second law — it's covered in detail in Section 3. See p. 175.

...and Integrate to find Velocity and Displacement from Acceleration

It's pretty similar if you're trying to go "back the other way", except you integrate rather than differentiate:

1) To find an equation for velocity, integrate the equation for acceleration with respect to time.

2) To find an equation for displacement, integrate the equation for velocity with respect to time.

DISPLACEMENT (s) $\xleftarrow{\text{Integrate}}$ **VELOCITY** (v) $\xleftarrow{\text{Integrate}}$ **ACCELERATION** (a)

EXAMPLE A particle P sets off from O and moves in a straight line along the x-axis so that at time t seconds, its velocity is v ms^{-1}, where $v = 12 - t^2$, measured in the direction of x increasing. At $t = 0$, $s = 0$. Find the time taken for P to return to O.

Velocity is given as a function of t, so:

$s = \int v\,\mathrm{dt} = 12t - \dfrac{t^3}{3} + C.$

Don't forget the constant. Most questions should give you some info so you can find it.

When $t = 0$, $s = 0$, so $0 = 12(0) - \dfrac{0^3}{3} + C \Rightarrow C = 0$.

Remember: $\int x^n\,dx = \dfrac{x^{n+1}}{n+1} + c$

P is at O when $s = 0$, i.e. when: $0 = 12t - \dfrac{t^3}{3} \Rightarrow 0 = t(36 - t^2)$

i.e. when $t = 0$, 6 or -6. So time taken for P to return to O is 6 seconds.

This can't be an answer, as you can't have a negative time.

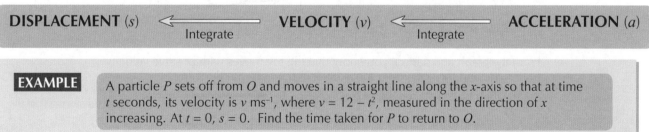

Displacement, Velocity and Acceleration

Sometimes the **Velocity** is Defined only for a **Particular Time Period**

If you're trying to find the displacement of an object for a <u>certain interval</u> of t then you can integrate the velocity using <u>definite integrals</u>. No faffing about with constants — hooray.

EXAMPLE

The graph shows the motion of a wind-up toy moving in a straight line. The velocity of the toy in the interval $0 \le t \le 7$ is given by $v = -t^2 + 6t$.

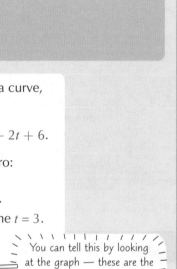

a) How can you tell that the toy's acceleration is not constant for $0 \le t \le 7$?

b) (i) Find an expression for the toy's acceleration at time t.
   (ii) Show that the toy reaches its maximum speed in the interval $0 \le t \le 7$ at $t = 3$, and find the speed.

c) Find the two times in the interval $0 \le t \le 7$ when the toy is stationary.

d) Find the toy's displacement from the origin after 7 seconds.

e) Find the total distance the toy travels during the first 7 seconds.

a) The gradient of the graph gives the toy's acceleration. As the graph is a curve, the gradient is not constant, and so neither is the toy's acceleration.

b) (i) Differentiate the toy's velocity to find the acceleration: $a = \dfrac{dv}{dt} = -2t + 6$.

   (ii) The toy's speed is at a maximum when acceleration is equal to zero:
   i.e. when $a = -2t + 6 = 0 \Rightarrow t = 3$.
   Putting $t = 3$ back into the equation for v gives $v = -(3)^2 + 6(3) = 9$.
   So the toy's maximum speed is $v_{max} = 9 \text{ ms}^{-1}$, and this occurs at time $t = 3$.

c) The toy is stationary when $v = 0$, i.e. when $-t^2 + 6t = t(-t + 6) = 0$
   So, the toy is stationary when $t = 0$ s and $t = 6$ s.

   You can tell this by looking at the graph — these are the values where the graph crosses the t-axis. But it's always best to double-check using algebra.

d) Integrate the velocity to find an expression for the toy's displacement:

$$s = \int v \, dt = \int_0^7 (-t^2 + 6t) \, dt = \left[-\frac{t^3}{3} + 3t^2 \right]_0^7$$
$$= \left[-\frac{7^3}{3} + 3(7)^2 \right] - \left[-\frac{0^3}{3} + 3(0)^2 \right] = \left(32\frac{2}{3} - 0 \right) = 32\frac{2}{3} \text{ m}$$

The limits O and 7 are used to find the displacement after 7 seconds.

e) From the graph and part c), you know that the toy moves with positive velocity until $t = 6$, and then begins to move back in the opposite direction.
   So, first find the displacement of the toy at $t = 6$:

$$s = \int_0^6 (-t^2 + 6t) \, dt = \left[-\frac{t^3}{3} + 3t^2 \right]_0^6 = \left[-\frac{6^3}{3} + 3(6)^2 \right] - 0 = \textbf{36 m}$$

This will be the <u>maximum positive displacement</u> of the toy in the interval $0 \le t \le 7$

From part d), you know the displacement of the toy at $t = 7$, so:

Total distance travelled $= 36 + \left(36 - 32\frac{2}{3} \right) = 36 + 3\frac{1}{3} = 39\frac{1}{3}$ m.

This is how far the toy has moved in the opposite direction between t = 6 and t = 7.

CGP driving tips #1 — differentiate velocity from displacement...

Calculus? In Mechanics? What fresh horror is this? Actually, it's really not that bad at all. Just make sure you know when to differentiate and when to integrate and then bang in the numbers you're given in the question to get the answer. Sorted.

M1 Section 2 — Practice Questions

Time for some more questions. A bit of advice — don't panic, take it step by step, and above all ~~don't get hurt~~ keep practising until it's second nature.

Warm-up Questions

Take $g = 9.8$ ms^{-2} in each of these questions.

1) A motorcyclist accelerates uniformly from 3 ms^{-1} to 9 ms^{-1} in 2 seconds.
   What is the distance travelled by the motorcyclist during this acceleration?

2) A runner starts from rest and accelerates at 0.5 ms^{-2} for 5 seconds. She maintains a constant velocity for 20 seconds then decelerates to a stop at 0.25 ms^{-2}.
   Draw a (t, v) graph to show the motion and find the distance the runner travelled.

3) The start of a journey is shown on the (t, v) graph to the right.
   Find the displacement when: a) $t = 3$ b) $t = 5$ c) $t = 6$

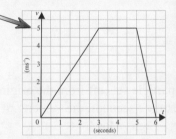

4) A particle sets off from the origin at $t = 0$ and moves along the x-axis with velocity $v = 8t^2 - 2t$. Find expressions for:
   a) the acceleration of the particle at time t,
   b) the displacement of the particle at time t.

Hopefully those questions above were no trouble, so it's time to have a go at the kind of questions you're likely to see in the exam. You'll find them below, in a different font and everything...

Exam Questions

Take $g = 9.8$ ms^{-2} in each of these questions.

1   A window cleaner of a block of flats accidentally drops his sandwich, which falls freely to the ground. The speed of the sandwich as it passes a high floor is u. After a further 1.2 seconds the sandwich is moving at a speed of 17 ms^{-1}. The distance between the consecutive floors of the building is h

   a)   Find the value of u.

   (3 marks)

   b)   It takes the sandwich another 2.1 seconds to fall the remaining 14 floors to the ground.
        Find h.

   (4 marks)

2   A train starts from rest at station A and travels with constant acceleration for 20 s. It then travels with constant speed V ms^{-1} for 2 minutes. It then decelerates with constant deceleration for 40 s before coming to rest at station B. The total distance between stations A and B is 2.1 km.

   a) Sketch a (t, v) graph for the motion of the train between stations A and B.

   (3 marks)

   b) Hence or otherwise find the value of V.

   (3 marks)

   c) Calculate the distance travelled by the train while decelerating.

   (2 marks)

   d) Calculate the train's acceleration during the first 20 s of motion.

   (3 marks)

M1 Section 2 — Practice Questions

And for all you kinemaniacs out there, here are three more questions for you to sink your teeth into.

3   A rocket is projected vertically upwards from a point 8 m above the ground at a speed of u ms^{-1} and travels freely under gravity. The rocket hits the ground at 20 ms^{-1}. Find:

  a)   the value of u,

  (3 marks)

  b)   how long it takes to hit the ground.

  (3 marks)

4   A particle sets off from the origin, O, at time $t = 0$ and moves in a straight line along the x-axis. At time t seconds, the velocity of the particle is given by $v = 9t - 3t^2$ ms^{-1} for $0 \leq t \leq 4$ and $v = -12$ ms^{-1} for $t > 4$.

  Find:

  a)   the time when the acceleration is zero in the interval $0 \leqslant t \leqslant 4$,

  (2 marks)

  b)   the displacement of the particle from O at $t = 4$,

  (3 marks)

  c)   the time when the particle returns to O for $t > 4$.

  (3 marks)

5   The following graph models the velocity of a car pulling away from a set of traffic lights. The car's velocity from time $t = 0$ s to $t = 3$ s is given by $v = 6t - t^2$ ms^{-1}.

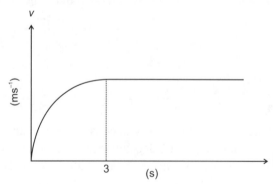

  a)   Write down an expression for the car's acceleration during the first 3 seconds of travel.

  (1 mark)

  b)   Find the distance the car moves during this time.

  (3 marks)

Newton's Laws

That clever chap Isaac Newton established 3 laws involving motion. You need to know <u>all</u> of them.

Newton's Laws of Motion

Newton's First Law

A body will <u>stay at rest</u> or <u>maintain a constant velocity</u> — unless an extra force acts to <u>change</u> that motion.

Newton's Second Law

$$F_{net} = ma$$

F_{net} (the <u>overall resultant force</u>) is equal to the mass multiplied by the acceleration. Also, F_{net} and a are in the same direction.

Newton's Third Law

For <u>two bodies</u> in contact with each other, the force each applies to the other is <u>equal in magnitude</u> but <u>opposite in direction</u>.

<u>Hint</u>: $F_{net} = ma$ is sometimes just written as $F = ma$, but it means the same thing.

F = ma equations are sometimes known as 'equations of motion'.

Resolve Forces in Perpendicular Directions

EXAMPLE

A mass of 4 kg at rest on a smooth horizontal plane is acted on by a horizontal force of 5 N. Find the acceleration of the mass and the normal reaction from the plane. Take $g = 9.8$ ms⁻².

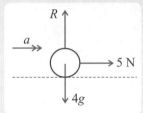

Resolve horizontally:

$F_{net} = ma$

$5 = 4a$

Always write $F_{net} = ma$ first.

$a = 1.25$ ms⁻² in the direction of the horizontal force

Resolve vertically:

$F_{net} = ma$, so $R - 4g = 4 \times 0$

$R = 4g = 39.2$ N

EXAMPLE

A particle of weight 30 N is being accelerated across a smooth horizontal plane by a force of 6 N acting at an angle of 25° to the horizontal, as shown. Given that the particle starts from rest, find:

    a) its speed after 4 seconds   b) the magnitude of the normal reaction with the plane.

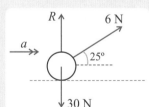

a) Resolve horizontally:

$F_{net} = ma$

$6\cos25° = \dfrac{30}{g}a$ so $a = 1.776...$ ms⁻²

$v = u + at$

$v = 0 + 1.776... \times 4 = 7.11$ ms⁻¹ (to 3 s.f.)

b) Resolve vertically:

$F_{net} = ma$

$R + 6\sin25° - 30 = \dfrac{30}{g} \times 0$

So $R = 30 - 6\sin25° = 27.5$ N (to 3 s.f.)

EXAMPLE

A horizontal force of magnitude 10 N accelerates an object of mass m kg along a rough horizontal surface at a rate of 5 ms⁻². Given that the coefficient of friction between the object and the surface is 0.5, find m.

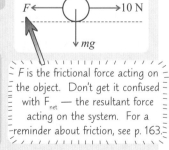

Resolve vertically:

$F_{net} = ma$

$R - mg = m \times 0$

So $R = mg$

The object is moving, so $F = \mu R$. (See p. 163).

Resolve horizontally:

$F_{net} = ma$

$10 - F = 5m$

$F = \mu R \Rightarrow 10 - \mu R = 5m$

$10 - \mu mg = 5m$

$10 = 5m + \mu mg$ *Using $R = mg$*

So $m = \dfrac{10}{5 + \mu g}$

$= \dfrac{10}{5 + (0.5 \times 9.8)}$

$= 1.01$ kg (3 s.f.)

F is the frictional force acting on the object. Don't get it confused with F_{net} — the resultant force acting on the system. For a reminder about friction, see p. 163.

Interesting Newton fact: Isaac Newton had a dog called Diamond...

Did you know that Isaac Newton and Stephen Hawking both held the same position at Cambridge University? And the dog fact about Newton is true — don't ask me how I know such things, just bask in my amazing knowledge of all things trivial.

Friction and Inclined Planes

Solving these problems involves careful use of $F_{net} = ma$, $F = \mu R$ and the equations of motion.

Use F = ma in Two Directions for Inclined Plane questions

For inclined slope questions, it's much easier to resolve forces parallel and perpendicular to the plane's surface.

EXAMPLE A mass of 600 g is propelled up the line of greatest slope of a smooth plane inclined at 30° to the horizontal. If its velocity is 3 ms⁻¹ after the propelling force has stopped, find the distance it travels before coming to rest and the magnitude of the normal reaction. Use $g = 9.8$ ms⁻².

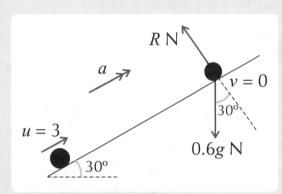

Resolve in ↗ direction:

$F_{net} = ma$

$-0.6g\sin30° = 0.6a$

Taking up the plane as +ve.

$a = -4.9$ ms⁻²

$v^2 = u^2 + 2as$

$0 = 3^2 + 2(-4.9)s$

So $s = 0.918$ m (3 s.f.)

Resolve in ↖ direction:

$F_{net} = ma$

$R - 0.6g\cos30° = 0.6 \times 0$

So $R = 5.09$ N

Remember that friction always acts in the opposite direction to the motion.

EXAMPLE A small body of weight 20 N accelerates from rest and moves a distance of 5 m down a rough plane angled at 15° to the horizontal. Draw a force diagram and find the coefficient of friction between the body and the plane given that the motion takes 6 seconds. Take $g = 9.8$ ms⁻².

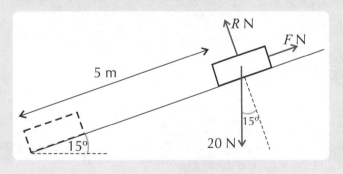

$u = 0$, $s = 5$, $t = 6$, $a = ?$

Use one of the equations of motion: $s = ut + \frac{1}{2}at^2$

$5 = (0 \times 6) + (\frac{1}{2}a \times 6^2)$ so $a = 0.2778$ ms⁻²

Resolving in ↖ direction:

$F_{net} = ma$

$R - 20\cos15° = \frac{20}{g} \times 0$

So: $R = 20\cos15° = $ **19.32 N**

Resolving in ↙ direction:

$F_{net} = ma$

$20\sin15° - F = \frac{20}{g} \times 0.2778$

$F = $ **4.609 N**

It's sliding, so $F = \mu R$

$4.609 = \mu \times 19.32$

$\mu = 0.24$ (to 2 d.p.)

Friction and Inclined Planes

Friction opposes motion, so it also increases the tension in whatever's doing the pulling...

EXAMPLE

A mass of 3 kg is being pulled up a plane inclined at 20° to the horizontal by a rope parallel to the surface. Given that the mass is accelerating at 0.6 ms⁻² and that the coefficient of friction is 0.4, find the tension in the rope. Take $g = 9.8$ ms⁻².

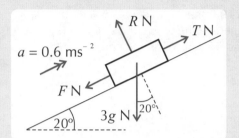

Resolving in ↖ direction:

$$F_{net} = ma$$
$$R - 3g\cos20° = 3 \times 0$$

so: $R = 3g\cos20°$

The mass is sliding, so $F = \mu R$

$$= 0.4 \times 3g\cos20° = 11.05 \text{ N (4 s.f.)}$$

Resolving in ↗ direction:

$$F_{net} = ma$$
$$T - F - 3g\sin20° = 3 \times 0.6$$
$$T = 1.8 + 11.05 + 3g\sin20° = 22.9 \text{ N (3 s.f.)}$$

Friction Opposes Limiting Motion

For a body <u>at rest</u> but on the point of moving <u>down</u> a plane, the friction force is <u>up</u> the plane. A body about to move <u>up</u> a plane is opposed by friction <u>down</u> the plane. Remember it well — it's about to come in handy.

EXAMPLE

A 4 kg box is placed on a 30° plane where $\mu = 0.4$. A force Q maintains equilibrium by acting up the plane parallel to the line of greatest slope. Find Q if the box is on the point of sliding:

a) up the plane   b) down the plane.

a)

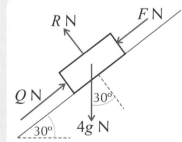

$$F_{net} = ma$$

Resolving in ↖ direction:
$$R - 4g\cos30° = 0$$
$$R = 4g\cos30°$$

$F = \mu R$
$$= 0.4 \times 4g\cos30°$$
$$= 1.6g\cos30°$$

Resolving in ↗ direction:
$$Q - 4g\sin30° - F = 4 \times 0$$
$$Q = 4g\sin30° + 1.6g\cos30°$$
$$= 33.2 \text{ N (3 s.f.)}$$

b)

Resolving in ↖ direction:
$$R = 4g\cos30°$$
$$F = 1.6g\cos30°$$

Resolving in ↗ direction:
$$Q - 4g\sin30° + F = 4 \times 0$$
$$Q = 4g\sin30° - 1.6g\cos30°$$
$$Q = 6.02 \text{ N (3 s.f)}$$

So for equilibrium $6.02 \text{ N} \le Q \le 33.2 \text{ N}$

Inclined planes — nothing to do with suggestible Boeing 737s...

The main thing to remember is that you can choose to resolve in any two directions as long as they're <u>perpendicular</u>. It makes sense to choose the directions that involve doing as little work as possible. Obviously.

Connected Particles

Like Laurel goes with Hardy and Posh goes with Becks, some particles are destined to be together...

Connected Particles act like One Mass

Particles connected together have the <u>same speeds</u> and <u>magnitudes of acceleration</u> as each other, as long as the connection <u>holds</u>. Train carriages moving together have the same acceleration.

EXAMPLE A 30 tonne locomotive engine is pulling a single 10 tonne carriage as shown. They are accelerating at 0.3 ms^{-2} due to the force P generated by the engine. It's assumed that there are no forces resistant to motion. Find P and the tension in the coupling.

Here's the pretty picture:

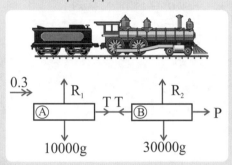

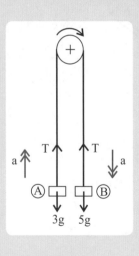

For A: $F_{net} = ma$

$T = 10\,000 \times 0.3$

$T = 3000$ N

If you weren't asked for the tension in the coupling, you could just consider the whole train as one object of mass 40 tonnes and use F = ma to find P.

For B: $F_{net} = ma$

$P - T = 30\,000 \times 0.3$

$P = 12000$ N

Pulleys (and 'Pegs') are always Smooth

In M1 questions, you can always assume that the <u>tension</u> in a string will be the <u>same</u> either side of a <u>smooth pulley</u>.

EXAMPLE Masses of 3 kg and 5 kg are connected by an inextensible string and hang vertically either side of a smooth pulley. They are released from rest. Find their acceleration and the time it takes for each to move 40 cm. State any assumptions made in your model. Take $g = 9.8$ ms^{-2}.

For A: $F_{net} = ma$

Resolving upwards: $T - 3g = 3a$ ①

For B: $F_{net} = ma$

Resolving downwards: $5g - T = 5a$

$T = 5g - 5a$ ②

Eliminating T from ① and ②: $(5g - 5a) - 3g = 3a$

$a = 2.45$ ms^{-2}

List variables: $u = 0$; $a = 2.45$; $s = 0.4$

Use an equation with u, a, s and t in it:

$s = ut + \frac{1}{2}at^2$

$0.4 = (0 \times t) + (\frac{1}{2} \times 2.45 \times t^2)$ So $t = \sqrt{\frac{0.8}{2.45}} = 0.571$ s (3 s.f.)

Assumptions: The 3 kg mass does not hit the pulley; the 5 kg mass does not hit the ground; there's no air resistance; the string is 'light' so has zero mass; the string doesn't break; the pulley is fixed.

Connected Particles

Use F = ma in the *Direction Each Particle Moves*

EXAMPLE

A mass of 3 kg is placed on a smooth horizontal table. A light inextensible string connects it over a smooth peg to a 5 kg mass which hangs vertically as shown. Find the tension in the string if the system is released from rest. Take $g = 9.8$ ms^{-2}.

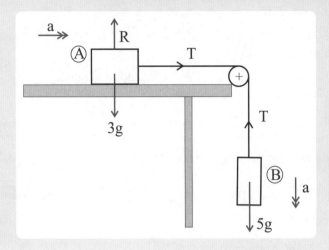

For A:
Resolve horizontally:

$F_{net} = ma$

$T = 3a$

$a = \dfrac{T}{3}$ ①

For B:
Resolve vertically:

$F_{net} = ma$

$5g - T = 5a$ ②

Sub ① into ②:

$5g - T = 5 \times \dfrac{T}{3}$

So $\dfrac{8}{3}T = 5g$

$T = 18.4$ N (to 3 s.f.)

Remember to use F ≤ μR on *Rough Planes*

More complicated pulley and peg questions have <u>friction</u> for you to enjoy too.

EXAMPLE

The peg system of the example above is set up again. However, this time a friction force, F, acts on the 3 kg mass due to the table top now being rough, with coefficient of friction $\mu = 0.5$. Find the new tension in the string when the particles are released from rest. Take $g = 9.8$ ms^{-2}.

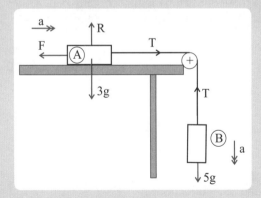

For B: Resolving vertically: $5g - T = 5a$ ①

For A: Resolving horizontally: $F_{net} = ma$
$T - F = 3a$ ②

Resolving vertically: $R - 3g = 0$

$R = 3g$

The particles are moving, so $F = \mu R = 0.5 \times 3g$
$= 14.7$ N

Sub this into ②: $T - 14.7 = 3a$

$a = \dfrac{1}{3}(T - 14.7)$

Sub this into ①: $5g - T = 5 \times \dfrac{1}{3}(T - 14.7)$

$8T = 147 + 73.5$

$T = 27.6$ N (to 3 s.f.)

Useful if you're hanging over a Batman-style killer crocodile pit...

It makes things a lot easier when you know that connected particles act like one mass, and that in M1 pulleys can always be treated as smooth. Those examiners occasionally do try to make your life easier, honestly.

Connected Particles

Particles A and B of mass 4 kg and 10 kg respectively are connected by a light inextensible string over a smooth pulley as shown. A force of 15 N acts on A at an angle of 25° to a rough horizontal plane where $\mu = 0.7$. When B is released from rest it takes 2 s to fall d m to the ground. Find d. Take $g = 9.8$ ms^{-2}.

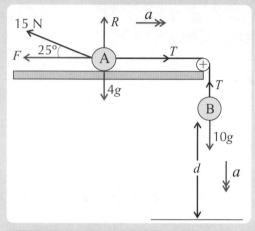

For A: Resolve vertically to find R:
$R = 4g - 15\sin 25° = 32.86$ N
$F = \mu R = 0.7 \times 32.86 = 23.00$ N

$F_{net} = ma$
$T - 23.00 - 15\cos 25° = 4a$
so $T = 4a + 36.59$ ①

For B: $F_{net} = ma$
$10g - T = 10a$
so $T = 98 - 10a$ ②

Substitute ① into ②:
$4a + 36.59 = 98 - 10a$
so $a = 4.39$ ms^{-2}

Using $s = ut + \frac{1}{2}at^2$: $s = d$, $u = 0$, $t = 2$, $a = 4.39$
so $d = (0 \times 2) + \frac{1}{2}(4.39 \times 2^2) = 8.8$ m (2 s.f.)

When B hits the ground A carries on moving along the plane. How long does it take A to stop after B hits the ground?

Speed of A when B hits the ground:
$v = u + at$: $u = 0$, $a = 4.39$, $t = 2$
$v = 0 + (4.39 \times 2) = 8.78$ ms^{-1}

Resolve to find new acceleration of A:
$-F - 15\cos 25° = 4a$

Acceleration, $a = \dfrac{-23 - 15\cos 25°}{4} = -9.15$ ms^{-2} (deceleration)

Time taken to stop:
$t = \dfrac{(v - u)}{a}$: $u = 8.78$, $v = 0$, $a = -9.15$
so $t = \dfrac{0 - 8.78}{-9.15} = 0.96$ s (to 2 s.f.)

To answer this question, you have to assume that A stops before it hits the pulley.

Rough Inclined Plane questions need Really Good force diagrams

You know the routine... resolve forces parallel and perpendicular to the plane... yawn.

A 3 kg mass is held in equilibrium on a rough ($\mu = 0.4$) plane inclined at 30° to the horizontal. It is attached by a light, inextensible string to a mass of M kg hanging vertically beneath a smooth pulley, as shown. Find M if the 3 kg mass is on the point of sliding up the plane. Take $g = 9.8$ ms^{-2}.

For B: Resolving vertically: $F_{net} = ma$
$Mg - T = M \times 0$
$T = Mg$

For A: Resolving in ↖ direction: $F_{net} = ma$
$R - 3g\cos 30° = 3 \times 0$
$R = 3g\cos 30°$

It's limiting friction, so: $F = \mu R = 0.4 \times 3g\cos 30°$
$= 10.18$ N

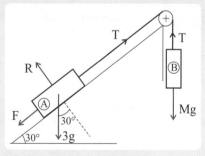

For A: Resolving in ↗ direction: $T - F - 3g\sin 30° = 3 \times 0$
$Mg - 10.18 - 3g\sin 30° = 0$
$M = 2.54$ kg (to 3 s.f.)

Connected particles — together forever... *isn't it beautiful?*

The key word here is <u>rough</u>. If a question mentions the surface is rough, then cogs should whirr and the word 'friction' should pop into your head. Take your time with force diagrams of rough inclined planes — I had a friend who rushed into drawing a diagram, and he ended up with a broken arm. But that was years later, now that I come to think of it.

Momentum

Momentum has Magnitude and Direction

Momentum is a measure of how much "umph" a <u>moving object</u> has, due to its <u>mass</u> and <u>velocity</u>.
Total momentum <u>before</u> a collision equals total momentum <u>after</u> a collision.
This idea is called "<u>Conservation of Momentum</u>".
Because it's a <u>vector</u>, the <u>sign</u> of the velocity in momentum is important.

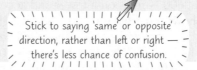

Momentum = Mass × Velocity

The unit of momentum is kgms⁻¹ or Ns

EXAMPLE

Particles A and B, each of mass 5 kg, move in a straight line with velocities 6 ms⁻¹ and 2 ms⁻¹ respectively. After colliding with B, A continues in the same direction with velocity 4.2 ms⁻¹. Find the velocity of B after impact.

Before

A 6 ms⁻¹ (5kg)   B 2 ms⁻¹ (5kg)

After

A 4.2 ms⁻¹ (5kg)   B v (5kg)

Before: Momentum A + Momentum B = $(5 \times 6) + (5 \times 2) = 40$

After: Momentum A + Momentum B = $(5 \times 4.2) + (5 \times v) = 21 + 5v$

Using conservation of momentum: $40 = 21 + 5v$

So: $v = 3.8$ ms⁻¹ in the same direction as before

Stick to saying 'same' or 'opposite' direction, rather than left or right — there's less chance of confusion.

Draw '<u>before</u>' and '<u>after</u>' diagrams to help you see what's going on.

EXAMPLE

Particles A and B of mass 6 kg and 3 kg are moving towards each other at speeds of 2 ms⁻¹ and 1 ms⁻¹ respectively. Given that B rebounds with speed 3 ms⁻¹ in the opposite direction to its initial velocity, find the velocity of A after the collision.

Before

A 2 ms⁻¹ (6kg)   1 ms⁻¹ B (3kg)

After

A v (6kg)   B 3 ms⁻¹ (3kg)

$(6 \times 2) + (3 \times -1) = (6 \times v) + (3 \times 3)$

$9 = 6v + 9$

$v = 0$

Masses Joined Together have the Same Velocity

Particles that <u>stick together</u> after impact are said to "<u>coalesce</u>". After that you can treat them as just <u>one object</u>.

EXAMPLE

Two particles of mass 40 g and M kg move towards each other with speeds of 6 ms⁻¹ and 3 ms⁻¹ respectively. Given that the particles coalesce after impact and move with a speed of 2 ms⁻¹ in the same direction as that of the 40 g particle's initial velocity, find M.

Before

A 6 ms⁻¹ (0.04kg)   3 ms⁻¹ B (M)

After

(M + 0.04) kg 2 ms⁻¹

$(0.04 \times 6) + (M \times -3) = [(M + 0.04) \times 2]$

$0.24 - 3M = 2M + 0.08$

$5M = 0.16$

$M = 0.032$ kg

Don't forget to convert all masses to the same units.

EXAMPLE

A lump of ice of mass 0.1 kg is slid across the smooth surface of a frozen lake with speed 4 ms⁻¹. It collides with a stationary stone of mass 0.3 kg. The lump of ice and the stone then move in opposite directions to each other with equal speeds. Find their speed.

Before

A 4 ms⁻¹ (0.1kg)   B 0 ms⁻¹ (0.3kg)

After

v (0.1kg)   B v (0.3kg)

$(0.1 \times 4) + (0.3 \times 0) = (0.1 \times -v) + 0.3v$

$0.4 = -0.1v + 0.3v$

$v = 2$ ms⁻¹

Ever heard of Hercules?

Well, he carried out 12 tasks. Nothing to do with momentum, but if you're feeling sorry for yourself for doing M1, think on.

M1 Section 3 — Practice Questions

Find the coefficient of friction between a student's pen and a sheet of paper. Model the pen as a rod and the paper as a rough plane... or else you could just answer the questions below, which would be a better use of your time.

Warm-up Questions

Take $g = 9.8$ ms^{-2} in each of these questions.

1) A horizontal force of 2 N acts on a 1.5 kg particle initially at rest on a smooth horizontal plane. Find the speed of the particle 3 seconds later.

2) A horizontal force P acting on a 2 kg mass generates an acceleration of 0.3 ms^{-2}. Given that the mass is in contact with a rough horizontal plane which resists motion with a force of 1 N, find P. Then find the coefficient of friction, μ, to 2 d.p.

3) A brick of mass 1.2 kg is sliding down a rough plane which is inclined at 25° to the horizontal. Given that its acceleration is 0.3 ms^{-2}, find the coefficient of friction between the brick and the plane. What assumptions have you made?

4) An army recruit of weight 600 N steps off a tower and accelerates down a "death slide" wire as shown. The recruit hangs from a light rope held between her hands and looped over the wire. The coefficient of friction between the rope and wire is 0.5. Given that the wire is 20 m long and makes an angle of 30° to the horizontal throughout its length, find how fast the recruit is travelling when she reaches the end of the wire.

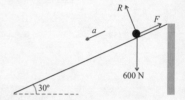

5) A 2 tonne tractor experiences a resistance force of 1000 N whilst driving along a straight horizontal road. If the tractor engine provides a forward force of 1500 N and it's pulling a 1 tonne trailer, find the resistance force acting on the trailer, and the tension in the coupling between the tractor and trailer, if they are moving with constant speed.

6) Two particles are connected by a light inextensible string, and hang in a vertical plane either side of a smooth pulley. When released from rest the particles accelerate at 1.2 ms^{-2}. If the heavier mass is 4 kg, find the weight of the other.

7) Two particles of mass 3 kg and 4 kg are connected by a light, inextensible string passing over a smooth pulley as shown. The 3 kg mass is on a smooth slope angled at 40° to the horizontal. Find the acceleration of the system if released from rest, and find the tension in the string. What force acting on the 3 kg mass parallel to the plane would be needed to maintain equilibrium?

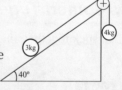

8) Each diagram represents the motion of two particles moving in a straight line. Find the missing mass or velocity (all masses are in kg and all velocities are in ms^{-1}).

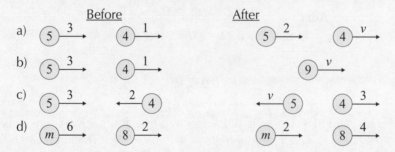

M1 Section 3 — Practice Questions

Right, those warm-up questions should have given you the momentum to get straight into these exam questions.
May the *ma* be with you...

Exam Questions

Take $g = 9.8$ ms^{-2} in each of these questions.

1   A crane moves a mass of 300 kg, A, suspended by two light cables AB and AC attached to a horizontal movable beam BC. The mass is moved in the direction of the line of the supporting beam BC during which time the cables maintain a constant angle of 40° to the horizontal, as shown.

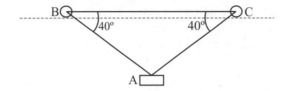

    a)   The mass is initially moving with constant speed. Find the tension in each cable.

(4 marks)

    b)   The crane then moves the mass with a constant acceleration of 0.4 ms^{-2}.
Find the tension in each cable.

(6 marks)

    c)   What modelling assumptions have you made in part b)?

(2 marks)

2   A horizontal force of 8 N just stops a mass of 7 kg from sliding down a plane inclined at 15° to the horizontal, as shown.

    a)   Calculate the coefficient of friction between the mass and the plane to 2 d.p.

(5 marks)

    b)   The 8 N force is now removed. Find how long the mass takes to slide a distance of 3 m down the line of greatest slope. Give your answer correct to 2 significant figures.

(7 marks)

3   a)   A car of mass 1500 kg is pulling a caravan of mass 500 kg. They experience resistance forces totalling 1000 N and 200 N respectively. The forward force generated by the car's engine is 2500 N. The coupling between the two does not break. Find:

        (i)   the acceleration of the car and caravan,

(3 marks)

        (ii)   the tension in the coupling.

(2 marks)

    b)   In another stage of the motion, the car and caravan are moving up a slope inclined at an angle of 2° to the horizontal. The forward force generated by the car's engine remains the same, and the resistance forces acting on the car and caravan also remain unchanged.

        (i)   Find the new acceleration of the car and caravan.

(3 marks)

        (ii)   Show that the tension in the coupling is unchanged.

(3 marks)

M1 Section 3 — Practice Questions

4   Two particles P and Q of masses 1 kg and m kg respectively are linked by a light inextensible string passing over a smooth pulley as shown. Particle P is on a rough slope inclined at 20° to the horizontal, where the coefficient of friction between P and the slope is 0.1.

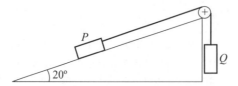

   a)   Given that P is about to slide down the plane, find the mass of Q.

   (5 marks)

   b)   Describe the motion of the system if the mass of Q is 1 kg.

   (5 marks)

5   Two particles of mass 0.8 kg and 1.2 kg are travelling in the same direction along a straight line with speeds of 4 ms⁻¹ and 2 ms⁻¹ respectively until they collide. After the collision the 0.8 kg mass has a velocity of 2.5 ms⁻¹ in the same direction. The 1.2 kg mass then continues with its new velocity until it collides with a mass of m kg travelling with a speed of 4 ms⁻¹ in the opposite direction to it.

   Given that both particles are brought to rest by this collision, find the mass m.

   (4 marks)

6   Two particles A and B are connected by a light inextensible string which passes over a smooth fixed pulley as shown. A has a mass of 7 kg and B has a mass of 3 kg. The particles are released from rest with the string taut, and A falls freely until it strikes the ground travelling at a speed of 5.9 ms⁻¹. A does not rebound after hitting the floor.

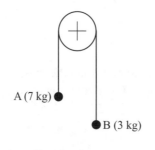

   a)   Find the time taken for A to hit the ground.

   (4 marks)

   b)   How far will B have travelled when A hits the ground?

   (2 marks)

   c)   Find the time (in s) from when A hits the ground until the string becomes taut again.

   (4 marks)

7   A coal wagon of mass 4 tonnes is rolling along a straight rail track at 2.5 ms⁻¹. It collides with a stationary wagon of mass 1 tonne. During the collision the wagons become coupled and move together along the track.

   a)   Find their speed after the collision.

   (2 marks)

   b)   State two assumptions made in your model.

   (2 marks)

General Certificate of Education
Advanced Subsidiary (AS) and Advanced Level

Mechanics M1 — Practice Exam One

Time Allowed: 1 hour 30 min

Graphical calculators may be used for this exam.

Unless told otherwise, whenever a numerical value of g is required, take g = 9.8 ms^{-2}.

There are 72 marks available for this paper.

Unless told otherwise, give any non-exact numerical answers to 3 significant figures.

1

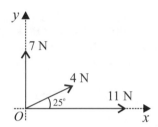

The diagram shows three forces acting at a point O on a horizontal plane. One force has magnitude 7 N and acts along the positive y-axis. The second force has magnitude 11 N and acts along the positive x-axis. The third force has magnitude 4 N and acts at an angle of 25° above the positive x-axis. Find:

a) the magnitude of the resultant of the three forces,

(5 marks)

b) the angle the resultant makes above the positive x-axis.

(3 marks)

2 A motorcyclist is travelling at 15 ms^{-1}. As he passes point A on a straight section of road, he accelerates uniformly for 4 s until he passes point B at 40 ms^{-1}. He then immediately decelerates at 2.8 ms^{-2} so that when he passes point C he is travelling at 26 ms^{-1}.
Find:

a) his acceleration between A and B,

(2 marks)

b) the time to travel from B to C,

(2 marks)

c) the distance from A to C.

(3 marks)

3   Two railway trucks A and B, with masses 3500 kg and 1500 kg respectively, are travelling towards each other on straight horizontal rails. Both trucks are travelling at 3 ms^{-1} when they collide. Assume that the trucks can be modelled as particles.

   a)   If the trucks couple together on impact and move together as a single body on the rails, find the speed and direction of the combined trucks immediately after the collision.

   (3 marks)

   b)   Assume that the trucks do not couple together following the collision, and instead, A moves with speed 1 ms^{-1} in the opposite direction to before the collision. Find the speed and direction of B immediately after the collision.

   (3 marks)

4   A car, of mass 1600 kg, is towing a horse box of mass 3000 kg along a straight, horizontal road. The car experiences a resistive force of magnitude 400 N and the horse box experiences a constant resistive force of magnitude R N. A driving force of magnitude 4300 N acts on the car. The vehicles accelerate at 0.8 ms^{-2}.

   a)   Assuming that the tow bar connecting the car to the horse box is horizontal, find:

      (i)   the tension, T, in the tow bar,

      (3 marks)

      (ii)   the resistance force, R, acting on the horse box.

      (3 marks)

   b)   When the car and horse box are travelling at a speed of 7 ms^{-1}, the horse box becomes detached from the car. Assuming that the only horizontal force now acting on the horse box is the resistive force R, find:

      (i)   the deceleration of the horse box,

      (2 marks)

      (ii)   the distance the horse box travels before it comes to rest.

      (3 marks)

5   A particle P sets off from the origin at $t = 0$ and starts to move along the x-axis in the direction of x increasing. After t seconds, P has velocity v ms^{-1}, where $v = 11t - 2t^2$ for $0 \leq t \leq 5$ and $v = -175 + 56t - 4t^2$ for $t > 5$. Find:

   a)   an expression for the acceleration of P for $0 \leq t \leq 5$,

   (2 marks)

   b)   the displacement of P from the origin at $t = 5$,

   (4 marks)

   c)   the maximum velocity of P for $t > 5$.

   (4 marks)

6   A cyclist starts from rest and accelerates at 1.5 ms⁻² for 8 s along a straight horizontal road and then continues at a constant speed. A motorist sets off from the same point as the cyclist at the same time and in the same direction, and accelerates at a constant rate for 6 s, reaching a maximum speed of V ms⁻¹. The car then decelerates at a constant rate until it comes to rest after a further 18 s. At the instant when the car comes to rest, it is overtaken by the cycle.

   a)   Calculate the greatest speed attained by the cyclist.

        (2 marks)

   b)   Sketch a (t, v) graph for the motion of the cyclist.

        (2 marks)

   c)   Sketch a (t, v) graph for the motion of the car.

        (2 marks)

   d)   Calculate the distance travelled by the cyclist before overtaking the car.

        (3 marks)

   e)   Calculate the value of V.

        (3 marks)

7   A particle A of mass 3 kg is placed on a rough plane inclined at an angle of $\tan^{-1}\frac{3}{4}$ to the horizontal and is attached by a light inextensible string to a second particle B of mass 4 kg.
      The string passes over a smooth pulley at the top of the inclined plane so that particle B hangs freely. When the system is released, particle B moves downwards vertically with an acceleration of 1.4 ms⁻² and A moves up the plane.

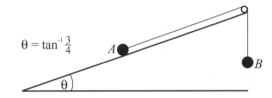

   a)   Draw a diagram showing clearly *all* the forces acting on the particles.

        (2 marks)

   Find:

   b)   the normal reaction between particle A and the plane, to 2 decimal places,

        (2 marks)

   c)   the tension in the string,

        (2 marks)

   d)   the friction force acting on particle A,

        (3 marks)

   e)   the coefficient of friction between particle A and the plane.

        (2 marks)

   Two seconds after the particles are released, the string breaks. A then continues up the plane until it comes instantaneously to rest. At no point does A reach the pulley. Find:

   f)   how far particle B moves from the start of the motion until the string breaks,

        (2 marks)

   g)   how far particle A moves from the instant the string breaks until it comes to rest.

        (5 marks)

General Certificate of Education
Advanced Subsidiary (AS) and Advanced Level

Mechanics M1 — Practice Exam Two

Time Allowed: 1 hour 30 min

Graphical calculators may be used for this exam.

Unless told otherwise, whenever a numerical value of g is required, take $g = 9.8$ ms^{-2}.

There are 72 marks available for this paper.

Unless told otherwise, give any non-exact numerical answers to 3 significant figures.

1   Three forces act at a point, O, as shown below.

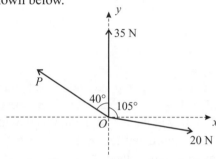

a)   Given that there is no net force in the direction of the x-axis, find P.

(2 marks)

b)   Find the magnitude and direction of the resultant force, R.

(3 marks)

R acts on a particle of mass 5 kg, causing it to move. Find:

c)   the acceleration, a, of the particle.

(2 marks)

d)   the time it takes the particle to move a distance of 6 m, given that the particle is initially at rest.

(3 marks)

2   The displacement, x m, of a particle from a fixed point O at time t s is $x = t^4 + 6t^3 - 24t^2 + 1$, where $t \geq 0$.
     Find:

a)   the particle's displacement at time $t = 1$ s,

(1 mark)

b)   the particle's velocity at time $t = 2$ s,

(3 marks)

c)   (i)   the time at which the particle's acceleration is zero,

(6 marks)

     (ii)   the velocity at this time.

(2 marks)

3   A small ring of mass m kg is threaded onto a rough, inextensible rope held taut and horizontal. The ring is held in limiting equilibrium by a string pulling upwards at an angle of 51.3° to the horizontal. The coefficient of friction between the ring and the rope is 0.6 and the magnitude of the frictional force is 1.5 N.

a)   Sketch a diagram showing the ring and the forces acting upon it.

(2 marks)

b)   Find the tension in the string, T, and the mass of the ring, m.

(6 marks)

4   A roller coaster moves from rest along a track with constant acceleration, taking 2 s to reach a speed of 6 ms⁻¹. It then travels at a constant speed for 15 s. The roller coaster decelerates uniformly to rest in 1 s as it reaches the top of the hill. It then waits for 5 s before accelerating uniformly down a vertical slope for 4 s, reaching a maximum speed of 30 ms⁻¹.

a)   Sketch a (t, v) graph representing the motion of the roller coaster.

(2 marks)

b)   Find the greatest acceleration experienced by the roller coaster.

(3 marks)

c)   What is the total distance travelled by the roller coaster?

(3 marks)

5

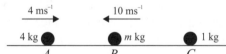

Two particles A and B of mass 4 kg and m kg respectively are moving towards each other on a smooth, horizontal surface. A has speed 4 ms⁻¹ and B has speed 10 ms⁻¹. A third particle, C, of mass 1 kg, is at rest. B lies between A and C.

a) A and B collide and their directions of motion are reversed. Immediately following the collision, A moves with speed 2 ms⁻¹ and B moves with speed v ms⁻¹. Use conservation of momentum to show that $mv = 24 - 10m$.

(3 marks)

b) B goes on to collide with C. B and C coalesce on impact and begin moving with speed 7 ms⁻¹ in the direction of B before this collision. Show that $mv = 7(m + 1)$.

(2 marks)

c)   Hence find:

(i)   the mass m,

(3 marks)

(ii)   the speed v.

(2 marks)

6   A rocket with mass 1 400 000 kg is launched vertically upwards by engines providing a force of 34 000 000 N.

   a)   Calculate the expected acceleration of the rocket, assuming that the only other force acting on the rocket is its weight.

   (2 marks)

   b)   The actual acceleration is measured at 12 ms^{-2}.
        Find the magnitude of the total resistive force, R, acting on the rocket.

   (2 marks)

   c)   Find the time taken to reach a height of 20 km. Give your answer to the nearest second.

   (2 marks)

   d)   At a height of 20 km, the engines stop firing, and the rocket moves freely under gravity (i.e. the resistive force can be ignored). Find the maximum height reached by the rocket.

   (4 marks)

   e)   State one modelling assumption you have made.

   (1 mark)

7

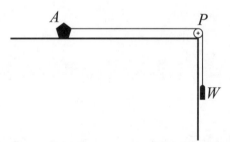

A particle, A, of mass 0.2 kg is attached to a weight, W, of mass 0.3 kg, by a light inextensible string which passes over a smooth pulley, P, as shown. When the system is released from rest, with the string taut, A and W experience an acceleration of 4 ms^{-2}. A moves across a rough horizontal plane and W falls vertically.

   a)   Find the coefficient of friction, μ, between A and the horizontal plane.

   (5 marks)

   W falls for h m until it hits the ground and does not rebound. A continues to move until it reaches P with speed 3 ms^{-1}. The initial distance between A and P is $\frac{7}{4}h$ m.

   b)   Find the distance h.

   (7 marks)

   c)   How did you use the information that the string is inextensible?

   (1 mark)

Algorithms

Welcome to the wonderful world of Decision Maths. And what a good decision it was too. This page is on algorithms, which aren't as scary as they sound. You've probably come across algorithms before, though you might not know it.

Algorithms are sets of Instructions

An <u>algorithm</u> is just a fancy mathematical name for a <u>set of instructions</u> for <u>solving</u> a problem. You come across lots of algorithms in everyday life — <u>recipes</u>, <u>directions</u> and <u>assembly instructions</u> are all examples of algorithms.

1) Algorithms start with an <u>input</u> (e.g. in a recipe, the input is the raw ingredients). You carry out the algorithm on the input, following the instructions <u>in order</u>.

Anyone should be able to follow an algorithm — not just the person who wrote it, or someone who understands the process fully.

2) Algorithms have an <u>end result</u> — something that you <u>achieve</u> by carrying out the algorithm (e.g. a cake). An algorithm is said to be <u>correct</u> if it achieves its end result.

3) Algorithms will <u>stop</u> when you've reached a <u>solution</u>, or produced your <u>finished product</u> — they're <u>finite</u>. They <u>must</u> have a <u>stopping condition</u> — an <u>instruction</u> that tells you to stop when you've reached a certain point.

4) Algorithms are often written so that <u>computers</u> could follow the instructions. <u>Computer programming</u> is an important application of Decision Maths.

In Maths, the End Result is the Solution

Most mathematical algorithms are general — they work for a range of different inputs. However, for simple cases, following the algorithm mightn't be the most efficient method.

Algorithms can be used to solve <u>mathematical problems</u> too.

1) The <u>input</u> in a mathematical algorithm is the <u>number</u> (or numbers) you start with. Your <u>end result</u> (output) is the <u>final number</u> you end up with — this'll be the <u>solution</u> to the original problem.

2) Any number you put in will have a <u>unique</u> output — you won't get different sets of solutions for the same input.

3) It's a good idea to <u>write down</u> the numbers each instruction produces in a <u>table</u> — sometimes the algorithm will <u>tell you</u> when to do this. This table is called a <u>trace table</u>.

The Russian Peasant algorithm Multiplies two numbers

The Russian Peasant algorithm is a well-known algorithm that multiplies two numbers together. And I've no idea what Russian peasants have to do with it.

1) Write down the two numbers that you are multiplying in a table. Call them x and y.

2) Divide x by 2 and write down the result underneath x, ignoring any halves.

E.g. if $x = 11$, when you divide it by 2 you write down 5, not 5.5.

3) Multiply y by 2 and write down the result underneath y.

4) Repeat steps 2) - 3) for the numbers in the new row. Keep going until the number in the x-column is 1.

This is an example of a stopping condition.

5) Work down your table and cross out every row that has an even value for x.

6) Add up the remaining numbers in the y-column (i.e. the ones that haven't been crossed out). This is the solution xy.

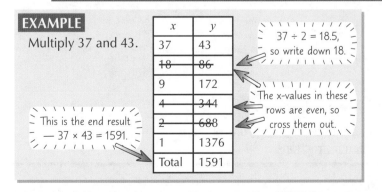

EXAMPLE

Multiply 37 and 43.

x	y
37	43
~~18~~	~~86~~
9	172
~~4~~	~~344~~
~~2~~	~~688~~
1	1376
Total	1591

37 ÷ 2 = 18.5, so write down 18.

The x-values in these rows are even, so cross them out.

This is the end result — 37 × 43 = 1591.

EXAMPLE

Multiply 21 and 52.

x	y
21	52
~~10~~	~~104~~
5	208
~~2~~	~~416~~
1	832
Total	1092

This is the end result — 21 × 52 = 1092.

Feel the beat of the rithm of the night...

For your homework tonight, I would like you to make me a cake please. My favourite's carrot cake with cream cheese icing.

Algorithms

There's a bit more background stuff you need to know about algorithms — it's the mathsiest bit in this section, so enjoy it while you can. Then it's onto pseudo-code, when you get to be a pseudo-computer.

The **Order** of an algorithm tells you how **Fast** it is

It's useful to know how long an algorithm takes to run — that way you can compare two algorithms and decide which is better.

1) The size of an algorithm is the number of inputs you have — so for an algorithm like the bubble sort (see p194), the size is how many numbers you have in your list. The size of an algorithm is usually written as n.

2) How long an algorithm takes to run is measured by its efficiency — this will be a function of n (e.g. $n^2 - n$). The time it takes depends on how many operations the algorithm involves — if there are lots of operations, it'll take longer. The efficiency gives you the worst case scenario (i.e. the maximum number of times you'll need to run the algorithm or carry out a particular operation for n inputs).

3) The order (or complexity) of an algorithm is a way of comparing how efficient algorithms are.

4) You work out the order by looking at the highest power of n in the function:
   - If the highest power is 1, e.g. $5n + 2$, the algorithm is of linear order (you'd write it as $O(n)$ or order 1).
   - If the highest power is 2, e.g. $5n^2 + 6n$, the algorithm is of quadratic order (you'd write $O(n^2)$ or order 2).
   - If the highest power is 3, e.g. $n^3 + 2n^2 + 3n$, the algorithm is of cubic order (you'd write $O(n^3)$ or order 3).

5) The order tells you how the time changes as the size (n) increases. If n is doubled, a linear order algorithm will take about twice as long, a quadratic order algorithm will take about $2^2 = 4$ times as long and a cubic order algorithm will take about $2^3 = 8$ times as long.

> **EXAMPLE** A computer uses a quadratic algorithm. It takes 1.8 seconds to carry out the algorithm on a set of 50 numbers. Estimate how long it will take when there are 250 numbers.
>
> In this example, $n = 50$. $250 = 5 \times 50$, so you have to multiply the time by $5^2 = 25$ as the algorithm is quadratic. So when there are 250 numbers, it will take $1.8 \times 25 = 45$ seconds to carry out the algorithm.

Some algorithms are written in **Pseudo-Code**

1) Algorithms can be written in lots of different ways — e.g. a set of written instructions, a flow chart (see next page), computer programming language or pseudo-code.

2) Pseudo-code is a bit like computer programming language, but less formal — it's written for a person, not a computer. It won't be written in full sentences though — just a set of brief instructions.

3) In the exam, you need to be able to follow an algorithm written in pseudo-code, but you won't have to write your own. You might have conditions like IF and THEN — you only do the THEN instruction if the IF bit's true.

There's an example of this in the questions on p198 — make sure you can follow it.

> **EXAMPLE** This is the pseudo-code for an algorithm that outputs the first 10 triangle numbers:
>
> STEP 1: Input X = 1 and Y = 2
> STEP 2: Print X
> STEP 3: Let X = X + Y
> STEP 4: Let Y = Y + 1
> STEP 5: If Y < 11, then return to STEP 2.
> STEP 6: Stop.
>
> *You start off with X = 1 and Y = 2, so you print 1, then X becomes 1 + 2 = 3 and Y becomes 3. 3 < 11, so you go back to step 2. This time, print 3, then X becomes 3 + 3 = 6 and Y becomes 4. You carry on like this until Y = 11.*
>
> Following this algorithm gives 1, 3, 6, 10, 15, 21, 28, 36, 45, 55.

4) Algorithms are pretty easy to alter — all you have to do is change one of the steps. You can do this on flow charts too, or on written instructions.

I'll have fish and chips twice please...

Say you had a cubic algorithm that was faster than a speeding bullet. Then if you doubled the size of the problem, it would take $2^3 = 8$ times as long. Which means that it would now be faster than a high-speed train, but not as fast as a bullet — good if you're trying to rescue someone tied to the train tracks, less good if you're trying to rescue someone from a bullet.

Flow Charts

Right, now you know all the background stuff, it's time to have some fun. Well, I say fun, but really it's just putting algorithms into flow charts and stuff like that.

Algorithms can be written as *Flow Charts*

Instead of giving instructions in <u>words</u> (like in the Russian Peasant example on p.191), some algorithms are written as <u>flow charts</u>. There are three different types of <u>boxes</u> which are used for different things:

(Start / Stop)   [Instruction]   < Decision >

The boxes are connected with <u>arrows</u> to guide you through the flow chart. 'Decision' boxes will ask a question, and for each one you have a <u>choice</u> of arrows, one arrow for '<u>yes</u>' and one for '<u>no</u>', which will take you to another box. Sometimes flow charts will include a loop which takes you back to an earlier stage in the chart. Loops are a way of <u>repeating steps</u> until the algorithm is <u>finished</u>.

Put the *Results* from the flow chart into a *Trace Table*

It can sometimes be a bit tricky keeping track of the <u>results</u> of a flow chart, especially if you have to go round a <u>loop</u> lots of times. It's a good idea to put your results into a <u>trace table</u> — it's much easier to see the <u>solutions</u> that way.

EXAMPLE

This flow chart works out the factors of a number, *a*.

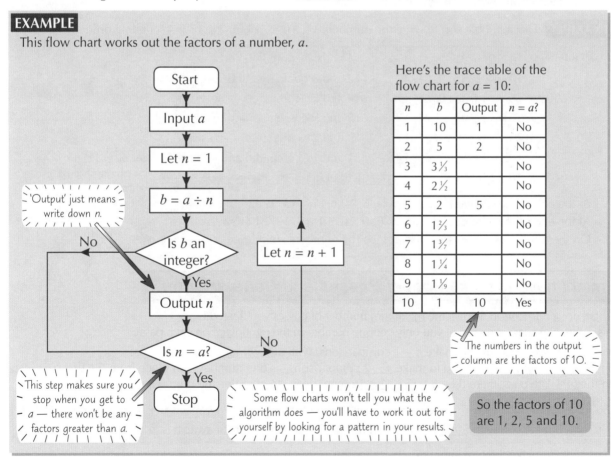

Here's the trace table of the flow chart for $a = 10$:

n	b	Output	$n = a$?
1	10	1	No
2	5	2	No
3	$3\frac{1}{3}$		No
4	$2\frac{1}{2}$		No
5	2	5	No
6	$1\frac{2}{3}$		No
7	$1\frac{3}{7}$		No
8	$1\frac{1}{4}$		No
9	$1\frac{1}{9}$		No
10	1	10	Yes

The numbers in the output column are the factors of 10.

'Output' just means write down *n*.

This step makes sure you stop when you get to *a* — there won't be any factors greater than *a*.

Some flow charts won't tell you what the algorithm does — you'll have to work it out for yourself by looking for a pattern in your results.

So the factors of 10 are 1, 2, 5 and 10.

Things seem to be flowing nicely...

Don't worry — you won't be expected to write algorithms in your exam, but you need to be able to use them. Some algorithms can look a bit confusing if there are lots of steps and decisions, but if you work through them slowly step by step they aren't too bad. Have a go at the one on this page for some different values of *a* — try *a* = 12, 17 and 18.

Sorting

You've probably been able to sort things into alphabetical or numerical order since you were knee-high to a hamster, but in D1 you need to know how to sort things using an algorithm. At least it'll be easy to check your answer.

A *Bubble Sort* compares *Pairs* of numbers

The bubble sort is an algorithm that sorts numbers (or letters). It's pretty easy to do, but it can be a bit fiddly, so take care.

The Bubble Sort

1) Look at the first two numbers in your list. If they're in the right order, you don't have to do anything with them. If they're the wrong way round, swap them. It might help you to make a note of which numbers you swap each time.

2) Move on to the next pair of numbers (the first will be one of the two you've just compared) and repeat step 1. Keep going through the list until you get to the last two numbers. This set of comparisons is called a pass.

If there are n numbers in your list, there will be $n - 1$ comparisons in the first pass.

3) When you've finished the first pass, go back to the beginning of the list and start again. You won't have to compare the last pair of numbers, as the last number is now in place. Each pass has one less comparison than the one before it. When there are no swaps in a pass, the list is in order.

Stop when there are *No More Swaps*

It's called the bubble sort because the highest numbers rise to the end of the list like bubbles (apparently). It'll all be a lot easier once you've been through an example...

EXAMPLE Use a bubble sort to write the numbers 14, 10, 6, 15, 9, 21, 17 in ascending order.

First pass:

<u>14, 10</u>, 6, 15, 9, 21, 17	14 and 10 compared and swapped
10, <u>14, 6</u>, 15, 9, 21, 17	14 and 6 compared and swapped
10, 6, <u>14, 15</u>, 9, 21, 17	14 and 15 compared — no swap
10, 6, 14, <u>15, 9</u>, 21, 17	15 and 9 compared and swapped
10, 6, 14, 9, <u>15, 21</u>, 17	15 and 21 compared — no swap
10, 6, 14, 9, 15, <u>21, 17</u>	21 and 17 compared and swapped
10, 6, 14, 9, 15, 17, 21	End of first pass.

At the end of the first pass, the highest number has moved to the end of the list.

At the end of the second pass the list is: 6, 10, 9, 14, 15, 17, 21 (2 swaps).
At the end of the third pass the list is: 6, 9, 10, 14, 15, 17, 21 (1 swap).
On the fourth pass there are no swaps, so the numbers are in ascending order.

There were 7 swaps in total.

You might have to make *Lots* of *Passes* and *Comparisons*

1) If there are n numbers in the list, the maximum number of passes you'll need is $n - 1$.
This is the worst case scenario (if you only get one number in the right place on each pass).

2) On the first pass, you have to make $n - 1$ comparisons, with a maximum of $n - 1$ swaps.
On the second pass, you'll have to make $n - 2$ comparisons, as one number is in place from the first pass, etc.
On the $(n - 1)$th pass, there'll be $n - (n - 1) = 1$ comparison, so after this the numbers will be in order.

So for a bubble sort with 7 numbers, max. number of comparisons (or swaps) is $6 + 5 + 4 + 3 + 2 + 1 = 21$
Or for a bubble sort with 50 numbers, max. number of comparisons (or swaps) is $\frac{1}{2} \times 49 \times 50 = 1225$

3) If you have to make the maximum number of swaps, it means that the original list was in reverse order.

4) You can also use the algorithm to put numbers in descending order — on each comparison, just put the higher number first instead.

For big lists, use the formula $S_k = \frac{1}{2}k(k + 1)$ for the sum of the first k whole numbers (though if $n = 50$, you want the sum of the first 49 numbers).

Double, double, toil and trouble, fire burn and cauldron bubble...

The efficiency of the bubble sort algorithm is the maximum number of comparisons you might have to make. It's given by the function $\frac{1}{2}(n - 1)n = \frac{1}{2}n^2 - \frac{1}{2}n$, so the bubble sort is a quadratic order algorithm — see p.192 for more about order.

Sorting

The bubble sort can get a bit boring after a while — sometimes when you swap one pair of numbers, you know that you're going to have to make another swap on the next pass. Fortunately the shuttle sort finds a way around that.

The **Shuttle Sort** is an **Improved** version of the **Bubble Sort**

The main problem with the bubble sort is that you have to make a lot of comparisons. The shuttle sort is a bit more efficient, as it reduces the overall number of comparisons needed.

The Shuttle Sort

1) Look at the first two numbers in your list. If they're in the right order, leave them as they are. If they're the wrong way round, swap them. This is your first pass.

2) Move on to the next pair of numbers (the first will be one of the two you've just compared) and repeat step 1.

A pass in a shuttle sort is different to a pass in a bubble sort.

3) If you made a swap on the second comparison, compare the number you've just swapped to the first number in the list. If they're the wrong way round, swap them. This is your second pass.

4) Now move on to the next pair of numbers (the third and fourth in the list) and compare them. If you make a swap, compare the number you've just swapped to the number before it, and swap if you need to. Keep working backwards until either you get to a number it can't be swapped with or you reach the beginning of the list. This is another pass completed.

5) Continue through the list, repeating step 4 until you get to the last number in the list. Each time, compare backwards until you can't swap the number anymore.

The shuttle sort usually needs fewer comparisons than the bubble sort — though you'll have to make the same number of swaps. After the first pass, the first 2 numbers will be in the right places. After the second pass, the first three numbers will be in the right places and so on. For a list of n numbers, you'll need to make $n - 1$ passes to get the list in order.

The **Shuttle Sort** will have the **Same Number** of **Swaps** as the **Bubble Sort**

Even though you'll have to make the same number of swaps as you would using the bubble sort, you'll make fewer comparisons — this means the shuttle sort's more efficient.

EXAMPLE   Use a shuttle sort to write the numbers 14, 10, 6, 15, 9, 21, 17 in ascending order.

This is the same set of numbers used in the bubble sort example on the previous page.

Pass	List	Comparison
First pass:	14, 10, 6, 15, 9, 21, 17	14 and 10 compared and swapped
Second pass:	10, 14, 6, 15, 9, 21, 17	14 and 6 compared and swapped
	10, 6, 14, 15, 9, 21, 17	10 and 6 compared and swapped
Third pass:	6, 10, 14, 15, 9, 21, 17	14 and 15 compared — no swap
Fourth pass:	6, 10, 14, 15, 9, 21, 17	15 and 9 compared and swapped
	6, 10, 14, 9, 15, 21, 17	14 and 9 compared and swapped
	6, 10, 9, 14, 15, 21, 17	10 and 9 compared and swapped
	6, 9, 10, 14, 15, 21, 17	6 and 9 compared — no swap
Fifth pass:	6, 9, 10, 14, 15, 21, 17	15 and 21 compared — no swap
Sixth pass:	6, 9, 10, 14, 15, 21, 17	21 and 17 compared and swapped
	6, 9, 10, 14, 15, 17, 21	15 and 17 compared — no swap
	6, 9, 10, 14, 15, 17, 21	End of shuttle sort.

The shuttle sort is also a quadratic algorithm.

There are 7 numbers, so you have to make 7 – 1 = 6 passes. It was much quicker than the bubble sort — there were only 11 comparisons (instead of 18). You still needed to make 7 swaps though.

Not quite as exciting as a space shuttle — more exciting than a shuttlecock...

The shuttle sort is trickier than a bubble sort, but it's more efficient. Make sure you don't get them mixed up — or even worse, combine the two. Attempting to do a buttle sort in the exam might make the examiners laugh, but it won't get you any marks.

Packing

Packing to go on holiday can be a pain. You've got so much to fit in your suitcase, and there's always the risk of your shampoo leaking. Well, you'll be pleased to know that there are a couple of algorithms that are about packing (admittedly not holiday packing, but I'm sure you could adjust them to make them work).

These algorithms are called *Bin Packing Algorithms*

1) In bin packing problems, you have a set of items that you need to fit into the minimum number of bins.

2) One of the most common examples is fitting boxes of different heights on top of each other into bins of a given height. You need to arrange the boxes to use the fewest bins possible.

3) Other examples include things like cutting specified lengths of wood from planks of a fixed length (you want to minimise the number of planks used), or loading items of different weights into lorries that have a maximum weight capacity (again, you want to use the smallest number of lorries possible).

4) There's often more than one solution that uses the minimum number of bins. These solutions all have the least wasted space.

One solution might be preferable to the others. E.g. evenly loading a group's rucksacks might be fairer than completely filling most people's and leaving one person's virtually empty.

The *First-Fit* algorithm puts the items in the *First Bin* they'll go in

The first-fit algorithm is quick and easy, but it probably won't give you the best possible solution. Here's how it works:

1) Take the first item in the list and put it in the first bin.

2) Move on to the next item, and put it in the first bin it'll fit into. It might fit in the first bin, or you might have to move on to another bin.

3) Repeat step 2) until all the items are in a bin. For each item, try the first bin before you move on to the next.

EXAMPLE The ad breaks in a TV programme can be no longer than 150 seconds. Use the first-fit algorithm to sort the adverts into the breaks, saying how many breaks are needed and how much time is wasted.

A: 90s   B: 75s   C: 30s   D: 65s   E: 120s   F: 45s   G: 60s

Ad break 1:   A: 90s, C: 30s   space left: ~~60s~~ 30s

Ad break 2:   B: 75s, D: 65s   space left: ~~75s~~ 10s

Ad break 3:   E: 120s   space left: 30s

Ad break 4:   F: 45s, G: 60s   space left: ~~105s~~ 45s

B won't fit in break 1, as there's only 60s left after A, so it goes in break 2. However, C < 60s, so it fits in break 1.

So the adverts can be fitted into 4 ad breaks, with 30 + 10 + 30 + 45 = 115s wasted.

The *First-Fit Decreasing* algorithm needs the items in *Descending Order*

1) The first-fit decreasing algorithm is very similar to the first-fit algorithm except you need to put the items in descending order first.

You can use one of the sorting algorithms on pages 194-195.

2) Once you've got your ordered list, you just carry out the first-fit algorithm above.

3) This algorithm usually gives you a better solution than the first-fit algorithm, but it still might not be the best.

EXAMPLE Ribbon comes in rolls of length 5m. For the lengths of ribbon given below, use the first-fit decreasing algorithm to work out how the lengths can be cut from the rolls. You should also say how many rolls are needed and how much ribbon is wasted. All lengths are in metres.

2.5   1.9   2.9   3.1   2.7   2.2   1.8   2.0

First, use a sorting algorithm to put the lengths in order. The new list is:

3.1   2.9   2.7   2.5   2.2   2.0   1.9   1.8

Now use the first-fit algorithm to sort the lengths into rolls:

Roll 1:   3.1, 1.9   length left: ~~1.9~~ 0

Roll 2:   2.9, 2.0   length left: ~~2.1~~ 0.1

Roll 3:   2.7, 2.2   length left: ~~2.3~~ 0.1

Roll 4:   2.5, 1.8   length left: ~~2.5~~ 0.7

The ribbon can be cut from 4 rolls, with 0 + 0.1 + 0.1 + 0.7 = 0.9m wasted.

If you solved this problem using the first-fit algorithm, you'd use 5 rolls and waste 5.9m of ribbon.

I've bin packing my suitcase for my holiday...

Sorry, sorry, that was terrible. Try not to confuse first-fit with first-past-the-post — one's a bin packing algorithm, the other's a voting system. If you get them mixed up, you might end up trying to see how many politicians you can fit in a box. Hmm...

D1 Section 1 — Practice Questions

That's the first section of D1 done and dusted — and I don't think it was that bad. Once you get your head round the fact that 'algorithm' is just a fancy word for 'set of instructions', you're over the first hurdle. Time now for a few questions to check you know your stuff. Here are some straightforward ones to start off with.

Warm-up Questions

1) For each of the following sets of instructions, identify the input and output.
   a) a recipe for vegetable soup,
   b) directions from Leicester Square to the Albert Hall,
   c) flat-pack instructions for building a TV cabinet.

2) Use the Russian Peasant algorithm to multiply 17 and 56.

3) What are diamond-shaped boxes in flow diagrams used for?

4) Use the flow chart on p.193 to work out the factors of 16.

5) Use a bubble sort to write the numbers 72, 57, 64, 54, 68, 71 in ascending order.
   How many passes do you need to make?

6) If you had to put a list of 10 numbers in order using a bubble sort,
   what is the maximum number of comparisons you'd need to make?

7) An algorithm has order $O(n^2)$. If it takes 0.4s to apply the algorithm to a set of 20 numbers,
   approximately how long will it take on a set of 60 numbers?

8) Use a shuttle sort to write the numbers 21, 11, 23, 19, 28, 26 in ascending order.

9) Six items of weights 5 kg, 11 kg, 8 kg, 9 kg, 12 kg, 7 kg need to be packed
   into boxes that can hold a maximum weight of 15 kg.
   a) Pack the items into the boxes using the first-fit algorithm. State how much space is wasted.
   b) Pack the items into the boxes using the first-fit decreasing algorithm. State how much space is wasted.

If those warm-up questions have left you hungry for more, here are some tasty exam-style questions for you to sink your teeth into. They'll need a bit more work than the warm-up questions, but it'll be worth it, I promise.

Exam Questions

1   77   83   96   105   78   89

    a)   Use a shuttle sort to arrange the list of numbers above into descending order.
           Give the number of comparisons and the number of swaps for each pass.

(5 marks)

    b)   The list of numbers above is to be sorted into descending order using a bubble sort.
        (i)   Which number(s) will definitely be in the correct position after the first pass?

(1 mark)

        (ii)   Write down the maximum number of passes and the maximum number of swaps
             needed to sort a list of 6 numbers into descending order.

(2 marks)

D1 Section 1 — Practice Questions

If you thought I'd leave you hanging with just <u>one exam question</u>, you're very much mistaken.
I'd <u>never</u> be that mean to you — and to prove it, here's another page full of <u>beautiful exam questions</u>.

Exam Questions

2   Consider the following algorithm:

Step 1:   Input A, B with $A < B$
Step 2:   Input $N = 1$
Step 3:   Calculate $C = A \div N$
Step 4:   Calculate $D = B \div N$
Step 5:   If both C and D are integers, output N
Step 6:   If $N = A$, then stop. Otherwise let $N = N + 1$ and go back to Step 3.

a)   Carry out the algorithm with $A = 8$ and $B = 12$. Record your results.

(3 marks)

b)   (i)   What does this algorithm produce?

(1 mark)

   (ii) Using your answer to part (i) or otherwise, write down the output that would be
          produced if you applied the algorithm to $A = 19$ and $B = 25$, and explain your answer.
          You do not need to carry out the algorithm again.

(2 marks)

3   A joiner has planks of wood that are 3 m long. He needs to cut pieces of wood from the planks in the
    following lengths:

1.2 m   2.3 m   0.6 m   0.8 m   1.5 m   1.0 m   0.9 m   2.5 m

a)   Use the first-fit bin packing algorithm to fit the lengths of wood onto the planks.
     State how many planks are needed and how much wood is wasted.

(3 marks)

b)   The joiner knows that the first-fit decreasing algorithm is quadratic.
     A computer takes 2.1 s to carry out the algorithm on a set of 30 numbers.
     Estimate how long it will take for 120 numbers.

(2 marks)

4   a)   Rearrange the following set of numbers into ascending order using a shuttle sort.

1.3   0.8   1.8   0.5   1.2   0.2   0.9

     State how many passes you made.

(5 marks)

b)   How many comparisons and swaps were made on the first pass?

(1 mark)

Graphs

You probably reckon you're an old pro at graphs. But the graphs coming up are rather different. For a start, there's not a scrap of squared paper in sight. Fret not — soon they'll be as innocuous to you as a bar chart.

Graphs have **Points** Connected by **Lines**

Here's the definition of a graph:

> A **graph** is made up of **points** (called **nodes** or **vertices**) joined by **lines** (called **arcs** or **edges**).

Graphs can be used to <u>model</u> or <u>solve</u> real-life problems. Here are a few examples:

Use Graphs to show **Connections** in **Geographical Problems**

In this graph, the vertices represent towns and the edges represent roads.

The graph doesn't show where the towns are in relation to each other — just how they are linked by roads.

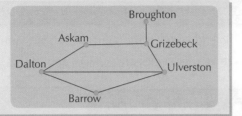

Weighted Graphs have a **Number** on Each Arc

1) <u>Weighted graphs</u>, or <u>networks</u>, have a number associated with each edge (called the <u>weight</u> of the edge).

2) Weights often give you <u>lengths</u> — like in this network showing points in a nature reserve and the footpaths joining them. They sometimes give you <u>costs</u> or <u>times</u> too.

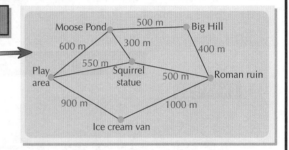

Digraphs have **Directed Edges**

Sometimes edges have <u>directions</u>, e.g. to show one-way streets. If they do, they're called <u>directed edges</u> and the graph is a <u>digraph</u> or a <u>directed graph</u>.

> A graph without any directed edges is sometimes referred to as an undirected graph. Whoopi-do.

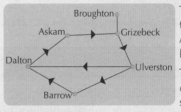

The edges on this digraph show the bus routes between the towns. A bus goes from Dalton to Askam, but not from Askam to Dalton.

There's no direction on the edge connecting Broughton and Grizebeck, so the buses run in both directions.

Graphs Can be **Connected** or **Not Connected**...

1) Two vertices are <u>connected</u> if there's a route between them.
2) A graph is <u>connected</u> if <u>all</u> its vertices are connected.

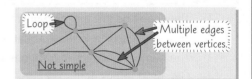

...**Simple** or **Not Simple**...

1) Graphs can have <u>more than one edge</u> between a pair of vertices. There can also be <u>loops</u> connecting vertices to themselves.

2) Graphs <u>without</u> any loops or multiple edges between vertices are called <u>simple graphs</u> (like the nature reserve and bus route examples above).

...**Complete** or **Not Complete**

Each vertex in a <u>complete graph</u> is joined <u>directly</u> to every other vertex by exactly one edge.

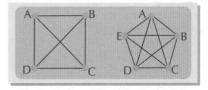

I've got geographical problems — I have no sense of direction...

The situations you can model with a graph are limited only by your imagination. In exams, they're limited only by the examiner's imagination. You might get a situation you've not seen before, but don't panic — just read the question carefully.

Graphs

More terminology coming up. Make sure you totally get it, or confusion will be the next thing coming up.

A **Path** is a Route in the Graph Which **Doesn't Repeat Any Vertices**

A path is a <u>sequence of edges</u> that flow on, end to end. The only thing is, you <u>can't</u> go through a vertex more than once.

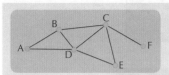

One possible path here is <u>ABDECF</u>. Another is <u>CBAD</u>.

DCECF <u>isn't</u> a path because you go through vertex C more than once.

A **Cycle** is a Path that **Brings you Back** to Your Starting Point

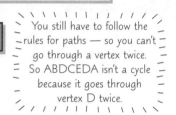

You still have to follow the rules for paths — so you can't go through a vertex twice. So ABDCEDA isn't a cycle because it goes through vertex D twice.

1) A <u>cycle</u> (or <u>circuit</u>) is a <u>closed path</u>. The <u>end</u> vertex is the same as the <u>start</u> vertex.
2) So on the graph above, <u>ABDA</u> is a cycle. Other cycles are <u>ABCDA</u> and <u>CEDBC</u>.

Subgraphs are Just **Bits of Another Graph**

1) These are absolute doddles. If you take a graph, and rub a few bits out, then you're left with a <u>subgraph</u>.
2) Here's the posh definition to learn:

A **subgraph** of graph G is a graph where all the vertices and edges belong to G.

EXAMPLE

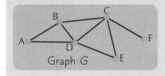 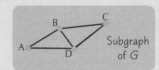 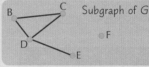 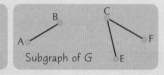

Trees are **Graphs** that have **No Cycles**

They also have to be <u>connected graphs</u> (see previous page).

Both graphs here are connected — but <u>only</u> the first is a <u>tree</u> (the graphical type of tree that is).

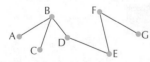 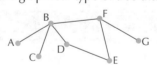

This is a tree — there are no cycles.

This one <u>isn't</u> a tree — there's a cycle (BDEFB.)

Spanning Trees are **Subgraphs** that are **Also Trees**

1) They can't be just any old subgraph though — they have to include <u>all the vertices</u>.
2) So if you're asked to draw a <u>spanning tree of a graph</u>, you can only delete <u>edges</u> from the original graph.
3) The number of <u>edges</u> in a spanning tree is always <u>one less</u> than the number of <u>vertices</u>.
4) Like most things in this section, a few diagrams speak a thousand words...

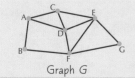

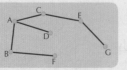

A spanning tree of G. There's no cycle, and it contains all the vertices from G.

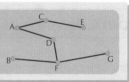

Another spanning tree of G. There are plenty more that could be drawn too.

A subgiraph — just the neck or a leg...

A page of lovely definitions. You'll need them very, very soon, so learn them and then scribble them out from memory. Then check back to the page to see what you missed. Graphs are all over the place — the London Underground map is one.

Graphs

If these graph definitions were a tunnel, you'd now be seeing a dot of light in the distance.

Planar Graphs can be Drawn so they Only Cross at Nodes

1) Planar graphs can be drawn on a plane in such a way that <u>the edges only cross at vertices</u>.

2) Be really careful if you're asked to say if a graph is <u>planar or not</u>.
E.g.

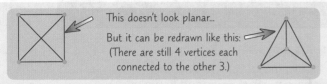

This doesn't look planar...
But it can be redrawn like this:
(There are still 4 vertices each connected to the other 3.)

3) This graph is <u>non-planar</u>:

Distance Matrices show the Weights between Vertices

1) To draw a distance <u>matrix</u> from a weighted digraph (p. 199), go through each space in the matrix and write down the <u>weight</u> between the two vertices. You only include <u>direct links</u> — don't start adding weights together.

2) Be really careful with <u>directed edges</u>. A weight on a directed edge only goes in <u>one</u> space of the matrix, as below.

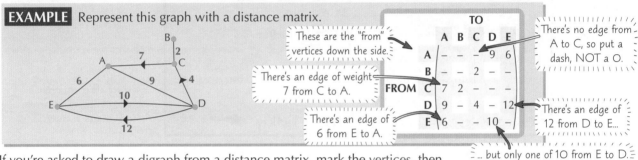

EXAMPLE Represent this graph with a distance matrix.

These are the "from" vertices down the side.

There's an edge of weight 7 from C to A.

There's an edge of 6 from E to A.

There's no edge from A to C, so put a dash, NOT a O.

There's an edge of 12 from D to E...

... but only one of 10 from E to D.

	TO				
FROM	A	B	C	D	E
A	–	–	–	9	6
B	–	–	2	–	–
C	7	2	–	–	–
D	9	–	4	–	12
E	6	–	–	10	–

3) If you're asked to draw a <u>digraph</u> from a distance matrix, mark the <u>vertices</u>, then go through the matrix, adding <u>edges</u> and <u>weights</u> in. If a weight only appears <u>once</u> in the matrix, the edge must be directed, so add an arrow.

The Order of a Node is the Number of Lines coming off it

1) Here's the formal definition:

This is sometimes called the 'degree' or 'valency' of a node or vertex.

> The **order** of a node is the number of edges connected to it.

EXAMPLE Calculate the order of each node in the graph below.

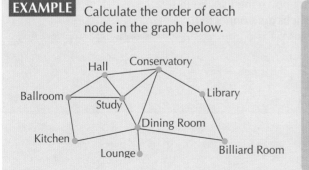

Node	Order
Ballroom	3
Billiard Room	2
Conservatory	4
Dining Room	5
Hall	3
Kitchen	2
Library	2
Lounge	1
Study	4

Rules of Orders

The sum of the orders is always <u>double</u> the number of edges.
(It's a count of how many edge ends there are.)

So, the sum of orders is always even.

Here, there are 13 edges and the sum of the orders is 26 (2 × 13).

2) A vertex with an <u>odd order</u> is <u>odd</u>, and one with an <u>even order</u> is — wait for it — <u>even</u>.
So the Billiard Room, Conservatory, Kitchen, Library and Study are all even, and the rest are odd.

Learn the definitions and it'll all become planar...

I didn't put the bit about the <u>sum of orders</u> always being <u>even</u> in *just* because it's fascinating. (Although it certainly is.) It actually comes up quite often in exam questions. They don't ask you straight out though. They'll phrase it in a cunning way. E.g. Why can't you have a graph consisting of three vertices with odd orders? Just stay calm and it'll be OK.

Minimum Spanning Trees

The stuff you've seen so far in this section might seem like it's been dreamed up by bored mathematicians to provide you with useless facts to learn. But this minimum spanning tree stuff is actually rather handy in the real world.

A *Minimum Spanning Tree* is the *Shortest* way to Connect All the Points

See page 200 if you've forgotten what spanning trees are. And remember — an arc is just another name for an edge.

A **minimum spanning tree** (MST) is a spanning tree where the total length of the arcs is as **small as possible**.

An MST is also known as a minimum connector.

Minimum spanning trees come in handy for cable or pipe-laying companies. If they need to connect several buildings in a town, say, they'd want to find the cheapest path — this may be the shortest route, or have the easiest ground to dig up.

Kruskal's Algorithm Finds Minimum Spanning Trees

Being absolutely certain that you've got the minimum spanning tree is tricky, so using an algorithm helps.

KRUSKAL'S ALGORITHM

1) List the arcs in ascending order of weight.

2) Pick the arc of least weight — this starts the tree.

3) Look at the next arc in your list.
   - if it forms a cycle, DON'T use it and go on to the next arc.
   - if it doesn't form a cycle, add it to the tree.

4) Repeat step 3 until you've joined all the vertices.

This is a 'greedy algorithm'. You make the choice that seems best at each stage, without worrying about later choices.

If there are n vertices in a network, there will always be (n − 1) arcs in an MST.

EXAMPLE Use Kruskal's algorithm to find a minimum spanning tree for this network.

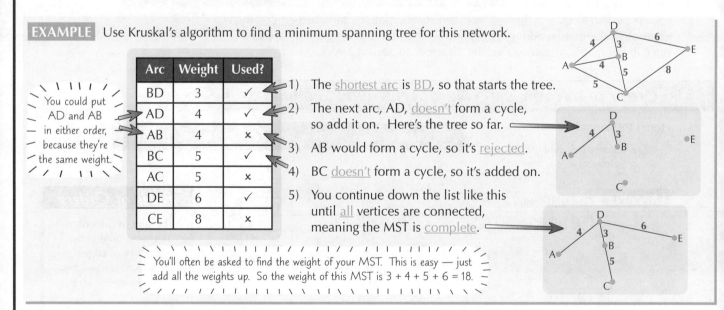

Arc	Weight	Used?
BD	3	✓
AD	4	✓
AB	4	✗
BC	5	✓
AC	5	✗
DE	6	✓
CE	8	✗

You could put AD and AB in either order, because they're the same weight.

1) The shortest arc is BD, so that starts the tree.

2) The next arc, AD, doesn't form a cycle, so add it on. Here's the tree so far.

3) AB would form a cycle, so it's rejected.

4) BC doesn't form a cycle, so it's added on.

5) You continue down the list like this until all vertices are connected, meaning the MST is complete.

You'll often be asked to find the weight of your MST. This is easy — just add all the weights up. So the weight of this MST is 3 + 4 + 5 + 6 = 18.

There are often a few different MSTs that can be found for a network — and you might be asked to find them.

In the list above, AB could have been used instead of AD, or AC instead of BC. All the different combinations of these arcs give three more MSTs:

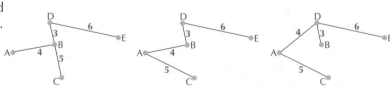

MST = Mathematical Stress and Tension...

All the minimum spanning trees for a network have the same total weight — if they didn't, they wouldn't all be minimums. Kruskal's algorithm works fine, but you can't do it straight from matrix forms of graphs, which is what computers often use. And if you've got a whopping network, this might be important. This is where Prim's algorithm is tops — see the next page...

Minimum Spanning Trees

Prim's algorithm does exactly the same job as Kruskal's algorithm. I'd love to say you only need to learn the one you like best, but that'd be a fib. You've got to learn them both, of course.

Prim's Algorithm *Finds Minimum Spanning Trees Too*

<u>PRIM'S ALGORITHM</u>

1) Pick a vertex, <u>any vertex</u> — this <u>starts</u> the tree.

2) Choose the arc of <u>least weight</u> that'll join a vertex <u>in the tree</u> to one <u>not yet</u> in the tree.

3) Repeat step 2 until you've joined <u>all</u> the vertices.

If there's more than one to pick from, just choose randomly.

EXAMPLE Use Prim's algorithm to find a minimum spanning tree for the network on the right.

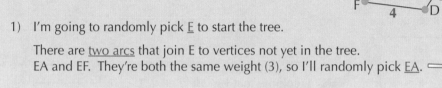

1) I'm going to randomly pick <u>E</u> to start the tree.

There are <u>two arcs</u> that join E to vertices not yet in the tree. EA and EF. They're both the same weight (3), so I'll randomly pick <u>EA</u>.

2) There are three arcs that join a vertex <u>in</u> the tree (A or E) to a vertex <u>outside</u> the tree: AB (2), AF (4), EF (3).

3) <u>AB</u> has the <u>least weight</u>, so that's the one to add.

4) Now the choice is from arcs AF (4), EF (3) or BC (6) — they join a vertex in the tree (A, B or E) to one not yet in the tree.

5) <u>EF</u> has the <u>least weight</u>, so it's added on next.

You <u>don't</u> have to check for cycles like you did with Kruskal's algorithm. Connecting to a vertex <u>outside</u> the tree will never make a cycle (one less thing to worry about).

6) Nearly there now — the next choice is from BC (6), FC (7) or FD (4).

7) <u>FD</u> has <u>least weight</u>, so that's the one to add.

8) Finally, C could be joined by BC (6), FC (7) or DC (5).

9) <u>DC</u> has the <u>least weight</u>, so that's the final arc.

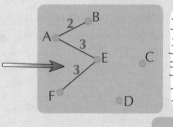

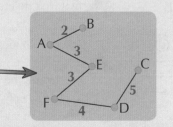

You might be asked to comment on how appropriate your solution is. E.g. imagine the arcs are bus routes of different lengths, and you're considering cancelling some. Even though the towns A-F are still all connected in the minimum spanning tree, people who live at B and work at C are likely to be very cross.

Wasn't Mr Prim one of the Mr Men?...

Practice, practice, practice is definitely the key for this algorithm too. There are only three steps to memorise, so that's not too tricky. You've just got to apply them accurately — so check you've considered all the possible arcs. Exam questions usually ask you to show your working, or to state the order that you add the arcs in, so winging it with a different method won't do.

Minimum Spanning Trees

The easiest way of putting a graph into a computer is to use a matrix. And the reason why Prim's algorithm is so useful is that it can be used on a <u>distance matrix</u>. It looks like a horrible mess of crossing out and circling randomly, but stay with me, and it'll all come clear.

Prim's Algorithm *Can be Used on* **Distance Matrices**

PRIM'S ALGORITHM

1) Pick <u>any vertex</u> to start the tree.
2) Cross out the <u>row</u> for the new vertex and circle the <u>column</u> for it.
3) Look for the <u>smallest weight</u> that's in <u>ANY circled column</u> AND <u>isn't</u> yet crossed out. Circle it. This is the <u>next arc</u> to add to the tree. The row it's in gives you the <u>new vertex</u>.
4) <u>Repeat</u> steps 2 and 3 until all the rows are crossed out.

EXAMPLE Use Prim's algorithm to find a minimum spanning tree for the graph represented by this distance matrix.

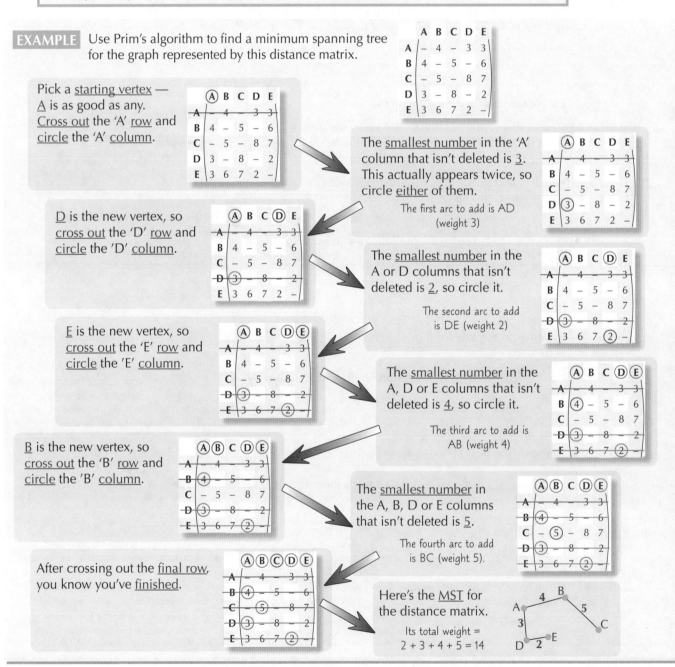

Pick a <u>starting vertex</u> — <u>A</u> is as good as any. <u>Cross out</u> the 'A' <u>row</u> and <u>circle</u> the 'A' <u>column</u>.

The <u>smallest number</u> in the 'A' column that isn't deleted is <u>3</u>. This actually appears twice, so circle <u>either</u> of them.

The first arc to add is AD (weight 3)

<u>D</u> is the new vertex, so <u>cross out</u> the 'D' <u>row</u> and <u>circle</u> the 'D' column.

The <u>smallest number</u> in the A or D columns that isn't deleted is <u>2</u>, so circle it.

The second arc to add is DE (weight 2)

<u>E</u> is the new vertex, so <u>cross out</u> the 'E' <u>row</u> and <u>circle</u> the 'E' column.

The <u>smallest number</u> in the A, D or E columns that isn't deleted is <u>4</u>, so circle it.

The third arc to add is AB (weight 4)

<u>B</u> is the new vertex, so <u>cross out</u> the 'B' <u>row</u> and <u>circle</u> the 'B' column.

The <u>smallest number</u> in the A, B, D or E columns that isn't deleted is <u>5</u>.

The fourth arc to add is BC (weight 5).

After crossing out the <u>final row</u>, you know you've <u>finished</u>.

Here's the <u>MST</u> for the distance matrix.

Its total weight = 2 + 3 + 4 + 5 = 14

This method also calculates the birthdate of your one true love...

When you're doing this yourself, you don't have to draw out the matrix a zillion times like I've done. Phew, I hear you say. I just wanted you to see all my steps. It took me ages, so do admire them all, and then have a practice for yourself.

Dijkstra's Algorithm

This is another of those algorithms that look really, really complicated. But when you've <u>learnt the steps</u>, you can string them together pretty rapidly. This one does a different job from the last two, so don't just skim the first bit.

Dijkstra's Algorithm Finds the Shortest Path between Two Vertices

1) If you're driving between <u>two cities</u> with a complicated road network between them, it's good to be able to work out which route is <u>quickest</u> (just like satnavs do).

2) <u>Dijkstra's algorithm</u> is a foolproof way to do this. Basically, you <u>label each vertex</u> with the length of the shortest path found so far from the starting point. If you find a <u>shorter path</u>, then you <u>change the label</u>. You keep doing this until you're sure that you've got the shortest distance to it.

> Weights can also represent costs — you might want to find the cheapest route.

DIJKSTRA'S ALGORITHM

> Once you've given a vertex a permanent label, you can't change it.

1) Give the <u>Start vertex</u> the <u>permanent label '0'</u>. This is also called a <u>final value</u>.

2) Find all the vertices <u>directly connected</u> to the vertex you've just given a permanent label to. Give each of these vertices a <u>temporary label</u> (also called a <u>working value</u>).

> Dijkstra's algorithm is quadratic (order $O(n^2)$), where n is the number of vertices — see page 192.

$$\text{Temporary label} = \frac{\text{Permanent label}}{\text{at previous vertex}} + \frac{\text{weight of arc}}{\text{between previous}} \atop \text{vertex and this one.}$$

If one of these vertices already has a temporary label, replace it <u>ONLY</u> if the new working value is <u>lower</u>.

3) Look at the <u>temporary labels</u> of vertices that <u>don't</u> have a permanent label yet. Pick the <u>smallest</u> and make this the <u>permanent label</u> of that vertex.

> If two vertices have the same smallest temporary labels, pick either.

4) Now repeat steps 2 and 3 until the <u>End vertex</u> has a <u>permanent label</u> (this is the shortest path length).

5) Trace the route <u>backwards</u> (from the End vertex to the Start vertex). An arc is on the path if:

> Weight of arc = Difference in permanent labels of the arc's vertices

---

EXAMPLE: Use Dijkstra's algorithm to find the shortest route between A and G.

In the exam, you'll be given a version of the graph to work out the answer on. It'll have <u>boxes</u> to complete at each vertex. Here's what goes in each box:

Order of becoming permanent	Permanent label
Temporary labels	

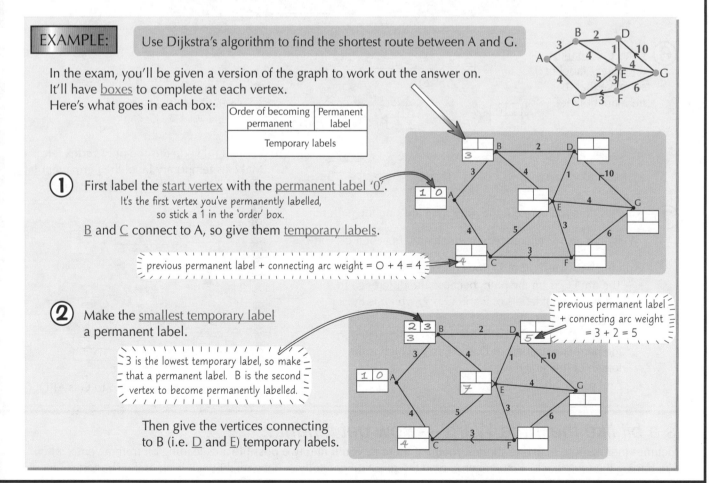

(1) First label the <u>start vertex</u> with the <u>permanent label '0'</u>.
It's the first vertex you've permanently labelled, so stick a 1 in the 'order' box.
<u>B</u> and <u>C</u> connect to A, so give them <u>temporary labels</u>.

> previous permanent label + connecting arc weight = 0 + 4 = 4

(2) Make the <u>smallest temporary label</u> a permanent label.

> 3 is the lowest temporary label, so make that a permanent label. B is the second vertex to become permanently labelled.

> previous permanent label + connecting arc weight = 3 + 2 = 5

Then give the vertices connecting to B (i.e. <u>D</u> and <u>E</u>) temporary labels.

Dijkstra's Algorithm

③ Again, make the <u>smallest temporary label</u> a permanent label.

> 4 is the lowest temporary label, so make that a permanent label. C is the third vertex to be labelled.

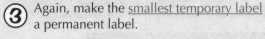

Then give all vertices without permanent labels connecting to C a temporary label. It's only <u>E</u>, because F is connected by a <u>directed edge</u> that only goes from <u>F to C</u>, not from C to F.

> 4 + 5 = 9, but this is greater than the current temporary label for E, so you DON'T replace it.

④ You're probably getting the idea now. Make the smallest temporary label a <u>permanent label</u>. In this case it's <u>5</u> (making D the <u>4th</u> vertex to be labelled).

Give all vertices without permanent labels connecting to D a temporary label. It's only E in this case. (G is connected by a <u>directed edge</u> running in the opposite direction. And of course B <u>already</u> has a permanent label.)

> 5 + 1 = 6 (you're coming from vertex D this time). This is smaller than the current temporary label for E, so you DO replace it.

⑤ <u>E</u> has the <u>smallest temporary label</u> (6), (in fact the only temporary label) so make that its <u>permanent label</u>.

Give the vertices connecting to <u>E</u> (F and G) temporary labels.

> 6 + 4 = 10

> 6 + 3 = 9

⑥ <u>F</u> has the <u>smallest temporary label</u> of 9, so make that its permanent label.

> 9 + 6 = 15. This is greater than the current temporary label for G, so you leave it as 10.

G (the <u>End vertex</u>) is the only vertex left. Make its temporary label the <u>permanent label</u> — this is the length of the <u>shortest route</u>.

⑦ Now it's time to figure out the <u>route</u>. An arc's on the path if:

> Weight of arc = Difference in permanent labels of arc's vertices

Working backwards from G (the <u>End vertex</u>):

* The arc <u>EG</u> is on the path, because the <u>difference</u> in the permanent labels of E and G is <u>4</u>, which is the length of the arc <u>EG</u>.
* The arc <u>DE</u> is on the path, because the <u>difference</u> in the permanent labels of D and E is <u>1</u>, which is the length of the arc <u>DE</u>.
* And so on, all the way back to <u>A</u>.

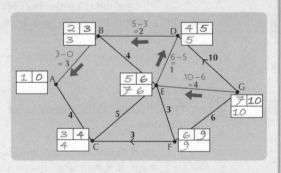

So the <u>shortest route</u> from A to G is <u>ABDEG</u>.

It's a bit like the Time Warp — now get it right...

Sometimes there's more than one shortest route. If there is, you'll find two possible arcs leading off from a vertex when you're tracing the route back. Remember to read the question carefully — they might want both of the shortest routes.

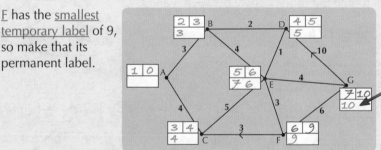

D1 Section 2 — Practice Questions

Right, now for this algorithm. 1) <u>Try</u> the questions. 2) <u>Check</u> your answers. 3) Reread the page on any you got <u>wrong</u>.
4) Repeat steps 1-3 until you get them all <u>right</u>.

Warm-up Questions

1) Explain what the following are: a) network, b) directed graph, c) tree, d) spanning tree

   Questions 2–7 are about the graph on the right.

2) Draw two subgraphs of the graph.

3) Explain why this graph is: a) planar, b) simple

4) Describe a possible path and a possible cycle in the graph.

5) The graph is currently connected. Delete some edges so that it isn't connected any more.

6) List the order of each node.
   Explain the link between the number of edges and the sum of the orders.

7) Add an arc so that there are only two odd nodes.

8) Here's a distance matrix. Draw the graph it represents.

9) Using Dijkstra's algorithm on
   the graph on page 205:

   a) Find the shortest route from A to F.

   b) Delete edge BD. Now find the
      shortest route from A to G.

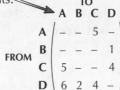

$$\begin{array}{c} \\ \textbf{FROM} \end{array} \begin{array}{c} \\ \\ \textbf{A} \\ \textbf{B} \\ \textbf{C} \\ \textbf{D} \end{array} \overset{\textbf{TO}}{\begin{pmatrix} \textbf{A} & \textbf{B} & \textbf{C} & \textbf{D} \\ - & - & 5 & - \\ - & - & - & 1 \\ 5 & - & - & 4 \\ 6 & 2 & 4 & - \end{pmatrix}}$$

Now for some questions just like you'll get in the exam. They really are the best sort of practice you can do.

Exam Questions

1 **Figure 1** shows the potential connections for a
   sprinkler system between greenhouses at a plant
   nursery.

   The numbers on each arc represent the cost in pounds
   of each connection.

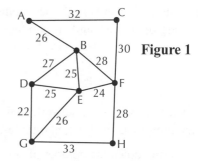

Figure 1

   a) Use Kruskal's algorithm to find a minimum spanning tree for the network in **Figure 1**.
      List the edges in the order that you consider them and indicate whether you are adding
      them to your minimum spanning tree.

      (3 marks)

   b) State the minimum cost of connecting the sprinkler system.

      (1 mark)

   c) Draw the minimum spanning tree obtained in a).

      (2 marks)

   d) If Prim's algorithm had been used to find the minimum spanning tree, starting from E,
      find which edge would have been the final edge added. Show your working.

      (2 marks)

   e) State two advantages of Prim's algorithm over Kruskal's algorithm for finding
      a minimum spanning tree.

      (2 marks)

D1 Section 2 — Practice Questions

Keep going. You can do it. No need for gas and air yet.

2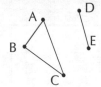

In a complete graph, each node is directly connected to every other node by exactly one edge.

In a connected graph, each node is connected, either directly or indirectly to every other node.

a) State the number of arcs that would need to be added to the graph above to make the graph complete.

(1 mark)

b) State the number of edges that would need to be added to the graph above to make the graph connected.

(1 mark)

c) How many edges does a minimum spanning tree for a graph with 5 nodes have?

(1 mark)

d) What is the sum of the orders of the nodes for the graph above?

(1 mark)

e) Explain why it is impossible to add edges to the graph above so that all nodes have an odd order.

(2 marks)

3 The table shows the lengths, in miles, of the roads between five towns.

a) Use Prim's algorithm, starting from A, to find a minimum spanning tree for this table. Write down the arcs in the order that they are selected.

(3 marks)

b) Draw your tree and state its total weight.

(2 marks)

c) State the number of other spanning trees that are the same length as your answer in part b).

(1 mark)

	A	B	C	D	E
A	–	14	22	21	18
B	14	–	19	21	20
C	22	19	–	21	15
D	21	21	21	–	24
E	18	20	15	24	–

4 This diagram shows a network of forest paths. The number on each edge represents the time, in minutes, required to walk along the path.

a) Write down the number of edges in a minimum spanning tree of the network shown.

(1 mark)

b) Use Dijkstra's algorithm to find the fastest route from A to I. State how long the route will take.

(6 marks)

c) A new path, requiring x minutes to walk along, is to be made between G and H. The new path reduces the time required to walk between A and I. Find and solve an inequality for x.

(2 marks)

d) Dijkstra's algorithm is adapted so that it is repeated a number of times, starting from each vertex in turn and going to a randomly selected second vertex. What is the order/complexity of the algorithm now?

(2 marks)

Traversable Graphs

You know that puzzle where you have to draw the shape on the right <u>without</u> taking your pencil off the paper?
Well, you're about to find out the logic behind it and exactly which points you can <u>start</u> drawing from.

Graphs can be **Eulerian**...

If **all** the vertices in a graph have an **even order**, the graph is **Eulerian**. ◄

The order, degree or valency of a vertex is the number of edges connected to it (see page 201).

1) These three graphs are all <u>Eulerian</u>.
   Every vertex is <u>even</u>.

   The numbers show the orders.

2) Eulerian graphs are <u>traversable</u>. This means it's <u>always possible</u> for you to start at <u>any point</u>, draw along each edge <u>exactly once</u> without taking your pen off the paper, and end up back at your <u>starting position</u>. Not every route works, but there'll definitely be some that do.

3) Or to look at it another way, if the graph represents <u>roads</u>, it's possible to walk down each of them <u>exactly once</u> before getting back to your <u>starting point</u>.

EXAMPLE Find a route that traverses the graph on the right.

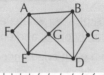

The graph is Eulerian. So you can start at any point.
A possible route is: AGDBCDEGBAFEA.
Another route is: EDCBDGAFEABGE. ◄

No matter which route you take, it'll always involve passing through the same number of vertices (13 in this case).

...Semi-Eulerian...

If **exactly two vertices** have an **odd order**, and the rest are even, the graph is **semi-Eulerian**.

1) These three graphs are all <u>semi-Eulerian</u>.
   There are exactly <u>two odd</u> vertices.

2) Semi-Eulerian graphs are <u>semi-traversable</u>. This means it's possible to go along every edge on the graph <u>exactly once</u>, but <u>ONLY</u> if you start at one odd vertex and end up at the <u>other</u> odd vertex.

EXAMPLE Find a route that traverses the graph on the right.

This graph is semi-Eulerian, so you have to start and end at the odd vertices (A and D).
A possible route is: ABDCA around the square, then ABDCA around the circle, then across the diagonal to D.

Remember — the sum of orders is always even (see page 201).
This means there'll always be an even number of odd vertices in a graph.
So you'll never have 3 or 5 odd vertices, but you might have 4 or 6.

...or **Neither**

1) If a graph has <u>more than two odd vertices</u>, you <u>can't</u> traverse it.

2) There's <u>no route</u> that travels along each edge exactly once. You have to go along some of them <u>twice</u>.

Some lovely non-Eulerian graphs. Try to find a route through them that goes along each edge exactly once. No taking your pen off the paper. See — you can't, can you?

Eul 'er now and it might stop 'er squeaking...

Right. So, Eulerian = traverse from any point and get back to starting point. Semi-Eulerian = traverse from one odd vertex to the other odd vertex. Non-Eulerian = you can't traverse. You have to go over some edges twice. And that's about it.

Route Inspection Problems

The route inspection problem is also called the Chinese postman problem. (It's named after a Chinese guy called Kwan Mei-Ko who discovered it in the 1960s. He wasn't a postman though — he was a mathematician.)

The **Route Inspection Algorithm** Finds the **Shortest Route** Covering **All Edges**

1) Route inspection problems ask you to find the shortest route through a network that goes along each edge before returning to the starting point.
2) It's the route that, say, a railway engineer would take if he had to inspect all the tracks.
3) In postman terms, the postman wants to find the shortest route that allows him to deliver letters to every street in a city, and brings him back to his starting point for a cup of tea.
4) And you'll never guess what. There are algorithms for solving these types of problems.
5) The first step is always to consider whether the graph is Eulerian, semi-Eulerian, or neither.

See the previous page.

A pre-1960s postman still manages to raise a smile, despite walking further than he has to each day.

Eulerian Graphs are Most **Straightforward**

Remember — in an Eulerian graph, all vertices have an even order.

Length of inspection route in an Eulerian graph = Weight of network

1) Eulerian graphs are traversable. So whatever point you start from, you can travel along each edge exactly once, and end up back at your start point.
2) Because you've gone down each edge once, you find the length of the route by just adding up all the edge weights.

> **EXAMPLE** Find an inspection route for the network on the right. Your route must start and finish at A. State the length of the route.
>
> The graph is Eulerian — the vertices all have even orders (they're all 4). So the graph is traversable, and a possible route is: ABCDABCDA (once round the quadrilateral, then once around the circle).
>
> Length of the route = sum of weights = 4 + 6 + 5 + 2 + 5 + 7 + 6 + 3 = 38

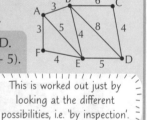

Semi-Eulerian Graphs are a **Bit Trickier**

In a semi-Eulerian graph, exactly two vertices have an odd order, remember.

In semi-Eulerian networks, you have to repeat the shortest path between the two odd vertices in an inspection route. You can think of it as adding arcs to make the network Eulerian so that it can be traversed.

This formula lets you find the length of the inspection route:

Length of inspection route in a semi-Eulerian graph = Weight of network + weight of the shortest path between the two odd vertices

> **EXAMPLE** Find an inspection route for the network on the right. Your route must start and finish at B. State the length of the route.
>
>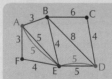
>
> The graph is semi-Eulerian — the odd vertices are A and D. The shortest path between them is AED, of length **10** (5 + 5). So extra edges AE and ED are added.
>
> A possible path is BCDEFABDEAEB.
>
> *This is worked out just by looking at the different possibilities, i.e. 'by inspection'.*
>
> *Rather than use the formula, you could just find the length of your path by adding all the weights.*
>
> The weight of the network = 3 + 6 + 4 + 5 + 4 + 3 + 5 + 4 + 8 = **42**
>
> Length of inspection route = Weight of network + weight of shortest path between odd vertices = 42 + 10 = **52**

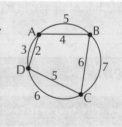

You only have to do this if you want to start and end at the same vertex. If you can pick and choose, just start at one odd vertex and end at the other. Then the length of the route will equal the network's weight (see the previous page).

Of course, during postal strikes, the postman stays put...

In the exam, you'll either be able to figure out the distance between the odd vertices by just looking, or you'll have worked it out earlier in the question using Dijkstra's algorithm (p.205). Right, now to find out what to do with non-Eulerian graphs...

Route Inspection Problems

The previous page told you how to find the shortest inspection route for Eulerian and semi-Eulerian networks. Now it's time to find out how to do it with <u>non-Eulerian networks</u>. It's a teensy bit more complicated — but I guess that's why it comes up more often in exam questions.

Learn the **Route Inspection Algorithm** for **Non-Eulerian** Networks

1) Non-Eulerian networks have <u>more than</u> two odd vertices.

2) In the exam, you'll probably be given a network with <u>four odd vertices</u>, but you could get one with <u>six</u>.

> <u>FINDING THE SHORTEST INSPECTION ROUTE FOR A NON-EULERIAN NETWORK:</u>
> With this method you can start at <u>any vertex</u>, and you'll end up at the <u>same one</u>.
> <u>Pair</u> the odd vertices in all the possible ways, find the pairing that gives you the
> <u>smallest total</u>, then <u>repeat the paths</u> between these pairs of vertices.

This'll become clearer with an example:

EXAMPLE Find an inspection route for the network below. Your route must start and finish at E. State the length of the route.

1) Pick out the vertices with <u>odd orders</u>.

   They're marked in pink on this network — A, B, C, D ⟹

2) <u>Pair</u> the vertices in <u>all the ways possible</u>.

   There are 3 ways to pair 4 vertices: AB + CD
   AC + BD
   AD + BC

3) Work out the <u>minimum total distance</u> for each pairing.

   E.g. for AB + CD, you find the smallest distance between AB, and the smallest distance between CD, and add them together:

   AB + CD = 5 + 4 = 9
   AC + BD = 8 + 8 = 16 ⟸ BD direct = 9, but BCD = 8.
   AD + BC = 12 + 4 = 16

   > There are loads of paths from A to D. By inspection, ACD is shortest (8 + 4 = 12), so use that one.

4) Pick the pairing with the <u>smallest total distance</u>.

   With a length of 9, it's <u>AB + CD</u> that has the smallest total. AB and CD will be the paths you repeat in the inspection route.

   > 6 odd vertices means 15 possible pairings, so it's important to be systematic. Learn this method and you won't miss any:
   > For A, B, C, D, E, F, use:
   > 1) AB, with the three pairings of C, D, E, F.
   > 2) AC, with the three pairings of B, D, E, F.
   > 3) AD, with the three pairings of B, C, E, F.
   > 4) AE, with the three pairings of B, C, D, F.
   > 5) AF, with the three pairings of B, C, D, E.

5) Add <u>extra edges</u> along each path in your pair.

   Add edges to repeat the path between <u>A and B</u> and to repeat the path between <u>C and D</u>.

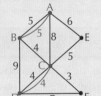

6) The graph is now <u>Eulerian</u> — so you can find an <u>inspection route</u> through it.

   A possible route starting and finishing at E = EABDCABCFDCE. ⟸ I've marked the pink paths for you.

   > Alternatively, you could just add up all the edges on your path. ⟹

7) Add the <u>lengths of the new edges</u> to the <u>weight of the network</u> to get the length of the inspection route.

   The length of the route = weight of network + length of extra edges
   = 51 + 9 = <u>60</u>

   > Weight of network = 5 + 6 + 8 + 4 + 5 + 9 + 4 + 7 + 3 = 51

He ain't heavy — so he's the best pairing possible...

Even if it's screamingly obvious which pairing is going to have the smallest value, always show the examiner that you've considered all the possible pairings and didn't just get lucky this once. Oh, and the most direct path mightn't be the shortest, so do check carefully, or it'll cock the whole thing up, and you'll shed marks like a German Shepherd sheds fur.

Route Inspection Problems

After asking you to find an inspection route for a network starting and finishing at <u>a certain point</u>, the examiners will often tell you to find the minimum inspection route if you can <u>start and finish wherever you like</u>.

Starting and Finishing at **Different Odd Vertices** Always **Shortens** the Route

In a network with <u>odd vertices</u>, the shortest route which goes down each path at least once always involves <u>starting at one odd vertex</u> and <u>ending at a different odd vertex</u>.

FINDING THE SHORTEST INSPECTION ROUTE STARTING AND ENDING AT DIFFERENT POINTS OF YOUR CHOICE:
You <u>start at one odd vertex</u> and <u>end at another odd vertex</u>. If you have <u>four</u> odd vertices, you <u>only</u> have to <u>repeat the path</u> between <u>one pair</u> of vertices. You want this path to be <u>as short as possible</u>. With <u>six</u> odd vertices, you'll have to repeat the paths between <u>two distinct pairs</u> of vertices. You need their <u>total</u> to be <u>as short as possible</u>.

EXAMPLE A feather duster salesman wants to travel along each street in a housing estate.
He can start his journey at any point, and end it at any point.
The graph represents the streets in the estate, and the numbers represent the lengths of each street in hundreds of metres.

(a) State the vertices that the salesman could start at to minimise his journey.

There are four odd vertices, and you're going to <u>start and end</u> at <u>two of them</u>, so this leaves one pair of odd vertices. You have to <u>repeat the path</u> between these two vertices, so make sure it's the <u>shortest possible</u>.

The odd vertices are <u>B, C, D, E</u>.
The distance between each possible pair is:
BC = 5, DE = 4, BD = 8, CE = 9, BE = 8, CD = 5

> With six odd vertices, you'll have 15 pairs. You have to pick the two with the smallest total, but they have to be totally separate vertices — e.g. BC and DE (not CD and DE).

The distance between <u>D and E</u> is shortest, at only 4. So that's the path you need to repeat.
So you start at <u>either</u> of vertices <u>B or C</u>, and end at the other.

(b) Find the length of his journey.

You just have to repeat the path between D and E.
So, total length of journey = weight of network + path between D and E
= 54 + 4 = <u>58</u>

Always <u>check the units</u> — the weights represent <u>hundreds of metres</u>, so the journey is actually <u>5800 metres</u> long, or <u>5.8 km</u>.

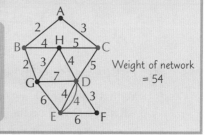

Weight of network = 54

Walking on **Both Sides** of the Street Makes it an **Eulerian Network**

1) Sometimes, the usual 'inspection route' or 'Chinese postman' problem is <u>changed</u> so that the person has to go down <u>each path twice</u>. Perhaps they'll be inspecting each pavement, or delivering leaflets to both sides of the streets.

2) This actually makes it <u>easier</u> to solve. It effectively <u>doubles</u> the edges at each vertex, making all the vertices <u>even</u>. The network is now <u>Eulerian</u>, so you can <u>traverse</u> it, and the length of the inspection route will just be <u>double the weight</u> of the network.

EXAMPLE The feather duster salesman decides to go down each street twice, once on each side.
What is the length of his new route?

Weight of original network = 54.
Weight of doubled network = 54 × 2 = 108
Length of new route = <u>10 800 metres</u>, or <u>10.8 km</u>.

> B was an odd vertex with 3 edges connected to it. It's now effectively even with 6 edges connected to it.

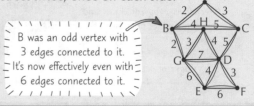

How's your network? — dunno, the fish just sort of get caught in it...

Remember — always read the question carefully to see what it's asking. Don't just scan it, say "Ah, Chinese postman" and jump in there. The examiners might have added a subtle twist. But to be kind, they'll often just tell you the network's weight.

D1 Section 3 — Practice Questions

Right. Time to see if you have the information from this section stuck in your head...

Warm-up Questions

1) Say whether each of these graphs is <u>Eulerian</u>, semi-Eulerian or <u>neither</u>.

   a) 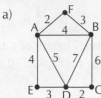 b) 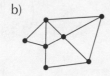 c)   d)

2) Identify the <u>odd</u> vertices in the graph on the right.
   Write down all the possible ways of <u>pairing</u> the odd vertices.

3) Find the length of the shortest "<u>Chinese postman</u>" route
   for each of these networks. Start and end at vertex A.

   a) 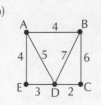 b) 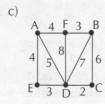 c)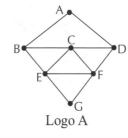

4) Repeat question 3. But this time you can start and finish at <u>any</u> vertices.
   State <u>which</u> vertices you're starting and finishing at.

5) For the graph on the right:
   a) identify the six odd vertices and find the distance between each possible pair,
   b) state which vertices may be started at for the shortest "<u>Chinese postman</u>" route.

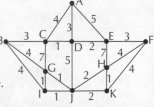

That's all the main skills brushed up on. Now it's time to see if you can apply them to some exam-style questions.

Exam Questions

1   A machinist is embroidering logos on sportsbags. The two logos are shown below.

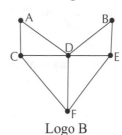

Logo A   Logo B

   a)   Say whether each logo consists of an Eulerian graph, a semi-Eulerian graph or neither.   *(2 marks)*

   b)   The sewing machine needle is positioned at any starting point, and sews a route without
        stitching any line more than once. It can be lifted and moved to a new starting point.
        (i)   For each logo, how many times must the needle be lifted?   *(2 marks)*
        (ii) For logo A, state an efficient starting vertex.   *(1 mark)*

   c)   For any non-Eulerian logo above, state the minimum number of arcs that
        must be added to it to make it Eulerian.   *(2 marks)*

D1 Section 3 — Practice Questions

These are your typical "Chinese postman" problems — of course they contain subtle variations. Just like in real exams.

2   The diagram on the right shows all the streets in a town, and their lengths in metres.

Angus is considering moving to the town and wants to walk down each street at least once. He parks his car at K.

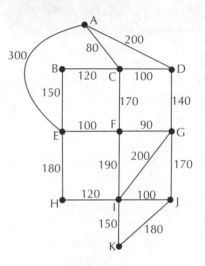

a)   Explain why it is not possible to walk down each street only once and return to the starting point.

(1 mark)

b)   Find the length of the shortest route Angus could follow, starting and finishing at K.

(6 marks)

c)   Angus's friend offers to drop him off at any point, and after he's walked down each street at least once, to pick him up from any point.

(i)   Find the length of the optimal route for Angus.

(2 marks)

(ii)   State the vertices from which Angus could start in order to achieve this optimal route.

(1 mark)

Total length of all
the roads = 2740 m

3   The diagram below shows the paths in a park, and the time taken to walk them in minutes.

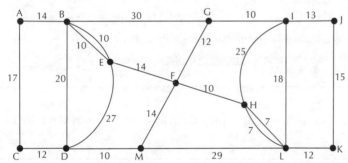

Alice the park keeper needs to walk down each path to check for storm-damaged trees.
She parks her car at F.

Time required to walk along all paths
= 336 minutes

a)   Find the time for the shortest route Alice could follow, starting and finishing at F.

(6 marks)

b)   If Alice starts at point B, and can finish at any point:

(i)   What point should she end at for the optimal route? Show your working.

(2 marks)

(ii)   How long will it take her to walk along all the paths now?

(1 mark)

4   The diagram on the right shows the distances between towns in miles.
The total road distance is 106 miles.

Jamie is inspecting the hedgerows along the roads.
He needs to go along each road, starting and finishing at A.

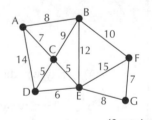

a)   Find the length of the optimal 'Chinese postman' route for Jamie.

(6 marks)

b)   There are ice-cream shops at points C and E.
If Jamie follows his optimal route, how many times will he pass an ice-cream shop?

(2 marks)

c)   Jamie decides it would be better if he went along each road twice.
What is the length of his new optimal route?

(1 mark)

Travelling Salesperson Problem

In the last section, you met the Chinese Postman problem. Well, this section's all about the Travelling Salesperson Problem (TSP). I'm not sure where the salesperson is from exactly, but he or she sure does get around.

Travelling Salespeople must visit Every Node

1) In a <u>Travelling Salesperson problem</u>, you need to visit <u>every vertex</u> in a network and end up back at your <u>starting point</u>.

E.g. a tourist wanting to visit all the landmarks in a city, starting and finishing at his hotel.

2) There isn't an algorithm guaranteed to find the <u>shortest</u> route (or 'tour'). And it's not usually practical to test each one as there tend to be too many.

3) Instead, you find a <u>lower and upper bound</u>, then a <u>reasonably good solution</u> between them. Luckily, there are <u>algorithms</u> for finding the lower and upper bound.

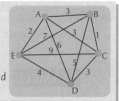

EXAMPLE
Two possible Travelling Salesperson routes starting from A are: AEDCBA (length 13) and ACBDEA (length 15).

> TACKLING TRAVELLING SALESPERSON PROBLEMS
> 1) Find a cycle (see p.200) that goes through each vertex using the <u>Nearest Neighbour Algorithm</u> (see the next page) — this is the <u>upper bound</u>.
> 2) Find the <u>lower bound</u> by using the <u>Lower Bound Algorithm</u> (see page 217).
> 3) The weight of the <u>optimum route</u> is: lower bound ≤ weight of optimum route ≤ upper bound

The Length of *Any Known Tour* is an *Upper Bound*

The <u>SMALLER</u> the <u>upper bound</u> the better.

This is because you want the interval between the upper and lower bounds to be as small as possible.

1) If the first tour you find has a length of <u>20</u>, this is your <u>initial upper bound</u>. You know it's a possible solution, but you don't know if it's the optimum one.

2) If your second tour has a length of <u>22</u>, then the upper bound <u>stays</u> at 20 — it's still the best so far.

3) But if you find a tour with a length of <u>17</u>, then this is an <u>improvement</u> so it becomes the new <u>upper bound</u>.

The *Nearest Neighbour Algorithm* Finds an *Upper Bound*

With the Nearest Neighbour algorithm, you basically choose the <u>unvisited</u> vertex <u>closest</u> to you each time. Once you've been to <u>all</u> the vertices, you go along the edge that takes you <u>straight back</u> to the starting point.

> THE NEAREST NEIGHBOUR ALGORITHM
> 1) Choose a <u>starting vertex</u> (you'll be told which one to use in an exam question).
> 2) Choose the <u>nearest unused vertex</u>.
> 3) Repeat Step 2 until you've visited <u>each vertex</u>.
> 4) Finish the cycle by <u>returning to the starting vertex</u>.

In real-life there won't always be a direct route back to the starting vertex — but exam questions always work out nicely.

EXAMPLE The graph shows the durations in hours of train journeys between five Russian towns. Ben wants to visit all five towns, spending the minimum amount of time on trains. Apply the Nearest Neighbour algorithm, starting at vertex A, to find an upper bound for Ben's optimum route.

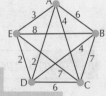

Applying the Nearest Neighbour algorithm <u>from A</u>:

Starting from a different vertex often gives a different result. E.g. applying the algorithm from <u>vertex C</u> gives the tour <u>CADEBC</u>, which has a duration of <u>23 hours</u>.

The closest vertex to A is <u>D</u> (2 hours).
The closest unused vertex to D is <u>E</u> (2 hours).
The closest unused vertex to E is <u>C</u> (7 hours).
The closest unused vertex to C is <u>B</u> (7 hours).
That's all the vertices visited, so back to <u>A</u> (6 hours).

<u>Upper bound</u> = total duration of ADECBA = <u>24 hours</u>.

Try to *Reduce* the Upper Bound with *Shortcuts*

If the sum of the weights of <u>two sides</u> of a triangle in the network are <u>less</u> than the <u>third side</u>, then there might be a <u>shortcut</u> to your tour.

E.g. if your tour involves edge PQ (weight = 9), it'd be quicker to go PRQ (weight = 8) — even if this means your tour goes through vertex R twice.

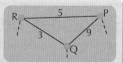

Travelling Salesperson Problem

Graphs can be <u>ridiculously complicated</u> when they're drawn out, so you'll often be given the information in a <u>matrix</u>.

You can use the **Nearest Neighbour Algorithm** Directly on a **Matrix**

1) Exam questions often give you the weights between vertices in <u>distance matrix form</u> (see p201).

2) Here's an example of how to apply the <u>Nearest Neighbour algorithm</u> to the matrix:

EXAMPLE Poppy is on holiday in New York and wants to see landmarks A-F. The time that it takes in minutes to get between each place on public transport is given in the matrix. Use the Nearest Neighbour algorithm <u>starting from C</u> to find an upper bound for Poppy's tour.

From\To	A	B	C	D	E	F
A	—	5	35	5	10	15
B	10	—	10	20	20	35
C	45	15	—	10	30	25
D	20	10	5	—	5	10
E	40	25	15	35	—	40
F	35	20	25	30	20	—

① Find <u>vertex C</u> in the 'From' column, and look across to find the <u>lowest number</u> (the time taken to get to the closest vertex). It's <u>10 mins to D</u>, so D is the next vertex in the tour.

You <u>don't</u> want to go to D again, so <u>cross out</u> this column. You don't want to go to C again until the <u>end</u>, so cross out that column too so you don't get muddled.

From\To	A	B	C	D	E	F
A	—	5	35	5	10	15
B	10	—	10	20	20	35
C	45	15	—	10	30	25
D	20	10	5	—	5	10
E	40	25	15	35	—	40
F	35	20	25	30	20	—

The times differ depending on which direction you're going in this matrix.

② Now you're at <u>D</u>, so find D in the 'From' column, and look across to find the shortest time to an <u>unvisited vertex</u> (i.e. not C). This is <u>5 mins to E</u>, so E is the next vertex in the tour. So far the tour is CDE. Now <u>cross out</u> column E so you don't accidentally revisit it.

From\To	A	B	C	D	E	F
A	—	5	35	5	10	15
B	10	—	10	20	20	35
C	45	15	—	10	30	25
D	20	10	5	—	5	10
E	40	25	15	35	—	40
F	35	20	25	30	20	—

③ Keep going with this until <u>all</u> the vertices are visited, then return to the <u>start vertex</u> (C). F is the last vertex visited — it's then 25 mins back to C. The whole tour is <u>CDEBAFC</u>, which takes 90 minutes. So 90 minutes is an upper bound.

Sometimes the Nearest Neighbour Algorithm is a **Bit Rubbish**

You Might End Up with **Really Long Distances** at the End

1) The Nearest Neighbour algorithm is a <u>greedy algorithm</u>, so you choose the best option <u>at any one moment</u>, rather than thinking about what's best in the long run.

2) This can mean you end up having to go along <u>really long</u> edges at the end. You'll often be able to see a better route just by looking.

EXAMPLE Use the Nearest Neighbour algorithm, <u>starting from vertex A</u>, to find an upper bound for the Travelling Salesperson problem for the network below.

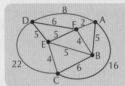

Applying the algorithm from A gives <u>AFBECDA</u>, which has a weight of <u>45</u>.

But that route zigzags, then goes along the really long route from C to D. Using common sense, you'd go in the circular route ABCEDFA (or AFDECBA). This has a weight of only 28.

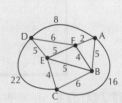

Or you might come to a **Grinding Halt**

Sometimes the algorithm <u>stalls</u> and you <u>don't</u> get a route visiting all the vertices. Often, the algorithm <u>will work</u> if you <u>change</u> the start vertex though.

EXAMPLE Show that the Nearest Neighbour algorithm, starting from vertex A, fails on this network.

Applying the algorithm from A gives ABEF, but then it <u>stalls</u>. You can't get to C or D.

But starting from E, the algorithm works — you get the tour <u>EFABCDE</u>.

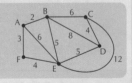

Everybody needs good Nearest Neighbour algorithms...

If you're not happy with your nearest neighbours, a good way to annoy them is to stand outside their window and change their TV channel with your remote. It'll drive them mad. Deny all knowledge about it if they mention it though.

Travelling Salesperson Problem

Now to find the lower bound. It's a completely different method from finding the upper bound, and it even involves your old friends from D1 Section 2 — Prim and Kruskal.

The **Lower Bound Algorithm** Involves Finding a **Minimum Spanning Tree**

1) The Lower Bound algorithm calculates the minimum possible weight for a Travelling Salesperson route.

2) There might not be a route of this weight, but there definitely won't be a shorter one.

> THE LOWER BOUND ALGORITHM
>
> 1) Choose a vertex, say A (you'll be told which one in an exam question). Find the two lowest weight edges joined to vertex A. Call their weights x and y.
>
> 2) Delete vertex A and all the edges joined to it. This is your 'reduced network'. Now find a minimum spanning tree (minimum connector) for the rest of the network and work out its weight. Call this W.
>
> 3) The Lower Bound = $W + x + y$

Edges joined to a vertex, are said to be incident to it.

Exam questions will often tell you to 'construct a minimum spanning tree on the reduced network'.

You do this with either Kruskal's or Prim's algorithm (see p202-204).

EXAMPLE By deleting vertex E, find a lower bound for the Travelling Salesperson problem on this network.

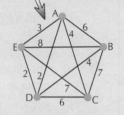

1) The two lowest weights joined to E are AE (3) and DE (2). So $x = 2$ and $y = 3$.

2) Delete vertex E and the incident edges. Now find a minimum spanning tree for the reduced network. I'm going to use Prim's algorithm, because I like it best.

> PRIM'S ALGORITHM
>
> 1) Pick a vertex, any vertex — this starts the tree. I'll start with A, ta.
>
> 2) Choose the arc of least weight that'll join a vertex in the tree to one not yet in the tree. Repeat this until you've joined all the vertices. That'll be AD (2), then AC (4), then DB (4).

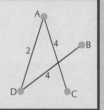

The weight, W, of the minimum spanning tree is $2 + 4 + 4 = \underline{10}$.

3) The Lower Bound = $W + x + y = 10 + 2 + 3 = \underline{15}$

3) If you're asked to find a lower bound from a distance matrix, start by crossing out the row and column of the deleted vertex. Then just use Prim's algorithm to find the minimum spanning tree (as on page 204).

The **Largest** Lower Bound is the **Best**

lower bound ≤ minimum weight of Travelling Salesperson tour ≤ upper bound

1) A small range of possible weights for the optimum tour is more useful than a large range — so you want your lower bound to be as large as possible.

2) To get the best lower bound, you should repeat the algorithm deleting a different vertex each time. Then you can pick the largest of the lower bounds.

On the network above, you get the lower bounds below. (You check them and I'll send you a chocolate bunny if you find an error.) Deleting A = lower bound 17. Deleting B = lower bound 18. Deleting C = lower bound 18. Deleting D = lower bound 17. So 18 is the best lower bound.

3) If you find a tour which has the same weight as your lower bound, you know you've stumbled upon an optimum tour.

4) And if your lower bound and your upper bound are the same, you know that value is the weight of the optimum tour.

The end of the section — bet you're bounding about with joy...

Solving a Travelling Salesman Problem has lots of bits. But exam questions tend to break it down into different parts, and often only ask you to do part of the process, say find an upper bound. If you're asked to find a lower bound, you might have already found a minimum spanning tree for the network earlier in the question, so you can use that as a starting point.

D1 Section 4 — Practice Questions

First the hors d'oeuvres...

Warm-up Questions

1) a) Give three different Travelling Salesperson routes for this network that start at A.

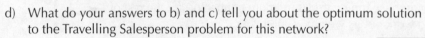

b) Apply the Nearest Neighbour algorithm from each vertex in turn. What is your best upper bound?

c) Find 5 lower bounds by deleting each vertex in turn and constructing a minimum spanning tree on the reduced network. What is your best lower bound?

d) What do your answers to b) and c) tell you about the optimum solution to the Travelling Salesperson problem for this network?

2) a) Apply the Nearest Neighbour algorithm starting from F to find an upper bound for this network.

b) Find a lower bound for this network by deleting vertex B.

	A	B	C	D	E	F
A	—	4	6	5	8	12
B	4	—	14	22	6	11
C	6	14	—	18	3	5
D	5	22	18	—	13	15
E	8	6	3	13	—	20
F	12	11	5	15	20	—

3) a) The Nearest Neighbour algorithm only finds a Travelling Salesperson route if started from three of these vertices. Which vertices are they?

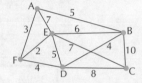

b) Find the best upper bound by starting the Nearest Neighbour algorithm from each of these vertices.

c) Find a lower bound for the network by deleting vertex E and all arcs incident to it.

Now the main course. (Don't save room for pudding. There isn't any.)

Exam Questions

1 A network is shown below.

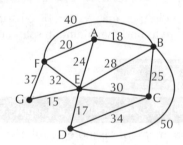

a) Find a minimum spanning tree for this network using Kruskal's algorithm. Draw your tree and state its weight.

(5 marks)

b) Use your answer to part a) to find a lower bound for the travelling salesperson problem. Delete vertex C and all arcs joined to it when forming your reduced network.

(3 marks)

c) Find an upper bound for the travelling salesperson problem on this network by applying the Nearest Neighbour algorithm. Start from vertex D.

(3 marks)

d) Show that the Nearest Neighbour algorithm fails when started from vertex C.

(2 marks)

D1 Section 4 — Practice Questions

Travelling Salesperson exam questions aren't usually too tricky. But you still need to practise, practise, practise.

2   The diagram on the right shows all the streets
     in a town, and their lengths in metres.
     Max wants to display a poster at each intersection.

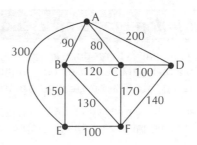

a)   Show that the Nearest Neighbour method fails if started from vertex C.

(1 mark)

b)   Find the length of the tour produced when the Nearest Neighbour algorithm
      is applied from vertex A.

(3 marks)

c)   Find the length of tour ABCDFEA.

(2 marks)

d)   Which of your answers to b) and c) is the best upper bound for Max's tour around the town?

(1 mark)

e)   Find a lower bound for the distance by deleting vertex D.
      Draw your minimum spanning tree.

(6 marks)

3   The diagram below shows the time taken to walk between park benches A-G in minutes.
     Alice the park keeper needs to inspect each bench for rot.

	A	B	C	D	E	F	G
A	—	15	10	7	6	7	4
B	15	—	8	5	12	13	14
C	10	8	—	6	15	18	2
D	7	5	6	—	7	5	13
E	6	12	15	7	—	3	10
F	7	13	18	5	3	—	6
G	4	14	2	13	10	6	—

a)   Starting from A, use Prim's algorithm to find a minimum spanning tree.
      Draw your minimum spanning tree, giving its total weight.

(6 marks)

b)   Using your answer to part a), calculate a lower bound for the duration of Alice's tour.
      You should delete vertex B and the arcs incident to it.

(3 marks)

c)   Use the Nearest Neighbour method starting from F to find an upper bound for Alice's tour.

(3 marks)

d)   Using your previous answers, draw a conclusion about the duration of the optimum tour.

(2 marks)

Linear Programs

Linear programming is a way of solving problems that have lots of inequalities, often to do with money or business. So if you're a budding entrepreneur, pay attention — this section could help you make your first million. Or just pass D1.

Linear Programming problems use Inequalities

The aim of linear programming is to produce an optimal solution to a problem, e.g. to find the solution that gives the maximum profit to a manufacturer, based on conditions that would affect it, such as limited time or materials. Before you start having a go at linear programming problems, there are a few terms you need to know.

1) In any problem, you'll have things that are being produced (or bought or sold etc.) — e.g. jars of jam or different types of books. The amount of each thing is represented by x, y, z etc — these are called the decision variables.

2) The constraints are the factors that limit the problem, e.g. a limited amount of workers available. The constraints are written as inequalities in terms of the decision variables. Most problems will have non-negativity constraints. This just means that the decision variables can't be negative. It makes sense really — you can't have −1 books.

> *Non-negativity constraints are sometimes called 'trivial' constraints.*

3) The objective function is what you're trying to maximise or minimise (e.g. maximise profit or minimise cost). It's usually in the form of a function written in terms of the decision variables.

4) A feasible solution is a solution that satisfies all the constraints. It'll give you a value for each of the decision variables. On a graph, the set of feasible solutions lie in the feasible region (see p.221).

5) You're aiming to optimise the objective function — that's finding a solution within the feasible region that maximises (or minimises) the objective function. This is the optimal solution, and there can be more than one.

Put the Information you're given into a Table

Linear programming questions can look a bit confusing because you're given a lot of information in one go. But if you put all the information in a table, it's much easier to work out the inequalities you need.

EXAMPLE

A company makes garden furniture, and produces both picnic tables and benches. It takes 5 hours to make a picnic table and 2 hours to paint it. It takes 3 hours to make a bench and 1 hour to paint it. In a week, there are 100 hours allocated to construction and 50 hours allocated to painting. Picnic tables are sold for a profit of £30 and benches are sold for a profit of £10. The company wants to maximise its weekly profit.

Putting this information into a table gives:

Item of furniture	Construction time (hours)	Painting time (hours)	Profit (£)
Picnic table	5	2	30
Bench	3	1	10
Total time available:	100	50	

> *This is an example of how linear programming can be used to solve real-life problems.*

Now use the table to identify all the different parts of the problem and come up with the inequalities:

- The decision variables are the number of picnic tables and the number of benches, so let x = number of picnic tables and y = number of benches.

- The constraints are the number of hours available for each stage of manufacture. Making a picnic table takes 5 hours, so x tables will take $5x$ hours. Making a bench takes 3 hours, so y tables will take $3y$ hours. There are a total of 100 hours available. From this, you get the inequality $5x + 3y \le 100$. Using the same method for the painting hours produces the inequality $2x + y \le 50$. You also need $x, y \ge 0$.

> *Don't forget the trivial constraints.*

- The objective function is to maximise the profit. Each picnic table makes a profit of £30, so x tables make a profit of £30x. Each bench makes a profit of £10, so y benches make a profit of £10y. Let P be the profit, then the aim is to maximise $P = 30x + 10y$.

I'd like −3 picnic tables please...

In fancy examiner speak, the example above could be written like this: 'maximise $P = 30x + 10y$ subject to the constraints $5x + 3y \le 100$, $2x + y \le 50$ and $x, y \ge 0$'. Watch out for constraints such as 'there have to be at least twice as many benches as picnic tables — this would be written as $2x \le y$. You might have to think about this one to get your head round it.

Feasible Regions

If you're a fan of <u>drawing graphs</u>, you'll love this page. It's a bit like the <u>graphical inequality problems</u> you came across at GCSE. Even if you're not that keen on graphs, or if the mere thought of them brings you out in a <u>rash</u>, don't worry — they're only <u>straight line graphs</u>.

Drawing **Graphs** can help solve **Linear Programming Problems**

<u>Plotting the constraints</u> on a <u>graph</u> is probably the easiest way to <u>solve</u> a linear programming problem — it helps you see the <u>feasible solutions</u> clearly. Get your ruler and graph paper ready.

1) Draw each of the <u>constraints</u> as a <u>line</u> on the graph. All you have to do is <u>change</u> the <u>inequality sign</u> to an <u>equals sign</u> and plot the line. If you find it easier, <u>rearrange</u> the equation into the form $y = mx + c$.

2) Then you have to <u>decide</u> which bit of the graph you <u>want</u> — whether the solution will be <u>above</u> or <u>below</u> the line. This will depend on the <u>inequality sign</u> — <u>rearrange</u> the inequality into the form $y = mx + c$, then think about which sign you'd use. For $y \le mx + c$ (or <), you want the bit <u>underneath</u> the line, and if it's $y \ge mx + c$ (or >) then you want the bit <u>above</u> the line. If you're not sure, put the <u>coordinates</u> of a point in one region (e.g. the origin) into the equation and see if it <u>satisfies</u> the inequality.

3) Once you've decided which bit you want, <u>shade</u> the region you <u>don't want</u>. This way, when you put all the constraints on the graph, the <u>unshaded region</u> (the bit you want) is easy to see.

4) If the inequality sign is < or >, use a <u>dotted line</u> — this means you <u>don't</u> include the line in the region. If the inequality sign is ≤ or ≥ then use a <u>normal</u> line, so the line is <u>included</u> in the range of solutions.

5) Once you've drawn <u>all</u> the constraints on the graph, you'll be able to solve the problem. Don't forget the <u>trivial constraints</u> — they'll limit the graph to the <u>first quadrant</u>.

The **Unshaded Area** is the **Feasible Region**

Your finished graph should have an area, <u>bounded</u> by the lines of the <u>constraints</u>, that <u>hasn't</u> been <u>shaded</u>. This is the <u>feasible region</u> — the <u>coordinates</u> of any point inside the <u>unshaded area</u> will satisfy <u>all</u> the constraints.

EXAMPLE

On a graph, show the constraints $x + y \le 5$, $3x - y \ge 2$, $y > 1$ and $x, y \ge 0$. Label the feasible region R.

Rearranging the inequalities into '$y = mx + c$' form and choosing the appropriate inequality sign gives: $y \le 5 - x$, $y \le 3x - 2$ and $y > 1$. The trivial constraints $x, y \ge 0$ are represented by the x- and y- axes.

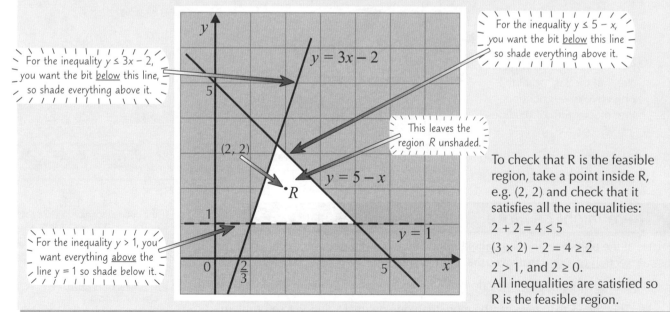

For the inequality $y \le 3x - 2$, you want the bit <u>below</u> this line, so shade everything above it.

For the inequality $y \le 5 - x$, you want the bit <u>below</u> this line so shade everything above it.

This leaves the region R unshaded.

For the inequality $y > 1$, you want everything <u>above</u> the line $y = 1$ so shade below it.

To check that R is the feasible region, take a point inside R, e.g. (2, 2) and check that it satisfies all the inequalities:

$2 + 2 = 4 \le 5$

$(3 \times 2) - 2 = 4 \ge 2$

$2 > 1$, and $2 \ge 0$.

All inequalities are satisfied so R is the feasible region.

It's feasible that I might become a film star...

...but not very likely — I'm a terrible actor. Anyway, although it's possible that you might get a linear programming problem with more than two variables, you won't have to draw graphs for these ones. You'll only have to graph 2-variable problems.

Optimal Solutions

Don't throw away your graphs just yet — you still need them for the next few pages. You're now getting on to the really useful bit — actually solving the linear programming problem.

Draw a line for the Objective Function

All the points in the feasible region (see previous page) satisfy all the constraints in the problem. You need to be able to work out which point (or points) also optimises the objective function. The objective function is usually of the form $Z = ax + by$, where Z either needs to be maximised (e.g. profit) or minimised (e.g. cost) to give the optimal solution.

The Objective Line Method

1. Draw the straight line $Z = ax + by$, choosing a fixed value of Z (a and b will be given in the question). This is called the objective line.

2. Move the line to the right, keeping it parallel to the original line. As you do this, the value of Z increases (if you move the line to the left, the value of Z decreases).

3. If you're trying to maximise Z, the optimal solution will be the last point within the feasible region that the objective line touches as you slide it to the right.

4. If you're trying to minimise Z, the optimal solution will be the last point within the feasible region that the objective line touches as you slide it to the left.

This is sometimes called the ruler method, as a good way to do it is to slide a ruler over the graph parallel to the objective line.

The objective lines have the Same Gradient

When you draw your first objective line, you can use any value for Z. Pick one that makes the line easier to draw — e.g. let Z be a multiple of both a and b so that the intercepts with the axes are easy to find.

EXAMPLE Using the example from the previous page, maximise the profit $P = 2x + 3y$.

First, choose a value for P, say $P = 6$. This means that the objective line goes through $(3, 0)$ and $(0, 2)$. Draw this line on the graph.

Slide the objective line to the right until it reaches the last point within R. At this point, P is maximised.

This is the first objective line, where $P = 6$.

From the diagram, you can see that the last point the objective line touches is the intersection of the lines $y = 5 - x$ and $y = 3x - 2$.

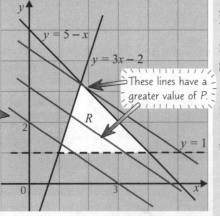

These lines have a greater value of P.

To find the point of intersection, solve these simultaneous equations. This will give you the optimal solution.

Substituting $y = 5 - x$ into $y = 3x - 2$
gives: $5 - x = 3x - 2$
$$7 = 4x \Rightarrow x = \tfrac{7}{4}$$

Putting $x = \tfrac{7}{4}$ into $y = 5 - x$ gives $y = \tfrac{13}{4}$.

Now put these values into the objective function to find P: $P = 2x + 3y$
$$= 2\left(\tfrac{7}{4}\right) + 3\left(\tfrac{13}{4}\right)$$
$$= \tfrac{14}{4} + \tfrac{39}{4} = \tfrac{53}{4} = 13.25$$

So the maximum value of P is 13.25, which occurs at $\left(\tfrac{7}{4}, \tfrac{13}{4}\right)$.

There might be More Than One optimal solution

If the optimal solution is on a dotted line, the actual solution will just be a point very very close to it. You don't need to worry about this though.

1) If the objective line is parallel to one of the constraints, you might end up with a section of a line that gives the optimal solution.

2) If this happens, any point along the line is an optimal solution (as long as it's inside the feasible region).

3) This shows that there can be more than one optimal solution to a problem.

Maximise your chance of passing D1...

Make sure you're happy with solving simultaneous equations — if not, have a look back at page 24. You won't have to solve any tricky quadratic equations for this section, but you need to be able to solve linear simultaneous equations quick-smart.

Optimal Solutions

If you object to using the <u>objective line</u>, there is another method. This one uses a lot more <u>simultaneous equations</u>, but you don't have to worry about keeping the ruler <u>parallel</u> or <u>stopping global warming</u> or anything like that.

Optimal Solutions are found at Vertices

The <u>optimal solution</u> for the example on the previous page was found at a <u>vertex</u> of the <u>feasible region</u>. This isn't a coincidence — if you have a go at some more linear programming problems, you'll find that the optimal solutions <u>always</u> occur at a vertex (or an <u>edge</u>) of the feasible region. This gives you another way to solve the problem.

The Vertex Method

1. **Find the x- and y-values of the <u>vertices</u> of the <u>feasible region</u>. You do this by solving the <u>simultaneous equations</u> of the <u>lines</u> that <u>intersect</u> at each vertex.**
2. **Put these values into the <u>objective function</u> $Z = ax + by$ to find the value of Z.**
3. **Look at the Z values and work out which is the <u>optimal value</u>. Depending on your objective function, this might be either the <u>smallest</u> (if you're trying to <u>minimise</u> Z) or the <u>largest</u> (if you're trying to <u>maximise</u> Z).**

If two vertices A and B produce the same Z value, this means that all points along the edge AB are also optimal solutions.

Test Every vertex

Even if it looks <u>obvious</u> from the graph, you still have to <u>test</u> each vertex of the feasible region. Sometime the <u>origin</u> will be one of the vertices — it's really easy to test, as the objective function will just be equal to $\underline{0}$ there. Don't forget vertices on the <u>x-</u> and <u>y-axes</u> too.

You can sometimes just read off the coordinates from your graph (as long as it's accurate).

EXAMPLE

Minimise $Z = 8x + 9y$, subject to the constraints $2x + y \geq 6$, $x - 2y \leq 2$, $x \leq 4$, $y \leq 4$ and $x, y \geq 0$.

Drawing these constraints on a graph produces the diagram below, where A, B, C and D are the vertices of the feasible region R:

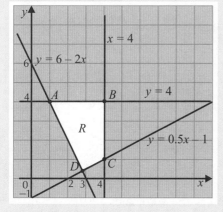

Point A is the intersection of the lines $y = 6 - 2x$ and $y = 4$, so A has coordinates $(1, 4)$.

Point B is the intersection of the lines $x = 4$ and $y = 4$, so B has coordinates $(4, 4)$.

Point C is the intersection of the lines $x = 4$ and $y = 0.5x - 1$, so C has coordinates $(4, 1)$.

Point D is the intersection of the lines $y = 6 - 2x$ and $y = 0.5x - 1$, which has coordinates $\left(\frac{14}{5}, \frac{2}{5}\right)$.

You need to use simultaneous equations to find the coordinates of D.

Putting these values into the objective function $Z = 8x + 9y$:

At A, $Z = (8 \times 1) + (9 \times 4) = 44$.

At B, $Z = (8 \times 4) + (9 \times 4) = 68$.

At C, $Z = (8 \times 4) + (9 \times 1) = 41$.

At D, $Z = (8 \times 2.8) + (9 \times 0.4) = 26$.

So the minimum value of Z is 26, which occurs when $x = \frac{14}{5}$ and $y = \frac{2}{5}$.

In this example, it was really <u>easy</u> to find the coordinates of A, B and C, as at least one of the values was <u>given</u> by the <u>equation of the line</u>. D was a bit harder, as it involved <u>simultaneous equations</u>, but it wasn't too bad.

Your optimal solution might mean that there are some <u>spare capacities</u> — some of the variables that haven't been <u>used up</u>. This usually happens with a <u>constraint</u> that isn't used when finding the <u>optimal solution</u> (i.e. it doesn't go through the vertex that provides the optimal solution). In a <u>real life problem</u>, you might have to <u>interpret</u> this — e.g. there might be <u>spare time</u>, or <u>leftover ingredients</u>.

I'm getting vertigo...

Some questions might give you two different objective functions and ask you to minimise cost and maximise profit for the same set of constraints. The vertex method is really useful here, as once you've worked out the coordinates of the vertices, you can easily put the values into both objective functions without having to do any more work (or draw on confusing lines).

Optimal Integer Solutions

The methods on the previous two pages are all very well and good, but I can't exactly make 2.5 teddy bears, even if it does <u>maximise my profit</u>. There must be a better way, one that doesn't involve <u>mutilating soft toys</u>...

Some problems need Integer Solutions

1) Sometimes it's fine to have <u>non-integer solutions</u> to linear programming problems — for example, if you were making different <u>fruit juices</u>, you could realistically have 3.5 litres of one type of juice and 4.5 litres of another.

2) However, if you were making <u>garden furniture</u>, you couldn't make 3.5 tables and 4.5 benches — so you need <u>integer solutions</u>.

3) You won't always be <u>told</u> whether a problem needs integer solutions — you might have to <u>work it out</u> for yourself. It's common sense really — just think about whether you can have <u>fractions</u> of the <u>decision variables</u>.

You can use the Objective Line Method or the Vertex Method

Some problems have optimal integer solutions that are far away from the vertices — but you don't need to worry about these for D1.

Both of the methods covered on pages 222-223 can be used to find an <u>optimal integer solution</u> — it just depends on how <u>clear</u> your <u>graph</u> is.

1) You use the <u>objective line method</u> in exactly the <u>same way</u> as before, but instead of looking for the last <u>vertex</u> the line touches, you need to look for the last <u>point</u> with <u>integer coordinates</u> in the <u>feasible region</u>. This might be hard to do if your graph isn't very <u>accurate</u>, or if the scale isn't <u>clear</u>.

2) The other way to find the optimal integer solution is to use the <u>vertex method</u> to find which vertex to use. Then, consider all the points with <u>integer coordinates</u> that are <u>close by</u>. Make sure you <u>check</u> whether these points still <u>satisfy</u> the <u>constraints</u> though — test this <u>before</u> you put the values into the objective function.

The Optimal Integer Solution must be Inside the Feasible Region

It's easy to forget that <u>not all</u> the solutions near the optimal vertex will be <u>inside</u> the <u>feasible region</u> — you can check either <u>by eye</u> on an <u>accurate graph</u>, or put the <u>coordinates</u> into each of the <u>constraints</u>.

> **EXAMPLE** The optimal solution to the problem on the previous page occurred at $\left(\frac{14}{5}, \frac{2}{5}\right)$ $(= (2.8, 0.4))$. Find the optimal integer solution.
>
> Looking at the integers nearby gives you the points (3, 0), (3, 1), (2, 0) and (2, 1) to test. However, the point (3, 0) doesn't satisfy the constraint $x - 2y \leq 2$, and (2, 0) and (2, 1) don't satisfy $2x + y \geq 6$, so the optimal integer solution is at (3, 1), where $Z = (8 \times 3) + (9 \times 1) = 33$.

EXAMPLE

A company makes baby clothes. It makes x sets of girls' clothes and y sets of boys' clothes, for a profit of £6 and £5 respectively, subject to the constraints $x + y \leq 9$, $3x - y \leq 9$, $y \leq 7$ and $x, y \geq 0$.
Maximise the profit, $P = 6x + 5y$

This example uses the vertex method, but you could also use the objective line method.

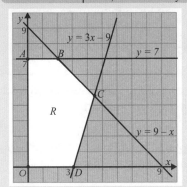

The feasible region is the area $OABCD$, with coordinates $O(0, 0)$, $A(0, 7)$, $B(2, 7)$, $C(4.5, 4.5)$ and $D(3, 0)$.

The value of P at each vertex is O: £0, A: £35, B: £47, C: £49.50 and D: £18.

The maximum value of P is £49.50, which occurs at (4.5, 4.5). However, making 4.5 sets of clothes is not possible, so an integer solution is needed.

The integer coordinates near C are (4, 5), (5, 5), (5, 4) and (4, 4). (5, 5) and (5, 4) don't satisfy the constraint $3x - y \leq 9$ so are outside the feasible region. At (4, 5), $P = £49$, and at (4,4), $P = £44$, so £49 is the maximum profit.

So the company needs to make 4 sets of girls' clothes and 5 sets of boys' clothes to make the maximum profit of £49.

My solution to a problem is to close my eyes and hope it'll go away...

Oo, I do like a nice integer now and then. Like a good cup of tea, integers can really brighten your morning. They're harder to dunk biscuits in, but they do provide sensible solutions to linear programming problems. Watch out for them in the exam.

The Simplex Method

Don't be fooled — the Simplex Method isn't as simple as its name would have you believe. You're probably going to have to read the next few pages a couple of times to get it into your head. It's pretty handy though and you'll feel really clever when you can do it without breaking a sweat.

You need to use Slack Variables

The Simplex Method is another way of solving linear programming problems. Instead of drawing a graph, you put all the information into a table (called a tableau) and solve it from there. The method's on the next page.

1) Before you put your information into a tableau, you need to introduce slack variables. These are just extra variables that turn the inequalities (e.g. $2x + y \leq 25$) into equalities (e.g. $2x + y + s = 25$).

2) The slack variables are usually s and t (though you might need u and v too if there are a lot of constraints).

3) You only need one slack variable per constraint — you wouldn't end up with an equation like $2x + y + s + t = 25$.

4) The slack variables are non-negative — that is, $s \geq 0$, $t \geq 0$ etc.

The slack variables represent the spare capacities (see p. 227).

Put the Variables into Columns in your Tableau

1) To set up the tableau, you need to put each variable in a separate column. You'll need a column for the objective function (e.g. the profit, P), then one for x and one for y (and one for z, if it's a three-variable problem) and one for each of the slack variables.

2) Each row of your tableau should represent one of the constraints. The top row will be the objective function, so the coefficient of P is 1 here. You need to rearrange the objective function to get all the variables on the same side (so $P = 3x + 2y$ becomes $P - 3x - 2y = 0$). In all the other rows, $P = 0$ (as P doesn't appear in the constraints).

3) The other rows will have values for the coefficients of x and y (and maybe z), and one of the slack variables.

4) There should be a column for the right-hand side (RHS) of each equation — this'll be 0 for the objective function.

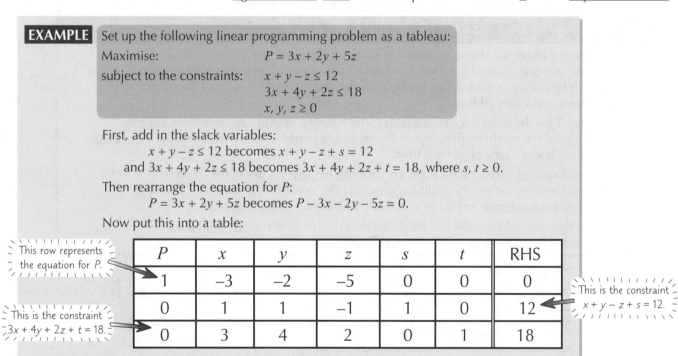

EXAMPLE Set up the following linear programming problem as a tableau:

Maximise: $P = 3x + 2y + 5z$

subject to the constraints: $x + y - z \leq 12$
$3x + 4y + 2z \leq 18$
$x, y, z \geq 0$

First, add in the slack variables:
$x + y - z \leq 12$ becomes $x + y - z + s = 12$
and $3x + 4y + 2z \leq 18$ becomes $3x + 4y + 2z + t = 18$, where $s, t \geq 0$.

Then rearrange the equation for P:
$P = 3x + 2y + 5z$ becomes $P - 3x - 2y - 5z = 0$.

Now put this into a table:

This row represents the equation for P.

This is the constraint $x + y - z + s = 12$.

This is the constraint $3x + 4y + 2z + t = 18$.

P	x	y	z	s	t	RHS
1	−3	−2	−5	0	0	0
0	1	1	−1	1	0	12
0	3	4	2	0	1	18

Give me some slack...

Now that wasn't too bad, was it? Unfortunately, it gets a little harder on the next page — brace yourself in preparation. You'll probably need a warming sweet drink and some glucose sweets. My Nan used to swear by barley sugars. But in fact, the best way to prepare yourself is to make sure you know how to set up these simplex tableaux really well.

The Simplex Method

Before you can really make a start with the Simplex method, you need to get to grips with <u>choosing a pivot</u>.

You have to choose **Pivots** from the **Tableau**

Choosing a <u>pivot</u> is the next step in <u>solving</u> a linear programming problem (once you've set up the <u>tableau</u>). It's important that you get this bit right, as it'll affect the rest of the solution if it's wrong.

Choosing a Pivot

1. **Look at the <u>top row</u> of your tableau (the row for the <u>objective function</u>). Pick a column that has a <u>negative value</u> in the top row (let's say you've picked column x for the rest of this method).**

2. **Now <u>divide</u> each value in the <u>RHS column</u> by the corresponding <u>x-value</u>. Ignore the <u>top row</u>, as the RHS is 0 here. Choose the x-value that gives the <u>smallest positive solution</u> when the RHS value is divided by it. This is your <u>pivot</u>.**   ← *If you get a negative value when you divide, you can't use this as your pivot.*

3. **The row that your pivot is in is called the <u>pivot row</u>.**

EXAMPLE   Choose a pivot for the following tableau:

1) First, look at the top row. The y-value is the only negative one, so pick the y-column.

2) Now divide each of the values in the RHS column by the y-value in the same row:
    $18 \div 2 = 9$, $15 \div 3 = 5$
    and $20 \div -4 = -5$. ← *You can't use the negative solution.*
    The smallest positive value is 5, so 3 is your pivot.

P	x	y	s	t	u	RHS
1	4	–1	0	0	0	0
0	3	2	1	0	0	18
0	2	③	0	1	0	15
0	5	–4	0	0	1	20

3) Circle the 3 in the y-column. The row this 3 is in is the pivot row.

Use your **Pivots** to **Solve** the problem

Choosing a pivot is only the <u>beginning</u>... Don't panic if you don't understand this method as you read it — it'll make more sense as you go through the <u>worked example</u> on the next page.

The Simplex Method

1. **First, choose a <u>pivot</u> (see above). <u>Divide</u> the whole of the <u>pivot row</u> by the pivot — this'll make the <u>new value</u> of the pivot <u>1</u>. Make all the <u>other values</u> in the <u>pivot column</u> 0 — you do this by <u>adding</u> or <u>subtracting multiples</u> of the <u>original pivot row</u> to all the other rows. This will give you a <u>new tableau</u>.**   ← *This is one iteration of the Simplex Method.*

2. **<u>Repeat</u> step 1 for the other <u>decision variables</u> which have a <u>negative value</u> in their <u>top row</u>, (i.e. if you used the x-column first, repeat for the y- and maybe z- columns) using the <u>new tableau</u>. You need to choose a <u>new pivot</u> each time.**

3. **Keep repeating steps 1 and 2 until there are <u>no more negative values</u> in the top row. At this point you've reached the <u>optimum solution</u>. The columns that have just 1s and 0s in are called <u>basis columns</u> and those that don't are called <u>non-basis columns</u>.**

4. **You can now work out the values of the decision variables from your <u>final tableau</u>. The RHS value in the <u>top row</u> will be the <u>maximum value</u> of P.**

P	x	y	s	t	RHS
①	0	0	2	3	⑭
0	0	①	½	0	③
0	①	0	0	2	⑤

Suppose this was your final tableau...

The variables in the top row of the non-basis columns (s and t in this case) have a value of O. So, s, t = O.

The values of the variables in the top row of the basis columns are found by reading down to the 1 and across to the value in the final column. So $P = 14$, $y = 3$ and $x = 5$.
This means that P is maximised (with a value of 14) when $y = 3$ and $x = 5$.

If the <u>slack variables</u> aren't zero, it means you've got <u>spare capacities</u> — there's an example like this at the bottom of the next page.

This is making my head pivot...

I know, I know, a nice big piece of cake would be better than this stuff, but the next example's about cake (if that helps).

The Simplex Method

Solve *Linear Programming Problems* using the *Simplex Method*

The best way to understand the Simplex Method is to follow through a <u>worked example</u>, then have a go for yourself.

EXAMPLE Jonny is making cakes to sell at a fair. Baking a small cake takes 1 hour and baking a large cake takes 2 hours. Decorating a small cake takes 2 hours, and decorating a large cake also takes 2 hours. There are 4 hours' baking time available and 6 hours' decorating time. A small cake sells for a profit of £2 and a large cake sells for a profit of £3. Use the Simplex Method to calculate how many cakes he should make in order to maximise his profits.

1) First, set this up as a linear programming problem: let x = number of small cakes and y = number of large cakes. So you want to maximise $P = 2x + 3y$, subject to the constraints $x + 2y \leq 4$, $2x + 2y \leq 6$, where $x, y \geq 0$.

2) Then add in the slack variables: $x + 2y \leq 4$ becomes $x + 2y + s = 4$ and $2x + 2y \leq 6$ becomes $2x + 2y + t = 6$, where $s, t \geq 0$. Now rearrange the objective function to get all the variables on one side: $P - 2x - 3y = 0$.

3) Put all the equations into the initial tableau:

4) Choose the pivot:
Both the x- and y- columns have negative values in the first row, so you could use either.
Using the x-column: $4 \div 1 = 4$, $6 \div 2 = 3$.

P	x	y	s	t	RHS	
1	−2	−3	0	0	0	(a)
0	1	2	1	0	4	(b)
0	②	2	0	1	6	(c)

It's a good idea to label your equations so you can keep track of what you do to them.

$3 < 4$, so use $x = 2$ as your pivot (and circle it).

Now divide the pivot row by 2 to make the x-value 1. Then add and subtract multiples of the original pivot row (row (c) above) to the other rows to make the x-values 0:

P	x	y	s	t	RHS	
1	0	−1	0	1	6	(d) = (a) + (c)
0	0	①	1	$-\frac{1}{2}$	1	(e) = (b) − ½(c)
0	1	1	0	$\frac{1}{2}$	3	(f) = (c) ÷ 2

This is the first iteration.

To make the x-value in the top row 0, you need to add row (c) to row (a): −2 + 2 = 0.

To make the x-value in the 2nd row 0, you need to take away half of row (c) from row (b).

5) Choose a pivot from this new tableau for the y-column: $1 \div 1 = 1$, $3 \div 1 = 3$, so use $y = 1$ in row (e) as the pivot. There's no need to do $6 \div -1$ as it'll give a negative value.

Now you have to make the pivot in the y-column 1, and the y-values in all the other rows 0 by adding or subtracting multiples of row (e):

This time, the y-value is already 1, so you don't have to do anything to this row.

P	x	y	s	t	RHS	
1	0	0	1	$\frac{1}{2}$	7	(g) = (d) + (e)
0	0	1	1	$-\frac{1}{2}$	1	(h) = (e)
0	1	0	−1	1	2	(i) = (f) − (e)

6) There are no more negative values in the top row, so you're ready to read off the solutions:
s and t are non-basis columns, so $s, t = 0$.
Reading off the basis columns using the method at the bottom of the previous page: $P = 7$, $x = 2$ and $y = 1$.

So P is maximised when $x = 2$ and $y = 1$, so Jonny needs to make 2 small cakes and 1 large cake. This gives a P value of 7, so the maximum profit is £7.

Sometimes you're left with spare capacities that you need to interpret.
E.g. if this was your tableau after the first iteration for a similar example:

P	x	y	s	t	RHS
1	3	0	2	0	10
0	2	1	½	0	6
0	2	0	0	1	2

1) x and s are non-basis columns so $x, s = 0$.

2) P, y and t are basis columns, so read off the values using the method at the bottom of the previous page: $P = 10$, $y = 6$, and $t = 2$.

So if the context was cakes as above, Jonny should make 6 large cakes and no small cakes to make a maximum profit of £10.
He'd have 2 hours' decorating time left over.

Exam questions often ask you to give the values of P, x, y and possibly z at the end of <u>one iteration</u>.
Just set the <u>non-basis</u> column variables to zero, and read off the <u>basis</u> column values in exactly the same way as above.

Always go for the large cake...
The Simplex Method looks harder than drawing the graph, but you can use it to solve problems with more than two variables.

D1 Section 5 — Practice Questions

The graph stuff in this section isn't too bad — once you've got your head round turning the constraints into inequalities, all you have to do is draw a graph and Bob's your uncle. I wish I had an Uncle Bob. The Simplex algorithm seems nonsensical, but it's OK when you get the hang of it. Anyway, here are some warm-up questions for you to have a go at.

Warm-up Questions

1) Give a brief definition of:
   a) decision variables
   b) objective function
   c) optimal solution

2) What does a dotted line on a graph show?

3) What is an objective line?

4) Give one example of a problem that doesn't need integer solutions, and one example that does.

5) A company makes posters in two sizes, large and small. It takes 10 minutes to print each large poster, and 5 minutes to print each small poster. There is a total of 250 minutes per day allocated to printing. It takes 6 minutes to laminate a large poster and 4 minutes for a small poster, with a total of 200 minutes laminating time. The company want to sell at least as many large posters as small, and they want to sell at least 10 small posters. Large posters are sold for a profit of £6 and small posters are sold for a profit of £3.50.
   a) Write this out as a linear programming problem. Identify the decision variables, constraints and objective function.
   b) Show the constraints for this problem graphically. Label the feasible region R.
   c) Maximise the profit, using either the objective line method or the vertex method. Don't worry about integer solutions for now.
   d) Use your answer to part c) to find the optimal integer solution.

6) a) Put the following linear programming problem into a tableau:
      maximise $P = 6x + 12y$, subject to the constraints $x + 3y \leq 7$, $2x + 3y \leq 8$, $x, y \geq 0$.
   b) Use the Simplex Method to solve the problem.

Exam questions try and scare you by throwing a lot of information at you all at once. Don't let them bully you, just take them one bit at a time and you'll soon get the better of them. Here are a few for you to do.

Exam Questions

1   Anna is selling red and white roses at a flower stall. She buys the flowers from a wholesaler, where red roses cost 75p each and white roses cost 60p each. Based on previous sales, she has come up with the following constraints:

   • She will sell both red roses and white roses.

   • She will sell more red roses than white roses.

   • She will sell a total of at least 100 flowers.

   • The wholesaler has 300 red roses and 200 white roses available.

   Let x be the number of red roses she buys and y be the number of white roses she buys. Formulate this information as a linear programming problem. Write out the constraints as inequalities and identify a suitable objective function, stating how it should be optimised. You do not need to solve this problem.

   (7 marks)

D1 Section 5 — Practice Questions

In the words of some little <u>Dickensian orphan</u>, 'please sir, I want some more'. Well, I'd be more than happy to oblige — here's another page full of <u>exciting exam questions</u>.

2   A company sells three packs of craft paper: bronze, silver and gold. Each pack is made up of three different types of paper: tissue paper, sugar paper and foil.

- The gold pack is made up of 6 sheets of foil, 15 sheets of sugar paper and 15 sheets of tissue paper.
- The silver pack is made up of 2 sheets of foil, 9 sheets of sugar paper and 4 sheets of tissue paper.
- The bronze pack is made up of 1 sheet of foil, 6 sheets of sugar paper and 1 sheet of tissue paper.
- Each day, there are 30 sheets of foil available, 120 sheets of sugar paper available and 60 sheets of tissue paper available.
- The company is trying to reduce the amount of foil used, so it uses at least three times as many sheets of sugar paper as of foil.

The company makes x gold packs, y silver packs and z bronze packs in a day.

a)   Apart from the trivial constraints, write out the other four constraints as inequalities in terms of x, y and z. Simplify each inequality where possible.

(8 marks)

b)   On Monday, the company decides to make the same number of silver packs as bronze packs.

   (i)   Show that your inequalities from part a) become
$$2x + y \leq 10$$
$$x + y \leq 8$$
$$3x + y \leq 12$$
$$2y \geq x$$

(3 marks)

   (ii)   On graph paper, draw a graph showing the constraints from part (i) above, as well as the trivial constraints. Label the feasible region R.

(5 marks)

   (iii)   Use your graph to work out the maximum number of packs the company can make on Monday.

(2 marks)

   (iv)   Gold packs are sold for a profit of £3.50, silver packs are sold for a profit of £2 and bronze packs are sold for a profit of £1. Use your answers to parts (ii) and (iii) to maximise the profit they make, and state how many of each type of pack they need to sell.

(3 marks)

3   The graph below shows the constraints of a linear programming problem. The feasible region is labelled R.

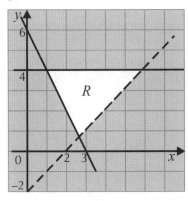

a)   Including the trivial constraints, find the inequalities that produce R.

(5 marks)

b)   Find the coordinates of each vertex of R.

(4 marks)

The aim is to minimise $C = 4x + y$.

c)   Find the optimal solution and state where this value occurs.

(3 marks)

D1 Section 5 — Practice Questions

And now for some <u>Simplex exam questions</u>. The Simplex stuff might have seemed the height of complicatedness, but the questions you actually get on it don't tend to be that bad. A bit of practice and you'll be laughing.

4   Look at the following linear programming problem:

         Maximise $\qquad\qquad P = -2x + 4y - 3z,$

         subject to the constraints $x + y + z \leq 16$

$$3x + 2y - z \leq 20$$
$$4x - 5y + z \leq 25$$
$$x, y, z, \geq 0.$$

    a)   Set up an initial Simplex tableau to show this information.

             (4 marks)

    b)   Explain why your pivot has to come from the y-column, and state the value of the pivot.

             (2 marks)

    c)   Using your tableau, carry out one iteration of the Simplex method.
         State the value of P you have found at this stage.

             (5 marks)

5   A decorating company decorates rooms defined as small or large.

    •   Each room has to be painted and wallpapered.

    •   Painting a small room takes 1 day, and painting a large room takes 3 days.

    •   Wallpapering a small room takes 2 days, and wallpapering a large room takes 4 days.

    •   There are 15 days' painting time and 22 days' wallpapering time available.

    •   The company makes a profit of £50 on every small room decorated, and £120 on every large room.

    a)   Write out the 4 constraints for this linear programming problem.

             (3 marks)

The company wants to maximise their profits.

    b)   State the objective function to be maximised.

             (1 mark)

    c)   Set up a Simplex tableau to show this information.

             (3 marks)

    d)   Use the Simplex method to solve the linear programming problem. Start by choosing a pivot
         from the x-column. Interpret your results within the context of the problem.

             (8 marks)

General Certificate of Education
Advanced Subsidiary (AS) and Advanced Level

Decision Mathematics D1 — Practice Exam One

Time Allowed: 1 hour 30 min

Graphical calculators may be used for this exam.

Give any non-exact numerical answers to an appropriate degree of accuracy.

There are 72 marks available for this paper.

1   The algorithm below calculates square roots correct to 2 decimal places.

Step 1:	Input A
Step 2:	Let N = 1
Step 3:	Let P = A ÷ N
Step 4:	Let Q = P + N
Step 5:	Let R = Q ÷ 2
Step 6:	If $|R - N| < 0.01$, then go to Step 10
Step 7:	If $|R - N| \geq 0.01$, then go to Step 8
Step 8:	Let N = R
Step 9:	Go to Step 3
Step 10:	Write R to 2 decimal places
Step 11:	Stop.

a)   Trace the algorithm for A = 2.

(6 marks)

b)   State the result you would obtain if you traced the algorithm for A = 9.

(1 mark)

2   The network below represents the main roads between towns in an area.
The weights on the edges represent distances in miles, and the vertices represent road junctions.

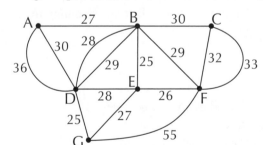

Total length of roads = 460 miles

a)   Duncan works in town C and lives in town G. On a copy of the diagram, use Dijkstra's
algorithm to find Duncan's shortest route home. Write down the route and give its length.

(7 marks)

b)   Duncan drives a truck which paints lines on roads. He is going to paint white lines on all
the roads. He uses the shortest route that travels down each road, starting from C and ending at G.
(i)   Which roads does Duncan need to drive along more than once?
(ii)   How many miles will Duncan drive?

(2 marks)

3   Stephanie is packing to go to university. She has boxes that can hold a maximum of 6 kg.
The items she needs to pack into the boxes have the following weights (in kg):

    1.8   3.5   2.6   4.1   1.2   0.8   2.0   2.4   3.1

a)   Use the first fit method to pack the items into the boxes.
State how many boxes are used and how much space is wasted.

(3 marks)

b)   Use the first fit decreasing method to pack the items again. You don't need to use an algorithm
to sort the items. State how many boxes are used and how much space is wasted.

(3 marks)

c)   Suggest a reason why the answer to part a) might be a more practical way of packing.

(1 mark)

4   The diagram shows the various cycle paths in a park. The bike hire shop is at G.
A floodlighting system is to be installed so that the cycle paths can be used after dark. There will be a light
at each intersection. The number on each edge represents the distance, in metres, between two intersections.

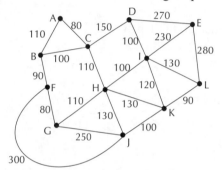

a)   Cabling must be laid along the paths so that each intersection is connected.
Starting from the bike hire shop (G), use Prim's algorithm to find a cabling layout
that will use a minimum amount of cable. List the paths in the order they are added.

(5 marks)

b)   Draw your minimum spanning tree and state its length.

(3 marks)

c)   The warden uses Kruskal's algorithm to find a minimum spanning tree.
Find the tenth and the eleventh edges that the warden adds to his spanning tree.

(3 marks)

5   In a simple graph, no two nodes are directly joined by more than one arc,
and nodes are never joined directly to themselves.
In a connected graph, every pair of nodes has a path between them.

a)   A graph has 4 nodes, A, B, C, D, and 4 arcs. Nodes A and B have orders of 1 and 3 respectively.
Draw two possible connected graphs, where one is simple and the other isn't.

(2 marks)

b)   Give an example of a cycle in your simple graph.

(1 mark)

c)   Explain why ABCBD is not a path in the graph below.

(1 mark)

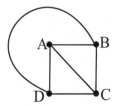

6   The diagram on the right shows a network.
The distances between the vertices are given on the edges.

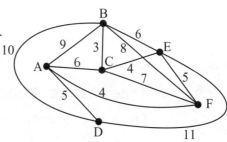

a)   Use the nearest neighbour algorithm to find an upper bound for your completed network.
Start from vertex A.

(3 marks)

b)   Find a minimum spanning tree for your network using Kruskal's algorithm.
Draw your tree and state its weight.

(4 marks)

c)   Hence find a lower bound for the completed network by deleting vertex B and all edges
incident to it.

(3 marks)

d)   Using your answers to parts a) and c), draw a conclusion about the length of the optimum tour.

(1 mark)

7   John makes greetings cards to sell at craft fairs. He makes x birthday cards and y blank cards.

Each birthday card costs 40p to make and each blank card costs 50p to make.
He has a total of £8 he can spend on materials for the cards.
He decides that he doesn't have enough time to make more than 18 cards in total.

a)   Write out the two constraints as inequalities in terms of x and y.

(2 marks)

b)   John makes a profit of £0.75 on each birthday card and £1.50 on each blank card.
Assume he sells all the cards he makes. He wants to maximise the profit, P.

Write out the objective function, P, in terms of x and y.

(1 mark)

c)   Set up an initial Simplex tableau to show this information.

(3 marks)

d)   Using a pivot from the y column, carry out one iteration of the Simplex method.
State the values of x, y and P that you have found at this stage.
Interpret your result in the context of the problem.

(6 marks)

Natalie is also making cards to sell.

Each birthday card also costs her 40p to make and each blank card costs her 50p to make.
Like John, she has a total of £8 she can spend on materials for the cards.

e)   Natalie doesn't limit the total number of cards she makes. Instead, she uses the constraints
represented by the inequalities $y \leq 8$ and $y \leq x$.
Write out in words what these constraints mean in terms of the number of birthday cards
and blank cards.

(2 marks)

f)   On graph paper, draw these three constraints, together with the
non-negativity constraints $x, y \geq 0$ and label the feasible region R.

(4 marks)

Natalie also makes a profit of £0.75 on each birthday card and £1.50 on each blank card.
Assume she sells all the cards she makes. She wants to maximise the profit, P.

g)   Use the graph from part f) to optimise the objective function. State how many birthday cards
and how many blank cards Natalie should make, and write down the maximum profit.

(5 marks)

General Certificate of Education
Advanced Subsidiary (AS) and Advanced Level

Decision Mathematics D1 — Practice Exam Two

Time Allowed: 1 hour 30 min

Graphical calculators may be used for this exam.

Give any non-exact numerical answers to an appropriate degree of accuracy.

There are 72 marks available for this paper.

1   281   276   255   290   263   287

    a)   Sort these numbers into ascending order using a shuttle sort.
        State the number of comparisons and swaps made on each pass.

(5 marks)

    b)   The original list is sorted into descending order using a bubble sort. Write down the maximum
        number of comparisons and the maximum number of passes needed.

(2 marks)

2   a)   Nicola has worked out the following lower bounds for a travelling salesperson problem:
        187, 213, 195, 199, 207, 182.

        (i)   State the best lower bound.

(1 mark)

        She has found the following upper bounds for the same problem: 234, 218, 226, 217, 229, 235.

        (ii) State the best upper bound.

(1 mark)

        (iii) From your answers to parts (i) and (ii), what can you conclude about the weight of the
             optimum tour for this problem?

(1 mark)

    b)   Stuart is a security guard for an office block. At the end of each day, he has to go round every
        office and lock up. The times (in minutes) it takes him to walk between offices are shown in the
        matrix below.

	A	B	C	D	E	F
A	–	6	7	5	11	2
B	6	–	4	12	8	6
C	7	4	–	9	10	13
D	5	12	9	–	3	7
E	11	8	10	3	–	1
F	2	6	13	7	1	–

        (i)   Find an upper bound for Stuart's quickest route using the Nearest Neighbour algorithm.
            Start at office B.

(4 marks)

        (ii) Use Prim's algorithm to find a minimum spanning tree, starting from office C.
            Show the order in which the edges are added and draw your tree, stating its weight.

(5 marks)

        (iii) Using your answer to part (ii), find a lower bound for Stuart's route.
            Delete vertex D and all edges incident to it.

(3 marks)

3 An algorithm for finding the next multiple of 9 from any integer A is represented by this flow chart:

a) Use the algorithm to show that the output for $A = 977$ is 981.

State the values of A and B at each pass through the flow chart.

(4 marks)

b) Write down the output when $A = 978$.

(1 mark)

c) Explain why no more than 9 passes through the algorithm will ever be needed.

(1 mark)

Start

Input A

Let B = sum of digits of A

Is B a 1-digit number? — Yes

Let $A = A + 1$

No

Let B = sum of digits of B

Does $B = 9$? — No

Yes

Output A

Stop

4

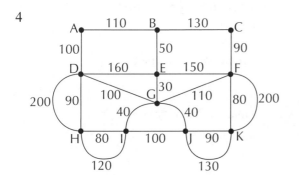

Total length of roads = 2200 m

The diagram shows the network of roads in a village.
The number on each edge is the length, in metres, of the road.

Rufus runs a roof repair company.

a) Rufus delivers leaflets advertising his business. He needs to walk along each road at least once, starting and finishing at H. Find the length of an optimal route for Rufus.

(6 marks)

b) If Rufus can start and finish the delivery at two distinct vertices,

(i) state which two vertices should be chosen to minimise the length of his new route.
Give a reason for your answer.

(2 marks)

(ii) Find the length of his new route.

(1 mark)

c) Rufus lives at H and needs to repair a roof at C. Use Dijkstra's algorithm to find the minimum driving distance between H and C. State the corresponding route.

(6 marks)

5   Scott draws a graph that has 8 vertices and 16 edges. All the vertices are even, and the graph is connected.

   a)   Is this graph Eulerian? Explain your answer.

   (2 marks)

   b)   Explain what he would have to do to make the graph semi-Eulerian.

   (1 mark)

   c)   How many edges will he need to draw a minimum spanning tree?

   (1 mark)

6   A charity is selling tickets to its annual charity ball. It has two corporate packages available: business class and premier.

   Each business class package includes 5 tickets and each premier package includes 10 tickets.

   Each business class package includes 2 bottles of wine and each premier package includes 8 bottles of wine.

   There are 300 tickets and 160 bottles of wine available.

   At least 5 of each type of package are sold, and at least 20 packages are sold in total.

   The charity sells x business class packages and y premier packages.

   a)   5 constraints are required when expressing this information as a linear programming problem.

   (i)   Show why the following constraints are required: $x + 2y \leq 60$, $x + 4y \leq 80$

   (2 marks)

   (ii)   State three other constraints that must also be used.

   (2 marks)

   b)   Each business class package makes a profit of £150 and each premier package makes a profit of £200. The charity wants to calculate the minimum and maximum profit from the ball.

   (i)   On graph paper, draw a diagram to represent this linear programming problem. Clearly label the feasible region and draw on an objective line.

   (6 marks)

   (ii)   Find the maximum profit from the ball. Write down how many of each type of package need to be sold to make this profit.

   (2 marks)

   (iii)   Find the minimum profit from the ball. Write down how many of each type of package need to be sold to make this profit.

   (2 marks)

7   Look at the following linear programming problem:

   Maximise $P = 4x + 3y + 2z$,

   subject to the constraints $x - y + 3z \leq 6$

   $2x - 4y - 5z \leq 20$

   $x, y, z \geq 0$.

   a)   Set up an initial Simplex tableau to show this information.

   (3 marks)

   b)   Explain why your pivot cannot come from the y-column.

   (1 mark)

   c)   Using a pivot from the x column, carry out one iteration of the Simplex method. State the values of x, y, z and P you have found at this stage.

   (6 marks)

   d)   Why does P have no finite maximum?

   (1 mark)

Answers

C1 Section 1 — Algebra Fundamentals

Warm-up Questions

1) a) a & b are constants, x is a variable.

   b) a & b are constants, x is a variable.

   c) a, b & c are constants, y is a variable.

   d) a is a constant, x & y are variables.

2) Identity symbol is $\equiv$.

3) A, C and D are identities.

4) a) x^8 b) a^{15} c) x^6 d) a^8 e) x^4y^3z f) $\dfrac{b^2c^5}{a}$

5) a) 4   b) 2   c) 8   d) 1   e) $\dfrac{1}{7}$

6) a) $x = \pm\sqrt{5}$ b) $x = -2 \pm \sqrt{3}$

7) a) $2\sqrt{7}$ b) $\dfrac{\sqrt{5}}{6}$ c) $3\sqrt{2}$ d) $\dfrac{3}{4}$

8) a) $\dfrac{8}{\sqrt{2}} = \dfrac{8}{\sqrt{2}} \times \dfrac{\sqrt{2}}{\sqrt{2}} = \dfrac{8\sqrt{2}}{2} = 4\sqrt{2}$

   b) $\dfrac{\sqrt{2}}{2} = \dfrac{\sqrt{2}}{(\sqrt{2})^2} = \dfrac{1}{\sqrt{2}}$

9) $136 + 24\sqrt{21}$

10) $3 - \sqrt{7}$

11) a) $a^2 - b^2$ b) $a^2 + 2ab + b^2$

   c) $25y^2 + 210xy$ d) $3x^2 + 10xy + 3y^2 + 13x + 23y + 14$

12) a) $xy(2x + a + 2y)$ b) $a^2x(1 + b^2x)$

   c) $8(2y + xy + 7x)$ d) $(x - 2)(x - 3)$

13) a) $\dfrac{52x + 5y}{60}$ b) $\dfrac{5x - 2y}{x^2y}$ c) $\dfrac{x^3 + x^2 - y^2 + xy^2}{x(x^2 - y^2)}$

14) a) $\dfrac{3a}{2b}$ b) $\dfrac{2(p^2 + q^2)}{p^2 - q^2}$ c)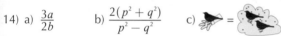

Exam Questions

1 a) $27^{\frac{1}{3}} = \sqrt[3]{27}$

      $= 3$ *[1 mark]*

   b) $27^{\frac{4}{3}} = (27^{\frac{1}{3}})^4$ *[1 mark]*

      $= 3^4 = 3 \times 3 \times 3 \times 3 = 9 \times 9$

      $= 81$ *[1 mark]*

2 a) $(5\sqrt{3})^2 = (5^2)(\sqrt{3})^2 = 25 \cdot 3$

      $= 75$ *[1 mark]*

   b) $(5 + \sqrt{6})(2 - \sqrt{6}) = 10 - 5\sqrt{6} + 2\sqrt{6} - 6$ *[1 mark]*

      $= 4 - 3\sqrt{6}$ *[1 mark]*

3 $10000\sqrt{10} = 10^4 \cdot 10^{\frac{1}{2}}$ *[1 mark]*

      $= 10^{4 + \frac{1}{2}}$ *[1 mark]*

      $= 10^{\frac{9}{2}}$

      so $k = \dfrac{9}{2}$ *[1 mark]*

4 Multiply top and bottom by $3 + \sqrt{5}$ to 'rationalise the denominator':

   $\dfrac{5 + \sqrt{5}}{3 - \sqrt{5}} = \dfrac{(5 + \sqrt{5})(3 + \sqrt{5})}{(3 - \sqrt{5})(3 + \sqrt{5})}$ *[1 mark]*

   $= \dfrac{15 + 5\sqrt{5} + 3\sqrt{5} + 5}{9 - 5}$ *[1 mark]*

   $= \dfrac{20 + 8\sqrt{5}}{4}$ *[1 mark]*

   $= 5 + 2\sqrt{5}$ *[1 mark]*

5 $2x^4 - 32x^2 = 2x^2(x^2 - 16)$

      $= 2x^2(x + 4)(x - 4)$

   [3 marks available in total — 1 mark for each correct factor]

6 $\dfrac{x + 5x^3}{\sqrt{x}} = x^{-\frac{1}{2}}(x + 5x^3)$ *[1 mark]*

      $= x^{\frac{1}{2}} + 5x^{\frac{5}{2}}$ *[1 mark]*

7 $\dfrac{(5 + 4\sqrt{x})^2}{2x} = \dfrac{25 + 40\sqrt{x} + 16x}{2x}$ *[1 mark]*

      $= \dfrac{1}{2}x^{-1}(25 + 40x^{\frac{1}{2}} + 16x)$ *[1 mark]*

      $= \dfrac{25}{2}x^{-1} + 20x^{-\frac{1}{2}} + 8,$

      so $P = 20$ and $Q = 8$ *[1 mark]*

C1 Section 2 — Quadratic Equations

Warm-up Questions

1) a) $(x + 1)^2$ b) $(x - 10)(x - 3)$

   c) $(x + 2)(x - 2)$ d) $(3 - x)(x + 1)$

   e) $(2x + 1)(x - 4)$ f) $(5x - 3)(x + 2)$

2) a) $(x - 2)(x - 1) = 0$, so $x = 2$ or 1

   b) $(x + 4)(x - 3) = 0$, so $x = -4$ or 3

   c) $(2 - x)(x + 1) = 0$, so $x = 2$ or -1

   d) $(x + 4)(x - 4) = 0$, so $x = \pm4$

   e) $(3x + 2)(x - 7) = 0$, so $x = -2/3$ or 7

   f) $(2x + 1)(2x - 1) = 0$, so $x = \pm1/2$

   g) $(2x - 3)(x - 1) = 0$, so $x = 3/2$ or 1

3) a) $(x - 2)^2 - 7$; minimum value $= -7$ at $x = 2$, and this crosses the x-axis at $x = 2 \pm \sqrt{7}$

   b) $\dfrac{21}{4} - \left(x + \dfrac{3}{2}\right)^2$; maximum value $= 21/4$ at $x = -3/2$, and this crosses the x-axis at $-\dfrac{3}{2} \pm \dfrac{\sqrt{21}}{2}$.

   c) $2(x - 1)^2 + 9$; minimum value $= 9$ at $x = 1$, and this doesn't cross the x-axis.

   d) $4\left(x - \dfrac{7}{2}\right)^2 - 1$; minimum value $= -1$ at $x = 7/2$, crosses the x-axis at $x = \dfrac{7}{2} \pm \dfrac{1}{2}$ i.e. $x = 4$ or 3

Answers

4) a) $b^2 - 4ac = 16$, so 2 roots

b) $b^2 - 4ac = 0$, so 1 root

c) $b^2 - 4ac = -8$, so no roots

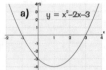 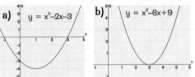

5) a) Using the quadratic formula with $a = 3$, $b = -7$ and $c = 3$:

$$x = \frac{-(-7) \pm \sqrt{(-7)^2 - (4 \times 3 \times 3)}}{(2 \times 3)}$$

$$= \frac{7 \pm \sqrt{49 - 36}}{6}$$

$$= \frac{7 \pm \sqrt{13}}{6}$$

so $x = \frac{7 + \sqrt{13}}{6}$, $x = \frac{7 - \sqrt{13}}{6}$.

b) Using the quadratic formula with $a = 2$, $b = -6$ and $c = -2$:

$$x = \frac{-(-6) \pm \sqrt{(-6)^2 - (4 \times 2 \times -2)}}{(2 \times 2)}$$

$$= \frac{6 \pm \sqrt{36 + 16}}{4}$$

$$= \frac{6 \pm \sqrt{52}}{4}$$

$$= \frac{6 \pm 2\sqrt{13}}{4}$$

$$= \frac{3 \pm \sqrt{13}}{2}$$

so $x = \frac{3 + \sqrt{13}}{2}$, $x = \frac{3 - \sqrt{13}}{2}$.

c) Using the quadratic formula with $a = 1$, $b = 4$ and $c = -6$:

$$x = \frac{-(4) \pm \sqrt{(4)^2 - (4 \times 1 \times -6)}}{(2 \times 1)}$$

$$= \frac{-4 \pm \sqrt{16 + 24}}{2}$$

$$= \frac{-4 \pm \sqrt{40}}{2}$$

$$= \frac{-4 \pm 2\sqrt{10}}{2}$$

$$= -2 \pm \sqrt{10}$$

so $x = -2 + \sqrt{10}$, $x = -2 - \sqrt{10}$.

6) $k^2 - (4 \times 1 \times 4) > 0$, so $k^2 > 16$ and so $k > 4$ or $k < -4$.

7) $4x^4 - 5x^2 + 1 = 4(x^2)^2 - 5(x^2) + 1$ so substitute $y = x^2$ to give:
$4y^2 - 5y + 1$. Now solve for y:

$(4y - 1)(y - 1) = 0$, so $y = \frac{1}{4}$ or $y = 1$.

So: $x^2 = \frac{1}{4}$ or $x^2 = 1$, and so $x = \pm\frac{1}{2}$ or $x = \pm 1$.

Exam Questions

1   For equal roots, $b^2 - 4ac = 0$ *[1 mark]*
       $a = 1$, $b = 2k$ and $c = 4k$
   so $(2k)^2 - (4 \times 1 \times 4k) = 0$ *[1 mark]*
          $4k^2 - 16k = 0$
          $4k(k - 4) = 0$ *[1 mark]*
   so $k = 4$ (as k is non-zero).   *[1 mark]*

2 a) For distinct real roots, $b^2 - 4ac > 0$ *[1 mark]*
     $a = p$, $b = p + 3$ and $c = 4$
  so $(p + 3)^2 - (4 \times p \times 4) > 0$ *[1 mark]*
       $p^2 + 6p + 9 - 16p > 0$
       $p^2 - 10p + 9 > 0$ *[1 mark]*

b) $p^2 - 10p + 9$ is a u-shaped quadratic, which crosses the
x-axis when $p^2 - 10p + 9 = 0$, that is when $(p - 9)(p - 1) = 0$
[1 mark], which occurs at $p = 9$ and $p = 1$ *[1 mark]*. As it's
u-shaped, $p^2 - 10p + 9 > 0$ when p is outside these values
[1 mark], that is when $p < 1$ or $p > 9$ *[1 mark]*.

3   Expanding the brackets on the RHS gives the quadratic
$mx^2 + 4mx + 4m + p$. Equating the coefficients of x^2 gives
$m = 5$ *[1 mark]*. Equating the coefficients of x gives
$n = 4m$, so $n = 20$ *[1 mark]*. Equating the constant terms
gives $14 = 4m + p \Rightarrow p = -6$ *[1 mark]*.

4 a) $a = 12 \div 2 = 6$ *[1 mark]*, so the completed square is
$(x - 6)^2 + b = x^2 - 12x + 36 + b$. Equating coefficients
gives $15 = 36 + b$, so $b = 15 - 36 = -21$ *[1 mark]*.
The final expression is $(x - 6)^2 - 21$.

b) (i)   The minimum occurs when the expression in brackets
is equal to 0, which means the minimum is the value of
b, which from (a) above is –21 *[1 mark]*.

(ii)   From above, the minimum occurs when the expression
in brackets is equal to 0, i.e. when $x = 6$ *[1 mark]*.

*Part (b) is dead easy once you've completed the square — you can
just take your values straight from there.*

5 a) Put $a = 1$, $b = -14$ and $c = 25$ into the quadratic formula:

$$x = \frac{-(-14) \pm \sqrt{(-14)^2 - (4 \times 1 \times 25)}}{(2 \times 1)}$$

$$= \frac{14 \pm \sqrt{196 - 100}}{2}$$

$$= \frac{14 \pm \sqrt{96}}{2}$$

$$= \frac{14 \pm 4\sqrt{6}}{2}$$

$$= 7 \pm 2\sqrt{6}$$

so $x = 7 + 2\sqrt{6}$, $x = 7 - 2\sqrt{6}$
*[3 marks available — 1 mark for putting correct values of
a, b and c into the quadratic formula, 1 mark each for final
x-values.]*

b)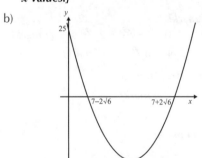

*[3 marks available — 1 mark for drawing u-shaped curve,
1 mark for using answers from a) as x-axis intercepts and
1 mark for correct y-axis intercept (0, 25).]*

c) As the graph is u-shaped, the inequality is < 0 when x is
between the two intercepts, i.e. $7 - 2\sqrt{6} \le x \le 7 + 2\sqrt{6}$
[1 mark].

6 a) (i) $m = 10 \div 2 = 5$ *[1 mark]*, so the expression becomes $-(5 - x)^2 + n = -25 + 10x - x^2 + n$. Equating coefficients gives $-27 = -25 + n$, so $n = -27 - (-25) = -2$ *[1 mark]*. The final expression is $-(5 - x)^2 - 2$.

   (ii) $(5 - x)^2 \geq 0$ for all values of x, so $-(5 - x)^2 \leq 0$. Therefore — $(5 - x)^2 - 2 < 0$ for all x, i.e. the function is always negative. *[1 mark]*

   b) (i) The y-coordinate is the maximum value, which is -2 *[1 mark]*, and this occurs when the expression in the brackets = 0.
   The x-value that makes the expression in the brackets 0 is 5 *[1 mark]*, so the coordinates of the maximum point are $(5, -2)$.

   (ii)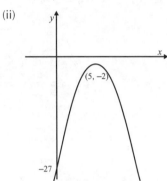

   [2 marks available — 1 mark for drawing n-shaped curve that sits below the x-axis, 1 mark for correct y-axis intercept (0, −27)]

7 Substitute $y = x^{\frac{1}{5}}$ *[1 mark]*, then $2y^2 - 3y - 2 = 0$.
   Factorise quadratic to get $(2y + 1)(y - 2) = 0$ *[1 mark]*.
   Solve for y to get $y = -\frac{1}{2}$ or $y = 2$ *[1 mark]*.
   So, $x^{\frac{1}{5}} = -\frac{1}{2}$ or $x^{\frac{1}{5}} = 2$
   $\Rightarrow x = (-\frac{1}{2})^5 = -\frac{1}{32}$ or $x = 2^5 = 32$ *[1 mark]*

C1 Section 3 —
Inequalities & Simultaneous Equations
Warm-up Questions

1) a) $x > -\frac{38}{5}$ b) $y \leq \frac{7}{8}$ c) $y \leq -\frac{3}{4}$

2) a) $x > \frac{5}{2}$ b) $x > -4$ c) $x \leq -3$

3) a) $-\frac{1}{3} \leq x \leq 2$ b) $x < 1 - \sqrt{3}$ or $x > 1 + \sqrt{3}$
   c) $x \leq -3$ or $x \geq -2$

4) a) $x \leq -3$ and $x \geq 1$ b) $x < -\frac{1}{2}$ and $x > 1$
   c) $-3 < x < 2$

5) a) $x = -3, y = -4$ b) $x = -\frac{1}{6}, y = -\frac{5}{12}$

6) a) The line and the curve meet at the points $(2, -6)$ and $(7, 4)$.
   b) The line is a tangent to the parabola at the point $(2, 26)$.
   c) The equations have no solution and so the line and the curve never meet.

7) a) $\left(\frac{1}{4}, -\frac{13}{4}\right)$ b) $(4, 5)$ c) $(-5, -2)$

Exam Questions

1 a) $3x + 2 \leq x + 6$
   $\qquad 2x \leq 4$ *[1 mark]*
   $\qquad x \leq 2$ *[1 mark]*

  b) $\qquad 20 - x - x^2 > 0$
   $(4 - x)(5 + x) > 0$ *[1 mark]*
   The graph crosses the x-axis at $x = 4$ and $x = -5$ *[1 mark]*. The coefficient of x^2 is negative so the graph is n-shaped *[1 mark]*.
   So $20 - x - x^2 > 0$ when $-5 < x < 4$ *[1 mark]*.

  c) From above, x will satisfy both inequalities when $-5 < x \leq 2$ *[1 mark]*.

   For this bit, all you need to do is use your answers to parts a) and b) and work out which values of x fit in them both.

2 a) $3 \leq 2p + 5 \leq 15$
   This inequality has 3 parts. Subtract 5 from each part to give: $-2 \leq 2p \leq 10$ *[1 mark]*.
   Now divide each part by 2 to give: $-1 \leq p \leq 5$
   [1 mark for −1 ≤ p and 1 mark for p ≤ 5].

  b) $q^2 - 9 > 0$
   $(q + 3)(q - 3) > 0$ *[1 mark]*
   The function is 0 at $q = -3$ and $q = 3$ *[1 mark]*.
   The coefficient of x^2 is positive so the graph is u-shaped.
   So $q^2 - 9 > 0$ when $q < -3$ or $q > 3$
   [1 mark for each correct inequality].

   Use D.O.T.S. (Difference of Two Squares) to factorise the quadratic — remember that $a^2 - b^2 = (a + b)(a - b)$.

3 a) $(3x + 2)(x - 5)$ *[1 mark]*

  b) $(3x + 2)(x - 5) \leq 0$
   The function is 0 at $x = -\frac{2}{3}$ and $x = 5$ *[1 mark]*.
   The coefficient of x^2 is positive so the graph is u-shaped, meaning the function is less than or equal to 0 between these x-values.
   I.e. $3x^2 - 13x - 10 \leq 0$ when $-\frac{2}{3} \leq x \leq 5$
   [2 marks, 1 for $-\frac{2}{3} \leq x$ and 1 for x ≤ 5].

4 First, take the linear equation and rearrange it to get x on its own: $x = 6 - y$ *[1 mark]*. Now substitute the equation for x into the quadratic equation:
   $\qquad (6 - y)^2 + 2y^2 = 36$ *[1 mark]*
   $\qquad 36 - 12y + y^2 + 2y^2 = 36$
   $\qquad\qquad 3y^2 - 12y = 0$
   $\qquad\qquad\quad y^2 - 4y = 0$
   $\qquad\qquad y(y - 4) = 0$ *[1 mark]*
   so $y = 0$ and $y = 4$. *[1 mark]*.
   Now you've got the y-values, put them back into the equation for x ($x = 6 - y$) to find the x-values.
   When $y = 0$, $x = 6 - y = 6 - 0 = 6$.
   When $y = 4$, $x = 6 - y = 6 - 4 = 2$.
   So solutions are $x = 6, y = 0$ *[1 mark]*
   and $x = 2, y = 4$ *[1 mark]*.

Answers

5 a) At points of intersection, $-2x + 4 = -x^2 + 3$ *[1 mark]*

$$x^2 - 2x + 1 = 0$$
$$(x - 1)^2 = 0 \quad \text{[1 mark]}$$

so $x = 1$ *[1 mark]*. When $x = 1$, $y = -2x + 4 = 2$, so there is one point of intersection at $(1, 2)$ *[1 mark]*.

b)

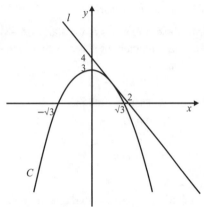

[5 marks available — 1 mark for drawing n-shaped curve, 1 mark for x-axis intercepts at $\pm\sqrt{3}$, 1 mark for maximum point of curve and y-axis intercept at (0, 3). 1 mark for line crossing the y-axis at (0, 4) and the x-axis at (2, 0). 1 mark for line and curve touching in one place.]

6 a)

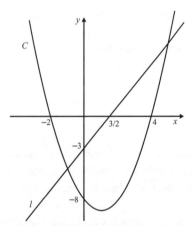

[5 marks available — 1 mark for drawing u-shaped curve, 1 mark for x-axis intercepts at –2 and 4 , 1 mark for y-axis intercept at (0, –8). 1 mark for line crossing the y-axis at (0, –3) and the x-axis at (3/2, 0). 1 mark for line and curve intersecting in two places.]

b) At points of intersection,

$$2x - 3 = (x + 2)(x - 4)$$
$$2x - 3 = x^2 - 2x - 8 \quad \text{[1 mark]}$$
$$0 = x^2 - 4x - 5 \quad \text{[1 mark]}$$

c) $x^2 - 4x - 5 = 0$

$$(x - 5)(x + 1) = 0 \quad \text{[1 mark]}$$

so $x = 5$, $x = -1$ *[1 mark]*.

When $x = 5$, $y = (2 \times 5) - 3 = 7$ and when $x = -1$, $y = (2 \times -1) - 3 = -5$, so the points of intersection are $(5, 7)$ *[1 mark]* and $(-1, -5)$ *[1 mark]*.

C1 Section 4 —
Coordinate Geometry and Graphs
Warm-up Questions

1) a) (i) $y + 1 = 3(x - 2)$ (ii) $y = 3x - 7$ (iii) $3x - y - 7 = 0$

   b) (i) $y + \frac{1}{3} = \frac{1}{5}x$ (ii) $y = \frac{1}{5}x - \frac{1}{3}$

   (iii) $3x - 15y - 5 = 0$

2) a) $y = \frac{3}{2}x - 4$ b) $y = -\frac{1}{2}x + 4$

3) The equation of the required line is $y = \frac{3}{2}x + \frac{15}{2}$.

4) a) $M = (\frac{2 + 12}{2}, \frac{5 - 1}{2}) = (7, 2)$

   b) $l = \sqrt{(7 - 2)^2 + (2 - 5)^2} = \sqrt{25 + 9} = \sqrt{34}$

5) a)   b)

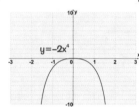   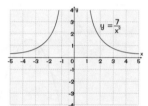

   c)   d)

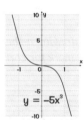   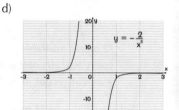

6)

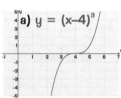   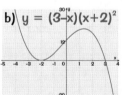

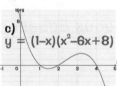   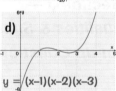

7) a)   b)

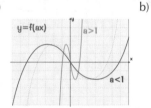   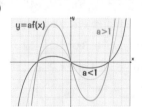

   c)   d)

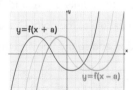   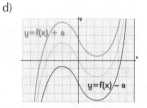

8) (a) 3, (0, 0)

(b) 2, (2, –4)

(c) 5, (–3, 4)

Exam Questions

1 a) Just rearrange into the form $y = mx + c$ and read off m:

$3y = 15 - 4x$

$y = -\frac{4}{3}x + 5$ *[1 mark]*

so the gradient of the line L is $-\frac{4}{3}$ *[1 mark]*.

b) Gradient of the line $= -1 \div -\frac{4}{3} = \frac{3}{4}$ *[1 mark]*

So $y = \frac{3}{4}x + c$.

Now use the x- and y- values of R to find C:

$1 = \frac{3}{4}(3) + c$

$1 = \frac{9}{4} + c$

$\Rightarrow c = -\frac{5}{4}$ *[1 mark]*

so the equation of the line is $y = \frac{3}{4}x - \frac{5}{4}$ *[1 mark]*

2 When the brackets are multiplied out, the first term is $2x^3$, so the graph is a positive cubic graph.

$y = 0$ when $x = 2$ or $x = -\frac{1}{2}$, so the graph touches the x-axis twice. When $x = 0$, $y = (1)(-2)^2 = 4$.

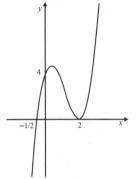

[4 marks available — 1 mark for correct shape, 1 mark for x-axis intercept at –1/2, 1 mark for graph touching the x-axis at 2 and 1 mark for correct y-axis intercept at 4.]

3 a)

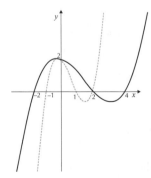

[3 marks available — 1 mark for horizontal stretch, 1 mark for x-axis intercepts at –2, 2 and 4, 1 mark for correct y-axis intercept at 2.]

b)

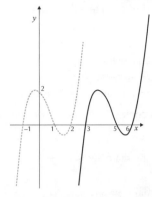

[2 marks available — 1 mark for horizontal translation to the right, 1 mark for x-axis intercepts at 3, 5 and 6]

4 a) Putting $(k, 1)$ into $2x - 14y + 6 = 0$ gives

$2k - 14 + 6 = 0$ *[1 mark]*, and so $k = 4$ *[1 mark]*.

b) $l = \sqrt{(x_2 - x_1)^2 + (y_2 - y_1)^2}$ *[1 mark]*

$= \sqrt{(4 + 3)^2 + (1 - 0)^2}$ *[1 mark]*

$= \sqrt{50} = 5\sqrt{2}$ *[1 mark]*.

c) Rewriting $2x + y + 5 = 0$ in the form $y = mx + c$ gives $y = -2x - 5$, and so read off the gradient $m = -2$ *[1 mark]*. As lines are parallel, can use same gradient *[1 mark]*. Putting this gradient and the coordinates of Q in the formula $y - y_1 = m(x - x_1)$ gives $y - 1 = -2(x - 4)$, i.e. the line $y = -2x + 9$. *[1 mark]*

5 a)

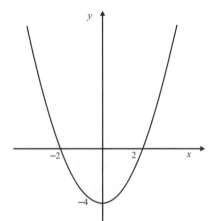

[2 marks available — 1 mark for x-axis intercepts at –2 and 2, 1 mark for correct y-axis intercept (0, –2)]

b) The curve is reflected in the x-axis *[1 mark]*, and stretched vertically by a scale factor of 2 *[1 mark]*.

c) $y = f(x) + 2$ *[1 mark]*

6 a) Using the formula $y - y_1 = m(x - x_1)$, with the coordinates of point S for the x- and y- values and $m = -2$,

$y - (-3) = -2(x - 7)$ *[1 mark]*

$y + 3 = -2x + 14$ *[1 mark]*

$y = -2x + 11$ *[1 mark]*

b) Putting $x = 5$ into $y = -2x + 11$ gives $y = 1$ *[1 mark]*, so T does lie on the line.

Answers

7 a) Rearrange equation and complete the square:
$x^2 - 2x + y^2 - 10y + 21 = 0$ *[1 mark]*
$(x - 1)^2 - 1 + (y - 5)^2 - 25 + 21 = 0$ *[1 mark]*
$(x - 1)^2 + (y - 5)^2 = 5$ *[1 mark]*
Compare with $(x - a)^2 + (y - b)^2 = r^2$:
centre = (1, 5) *[1 mark]*, radius = $\sqrt{5}$ *[1 mark]*.

b) The point (3, 6) and centre (1, 5) both lie on the diameter.
Gradient of the diameter = $\frac{6 - 5}{3 - 1} = 0.5$.
Q $(q, 4)$ also lies on the diameter, so $\frac{4 - 6}{q - 3} = 0.5$.
$-2 = 0.5q - 1.5$
So $q = (-2 + 1.5) \div 0.5 = -1$.
[3 marks available — 1 mark for finding the gradient of the diameter, 1 mark for linking this with the point Q, and 1 mark for correct calculation of q.]

c) Tangent at Q is perpendicular to the diameter at Q, so
gradient $m = -\frac{1}{0.5} = -2$
$y - y_1 = m(x - x_1)$, and $(-1, 4)$ is a point on the line, so:
$y - 4 = -2(x + 1)$
$y - 4 = -2x - 2$
$2x + y - 2 = 0$ is the equation of the tangent.
[5 marks available — 1 mark for gradient = −1 ÷ gradient of diameter, 1 mark for correct value for gradient, 1 mark for substituting Q in straight-line equation, 2 marks for correct substitution of values in the correct form, or 1 mark if not in the form ax + by + c = 0.]

8 a) Gradient of $LK = \frac{8 - 6}{5 - 2} = \frac{2}{3}$ *[1 mark]*
so gradient of $l_1 = -1 \div \frac{2}{3} = -\frac{3}{2}$ *[1 mark]*.

Now, putting this gradient and the x- and y- coordinates of L into the formula $y - y_1 = m(x - x_1)$ gives:
$$y - 6 = -\frac{3}{2}(x - 2)$$
$$y = -\frac{3}{2}x + 3 + 6$$
$$y = -\frac{3}{2}x + 9 \quad \text{[1 mark]}$$
$$\Rightarrow 3x + 2y - 18 = 0 \quad \text{[1 mark]}$$

b) Putting $x = 0$ into $y = -\frac{3}{2}x + 9$ gives $y = 9$ *[1 mark]*,
so $M = (0, 9)$ *[1 mark]*.

c) Putting $y = 0$ into $3x + 2y - 18 = 0$ gives $x = 6$
[1 mark], so $N = (6, 0)$ *[1 mark]*.

C1 Section 5 — Differentiation

Warm-up Questions

1) a) $\frac{dy}{dx} = 2x$ b) $\frac{dy}{dx} = 4x^3 + \frac{1}{2\sqrt{x}}$
c) $\frac{dy}{dx} = -\frac{14}{x^3} + \frac{3}{2\sqrt{x^3}} + 36x^2$

2) a) $\frac{dy}{dx} = 4x = 8$
b) $\frac{dy}{dx} = 8x - 1 = 15$
c) $\frac{dy}{dx} = 3x^2 - 14x = -16$

3) Differentiate $v = 17t^2 - 10t$ to give: $\frac{dv}{dt} = 34t - 10$
so, when $t = 4$, $\frac{dv}{dt} = 126$ ml/s.

4) The tangent and normal must go through (16, 6).
Differentiate to find $\frac{dy}{dx} = \frac{3}{2}\sqrt{x} - 3$, so gradient at (16, 6) is 3.
Therefore tangent can be written $y_T = 3x + c_T$;
putting $x = 16$ and $y = 6$ gives $6 = 3 \times 16 + c_T$, so $c_T = -42$,
and the equation of the tangent is $y_T = 3x - 42$.
The gradient of the normal must be $-\frac{1}{3}$, so the equation of
the normal is $y_N = -\frac{1}{3}x + c_N$
Substituting in the coordinates of the point (16, 6)
gives $6 = -\frac{16}{3} + c_N \Rightarrow c_N = \frac{34}{3}$; so the normal is
$y_N = -\frac{1}{3}x + \frac{34}{3} = \frac{1}{3}(34 - x)$.

5) For both curves, when $x = 4$, $y = 2$, so they meet at
(4, 2).   Differentiating the first curve gives
$\frac{dy}{dx} = x^2 - 4x - 4$, which at $x = 4$ is equal to –4.
Differentiating the other curve gives $\frac{dy}{dx} = \frac{1}{2\sqrt{x}}$, and so the
gradient at (4, 2) is ¼. If you multiply these two gradients
together you get –1, so the two curves are perpendicular at
$x = 4$.

6) $\frac{dy}{dx} = 3x^2 - \frac{3}{x^2}$; this is zero at (1, 4) and (–1, –4).
$\frac{d^2y}{dx^2} = 6x + \frac{6}{x^3}$; at $x = 1$ this is positive
so (1, 4) is a minimum; at $x = -1$ this is negative,
so (–1, –4) is a maximum.

7) Maximum is when $\frac{dh}{dm} = 0$.
So, $\frac{m}{5} - \frac{m^2}{300} = \frac{m}{5}\left(1 - \frac{m}{60}\right) = 0$
Since $m \neq 0$, $1 - \frac{m}{60} = 0 \Rightarrow m = 60$
$h_{max} = \frac{60^2}{10} - \frac{60^3}{900} = \frac{3600}{10} - \frac{216000}{900} = 360 - 240 = 120$ m

Those questions covered the basics of differentiation, so if you got them all correct, bravely venture into the murky realm of Exam Questions. If you struggled, have a cuppa to fuel your noggin — then read the section again until it all makes sense.

Exam Questions

1 a) Rewrite all the terms as powers of x:
$y = x^7 + \frac{2}{x^3} = x^7 + 2x^{-3}$ *[1 mark]*
and then differentiate each term:
$\frac{dy}{dx} = 7x^6 + (-3)2x^{-4}$
$= 7x^6 - \frac{6}{x^4}$ *[1 mark]*

b) This is a second-order derivative
— just differentiate the answer for part a):
$\frac{d^2y}{dx^2} = \frac{d}{dx}(7x^6 - 6x^{-4})$ *[1 mark]*
$= (7 \times 6)x^5 - (6 \times -4)x^{-5}$
$= 42x^5 + \frac{24}{x^5}$ *[1 mark]*

2 Rewrite the expression in powers of x, so it becomes $x^{-\frac{1}{2}} + x^{-1}$ *[1 mark]*. Then differentiate to get $\frac{dy}{dx} = -\frac{1}{2}x^{-\frac{3}{2}} - x^{-2}$ *[1 mark for each correct term]*.

Putting $x = 4$ into the derivative gives:

$-\frac{1}{2}4^{-\frac{3}{2}} - 4^{-2} = -\frac{1}{2}(\sqrt{4})^{-3} - \frac{1}{4^2}$

$= -\frac{1}{2} \cdot \frac{1}{2^3} - \frac{1}{16} = -\frac{1}{2} \cdot \frac{1}{8} - \frac{1}{16}$

$= -\frac{1}{16} - \frac{1}{16} = -\frac{1}{8}$

[1 method mark, 1 answer mark]

3 a) Rewrite the expression in powers of x, so it becomes:

$\frac{x^2 + 3x^{\frac{3}{2}}}{x^{\frac{1}{2}}}$ *[1 mark]*

Then divide the top of the fraction by the bottom:

$\frac{x^2}{x^{\frac{1}{2}}} + \frac{3x^{\frac{3}{2}}}{x^{\frac{1}{2}}}$

$= x^{\frac{3}{2}} + 3x$

So $p = \frac{3}{2}$ *[1 mark]* and $q = 1$ *[1 mark]*.

b) Use your answer to part a) to rewrite the equation as:

$y = 3x^3 + 5 + x^{\frac{3}{2}} + 3x$ *[1 mark]*.

Then differentiate each term to give:

$\frac{dy}{dx} = 9x^2 + \frac{3}{2}x^{\frac{1}{2}} + 3$ *[1 mark for each correct term]*.

4 a) $\frac{dy}{dx} = 6x^2 - 8x - 4$

[2 marks for all 3 terms correct or 1 mark for 2 terms.]

b) To find the gradient, put $x = 2$ into the answer to part (a): $6(2^2) - 8(2) - 4 = 24 - 16 - 4 = 4$ *[1 mark]*.

c) The gradient of the normal is $-1 \div$ the gradient of the tangent $= -1 \div 4 = -\frac{1}{4}$ *[1 mark]*. At $x = 2$, the y-value is $2(2^3) - 4(2^2) - 4(2) + 12 = 16 - 16 - 8 + 12 = 4$ *[1 mark]*. Putting these values into the formula $(y - y_1) = m(x - x_1)$ gives $(y - 4) = -\frac{1}{4}(x - 2) \Rightarrow y = -\frac{1}{4}x + \frac{1}{2} + 4 \Rightarrow y = -\frac{1}{4}x + 4\frac{1}{2}$ *[1 mark]*.

You could also give your answer in the form $x + 4y = 18$ by multiplying through by 4 to get rid of the fractions.

5 a) $\frac{dy}{dx} = (3 \times mx^{(3-1)}) - (2 \times x^{(2-1)}) + 8(1 \times x^{(1-1)})$

$= 3mx^2 - 2x + 8$

[1 method mark, 1 answer mark]

b) Rearranging the equation of the line parallel to the normal gives the equation: $y = 3 - 4x$, so it has a gradient of -4 *[1 mark]*. The normal also has gradient -4 because it is parallel to this line *[1 mark]*. The gradient of the tangent is $-1 \div$ the gradient of the normal $= -1 \div -4 = \frac{1}{4}$ *[1 mark]*.

c) (i) So you know that when $x = 5$, the gradient $3mx^2 - 2x + 8 = \frac{1}{4}$. *[1 mark]*

Now find the value of m:

$m(3 \times 5^2) - (2 \times 5) + 8 = \frac{1}{4}$ *[1 mark]*

$75m - 2 = \frac{1}{4}$

$m = \frac{9}{4} \times \frac{1}{75} = \frac{9}{300} = \frac{3}{100} = 0.03$ *[1 mark]*

(ii) When $x = 5$, then:

$y = (\frac{3}{100} \times 5^3) - (5^2) + (8 \times 5) + 2$ *[1 mark]*

$= \frac{375}{100} - 25 + 40 + 2$

$= \frac{375}{100} + 17 = \frac{2075}{100}$

$= 20.75$ *[1 mark]*

They've given you all the information you need, in a funny roundabout kinda way. Get comfortable figuring out gradients of normals and tangents and then applying them to curves — otherwise the exam will be very UNcomfortable. You have been warned...

6 a) Find the value of x that gives the minimum value of y — the stationary point of curve y.

Differentiate, and then solve $\frac{dy}{dx} = 0$:

$\frac{dy}{dx} = \frac{1}{\sqrt{x}} - \frac{8}{x^2}$ *[1 mark for each term]*

$\frac{1}{\sqrt{x}} - \frac{8}{x^2} = 0$ *[1 mark]* $\Rightarrow \frac{1}{\sqrt{x}} = \frac{8}{x^2}$

$x^2 \div x^{1/2} = 8 \Rightarrow x^{3/2} = 8$ *[1 mark]*

$x = (\sqrt[3]{8})^2 = 2^2 = 4.$ *[1 mark]*

So 4 miles per hour gives the minimum coal consumption.

b) $\frac{d^2y}{dx^2} = \frac{16}{x^3} - \frac{1}{2\sqrt{x^3}}$ *[1 mark]*

At the stationary point $x = 4$,

so $\frac{16}{4^3} - \frac{1}{2\sqrt{4^3}} = \frac{16}{64} - \frac{1}{2\sqrt{64}} = \frac{1}{4} - \frac{1}{16} = \frac{3}{16} > 0$,

therefore the stationary point is a minimum. *[1 mark]*

c) $y = 2\sqrt{4} + \frac{8}{4} = 4 + 2 = 6$ *[1 mark]*

7 a) $y = 6 + \frac{4x^3 - 15x^2 + 12x}{6} = 6 + \frac{2}{3}x^3 - \frac{5}{2}x^2 + 2x$

$\frac{dy}{dx} = 2x^2 - 5x + 2$

[1 mark for each correct term]

b) Stationary points occur when $2x^2 - 5x + 2 = 0$. *[1 mark]* Factorising the equation gives: $(2x - 1)(x - 2) = 0$

So stationary points occur when $x = 2$ *[1 mark]* and $x = \frac{1}{2}$ *[1 mark]*.

When $x = 2$:

$y = 6 + \frac{4(2^3) - 15(2^2) + (12 \times 2)}{6} = 5\frac{1}{3}$ *[1 mark]*

When $x = \frac{1}{2}$:

$y = 6 + \frac{4\left(\frac{1}{2}\right)^3 - 15\left(\frac{1}{2}\right)^2 + 12\left(\frac{1}{2}\right)}{6} = 6\frac{11}{24}$ *[1 mark]*

So coordinates of the stationary points on the curve are $\left(2, 5\frac{1}{3}\right)$ and $\left(\frac{1}{2}, 6\frac{11}{24}\right)$.

c) Differentiate again to find $\frac{d^2y}{dx^2} = 4x - 5$. *[1 mark]*

When $x = 2$ this gives $\Rightarrow 4(2) - 5 = 3$, which is positive, therefore the curve is minimum at $\left(2, 5\frac{1}{3}\right)$. *[1 mark]*

When $x = \frac{1}{2}$ this gives $\Rightarrow 4(\frac{1}{2}) - 5 = -3$, which is negative, so the maximum is at $\left(\frac{1}{2}, 6\frac{11}{24}\right)$. *[1 mark]*

Answers

8 a) First step, multiply out function to get $y = \frac{1}{3}x^3 + x^2 - 3x - 9$

$\frac{dy}{dx} = x^2 + 2x - 3 = 0$ at the stationary point. *[1 mark]*

$x^2 + 2x - 3 = (x - 1)(x + 3) = 0$

$\Rightarrow x = 1$ and $x = -3$ at the stationary points *[1 mark]*

$x = 1 \Rightarrow y = \frac{1}{3}(1)^3 + (1)^2 - 3(1) - 9 = \frac{1}{3} + 1 - 3 - 9 = -10\frac{2}{3}$

$x = -3 \Rightarrow y = \frac{1}{3}(-3)^3 + (-3)^2 - 3(-3) - 9$

$= -\frac{27}{3} + 9 + 9 - 9 = 0$

So the stationary points have coordinates:

$(1, -10\frac{2}{3})$ *[1 mark]* and $(-3, 0)$ *[1 mark]*

b) $\frac{d^2y}{dx^2} = 2x + 2$ *[1 mark]*

At $x = 1$, $\frac{d^2y}{dx^2} = 4 > 0$, so it's a minimum *[1 mark]*

At $x = -3$, $\frac{d^2y}{dx^2} = -4 < 0$, so it's a maximum *[1 mark]*

c) y is a positive cubic function, with stationary points as found in parts a) and b). The curve crosses the y-axis when $x = 0$, so $y = -9$ *[1 mark]*. The initial cubic equation can be factorised to find where it intersects/touches the x-axis:

$y = (\frac{1}{3}x - 1)(x^2 + 6x + 9)$

$y = (\frac{1}{3}x - 1)(x + 3)^2$

so $y = 0$ when $x = 3$ and -3 *[1 mark]*.

The sketch looks like this: *[1 mark]*

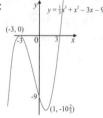

9 a) Surface area $= [2 \times (d \times x)] + [2 \times (d \times \frac{x}{2})] + [x \times \frac{x}{2}]$

$= 2dx + \frac{2dx}{2} + \frac{x^2}{2}$ *[1 mark]*

surface area $= 54$ so $3dx + \frac{x^2}{2} = 54$

$\Rightarrow x^2 + 6dx = 108$ *[1 mark]*

$d = \frac{108 - x^2}{6x}$ *[1 mark]*

Volume $=$ width $\times$ height $\times$ depth $= \frac{x}{2} \times x \times d$

$= \frac{x^2}{2} \times \frac{108 - x^2}{6x} = \frac{108x^2 - x^4}{12x} = 9x - \frac{x^3}{12}$ *[1 mark]*

b) Differentiate V and then solve for when $\frac{dV}{dx} = 0$:

$\frac{dV}{dx} = 9 - \frac{x^2}{4}$ *[1 mark for each correct term]*

$9 - \frac{x^2}{4} = 0$ *[1 mark]*

$\Rightarrow \frac{x^2}{4} = 9$

$\Rightarrow x^2 = 36$

$\Rightarrow x = 6$ *[1 mark]*

c) $\frac{d^2V}{dx^2} = -\frac{x}{2}$ *[1 mark]*

so when $x = 6$, $\frac{d^2V}{dx^2} = -3$ *[1 mark]*

$\frac{d^2V}{dx^2}$ is negative, so it's a maximum point. *[1 mark]*

$x = 6$ at V_{max}, so $V_{max} = (9 \times 6) - \frac{6^3}{12}$

$= 54 - \frac{216}{12} = 54 - 18 = 36$ m³ *[1 mark]*

10 a) $f'(x) = 2x^3 - 54$ *[1 mark]*

At the stationary point,

$f'(x) = 0 \Rightarrow 2x^3 = 54 \Rightarrow x^3 = 27 \Rightarrow x = 3$ *[1 mark]*,

which gives: $y = f(3) = \frac{1}{2}(3)^4 - 54(3) = \frac{1}{2}(81) - 162$

$= -121.5$ *[1 mark]*

So coordinates of the stationary point are $(3, -121.5)$.

b) $f''(x) = 6x^2$ *[1 mark]* so at the stationary point:

$f''(3) = 6 \times 9 = 54$, which is positive, so it is a minimum. *[1 mark]*

c) (i) As the stationary point is a minimum, $f'(x) > 0$ to the right of the stationary point. So the function is increasing when $x > 3$ *[1 mark]*

(ii) As the stationary point is a minimum, $f'(x) < 0$ to the left of the stationary point. So the function is decreasing when $x < 3$ *[1 mark]*

d) Intersects the x-axis when:

$y = \frac{1}{2}x^4 - 54x = 0$

$x(\frac{1}{2}x^3 - 54) = 0$

$\Rightarrow x = 0$

or $\frac{1}{2}x^3 = 54$

$\Rightarrow x = \sqrt[3]{108} = 3\sqrt[3]{4}$ *[1 mark]*

So the graph looks like this ↗

[1 mark]

C1 — Practice Exam One

1 a) Rearrange according to Laws of Indices (if you've forgotten, they've got their very own page in Section 1):

$36^{-\frac{1}{2}} = \frac{1}{36^{\frac{1}{2}}} = \frac{1}{\sqrt{36}}$ *[1 mark]*

$= \frac{1}{6}$ *[1 mark]*

b) First simplify the surd on the bottom of the fraction:

$\sqrt[m]{a^n} = a^{\frac{n}{m}}$ so $\sqrt{a^4} = a^2$ *[1 mark]*

Then rewrite the entire expression so that you're only multiplying things (remember that $\div a^n = \times a^{-n}$):

$\frac{a^6 \times a^3}{a^2} \div a^{\frac{1}{2}} = a^6 \times a^3 \times a^{-2} \times a^{-\frac{1}{2}}$ *[1 mark]*

Finally, add the powers together, because $a^m \times a^n = a^{m+n}$:

$= a^{6+3-2-\frac{1}{2}} = a^{\frac{13}{2}}$ *[1 mark]*

Lots of laws to remember there. Make sure you don't multiply powers when you should be adding, and vice versa.

2 Multiply out the brackets first:

$(5\sqrt{5} + 2\sqrt{3})^2 = (5\sqrt{5} + 2\sqrt{3})(5\sqrt{5} + 2\sqrt{3})$

$= (5\sqrt{5})^2 + 2(5\sqrt{5} \times 2\sqrt{3}) + (2\sqrt{3})^2$

So now you've got three terms to deal with, and they're all a little bit nasty. The first term is:

$(5\sqrt{5})^2 = 5\sqrt{5} \times 5\sqrt{5}$

$= 5 \times 5 \times \sqrt{5} \times \sqrt{5}$

$= 5 \times 5 \times 5$

$= 125$ *[1 mark]*

The second term is:

$2(5\sqrt{5} \times 2\sqrt{3}) = 2 \times 5 \times 2 \times \sqrt{5} \times \sqrt{3}$

$= 20\sqrt{15}$ *(don't forget, $\sqrt{5} \times \sqrt{3} = \sqrt{5 \times 3}$)*   *[1 mark]*

And the third term is:

$2\sqrt{3} \times 2\sqrt{3} = 2 \times 2 \times \sqrt{3} \times \sqrt{3}$
$= 2 \times 2 \times 3 = 12$ *[1 mark]*

So all you have to do now is add the three terms together:

$125 + 20\sqrt{15} + 12 = 137 + 20\sqrt{15}$ *[1 mark]*

So $a = 137$, $b = 20$ and $c = 15$.

3   a) $\frac{dy}{dx} = 12x^3 - 2$ *[1 mark for each correct term]*

b) $y = x^3 - 2x^2 + 4x - 8$

$\frac{dy}{dx} = 3x^2 - 4x + 4$ *[1 mark for expanding brackets, 2 marks for correct differentiation of all terms or 1 mark for correct differentiation of 2 terms]*

4   As one of these equations is a quadratic, you need the substitution method, so rearrange to get y on its own:

$y + x = 7$
$y = 7 - x$ *[1 mark]*

And now substitute that into the quadratic to get:

$7 - x = x^2 + 3x - 5$ *[1 mark]*

Rearrange again to get everything on one side of the equation, and then factorise it:

$0 = x^2 + 4x - 12$
$(x + 6)(x - 2) = 0$ *[1 mark]*

Which gives two values : $x = -6$ and $x = 2$ *[1 mark]*

Don't forget to find the corresponding values of y as well:

$y = 7 - x$
So when $x = -6$
$y = 7 - -6 = 7 + 6$
$y = 13$
And when $x = 2$
$y = 7 - 2$
$y = 5$ *[1 mark]*

So the equations meet at (–6, 13) and (2, 5).

Simultaneous equations — you should be able to do them standing on your head... although don't try that in the exam...

5   a) k is the y-value when $x = 4$, so substitute $x = 4$ into the equation of the line to find y:

$y + (2 \times 4) - 5 = 0$
$y = 5 - 8$
$y = -3$ so $k = -3$ *[1 mark]*

b) Remember — the gradients of two perpendicular lines multiply together to make –1. This means that the gradient of the new line will be: $\dfrac{-1}{\text{the gradient of AB}}$

The gradient of a straight line is the coefficient of x when the equation of the line is written in the form $y = mx + c$.
$y + 2x - 5 = 0$ becomes $y = -2x + 5$, so the gradient of AB = –2. *[1 mark]*
Now you know the gradient of the new line will be $\dfrac{-1}{-2}$, which equals $\dfrac{1}{2}$. *[1 mark]*

Finally, get the equation of the new line using $y - y_1 = m(x - x_1)$ and A (1, 3) — the point it passes through: $y - 3 = \frac{1}{2}(x - 1)$ *[1 mark]*

$y = \frac{1}{2}x - \frac{1}{2} + 3 = \frac{1}{2}x + \frac{5}{2}$

$y = \frac{x + 5}{2}$ *[1 mark]*

Remember the process, remember the formulas, and you'll be fine. But the only way to make sure you know it is practice. If you forgot anything, go back to the coordinate geometry section and go through it 'til it sinks in...

6   a) $4x + 7 > 7x + 4$
Subtract $4x + 4$ from both sides which gives
$3 > 3x$ *[1 mark]*
$1 > x$ or $x < 1$ *[1 mark]*

b) You've got to find the minimum value of $(x - 5)(x - 3)$ and when k is less than that, $(x - 5)(x - 3) > k$ will be true for all possible values of x.
As always, it helps to sketch a graph and think about what the function looks like:

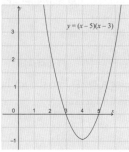

Remember, it's a symmetrical graph, so the minimum is halfway between $x = 3$ and $x = 5$
— i.e. when $x = 4$.   *[1 mark]*
Put this x-value into the equation to find the lowest possible y-value: $(x - 5)(x - 3) = (4 - 5)(4 - 3)$ *[1 mark]*
$= -1 \times 1 = -1$ *[1 mark]*
So for the range of values $k < -1$ it is true that
$(x - 5)(x - 3) > k$ for all possible values of x.

You can also find the minimum value by differentiating, or by completing the square — when you've got your quadratic in the form $(x + m)^2 + n$, the minimum value occurs at n.

7   Let $y = x^{\frac{1}{3}}$ *[1 mark]*, then the equation becomes
$2y^2 + 5y - 3 = 0$
Factorise to get: $(2y - 1)(y + 3) = 0$ *[1 mark]*
$\Rightarrow y = \frac{1}{2}, y = -3$ *[1 mark]*
$\Rightarrow x^{\frac{1}{3}} = \frac{1}{2}, x^{\frac{1}{3}} = -3$
$\Rightarrow x = (\frac{1}{2})^3, x = (-3)^3$ *[1 mark]*
$\Rightarrow x = \frac{1}{8}, x = -27$ *[1 mark]*

Answers

8 a) The centre of the circle must be the midpoint of AB, since AB is a diameter. Midpoint of AB is:
$\left(\frac{2+0}{2}, \frac{1+-5}{2}\right) = (1, -2)$ *[1 mark]*

The radius is half of the diameter, so half of length AB. Use Pythagoras' theorem to find the distance:
$AB = \sqrt{(2-0)^2 + (1-(-5))^2}$
$AB = \sqrt{40} = 2\sqrt{10}$ *[1 mark]*
$Radius = \frac{2\sqrt{10}}{2} = \sqrt{10}$ *[1 mark]*

b) The general equation for a circle with centre (a, b) and radius r is: $(x - a)^2 + (y - b)^2 = r^2$.
So for a circle centre $(1, -2)$ and radius $\sqrt{10}$ that gives:
$(x - 1)^2 + (y + 2)^2 = 10.$ *[1 mark]*
Multiply out to get the form given in the question:
$(x - 1)(x - 1) + (y + 2)(y + 2) = 10$ *[1 mark]*
$x^2 - 2x + 1 + y^2 + 4y + 4 = 10$
$x^2 + y^2 - 2x + 4y - 5 = 0$ *[1 mark]*

c) Find the equations of the tangent at A and the normal at C and then solve them simultaneously to find where the lines cross.
The tangent at A is at right angles to the diameter at A.
The diameter at A has the gradient:
$\frac{1 - -5}{2 - 0} = 3$
so the tangent has the gradient $-\frac{1}{3}$ *[1 mark]*
Put the gradient $-\frac{1}{3}$ and point A $(2, 1)$ into the formula for the equation of a straight line and rearrange:
$y - y_1 = m(x - x_1)$
$y - 1 = -\frac{1}{3}(x - 2)$
$\Rightarrow y = \frac{5}{3} - \frac{x}{3}$ *[1 mark]*
A normal passes through the centre, so the gradient of the normal through C is the gradient of the line from the centre to C
$= \frac{-1 - -2}{4 - 1} = \frac{1}{3}$ *[1 mark]*
Using the straight line formula at C $(4, -1)$:
$y - -1 = \frac{1}{3}(x - 4)$
$y = \frac{x}{3} - \frac{7}{3}$ *[1 mark]*
Solve the two equations simultaneously to find the point of intersection:
$\frac{5}{3} - \frac{x}{3} = \frac{x}{3} - \frac{7}{3}$ *[1 mark]*
$\frac{5}{3} + \frac{7}{3} = \frac{2x}{3}$
$12 = 2x$
$6 = x$ *[1 mark]*

When $x = 6$, $y = \frac{6}{3} - \frac{7}{3} = -\frac{1}{3}$ *[1 mark]*
so D has coordinates $\left(6, -\frac{1}{3}\right)$

9 a) To find the coordinates of A, solve the two lines as simultaneous equations:
$l_1: x - y + 1 = 0$
$l_2: 2x + y - 8 = 0$
Add the two equations together to get rid of y:
$x + 2x + 1 - 8 - y + y = 0$ *[1 mark]*
$3x - 7 = 0$
$x = \frac{7}{3}$ *[1 mark]*
Now put $x = \frac{7}{3}$ back into l_1 to find y:
$\frac{7}{3} - y + 1 = 0$
$y = \frac{7}{3} + 1 = \frac{10}{3}$ So A is $\left(\frac{7}{3}, \frac{10}{3}\right)$ *[1 mark]*
Still with me? Deep breath... there's a whole lot more geometry a-coming your way...

b) There's a lot of information here, so draw a quick sketch to make things a bit clearer:

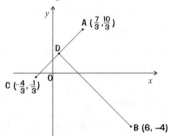

To find the equation of line BD, you need its gradient. But before you can find the gradient, you need to find the coordinates of point D — the midpoint of AC. To find the midpoint of two points, find the average of the x-values and the average of the y-values:
$D = \left(\frac{x_a + x_c}{2}, \frac{y_a + y_c}{2}\right) = \left(\frac{\frac{7}{3} + \frac{-4}{3}}{2}, \frac{\frac{10}{3} + \frac{-1}{3}}{2}\right)$ *[1 mark]*
$D = \left(\frac{1}{2}, \frac{3}{2}\right)$ *[1 mark]*
To find the gradient (m) of BD, use this rule: $m_{BD} = \frac{y_D - y_B}{x_D - x_B}$
Gradient $= \frac{\frac{3}{2} - -4}{\frac{1}{2} - 6} = \frac{\frac{3}{2} + \frac{8}{2}}{\frac{1}{2} - \frac{12}{2}} = \frac{3 + 8}{1 - 12} = -1$ *[1 mark]*
Now you can find the equation of BD. Input the known values of x and y at B $(6, -4)$ and the gradient (-1) into $y = mx + c$, which gives:
$-4 = (-1 \times 6) + c$ *[1 mark]*
$-4 + 6 = c$
$c = 2$
So the equation for BD is $y = -x + 2$ *[1 mark]*
But the question asks for it in the form $ax + by + c = 0$
So rearrange to get: $x + y - 2 = 0$ *[1 mark]*
Line blah, point blah, midpoint blah... it's easy to feel bamboozled when reading a long list of geometry babble, which is why it helps to DRAW A GRAPH. It's up to you, but I know what I'd do...

Answers

c) Look at the sketch above. To prove triangle ABD is a right-angled triangle, you need to prove that lines AD and BD are perpendicular — in other words, prove the product of their gradients equals –1.

You already know the gradient of BD = –1.
Use the same rule to find the gradient of AD:

$$m_{AD} = \frac{y_D - y_A}{x_D - x_A} = \frac{\frac{3}{2} - \frac{10}{3}}{\frac{1}{2} - \frac{7}{3}} = \frac{\frac{9}{6} - \frac{20}{6}}{\frac{3}{6} - \frac{14}{6}} = \frac{9 - 20}{3 - 14} = 1 \quad \textbf{[1 mark]}$$

$$m_{BD} \times m_{AD} = -1 \times 1 = -1 \quad \textbf{[1 mark]}$$

So triangle ABD is a right-angled triangle.

10 a) Start by finding a — it's the coefficient of x halved:

$x^2 - 6x + 5 = (x - 3)^2 + b$ **[1 mark]**

Multiply out to get $x^2 - 6x + 9 + b = x^2 - 6x + 5$

Simplify to find b: $9 + b = 5$ so $b = 5 - 9 = -4$
So the answer is $x^2 - 6x + 5 = (x - 3)^2 - 4$ **[1 mark]**

Completing the square should be like riding a bike — you never forget how to do it. So if you did forget, go back to the quadratics section and start pedalling...

b) To factorise $x^2 - 6x + 5$ you need two numbers that add up to –6 and multiply to give 5. Easy peasy...

$x^2 - 6x + 5 = (x - 1)(x - 5)$ **[2 marks for correct answer, or 1 mark if there's a sign error]**

c) Start by differentiating $y = x^2 - 6x + 5$:

$\frac{dy}{dx} = 2x - 6$ **[1 mark]**

At the stationary point, $\frac{dy}{dx} = 0$

$\Rightarrow 2x - 6 = 0$

$\Rightarrow x = 3$ **[1 mark]**

$\Rightarrow y = 3^2 - 6(3) + 5 = -4$ **[1 mark]**

So the coordinates of the stationary point are (3, –4).

d) We already know from part c) that there's a stationary point at (3, –4), and it must be a minimum — the coefficient of x^2 is positive, so it's a u-shaped graph.
To sketch the graph, find where the curve cuts the two axes:
When the line cuts the x-axis, $y = 0$. i.e. $x^2 - 6x + 5 = 0$
Use your answer to part b) to give...
$(x - 1)(x - 5) = 0$
so $x = 1$ or $x = 5$,
i.e. the graph cuts the x-axis at (1, 0) and (5, 0).
Now, when $x = 0$, $y = 0^2 - (6 \times 0) + 5$, so the graph cuts the y-axis at (0, 5).

Don't just start scribbling any old curve, make sure you've plotted the important points and labelled them clearly — otherwise no lovely marks for you.

Now you're all ready to sketch the graph:

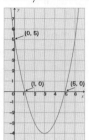

[3 marks available — 1 mark for correct shape with the minimum point in the correct quadrant, 1 mark for correct y-axis intercept, 1 mark for correct x-axis intercepts]

11 If the quadratic $ax^2 + bx + c = 0$ has no real roots, this means the discriminant gives a negative value:
$b^2 - 4ac < 0$ **[1 mark]**. So:
$(-4)^2 - [4 \times 1 \times (k - 1)] < 0$ **[1 mark]**
$\Rightarrow 16 - (4k - 4) < 0$
$\Rightarrow 20 - 4k < 0$ **[1 mark]**
$20 < 4k$
$k > 5$ **[1 mark]**

It's no good just remembering the discriminant formula — you also have to know what the result tells you. If you don't know the meaning of negative discriminants, head back to the quadratics section...

C1 — Practice Exam Two

1 a) Just multiply out the brackets:
$(\sqrt{3} + 1)(\sqrt{3} - 1) = 3 - \sqrt{3} + \sqrt{3} - 1$ **[1 mark]**
$= 2$ **[1 mark]**

b) To rationalise the denominator, you want to get rid of the surd on the bottom line of the fraction. To do this, use the difference of two squares — e.g. if the denominator's $\sqrt{a} + b$, you multiply by $\sqrt{a} - b$:

$\frac{\sqrt{3}}{\sqrt{3} + 1} \times \frac{\sqrt{3} - 1}{\sqrt{3} - 1}$ **[1 mark]**

$= \frac{3 - \sqrt{3}}{2}$ **[1 mark]**

(the bottom bit is substituted in from part a) **[1 mark]**

2 a) $\frac{x^2 + 2x}{\sqrt{x}} = x^{-\frac{1}{2}}(x^2 + 2x) = x^{\frac{3}{2}} + 2x^{\frac{1}{2}}$ **[1 mark for each correct term]**, so $m = \frac{3}{2}$ and $n = \frac{1}{2}$.

b) From part (a) above, $y = x^{\frac{3}{2}} + 2x^{\frac{1}{2}} + 3x^3 - x$.
Differentiating this gives
$\frac{dy}{dx} = \frac{3}{2}x^{\frac{1}{2}} + \left(2 \cdot \frac{1}{2}\right)x^{-\frac{1}{2}} + (3 \cdot 3)x^2 - 1$

$= \frac{3}{2}x^{\frac{1}{2}} + x^{-\frac{1}{2}} + 9x^2 - 1$

[4 marks available — 1 mark for each correct term]

Answers

3   Let $y = x^{\frac{1}{2}}$ *[1 mark]*, then the equation becomes
$4y^2 - 8y + 3 = 0$
Factorise to get: $(2y - 3)(2y - 1) = 0$ *[1 mark]*
$\Rightarrow y = \frac{3}{2}, y = \frac{1}{2}$ *[1 mark]*
$\Rightarrow x^{\frac{1}{2}} = \frac{3}{2}, x^{\frac{1}{2}} = \frac{1}{2}$
$\Rightarrow x = \left(\frac{3}{2}\right)^2, x = \left(\frac{1}{2}\right)^2$ *[1 mark]*
$\Rightarrow x = \frac{9}{4}, x = \frac{1}{4}$ *[1 mark]*

4   a)   Complete the square by halving the coefficient of x to find the number in the brackets (m):
$x^2 - 7x + 17 = \left(x - \frac{7}{2}\right)^2 + n$
Now simplify this equation to find n:
$n = x^2 - 7x + 17 - \left[\left(x - \frac{7}{2}\right)^2\right]$
$n = x^2 - 7x + 17 - x^2 + \frac{14x}{2} - \frac{49}{4}$
$n = 17 - \frac{49}{4} = \frac{19}{4}$ *[1 mark]*
So you can express $x^2 - 7x + 17$ as:
$\left(x - \frac{7}{2}\right)^2 + \frac{19}{4}$ *[1 mark]*
The maximum value of $f(x)$ will be when the denominator is as small as possible — so you want the minimum value of $x^2 - 7x + 17$. Using the completed square above, you can see that the minimum value is $\frac{19}{4}$ because the squared part can equal but never be below 0 *[1 mark]*.
So max value of $f(x)$ is $\frac{1}{19/4} = 1 \times \frac{4}{19} = \frac{4}{19}$ *[1 mark]*.
You've got to put on your thinking cap for that one — but they give you a big hint by getting you to complete the square first.

   b)   If the function only has one root, then $b^2 - 4ac = 0$ *[1 mark]*. For this equation, $a = 3$, $b = k$ and $c = 12$.
Use this formula to find k:
$k^2 - (4 \times 3 \times 12) = 0$ *[1 mark]*
$k^2 - 144 = 0$
$k^2 = 144$
$k = \pm 12$ *[1 mark]*
Of course, it's no good remembering the general formula if you don't know what a, b and c stand for. Imagine forgetting that it's $ax^2 + bx + c$ — you'd feel a right wally.

5   a)   A sketch will definitely help here:

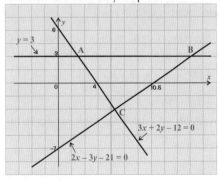

Finding the coordinates of points A, B and C is just a small matter of simultaneous equations. A and B are simple — you already know their y-value is 3, so:
Point A is the point where $y = 3$ and $3x + 2y - 12 = 0$ meet:
$3x + (2 \times 3) - 12 = 0$
$3x + 6 = 12$
$3x = 6$
$x = 2$
Point $A = (2, 3)$ *[1 mark]*
Point B is the point where $y = 3$ and $2x - 3y - 21 = 0$ meet:
$2x - (3 \times 3) - 21 = 0$
$2x = 30$
$x = 15$
Point $B = (15, 3)$ *[1 mark]*
Point C is slightly trickier — you've got to solve a pair of simultaneous equations:
Label the equations: $2x - 3y - 21 = 0$ (a)
$3x + 2y - 12 = 0$ (b)
It's easy to get muddled with all those 3s, 2s and 1s. Just a slip of concentration and then — whoopsy — you've solved $3x - 2y + 12 = O$, and that's no use to anyone...
Multiply (a) by 2 and (b) by 3 to equalise the coefficients of y:
$4x - 6y - 42 = 0$
$9x + 6y - 36 = 0$
Now add together to get rid of y:
$4x + 9x - 6y + 6y - 42 - 36 = 0$ *[1 mark]*
$13x - 78 = 0$
$13x = 78$
$x = 6$ *[1 mark]*
Substitute this value of x into (a) or (b):
$(3 \times 6) + 2y - 12 = 0$
$18 - 12 + 2y = 0$
$2y = -6$
$y = -3$
So C has the coordinates $(6, -3)$. *[1 mark]*

   b)   To show that the triangle is right-angled, you need to prove that the gradients of two of the lines multiply together to make -1. Looking at the sketch, the right angle looks like it's at C, so use lines BC and AC:
BC: $2x - 3y - 21 = 0$
$3y = 2x - 21$
$y = \frac{2}{3}x - 7$
So the gradient of BC $= \frac{2}{3}$.
AC: $3x + 2y - 12 = 0$
$2y = 12 - 3x$
$y = 6 - \frac{3}{2}x$
So the gradient of AC $= -\frac{3}{2}$ *[1 mark]*.
$\frac{2}{3} \times -\frac{3}{2} = -1$ *[1 mark]*
The lines that meet at C are perpendicular, so the triangle must be right-angled.

That gradient rule is proving useful, isn't it — you can find equations of normals and tangents and prove right angles, and it might even be the password for the magical kingdom of Narnia...

c) Point D has the coordinates $(3, d)$ so it must lie on the line $x = 3$. If you draw this on your sketch, you can see D must lie above line AB or below line AC to lie outside the triangle.

For $(3, d)$ to be above the line $y = 3$, $d > 3$. **[1 mark]**
Now work out the values of d that would give D as below the line AC. If D was on the line AC, then $(3, d)$ would satisfy the equation of AC:
$3x + 2y - 12 = 0$ when $x = 3$ and $y = d$
$(3 \times 3) + 2d - 12 = 0$ **[1 mark]**
$9 + 2d - 12 = 0$
$2d = 3$
$d = 1.5$
But D has to be below line AC, so d has to be less than 1.5.
So you've shown that either $d > 3$ or $d < 1.5$ **[1 mark]**.

6 a) When $f(x) = ax^2 + bx + c$ has no real roots, you know that $b^2 - 4ac < 0$. Here, $a = -j$, $b = 3j$ and $c = 1$ **[1 mark]**.
Therefore $(3j)^2 - (4 \times -j \times 1) < 0$ **[1 mark]**
$9j^2 + 4j < 0$ **[1 mark]**

b) To find the values where $9j^2 + 4j < 0$, you need to start by solving $9j^2 + 4j = 0$: $j(9j + 4) = 0$, so $j = 0$ **[1 mark]**
or $9j = -4 \Rightarrow j = -\frac{4}{9}$ **[1 mark]**. The graph looks like this:

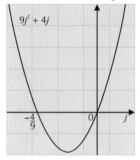

From the graph, you can see that $9j^2 + 4j < 0$ when $-\frac{4}{9} < j < 0$ **[1 mark]**.
If you made a mistake, do not pass GO, do not collect £200, and move your tiny top hat back to the pages on quadratic inequalities...

7 a) Start by differentiating $y = f(x)$:
$\frac{dy}{dx} = 3x^2 - 3$ **[2 marks — 1 mark for each correct term]**
The stationary points are where $\frac{dy}{dx} = 0$ **[1 mark]**
$\Rightarrow 3x^2 - 3 = 0$
$\Rightarrow 3(x^2 - 1) = 0$
$\Rightarrow 3(x - 1)(x + 1) = 0$ **[1 mark]**
$\Rightarrow x = 1, x = -1$
$x = 1 \Rightarrow y = 1^3 - 3(1) + 2 = 0$
$x = -1 \Rightarrow y = (-1)^3 - 3(-1) + 2 = 4$
So the stationary points are $(1, 0)$ and $(-1, 4)$.
[2 marks — 1 mark for each correct pair of coordinates]

b) Differentiate again to find out whether each stationary point is a maximum or a minimum:
$\frac{d^2y}{dx^2} = 6x$ **[1 mark]**
At $x = 1$,
$\frac{d^2y}{dx^2} = 6 > 0$, so the point $(1, 0)$ is a minimum **[1 mark]**
At $x = -1$,
$\frac{d^2y}{dx^2} = -6 < 0$, so the point $(-1, 4)$ is a maximum **[1 mark]**

c) The graph of $f(x)$ increases as x increases until it reaches the maximum at $(-1, 4)$, then decreases until it reaches the minimum at $(1, 0)$, where it starts increasing again.
So $f(x)$ increases as x increases for $x < -1$ **[1 mark]** and for $x > 1$ **[1 mark]**.
If you get stuck on a question like part c) do a quick sketch of the curve — that'll usually make things crystal clear.

8 a) A is on the y-axis, so the x-coordinate is 0. Just put $x = 0$ into the equation and solve:
$0^2 - (6 \times 0) + y^2 - 4y = 0$ **[1 mark]**
$y^2 - 4y = 0$
$y(y - 4) = 0$
$y = 0$ or $y = 4$
$y = 0$ is the origin, so A is at $(0, 4)$ **[1 mark]**

b) You're basically completing the square for x and y separately, so halve the coefficient of x to find a, and halve the coefficient of y to find b. For each one you'll end up with a number you don't want, which you need to take away each time:

Completing the square for $x^2 - 6x$ gives $(x - 3)^2$ but $(x - 3)^2 = x^2 - 6x + 9$ so you need to take 9 away:
$(x - 3)^2 - 9$ **[1 mark]**
Now the same for $y^2 - 4y$: $(y - 2)^2 = y^2 - 4y + 4$ so take away 4 which gives: $(y - 2)^2 - 4$ **[1 mark]**

Put these new expressions back into the original equation:
$(x - 3)^2 - 9 + (y - 2)^2 - 4 = 0$
$\Rightarrow (x - 3)^2 + (y - 2)^2 = 13$ **[1 mark]**

c) In the general equation for a circle $(x - a)^2 + (y - b)^2 = r^2$, the centre is (a, b) and the radius is r. So for the equation in part b) — $a = 3$, $b = 2$, $r = \sqrt{13}$.
Hence, the centre is $(3, 2)$ **[1 mark]**
and the radius is $\sqrt{13}$. **[1 mark]**

Answers

d) The tangent is perpendicular to the radius.
The radius between A $(0, 4)$ and centre $(3, 2)$

has a gradient of: $\frac{y_2 - y_1}{x_2 - x_1} = \frac{2 - 4}{3 - 0} = -\frac{2}{3}$ *[1 mark]*

Using the gradient rule, the tangent at A has a gradient of:

$\frac{-1}{-\frac{2}{3}} = \frac{3}{2}$ *[1 mark]*

Finally use $y - y_1 = m(x - x_1)$ to find the equation of the tangent to the circle at point A:

$y - 4 = \frac{3}{2}(x - 0)$ *[1 mark]*

$y = \frac{3}{2}x + 4$ *[1 mark]*

The tangent is perpendicular to the radius? That sounds like a useful life fact — like how to boil an egg or tie your laces. If you didn't know it, go back to the circles stuff on p34-35 and learn it...

9 a) To find the tangent you first need to find the gradient, so differentiate the equation of the curve:

$\frac{d(x^3 - 2x^2 + 4)}{dx} = 3x^2 - 4x$ *[1 mark]*

When $x = 1$ then the gradient =
$(3 \times 1^2) - (4 \times 1) = 3 - 4$
$= -1$ *[1 mark]*
When $x = 1$, $y = 1^3 - (2 \times 1^2) + 4 = 1 - 2 + 4 = 3$
Use these values and the equation $y - y_1 = m(x - x_1)$ to find the equation of the tangent at $x = 1$:
$y - 3 = -1(x - 1)$
$y = -x + 1 + 3$
$y = 4 - x$ *[1 mark]*

b) First find the gradient of the tangent at $x = 2$:
$(3 \times 2^2) - (4 \times 2) = 12 - 8 = 4$
Using the gradient rule:

Gradient of normal $= \dfrac{-1}{\text{gradient of tangent}}$ *[1 mark]*

So gradient of normal $= -\frac{1}{4}$ *[1 mark]*

When $x = 2$, $y = 2^3 - (2 \times 2^2) + 4 = 4$
Use these values and the equation $y - y_1 = m(x - x_1)$ to find the equation of the normal at $x = 2$:

$y - 4 = -\frac{1}{4}(x - 2)$

$y = \frac{1}{2} - \frac{x}{4} + 4$

$y = \frac{9}{2} - \frac{x}{4}$ *[1 mark]*

All this talk about tangents is making me want a tangerine... 'scuse me, just off to the grocer's...

c) First find where both lines cross the x-axis:
Tangent: $y = 4 - x$ so when $y = 0$:
$4 - x = 0 \Rightarrow x = 4$
The tangent cuts the x-axis at $(4, 0)$.

Normal: $y = \frac{9}{2} - \frac{x}{4}$ so when $y = 0$:

$\frac{9}{2} - \frac{x}{4} = 0 \Rightarrow \frac{9}{2} = \frac{x}{4} \Rightarrow x = 4 \times \frac{9}{2} = 18$
The normal cuts the x-axis at $(18, 0)$.
So the distance between the two intercepts
$= 18 - 4$
$= 14$ *[2 marks for correct answer, or 1 mark for correct method]*

d) (i) The graph of $f(x - a)$ is $f(x)$ translated to the right by a units. So to translate the graph of $y = x^3 - 2x^2 + 4$ right by 3 units, replace each x with $(x - 3)$:
$y = (x - 3)^3 - 2(x - 3)^2 + 4$ *[1 mark]*
$= (x - 3)(x^2 - 6x + 9) - 2(x^2 - 6x + 9) + 4$
$= x^3 - 9x^2 + 27x - 27 - 2x^2 + 12x - 18 + 4$
$= x^3 - 11x^2 + 39x - 41$ *[1 mark]*

(ii) The graph of $af(x)$ is the graph of $f(x)$ stretched along the y-axis by a factor of a. So to stretch the graph of $y = x^3 - 2x^2 + 4$ along the y-axis by a factor of 2, multiply the RHS of the equation by 2:
$y = 2(x^3 - 2x^2 + 4)$
$= 2x^3 - 4x^2 + 8$ *[1 mark]*

Oh my giddy goat, we've finished. You'd better go and have a lie down, otherwise all the numbers will fall out of your head and we'd have to start again...

Answers

C2 Section 1 — Polynomials
Warm-up Questions

1) a) $f(x) = (x + 2)(3x^2 - 10x + 15) - 36$

   b) $f(x) = (x + 2)(x^2 - 3) + 10$

   c) $f(x) = (x + 2)(2x^2 - 4x + 14) - 31$

2) a) (i) You just need to find f(–1).
         This is $-6 - 1 + 3 - 12 = -16$.

      (ii) Now find f(1). This is $6 - 1 - 3 - 12 = -10$.

      (iii) Now find f(2). This is $48 - 4 - 6 - 12 = 26$.

   b) (i) $f(-1) = -1$

      (ii) $f(1) = 9$

      (iii) $f(2) = 38$

   c) (i) $f(-1) = -2$

      (ii) $f(1) = 0$

      (iii) $f(2) = 37$

3) a) You need to find f(–2). This is
      $(-2)^4 - 3(-2)^3 + 7(-2)^2 - 12(-2) + 14$
      $= 16 + 24 + 28 + 24 + 14 = 106$.

   b) You need to find f(–4/2) = f(–2). You found this in part a,
      so remainder = 106. You might also have noticed that
      $2x + 4$ is a multiple of $x + 2$ (from part a), so the remainder
      must be the same.

   c) You need to find f(3). This is
      $(3)^4 - 3(3)^3 + 7(3)^2 - 12(3) + 14$
      $= 81 - 81 + 63 - 36 + 14 = 41$.

   d) You need to find f(6/2) = f(3). You found this in part c),
      so remainder = 41. You might also have noticed that $2x - 6$
      is a multiple of $x - 3$, so the remainder must be the same.

4) a) You need to find f(1) — if f(1) = 0, then $(x - 1)$ is a factor:
      $f(1) = 1 - 4 + 3 + 2 - 2 = 0$, so $(x - 1)$ is a factor.

   b) You need to find f(–1) — if f(–1) = 0, then $(x + 1)$ is a factor:
      $f(-1) = -1 - 4 - 3 + 2 - 2 = -8$, so $(x + 1)$ is not a factor.

   c) You need to find f(2) — if f(2) = 0, then $(x - 2)$ is a factor:
      $f(2) = 32 - (4 \times 16) + (3 \times 8) + (2 \times 4) - 2$
      $= 32 - 64 + 24 + 8 - 2 = -2$, so $(x - 2)$ is not a factor.

   d) The remainder when you divide by $(2x - 2)$ is the same as
      the remainder when you divide by $x - 1$.
      $(x - 1)$ is a factor (i.e. remainder = 0), so $(2x - 2)$ is also a
      factor.

5) If $f(x) = 2x^4 + 3x^3 + 5x^2 + cx + d$, then to make sure f(x) is
   exactly divisible by $(x - 2)(x + 3)$, you have to make sure
   $f(2) = f(-3) = 0$.
   $f(2) = 32 + 24 + 20 + 2c + d = 0$, i.e. $\underline{2c + d = -76}$.
   $f(-3) = 162 - 81 + 45 - 3c + d = 0$, i.e. $\underline{3c - d = 126}$.
   Add the two underlined equations to get: $5c = 50$,
   and so $c = 10$. Then $d = -96$.

Exam Questions

1 a) (i) Remainder $= f(1) = 2(1)^3 - 5(1)^2 - 4(1) + 3$ *[1 mark]*
        $= -4$ *[1 mark]*.

   (ii) Remainder $= f\left(-\frac{1}{2}\right) = 2\left(-\frac{1}{8}\right) - 5\left(\frac{1}{4}\right) - 4\left(-\frac{1}{2}\right) + 3$
        [1 mark] $= \frac{7}{2}$ *[1 mark]*.

   b) If f(–1) = 0 then $(x + 1)$ is a factor.
      $f(-1) = 2(-1)^3 - 5(-1)^2 - 4(-1) + 3$ *[1 mark]*
      $= -2 - 5 + 4 + 3 = 0$, so $(x + 1)$ is a factor of f(x).
      [1 mark]

   c) $(x + 1)$ is a factor, so divide $2x^3 - 5x^2 - 4x + 3$ by $x + 1$:
      $2x^3 - 5x^2 - 4x + 3 - \underline{2x^2}(x + 1) = 2x^3 - 5x^2 - 4x + 3 - 2x^3 - 2x^2$
      $= -7x^2 - 4x + 3$.
      $-7x^2 - 4x + 3 - (\underline{-7x})(x + 1) = -7x^2 - 4x + 3 + 7x^2 + 7x$
      $= 3x + 3$. Finally $3x + 3 - \underline{3}(x + 1) = 0$.
      so $2x^3 - 5x^2 - 4x + 3 = (2x^2 - 7x + 3)(x + 1)$.

      This is the method from p.54.

      Factorising the quadratic expression gives:
      $f(x) = (2x - 1)(x - 3)(x + 1)$.

      [4 marks available — 1 mark for dividing by x + 1 to find
      quadratic factor, 1 mark for correct quadratic factor,
      1 mark for attempt to factorise quadratic, 1 mark for
      correct factorisation of quadratic.]

2 a) $f(p) = (4p^2 + 3p + 1)(p - p) + 5$
        $= (4p^2 + 3p + 1) \times 0 + 5$
        $= 5$ *[1 mark]*.

   b) $f(-1) = -1$.
      $f(-1) = (4(-1)^2 + 3(-1) + 1)((-1) - p) + 5$
          $= (4 - 3 + 1)(-1 - p) + 5$
          $= 2(-1 - p) + 5 = 3 - 2p$ *[1 mark]*
      So: $3 - 2p = -1$, $p = 2$ *[1 mark]*.

   c) $f(x) = (4x^2 + 3x + 1)(x - 2) + 5$
      $f(1) = (4 + 3 + 1)(1 - 2) + 5 = -3$ *[1 mark]*.

C2 Section 2 — Sequences and Series
Warm-up Questions

1) a) nth term = $4n - 2$ b) nth term = $0.5n - 0.3$

   c) nth term = $-3n + 24$ d) nth term = $-6n + 82$

2) First work out n: $a = 5$, $l = 65$, $d = 3$
   so, $65 = 5 + 3(n - 1)$
   so, $n = 21$
   Now use: $S_{21} = 21 \times \dfrac{(5 + 65)}{2}$
   so, $S_{21} = 735$

3) a) 1st term $= a = 7$
      5th term $= a + 4d = 7 + 4d = 23$
      $\Rightarrow$ $4d = 16$
      $\Rightarrow$ $d = 4$

   b) 15th term $= 7 + 14(4) = 63$

   c) 10th term $= l = 7 + 9(4) = 43$
      So $S_{10} = 10 \times \dfrac{7 + 43}{2} = 250$

Answers

4) $S_{10} = 205$

5) a) $a = 2, r = -3$

You find r by putting the information you're given into the formula for u_2: $u_2 = u_1 \times r$, so $-6 = 2 \times r \Rightarrow r = -3$.

10th term, $u_{10} = ar^9$

$= 2 \times (-3)^9 = -39366$

b) $S_{10} = \dfrac{2(1 - (-3)^{10})}{1 - (-3)} = \dfrac{1 - (-3)^{10}}{2} = -29524$

6) a) $a = 2, r = 4$, so $S_{12} = \dfrac{2(4^{12} - 1)}{4 - 1} = 11,184,810$

b) $a = 30, r = \frac{1}{2}$, so $S_{12} = \dfrac{30\left(1 - \left[\frac{1}{2}\right]^{12}\right)}{1 - \frac{1}{2}} = 59.985$ (to 3 d.p.)

7) $a = 2, r = 3$

You need $ar^{n-1} = 1458$, i.e. $2 \times 3^{n-1} = 1458$, i.e. $3^{n-1} = 729$.

Then, use logs to find that:

$\log 3^{n-1} = \log 729$

$(n - 1)\log 3 = \log 729$

$n - 1 = \dfrac{\log 729}{\log 3}$

$n - 1 = 6$, i.e. $n = 7$, the 7th term $= 1458$.

See Section 4 for more on logs

8) $(2 + 3x)^5 = 2^5\left(1 + \frac{3}{2}x\right)^5$

$= 2^5\left[1 + \frac{5}{1}\left(\frac{3}{2}x\right) + \frac{5 \times 4}{1 \times 2}\left(\frac{3}{2}x\right)^2 + ...\right]$

x^2 term is $2^5 \times \frac{5 \times 4}{1 \times 2}\left(\frac{3}{2}x\right)^2$

so coefficient is $2^5 \times \dfrac{5 \times 4}{1 \times 2} \times \dfrac{3^2}{2^2} = 720$

Exam Questions

1 a) $h_2 = h_{1+1} = 2 \times 5 + 2 = 12$ *[1 mark]*

$h_3 = h_{2+1} = 2 \times 12 + 2 = 26$ *[1 mark]*

$h_4 = 2h_3 + 2 = 54$ *[1 mark]*

b) $\sum_{r=3}^{6} h_r = h_3 + h_4 + h_5 + h_6$

$h_5 = 2h_4 + 2 = 110$ *[1 mark]*

$h_6 = 2(110) + 2 = 222$

so $\sum_{r=3}^{6} h_r = 26 + 54 + 110 + 222$ *[1 mark]*

$= 412$ *[1 mark]*

Nothing hard here, just pop the numbers in. Pop, pop, pop...

2 a) $a_2 = 3k + 11$ *[1 mark]*

$a_3 = 3a_2 + 11$

$= 3(3k + 11) + 11 = 9k + 33 + 11$

$= 9k + 44$ *[1 mark]*

$a_4 = 3a_3 + 11$

$= 3(9k + 44) + 11$

$= 27k + 143$ *[1 mark]*

b) $\sum_{r=1}^{4} a_r = k + (3k + 11) + (9k + 44) + (27k + 143)$

$= 40k + 198$ *[1 mark]*

$40k + 198 = 278$

$40k = 278 - 198 = 80$ *[1 mark]*

$k = 2$ *[1 mark]*

3   Use the nth term formula: $a_n = a_1 + (n - 1)d$:

$a + (7 - 1)d = a + 6d$ *[1 mark]*

You know that $a_7 = 580$ so

$a + 6d = 580$ *[1 mark]*

And you know that $S_{15} = 9525$, so using the series formula:

$S_{15} = \dfrac{15}{2}[2a + (15 - 1)d] = 9525$ *[1 mark]*

$= \dfrac{15}{2}(2a + 14d) = 9525$, i.e. $15a + 105d = 9525$

then you can divide everything by 15 to give:

$a + 7d = 635$ *[1 mark]*

then solve them simultaneously:

$(a + 7d) - (a + 6d) = d = 635 - 580$ *[1 mark]*

$d = 55$ *[1 mark]*

and finally use this value of d to find a:

$a + (6 \times 55) = 580$

$a = 580 - 330$

$= 250$ *[1 mark]*

A lot of steps needed for that one, but don't panic if the question seems complicated. If you're stuck, write down all the sequence and series formulas — then see what formulas you can fill in using the info in the question. A light bulb should go 'bing'. Hopefully...

4 a) $a_{31} = 22 + (31 - 1)(-1.1)$ *[1 mark]*

$= 22 + 30(-1.1)$

$= 22 - 33 = -11$ *[1 mark]*

b) $a_k = 0$

$a_1 + (k - 1)d = 0$

$22 + (k - 1) \times -1.1 = 0$ *[1 mark]*

$k - 1 = \dfrac{-22}{-1.1} = \dfrac{220}{11} = 20$

$k = 20 + 1 = 21$ *[1 mark]*

c)   We want to find the first value of n for which $S_n < 0$.

Using the formula for sum of a series:

$S_n = \dfrac{n}{2}[2 \times 22 + (n - 1)(-1.1)] < 0$ *[1 mark]*

$S_n = \dfrac{n}{2}(44 - 1.1n + 1.1) < 0$

$\dfrac{n}{2}(45.1 - 1.1n) < 0$ *[1 mark]*

$\dfrac{n}{2}(45.1 - 1.1n) = 0$

$\Rightarrow \dfrac{n}{2} = 0$ or $45.1 - 1.1n = 0$

$\Rightarrow n = 0$ or $n = 41$ *[1 mark]*

The coefficient of n^2 is negative so graph is n-shaped.

Need to find negative part, so $n < 0$ or $n > 41$.

Since n cannot be negative then $n > 41$.

Now we just want the first (i.e. lowest) value of n for which this is true, which is $n = 42$. *[1 mark]*

Answers

5 a) $a = 6$
$d = 8$ *[1 mark]*
$a_n = 6 + 8(n - 1)$ *[1 mark]*
$= 8n - 2$ *[1 mark]*

b) $S_{10} = \frac{10}{2}[2 \times 6 + (10 - 1)8]$ *[1 mark]*
$= 5 \times (12 + 72)$ *[1 mark]*
$= 420$ *[1 mark]*

c) First find an expression for S_k:
$S_k = \frac{k}{2}[2 \times 6 + 8(k - 1)]$
$= \frac{k}{2} \times (12 + 8k - 8)$
$= \frac{k}{2}(8k + 4)$ *[1 mark]*
$= \frac{8k^2 + 4k}{2} = 4k^2 + 2k$ *[1 mark]*

Then, you know that the total sum will be less than 2450, because he hadn't yet reached that limit by day k, so:
$4k^2 + 2k < 2450$
$\Rightarrow 2k^2 + k < 1225$
$\Rightarrow 2k^2 + k - 1225 < 0$
$\Rightarrow (2k - 49)(k + 25) < 0$ *[1 mark]*

Don't forget the difference between series and sequences. Part c is about a series — the cumulative sum. So don't use the wrong equations, or you'll get very muddled indeed.

d) Since $(2k - 49)(k + 25) < 0$,
$2k - 49 = 0$ or $k + 25 = 0$
$k = 24.5$ or $k = -25$ *[1 mark]*
Coefficient of k^2 is positive so graph is u-shaped.
Need negative part, so $-25 < k < 24.5$.
k will be the largest whole number that satisfies the inequality, i.e. $k = 24$. *[1 mark]*

6 $(4 + 3x)^{10}$
$= 4^{10}\left[1 + \frac{10}{1}\left(\frac{3}{4}x\right) + \frac{10 \times 9}{1 \times 2}\left(\frac{3}{4}x\right)^2 + \frac{10 \times 9 \times 8}{1 \times 2 \times 3}\left(\frac{3}{4}x\right)^3 \right.$
$\left. + \frac{10 \times 9 \times 8 \times 7}{1 \times 2 \times 3 \times 4}\left(\frac{3}{4}x\right)^4 + ...\right]$

So the x coefficient $= 4^{10} \times \frac{10}{1} \times \frac{3}{4} = 7864320$ *[1 mark]*
x^2 coefficient $= 4^{10} \times \frac{90}{2} \times \frac{9}{16} = 26542080$ *[1 mark]*
x^3 coefficient $= 4^{10} \times \frac{720}{6} \times \frac{27}{64} = 53084160$ *[1 mark]*
x^4 coefficient $= 4^{10} \times \frac{5040}{24} \times \frac{81}{256} = 69672960$ *[1 mark]*

No problems there... as long as you've got binomial expansion straight in your head. If it's still a tangle of factors, powers and garden gnomes, go back and sort it out — you'll be glad you did.

7 a) $\left(\frac{1}{2x} + \frac{x}{2}\right)^3 = \left(\frac{1}{2x}\right)^3 + 3\left(\frac{1}{2x}\right)^2\left(\frac{x}{2}\right) + 3\left(\frac{1}{2x}\right)\left(\frac{x}{2}\right)^2 + \left(\frac{x}{2}\right)^3$
$= \frac{1}{8x^3} + \frac{3}{8x} + \frac{3x}{8} + \frac{x^3}{8}$
[3 marks available — 1 mark for correct use of formula, 1 mark for correct coefficients, 1 mark for correct simplified final answer].

b) $(2 + x^2)\left(\frac{1}{2x} + \frac{x}{2}\right)^3 = (2 + x^2)\left(\frac{1}{8x^3} + \frac{3}{8x} + \frac{3x}{8} + \frac{x^3}{8}\right)$.
The only parts of this multiplication which will give an x term are $2\left(\frac{3x}{8}\right)$ and $x^2\left(\frac{3}{8x}\right)$. *[1 mark]*
So, x term will be: $2\left(\frac{3x}{8}\right) + x^2\left(\frac{3}{8x}\right) = x\left(\frac{6}{8} + \frac{3}{8}\right)$ *[1 mark]*
and the coefficient of x is $\frac{9}{8}$ *[1 mark]*.

8 a) The ratio $= 1.3$, which is > 1, so the sequence is divergent. *[1 mark]*

b) $u_3 = 12 \times 1.3^2 = 20.28$ *[1 mark]*
$u_{10} = 12 \times 1.3^9 = 127.25$ *[1 mark]*

9 a) $S_\infty = \frac{a}{1 - r} = \frac{20}{1 - \frac{3}{4}} = \frac{20}{\frac{1}{4}} = 80$
[2 marks available — 1 mark for formula, 1 mark for correct answer]

b) $u_{15} = ar^{14} = 20 \times \left(\frac{3}{4}\right)^{14} = 0.356$ (to 3 sig. fig.)
[2 marks available — 1 mark for formula, 1 mark for correct answer]

c) Use the formula for the sum of a geometric series to write an expression for S_n:
$S_n = \frac{a(1 - r^n)}{1 - r} = \frac{20\left(1 - \frac{3^n}{4}\right)}{1 - \frac{3}{4}}$ *[1 mark]*
so $\frac{20\left(1 - \frac{3^n}{4}\right)}{1 - \frac{3}{4}} > 79.76$
Now rearrange and use logs to get n on its own:
$\frac{20\left(1 - \frac{3^n}{4}\right)}{1 - \frac{3}{4}} > 79.76 \Rightarrow 20\left(1 - \frac{3^n}{4}\right) > 19.94$
$\Rightarrow 1 - \frac{3^n}{4} > 0.997 \Rightarrow 0.003 > 0.75^n$ *[1 mark]*
$\Rightarrow \log 0.003 > n \log 0.75$ *[1 mark]*
$\Rightarrow \frac{\log 0.003}{\log 0.75} < n$ *[1 mark]*
Bit tricky that last bit. If $x < 1$, then $\log x$ has a negative value — and when dividing by a negative value on either side of an inequality sign you need to change the direction of the inequality.
$\frac{\log 0.003}{\log 0.75} = 20.1929....$
so $n > 20.1929....$
But n must be an integer, as it is a term not a value, therefore $n = 21$ *[1 mark]*
Don't get too calculator-happy and forget that n will be an integer — you'd have lost that mark if you'd just put 20.1929...

10 a) $u_n = ar^{n-1}$ where $a = 1$ and $r = 1.5$,
so $u_5 = 1 \times (1.5)^4$ *[1 mark]*
$= 5.06$ km to the nearest 10m *[1 mark]*
Make sure you get the ratios right here. If the values increase by 0.5 each time then the ratio is 1.5 — a ratio of 0.5 would decrease the value.

b) $a = 2$ and $r = 1.2$ *[1 mark]*
$u_9 = 2 \times (1.2)^8 = 8.60$ km
$u_{10} = 2 \times (1.2)^9 = 10.32$ km *[1 mark]*
$u_9 < 10$ km and $u_{10} > 10$ km
so day 10 is the first day Chris runs more than 10 km *[1 mark]*.

Answers

c) In 10 days, Alex ran a total of 30 km   *[1 mark]*

Use the formula for the sum of first n terms: $S_n = \dfrac{a(1-r^n)}{1-r}$.

Chris ran a total of: $\dfrac{2(1-1.2^{10})}{1-1.2} = 51.917\,\text{km}$ *[1 mark]*

Heather ran a total of: $\dfrac{1(1-1.5^{10})}{1-1.5} = 113.330\,\text{km}$
[1 mark]

So they raised £(30 + 51.917 + 113.330)
$= £195.25$ *[1 mark]*

11 a) $S_\infty = \dfrac{a}{1-r}$ and $u_2 = ar$ *[1 mark]*

So $36 = \dfrac{a}{1-r}$ i.e. $36 - 36r = a$ *[1 mark]*

and $5 = ar$. *[1 mark]*
Substituting for a gives: $5 = (36 - 36r)r = 36r - 36r^2$
i.e. $36r^2 - 36r + 5 = 0$ *[1 mark]*

b) Factorising gives: $(6r - 1)(6r - 5) = 0$

So $r = \dfrac{1}{6}$ or $r = \dfrac{5}{6}$. *[1 mark for each correct value]*

If $r = \dfrac{1}{6}$ and $ar = 5$ then $\dfrac{a}{6} = 5$ i.e. $a = 30$

If $r = \dfrac{5}{6}$ and $ar = 5$ then $\dfrac{5a}{6} = 5$ i.e. $a = 6$

[1 mark for each correct value]

Keep an eye on what you're being asked to find. Values in a sequence can be any number (oh, the possibilities), but the term positions are always whole numbers. So if you calculate a position and end up with a decimal number... something's not right.

C2 Section 3 — Circles and Trigonometry
Warm-up Questions

1) $\cos 30° = \dfrac{\sqrt{3}}{2}$, $\sin 30° = \dfrac{1}{2}$, $\tan 30° = \dfrac{1}{\sqrt{3}}$

$\cos 45° = \dfrac{1}{\sqrt{2}}$, $\sin 45° = \dfrac{1}{\sqrt{2}}$, $\tan 45° = 1$

$\cos 60° = \dfrac{1}{2}$, $\sin 60° = \dfrac{\sqrt{3}}{2}$, $\tan 60° = \sqrt{3}$

2) Sine Rule: $\dfrac{x}{\sin X} = \dfrac{y}{\sin Y} = \dfrac{z}{\sin Z}$

Cosine Rule: $x^2 = y^2 + z^2 - 2yz\cos X$

Area: $\dfrac{1}{2}xy\sin Z$

3) $\tan x = \dfrac{\sin x}{\cos x}$; $\cos^2 x = 1 - \sin^2 x$

4) a) B = 125°, a =3.66 m, c = 3.10 m, area is 4.64 m²

  b) r = 20.05 km, P = 1.49°, Q = 168.51°

5) Freda's angles are 22.3°, 49.5°, 108.2°

6)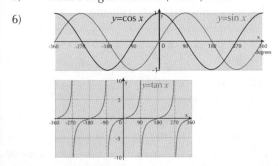

7) a) *[graph: $y = \tfrac{1}{2}\cos x$]*

  b) *[graph: $y = \tan 3x$]*

8) a) (i) $\theta = 240°,\ 300°$.

     (ii) $\theta = 135°,\ 315°$.

     (iii) $\theta = 135°,\ 225°$.

  b) (i) $\theta = 33.0°,\ 57.0°,\ 123.0°,\ 147.0°,\ -33.0°,\ -57.0°,$
          $-123.0°,\ -147.0°$

     (ii) $\theta = 179.8°$

9) $x = 70.5°,\ 120°,\ 240°,\ 289.5°$.

10) $x = -30°$

11) $(\sin y + \cos y)^2 + (\cos y - \sin y)^2$
    $\equiv (\sin^2 y + 2\sin y\cos y + \cos^2 y) +$
          $(\cos^2 y - 2\cos y \sin y + \sin^2 y)$
    $\equiv 2(\sin^2 y + \cos^2 y) \equiv 2$

12) $\dfrac{\sin^4 x + \sin^2 x\cos^2 x}{\cos^2 x - 1} \equiv -1$

LHS:
$\dfrac{\sin^2 x(\sin^2 x + \cos^2 x)}{(1 - \sin^2 x) - 1}$

$\equiv \dfrac{\sin^2 x}{-\sin^2 x} \equiv -1 \equiv$ RHS

Exam Questions

1 a) Using the cosine rule with $\triangle AMC$:
    $a^2 = b^2 + c^2 - 2bc\cos A$
    $2.30^2 = 2.20^2 + 2.20^2 - (2 \times 2.20 \times 2.20 \times \cos\theta)$
    $\cos\theta = \dfrac{5.29 - 4.84 - 4.84}{-9.68} = 0.4535...$
    $\theta = \cos^{-1} 0.4535... = 1.10$ rad to 3 s.f.

   [2 marks available — 1 mark for correct substitution into cosine rule formula, and 1 mark for correct answer in radians.]

   ...or, you could divide it into 2 right-angled triangles and then use: $\theta = 2\sin^{-1}\dfrac{1.15}{2.20} = 1.10$ rad. Whatever works.

  b) Arc length $S = r\theta = 2.20 \times 1.10$ *[1 mark]*
    $= 2.42$ m *[1 mark]*.
    Perimeter of slab = 2.42 + 1.5 + 1.5 = 5.42 m
    [1 mark].

c) Area of slab =
Area $\triangle ABC$ + Area $\triangle AMC$ − Area sector AMC.
Area of the triangles can be found using $\frac{1}{2}ab\sin C$.
Area of sector can be found using $\frac{1}{2}r^2\theta$.
So area of slab = $\left(\frac{1}{2} \times 1.50 \times 1.50 \times \sin 1.75\right)$ +
$\left(\frac{1}{2} \times 2.20 \times 2.20 \times \sin 1.10\right) - \left(\frac{1}{2} \times 2.20^2 \times 1.10\right)$
= 1.107 + 2.157 − 2.662 = 0.602 m² to 3 s.f.

[5 marks available — 1 mark for correct calculation of each of the three shapes, 1 mark for combining the three shapes in the correct way, 1 mark for correct final answer.]

2 a) $3\cos x = 2\sin x$, and $\tan x = \frac{\sin x}{\cos x}$,
You need to substitute tan in somewhere, so look at how you can rearrange to get sin/cos in the equation...
Divide through by $\cos x$ to give:
$3\frac{\cos x}{\cos x} = 2\frac{\sin x}{\cos x}$
$\Rightarrow 3 = 2\tan x$
$\Rightarrow \tan x = \frac{3}{2}$ (or = 1.5).
[2 marks available — 1 mark for correct substitution of tan x, 1 mark for correct final answer.]

b) Using $\tan x = 1.5$
$x = 56.3°$ *[1 mark]*
and a 2nd solution can be found from
$x = 180° + 56.3° = 236.3°$ *[1 mark]*.

Don't forget the other solution! Either use the CAST diagram or sketch a graph to help.

3 a) Angle MJH between the radius and tangent is a right angle, so use trig ratios to calculate angle JMH (or θ).
E.g. Using Pythagoras, $MJ = \sqrt{(0--4)^2 + (7-4)^2} = 5$.
$JH = \sqrt{(6-0)^2 + (-1-7)^2} = 10$.
$\tan\theta = \frac{10}{5} = 2$
$\theta = \tan^{-1}2 = 1.1071$ rad (to 4 d.p.)

[4 marks available — 1 mark for identifying that MJH is a right angle and that trig ratios can be used, 1 mark for calculation of two lengths of the triangle, 1 mark for correct substitution into a trig ratio, and 1 mark for correct answer in radians.]

b) Arc length $S = r\theta$ *[1 mark]*
Angle of sector = $\theta = 1.1071$ rad and $r = 5$ (both from (b))
so $S = 5 \times 1.1071 = 5.54$ to 3 s.f. *[1 mark]*.

4 a) Area of cross-section = $\frac{1}{2}r^2\theta$
$= \frac{1}{2} \times 20^2 \times \frac{\pi}{4} = 50\pi$ cm².
Volume = area of cross-section × height, so
$V = 50\pi \times 10 = 500\pi$ cm³.

[3 marks available — 1 mark for correct use of area formula, 1 mark for 50π, and 1 mark for correct final answer.]

b) Surface area is made up of 2 × cross-sectional area + 2 × side rectangles + 1 curved end rectangle.
Cross-sectional area = 50π (from part (a))
Area of each side rectangle = $10 \times 20 = 200$
Area of end rectangle = 10 × arc length
$= 10 \times \left(20 \times \frac{\pi}{4}\right)$
$= 50\pi$.
$S = (2 \times 50\pi) + (2 \times 200) + 50\pi = (150\pi + 400)$ cm².

[5 marks available — 1 mark for each correct shape area, 1 mark for correct combination, and 1 mark for correct final answer.]

5 $\sin 2x = -\frac{1}{2}$, so look for solutions in the range $0 \le 2x \le 4\pi$ *[1 mark]*.

It's easier to see what's going on by drawing a graph for this one:

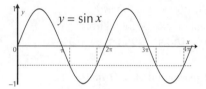

The graph shows there are 4 solutions between 0 and 4π. Putting $\sin 2x = -\frac{1}{2}$ into your calculator gives you the solution $2x = -\frac{\pi}{6}$, but this is outside the range *[1 mark]*. From the graph, you can see that the solutions within the range occur at $\pi + \frac{\pi}{6}$, $2\pi - \frac{\pi}{6}$, $3\pi + \frac{\pi}{6}$ and $4\pi - \frac{\pi}{6}$ *[1 mark]*, so $2x = \frac{7\pi}{6}$, $\frac{11\pi}{6}$, $\frac{19\pi}{6}$ and $\frac{23\pi}{6}$ *[1 mark]*.
Dividing by 2 gives:
$x = \frac{7\pi}{12}$, $\frac{11\pi}{12}$, $\frac{19\pi}{12}$ and $\frac{23\pi}{12}$ *[2 marks for all 4 correct, 1 mark for 2 correct]*

6 a)

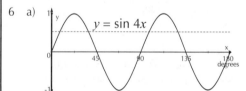

[2 marks available — 1 mark for correct y = sin x graph, 1 mark for 2 repetitions of the sine wave between 0 and 180°.]

b) E.g. $\sin 4x = 0.5$
$4x = 30°$
$x = 7.5°$ is one solution. *[1 mark]*
The graph in (a) shows there are 4 solutions between 0 and 180°, which, by the symmetry of the graph, lie 7.5° from where the graph cuts the x-axis, as follows:
$x = 45° - 7.5° = 37.5°$. *[1 mark]*
$x = 90° + 7.5° = 97.5°$. *[1 mark]*
$x = 135° - 7.5° = 127.5°$ *[1 mark]*

Answers

7 a) $2(1 - \cos x) = 3 \sin^2 x$, and $\sin^2 x = 1 - \cos^2 x$.
$\Rightarrow 2(1 - \cos x) = 3(1 - \cos^2 x)$ *[1 mark]*.

You need to get the whole equation into either sin or cos to get something useful at the end, so get used to spotting places to use the trig identities.

$\Rightarrow 2 - 2 \cos x = 3 - 3 \cos^2 x$
$\Rightarrow 3 \cos^2 x - 2 \cos x - 1 = 0$ *[1 mark]*.

   b) From (a), the equation can be written as:
$3 \cos^2 x - 2 \cos x - 1 = 0$

Now this looks suspiciously like a quadratic equation, which can be factorised...

$(3 \cos x + 1)(\cos x - 1) = 0$
$\Rightarrow \cos x = -\frac{1}{3}$ *[1 mark]* or $\cos x = 1$ *[1 mark]*
For $\cos x = -\frac{1}{3}$
   $x = 109.5°$ (to 1 d.p.) *[1 mark]*,
and a 2nd solution can be found from
   $x = (360° - 109.5°) = 250.5°$ *[1 mark]*.
For $\cos x = 1$
   $x = 0°$ *[1 mark]* and $360°$ *[1 mark]*.

8 a) Using the cosine rule:
$a^2 = b^2 + c^2 - 2bc\cos A$
If XY is a, then angle $A = 180° - 100° = 80°$.
$XY^2 = 150^2 + 250^2 - (2 \times 150 \times 250 \times \cos 80°)$
$XY^2 = 71976.3867$
$XY = \sqrt{71976.3867} = 268.28$ m (to 2 d.p.)
$= 268$ m to the nearest m.

[2 marks available — 1 mark for correct substitution into cosine rule formula, and 1 mark for correct answer.]

   b) Using the sine rule:
$\frac{a}{\sin A} = \frac{b}{\sin B}$, so $\frac{250}{\sin\theta} = \frac{268.2842 \text{ (from (a))}}{\sin 80°}$.
Rearranging gives:
$\frac{\sin\theta}{\sin 80°} = \frac{250}{268.2842} = 0.93$ to 2 d.p.
[3 marks available — 1 mark for correct substitution into sine rule formula, 1 mark for rearrangement into the correct form, and 1 mark for correct final answer.]

9      $2 - \sin x = 2 \cos^2 x$, and $\cos^2 x = 1 - \sin^2 x$
$\Rightarrow 2 - \sin x = 2(1 - \sin^2 x)$
$\Rightarrow 2 - \sin x = 2 - 2 \sin^2 x$
$\Rightarrow 2\sin^2 x - \sin x = 0$

Now simply factorise and all will become clear...

$\sin x(2 \sin x - 1) = 0 \Rightarrow \sin x = 0$ or $\sin x = \frac{1}{2}$.
For $\sin x = 0$, $x = 0$, π and 2π.
For $\sin x = \frac{1}{2}$, $x = \frac{\pi}{6}$ and $\pi - \frac{\pi}{6} = \frac{5\pi}{6}$.
[6 marks available — 1 mark for correct substitution using trig identity, 1 mark for factorising quadratic in sin x, 1 mark for finding correct values of sin x, 1 mark for all three solutions when sin x = 0, 1 mark for each of the other 2 correct solutions.]

10 a) $(1 + 2 \cos x)(3 \tan^2 x - 1) = 0$
$\Rightarrow 1 + 2 \cos x = 0 \Rightarrow \cos x = -\frac{1}{2}$.
OR:
$3 \tan^2 x - 1 = 0 \Rightarrow \tan^2 x = \frac{1}{3} \Rightarrow \tan x = \frac{1}{\sqrt 3}$ or $-\frac{1}{\sqrt 3}$.
For $\cos x = -\frac{1}{2}$
   $x = \frac{2\pi}{3}$ and $-\frac{2\pi}{3}$.

Drawing the cos x graph helps you find the second one here, and don't forget the limits are $-\pi \le x \le \pi$.

For $\tan x = \frac{1}{\sqrt 3}$
$x = \frac{\pi}{6}$ and $-\pi + \frac{\pi}{6} = -\frac{5\pi}{6}$.
For $\tan x = -\frac{1}{\sqrt 3}$
$x = -\frac{\pi}{6}$ and $-\frac{\pi}{6} + \pi = \frac{5\pi}{6}$.
Again, look at the graph of tan x if you're unsure.

[6 marks available — 1 mark for each correct solution.]

   b) $\sqrt 2 \cos x = \frac{1}{\tan x}$, and $\tan x = \frac{\sin x}{\cos x}$, so $\frac{1}{\tan x} = \frac{\cos x}{\sin x}$.
$\Rightarrow \sqrt 2 \cos x = \frac{\cos x}{\sin x}$ *[1 mark]*.
$\Rightarrow \sqrt 2 = \frac{1}{\sin x}$
$\Rightarrow \sin x = \frac{1}{\sqrt 2}$ *[1 mark]*.
$x = \frac{\pi}{4}$ *[1 mark]* and a 2nd solution can be found from
$x = \pi - \frac{\pi}{4} = \frac{3\pi}{4}$ *[1 mark]*.

C2 Section 4 — Logs and Exponentials
Warm-up Questions

1) a) $3^3 = 27$ so $\log_3 27 = 3$

   b) To get fractions you need negative powers
$3^{-3} = 1/27$
$\log_3 (1/27) = -3$

   c) Logs are subtracted so divide
$\log_3 18 - \log_3 2 = \log_3 (18 \div 2)$
$= \log_3 9$
$= 2$ $(3^2 = 9)$

2) a) Logs are added so you multiply —
remember $2 \log 5 = \log 5^2$.
$\log 3 + 2 \log 5 = \log (3 \times 5^2)$
$= \log 75$

   b) Logs are subtracted so you divide and the power half means square root
$\frac{1}{2} \log 36 - \log 3 = \log (36^{\frac{1}{2}} \div 3)$
$= \log (6 \div 3)$
$= \log 2$

   c) Logs are subtracted so you divide and the power quarter means fourth root
$\log 2 - \frac{1}{4} \log 16 = \log (2 \div 16^{\frac{1}{4}})$
$= \log (2 \div 2)$
$= \log 1 = 0$

Answers

3) This only looks tricky because of the algebra, just remember the laws: $\log_b (x^2 - 1) - \log_b (x - 1) = \log_b \{(x^2 - 1)/(x - 1)\}$
Then use the difference of two squares:
$(x^2 - 1) = (x - 1)(x + 1)$ and cancel to get
$\log_b (x^2 - 1) - \log_b (x - 1) = \log_b (x + 1)$

4) a) Filling in the answers is just a case of using the calculator

x	−3	−2	−1	0	1	2	3
y	0.0156	0.0625	0.25	1	4	16	64

Check that it agrees with what we know about the graphs. It goes through the common point (0, 1), and it follows the standard shape.

b) Then you just need to draw the graph, and use a scale that's just right.

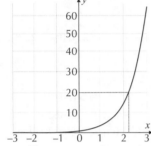

c) The question tells you to use the graph to get your answer, so you'll need to include the construction lines, but check the answer with a calculator.

$x = \log 20 / \log 4 = 2.16$, but you can't justify this accuracy if your graph's not up to it, so 2.2 is a good estimate.

5) a) $x = \log_{10} 240 / \log_{10} 10 = \log_{10} 240 = 2.380$

b) $x = 10^{5.3} = 199526.2... = 200000$ (to 3 s.f.)

c) $2x + 1 = \log_{10} 1500 = 3.176$, so $2x = 2.176$, so $x = 1.088$

d) $(x - 1) \log 4 = \log 200$, so $x - 1 = \log 200 / \log 4 = 3.822$, so $x = 4.822$

6) First solve for $1.5^P > 1\,000\,000$
$P \times \log_{10} 1.5 > \log_{10} 1\,000\,000$,
so $P > (\log_{10} 1\,000\,000) / (\log_{10} 1.5)$, $P > 34.07$.
We need the next biggest integer, so this will be $P = 35$.

Exam Questions

1 a) (i) $\log_a 20 - 2 \log_a 2$
$= \log_a 20 - \log_a (2^2)$ *[1 mark]*
$= \log_a (20 \div 2^2)$ *[1 mark]*
$= \log_a 5$ *[1 mark]*

(ii) $\frac{1}{2} \log_a 16 + \frac{1}{3} \log_a 27$
$= \log_a (16^{\frac{1}{2}}) + \log_a (27^{\frac{1}{3}})$ *[1 mark]*
$= \log_a (16^{\frac{1}{2}} \times 27^{\frac{1}{3}})$ *[1 mark]*
$= \log_a (4 \times 3) = \log_a 12$ *[1 mark]*

b) (i) $\log_2 64 = 6$ *[1 mark]* (since $2^6 = 64$)

(ii) $2 \log_3 9 = \log_3 (9^2) = \log_3 81$ *[1 mark]*
$\log_3 81 = 4$ *[1 mark]* (since $3^4 = 81$)

2 a) $2^x = 9$, so taking logs of both sides gives
$\log 2^x = \log 9$

This is usually the first step in getting x on its own — then you can use your trusty log laws...

$\Rightarrow x \log 2 = \log 9$
$\Rightarrow x = \dfrac{\log 9}{\log 2} = 3.17$ to 2 d.p.
[3 marks available — 1 mark for taking logs of both sides, 1 mark for x log 2 = log 9, and 1 mark for correct final answer.]

b) $2^{2x} = (2^x)^2$ (from the power laws) *[1 mark]*,
so let $y = 2^x$ and $y^2 = 2^{2x}$. This gives a quadratic in y:
$y^2 - 13y + 36 = 0$

Now the big question is — will it factorise? You betcha...

$(y - 9)(y - 4) = 0$, so $y = 9$ or $y = 4$, that is,
$\Rightarrow 2^x = 9$ *[1 mark]* or $2^x = 4$ *[1 mark]*

From (a), for $2^x = 9$, $x = 3.17$ to 2 d.p. *[1 mark]*
and for $2^x = 4$, $x = 2$ (since $2^2 = 4$) *[1 mark]*.

3 $\log_7 (y + 3) + \log_7 (2y + 1) = 1$
$\Rightarrow \log_7 ((y + 3)(2y + 1)) = 1$

To remove the $\log_7$, do 7 to the power of each side:
$(y + 3)(2y + 1) = 7^1 = 7$

Multiply out, rearrange, and re-factorise:
$2y^2 + 7y + 3 = 7$
$\Rightarrow 2y^2 + 7y - 4 = 0$
$\Rightarrow (2y - 1)(y + 4) = 0$
$\Rightarrow y = \frac{1}{2}$ or $y = -4$,
but since $y > 0$, $y = \frac{1}{2}$ is the only solution.
[5 marks available — 1 mark for combining the two logs, 1 mark for 7 to the power of each side, 1 mark for the correct factorisation of the quadratic, 1 mark for correct solutions and 1 mark for stating that only y = ½ is a valid solution.]

4 a) $\log_3 x = -\frac{1}{2}$, so do 3 to the power of each side to remove the log:
$x = 3^{-\frac{1}{2}}$ *[1 mark]*
$\Rightarrow x = \dfrac{1}{3^{\frac{1}{2}}}$ *[1 mark]* $\Rightarrow x = \dfrac{1}{\sqrt{3}}$ *[1 mark]*.

b) $2 \log_3 x = -4$
$\Rightarrow \log_3 x = -2$, and 3 to the power of each side gives:
$x = 3^{-2}$ *[1 mark]*
$\Rightarrow x = \dfrac{1}{9}$ *[1 mark]*

5 a) $6^{(3x + 2)} = 9$, so taking logs of both sides gives:
$(3x + 2) \log 6 = \log 9$ *[1 mark]*
$\Rightarrow 3x + 2 = \dfrac{\log 9}{\log 6} = 1.2262...$ *[1 mark]*
$\Rightarrow x = (1.2262... - 2) \div 3 = -0.258$ to 3 s.f. *[1 mark]*

Answers

b) $3^{(y^2-4)} = 7^{(y+2)}$, so taking logs of both sides gives:

$(y^2 - 4)\log 3 = (y + 2)\log 7$ *[1 mark]*

$\Rightarrow \dfrac{(y^2-4)}{(y+2)} = \dfrac{\log 7}{\log 3} = 1.7712...$ *[1 mark]*

The top of the fraction is a 'difference of two squares' so it will simplify as follows...

$\dfrac{(y-2)(y+2)}{(y+2)} = 1.7712...$ *[1 mark]*

$\Rightarrow y - 2 = 1.7712...$ *[1 mark]* $\Rightarrow y = 3.77$ to 3 s.f. *[1 mark]*

6 a) $\log_4 p - \log_4 q = \dfrac{1}{2}$, so using the log laws:

$\log_4\left(\dfrac{p}{q}\right) = \dfrac{1}{2}$

Doing 4 to the power of both sides gives:

$\dfrac{p}{q} = 4^{\frac{1}{2}} = \sqrt{4} = 2$

$\Rightarrow p = 2q$

[3 marks available — 1 mark for combining the two logs, 1 mark for 4 to the power of each side, 1 mark for the correct final working.]

b) Since $p = 2q$ (from (a)), the equation can be written:

$\log_2(2q) + \log_2 q = 7$ *[1 mark]*

This simplifies to:

$\log_2(2q^2) = 7$ *[1 mark]*

Doing 2 to the power of both sides gives:

$2q^2 = 2^7 = 128$ *[1 mark]*

$\Rightarrow q^2 = 64$, $\Rightarrow q = 8$ (since p and q are positive) *[1 mark]*

$p = 2q \Rightarrow p = 16$ *[1 mark]*

C2 Section 5 — Integration
Warm-up Questions

1) a) $2x^5 + C$　　b) $\dfrac{3x^2}{2} + \dfrac{5x^3}{3} + C$　　c) $\dfrac{3}{4}x^4 + \dfrac{2}{3}x^3 + C$

2) Integrating gives $y = 3x^2 - 7x + C$; then substitute $x = 1$ and $y = 0$ to find that $C = 4$. So the equation of the curve is $y = 3x^2 - 7x + 4$.

3) Check whether there are limits to integrate between. If there are, then it's a definite integral; if not, it's an indefinite integral.

4) a) $\displaystyle\int_0^1 (4x^3 + 3x^2 + 2x + 1)\,dx$

$= [x^4 + x^3 + x^2 + x]_0^1$

$= 4 - 0 = 4$

b) $\displaystyle\int_1^2\left(\dfrac{8}{x^5} + \dfrac{3}{\sqrt{x}}\right)dx = \left[-\dfrac{2}{x^4} + 6\sqrt{x}\right]_1^2$

$= \left(-\dfrac{2}{16} + 6\sqrt{2}\right) - (-2 + 6) = -\dfrac{33}{8} + 6\sqrt{2}$

c) $\displaystyle\int_1^6 \dfrac{3}{x^2}\,dx = \left[\dfrac{-3}{x}\right]_1^6 = -\dfrac{1}{2} - (-3) = \dfrac{5}{2}$

5) a) $\displaystyle\int_{-3}^3 (9 - x^2)\,dx = \left[9x - \dfrac{x^3}{3}\right]_{-3}^3$

$= 18 - (-18) = 36$

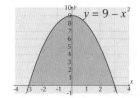

b) $\displaystyle\int_1^\infty \dfrac{3}{x^2}\,dx = \left[-\dfrac{3}{x}\right]_1^\infty$

$= 0 - (-3) = 3$

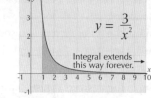

6) $\displaystyle\int_1^8 y\,dx = \int_1^8 x^{-\frac{1}{3}}\,dx = \left[\dfrac{3}{2}x^{\frac{2}{3}}\right]_1^8$

$= \left(\dfrac{3}{2} \times 8^{\frac{2}{3}}\right) - \left(\dfrac{3}{2} \times 1^{\frac{2}{3}}\right) = \left(\dfrac{3}{2} \times 4\right) - \left(\dfrac{3}{2} \times 1\right) = \dfrac{9}{2}$

7) a) $h = \dfrac{(3 - 0)}{3} = 1$

$x_0 = 0$: $y_0 = \sqrt{9} = 3$

$x_1 = 1$: $y_1 = \sqrt{8} = 2.8284$

$x_2 = 2$: $y_2 = \sqrt{5} = 2.2361$

$x_3 = 3$: $y_3 = \sqrt{0} = 0$

$\displaystyle\int_a^b y\,dx \approx \dfrac{1}{2}[(3 + 0) + 2(2.8284 + 2.2361)]$

$= 6.5645 \approx 6.56$

b) $h = \dfrac{(1.2 - 0.2)}{5} = 0.2$

$x_0 = 0.2$: 　　$y_0 = 0.2^{0.04} = 0.93765$

$x_1 = 0.4$: 　　$y_1 = 0.4^{0.16} = 0.86363$

$x_2 = 0.6$: 　　$y_2 = 0.6^{0.36} = 0.83202$

$x_3 = 0.8$: 　　$y_3 = 0.8^{0.64} = 0.86692$

$x_4 = 1$: 　　$y_4 = 1^1 = 1$

$x_5 = 1.2$: 　　$y_5 = 1.2^{1.44} = 1.30023$

$\displaystyle\int_a^b y\,dx \approx \dfrac{0.2}{2}\left[\begin{array}{l}(0.93765 + 1.30023)\\ + 2(0.86363 + 0.83202 + 0.86692 + 1)\end{array}\right]$

$= 0.1 \times 9.36302 \approx 0.936$

8) a) $A = \displaystyle\int_0^2 (x^3 - 5x^2 + 6x)\,dx$

$= \left[\dfrac{x^4}{4} - \dfrac{5}{3}x^3 + 3x^2\right]_0^2 = \dfrac{8}{3}$

b) $A = \displaystyle\int_1^4 2\sqrt{x}\,dx = \left[\dfrac{4}{3}x^{\frac{3}{2}}\right]_1^4 = \dfrac{28}{3}$

c) $A = \displaystyle\int_0^2 2x^2\,dx + \int_2^6 (12 - 2x)\,dx$

$= \left[\dfrac{2}{3}x^3\right]_0^2 + [12x - x^2]_2^6$

$= \dfrac{16}{3} + 16 = \dfrac{64}{3}$

Instead of integrating $(12 - 2x)$ between 2 and 6, you could have found the area of the triangle with base 4 and height 8.

d) $A = \displaystyle\int_1^4 (x + 3)\,dx - \int_1^4 (x^2 - 4x + 7)\,dx$

$= \left[\dfrac{x^2}{2} + 3x\right]_1^4 - \left[\dfrac{x^3}{3} - 2x^2 + 7x\right]_1^4$

$= \dfrac{33}{2} - 12 = \dfrac{9}{2}$

Exam Questions

1 a) $f(x) = \dfrac{x^{\frac{1}{2}}}{\frac{1}{2}} + 4x - \dfrac{5x^4}{4} + C$

and then simplify each term further if possible...

$= 2\sqrt{x} + 4x - \dfrac{5x^4}{4} + C$

[3 marks available — 1 mark for each term. Lose 1 mark if C missing or terms not simplified, e.g. ÷½ not converted to ×2. Note — you don't need to put surds in for it to be simplified — indices are fine.]

b) First rewrite everything in terms of powers of x:

$f'(x) = 2x + 3x^{-2}$

Now you can integrate each term (don't forget to add C):

$f(x) = \frac{2x^2}{2} + \frac{3x^{-1}}{-1} + C$

Then simplify each term:

$f(x) = x^2 - \frac{3}{x} + C$

[2 marks available — 1 mark for each term.
Lose 1 mark if C missing or terms not simplified.]

c) Following the same process as in part b):

$f'(x) = 6x^2 - \frac{1}{3}x^{-\frac{1}{2}}$

$f(x) = \frac{6x^3}{3} + \frac{1}{3}(x^{\frac{1}{2}} \div \frac{1}{2}) + C$

$f(x) = 2x^3 + \frac{2}{3}\sqrt{x} + C$

[2 marks available — 1 mark for each term.
Lose 1 mark if C missing or terms not simplified.]

2 a) Multiply out the brackets and simplify the terms:

$(5 + 2\sqrt{x})^2 = (5 + 2\sqrt{x})(5 + 2\sqrt{x})$

$= 25 + 10\sqrt{x} + 10\sqrt{x} + 4x$

$= 25 + 20\sqrt{x} + 4x$

So $a = 25$, $b = 20$ and $c = 4$

[3 marks: one for each constant]

b) Integrate your answer from a), treating each term separately:

$\int (25 + 20\sqrt{x} + 4x)\,dx = 25x + \left(20x^{\frac{3}{2}} \div \frac{3}{2}\right) + \left(\frac{4x^2}{2}\right) + C$

$= 25x + \frac{40\sqrt{x^3}}{3} + 2x^2 + C$

[3 marks available — 1 for each term.
Lose 1 mark if C missing or answers
not simplified (surds not necessary)]

Don't forget to add C, don't forget to add C, don't forget to add C.
Once, twice, thrice I beg of you, because it's very important.

3   To find $f(x)$ you integrate $f'(x)$, but it helps to write all terms in powers of x, so $5\sqrt{x} = 5x^{\frac{1}{2}}$ and $\frac{6}{x^2} = 6x^{-2}$ *[1 mark]*

Now integrate each term:

$\int (2x + 5x^{\frac{1}{2}} + 6x^{-2})\,dx = \frac{2x^2}{2} + \left(5x^{\frac{3}{2}} \div \frac{3}{2}\right) + \left(\frac{6x^{-1}}{-1}\right) + C$

$f(x) = x^2 + \frac{10\sqrt{x^3}}{3} - \frac{6}{x} + C$

[2 marks for correct terms, 1 mark for +C]

You've been given a point on the curve so you can calculate the value of C:

If $y = 7$ when $x = 3$, then

$3^2 - \frac{6}{3} + \frac{10\sqrt{3^3}}{3} + C = 7$ *[1 mark]*

$9 - 2 + 10\sqrt{3} + C = 7$

$7 + 10\sqrt{3} + C = 7$

$C = -10\sqrt{3}$

$f(x) = x^2 - \frac{6}{x} + \frac{10\sqrt{x^3}}{3} - 10\sqrt{3}$ *[1 mark]*

4 a) Rearrange the terms so each is written as a power of x, showing your working:

$\frac{1}{\sqrt{36x}} = \frac{1}{\sqrt{36}\sqrt{x}} = \frac{1}{6} \times \frac{1}{\sqrt{x}} = \frac{1}{6}x^{-\frac{1}{2}}$ *[1 mark]*

$2\left(\sqrt{\frac{1}{x^3}}\right) = 2\left(\frac{1}{x^3}\right)^{\frac{1}{2}} = 2(x^{-3})^{\frac{1}{2}}$

$= 2(x^{(-3 \times \frac{1}{2})}) = 2x^{-\frac{3}{2}}$ *[1 mark]*

This shows that $f'(x) = \frac{1}{6}x^{-\frac{1}{2}} - 2x^{-\frac{3}{2}}$ — so $A = \frac{1}{6}$ and $B = 2$
[1 mark]

b) Integrate f'(x) to find f(x):

$f(x) = \left(\frac{1}{6} \times x^{\frac{1}{2}} \div \frac{1}{2}\right) - \left(2x^{-\frac{1}{2}} \div -\frac{1}{2}\right) + C$ *[1 mark]*

$= \frac{1}{3}x^{\frac{1}{2}} + \left(-2 \div -\frac{1}{2}\right)\left(\frac{1}{\sqrt{x}}\right) + C$

$= \frac{\sqrt{x}}{3} + \frac{4}{\sqrt{x}} + C$ *[1 mark]*

Now use the coordinates (1, 7) to find the value of C:

$7 = \frac{\sqrt{1}}{3} + \frac{4}{\sqrt{1}} + C$ *[1 mark]*

$7 - \frac{1}{3} - 4 = C$

$C = \frac{8}{3}$

So $y = \frac{\sqrt{x}}{3} + \frac{4}{\sqrt{x}} + \frac{8}{3}$ *[1 mark]*

Well, aren't we having lovely integrating fun. Keep toddling
through, and it'll be time for tea and biscuits in no time.

5 a) The tangent at (1, 2) has the same gradient as the curve at that point, so use $f'(x)$ to calculate the gradient:

$f'(1) = 1^3 - 2$ *[1 mark]*

$= -1$ *[1 mark]*

Put this into the straight-line equation $y - y_1 = m(x - x_1)$:

$y - 2 = -1(x - 1)$ *[1 mark]*

$y = -x + 1 + 2$

$y = -x + 3$ *[1 mark]*

No need to go off on a tangent here — just find the gradient and
then find the equation. Boom. Done. And move swiftly on...

b) $f(x) = \int \left(x^3 - \frac{2}{x^2}\right)dx = \int (x^3 - 2x^{-2})dx$ *[1 mark]*

$= \frac{x^4}{4} - 2\frac{x^{-1}}{-1} + C = \frac{x^4}{4} + 2x^{-1} + C$ *[1 mark]*

$= \frac{x^4}{4} + \frac{2}{x} + C$

Now use the coordinates (1, 2) to find the value of C:

$2 = \frac{1^4}{4} + \frac{2}{1} + C$ *[1 mark]*

$2 - \frac{1}{4} - 2 = C$

$C = -\frac{1}{4}$ *[1 mark]*

So $f(x) = \frac{x^4}{4} + \frac{2}{x} - \frac{1}{4}$ *[1 mark]*

Answers

6 a) Multiply out the brackets in $f'(x)$:
   $(x - 1)(3x - 1) = 3x^2 - x - 3x + 1$
   $= 3x^2 - 4x + 1$ *[1 mark]*

   Now $f(x) = \int (3x^2 - 4x + 1)dx$
   $= \frac{3x^3}{3} - \frac{4x^2}{2} + \frac{x}{1} + C$ *[1 mark]*
   $= x^3 - 2x^2 + x + C$ *[1 mark]*
   Input the x and y coordinates to find C:
   $10 = 3^3 - 2(3^2) + 3 + C$ *[1 mark]*
   $10 - 27 + 18 - 3 = C$
   $C = -2$ *[1 mark]*
   So $f(x) = x^3 - 2x^2 + x - 2$ *[1 mark]*

   b) First calculate the gradient of $f(x)$ when $x = 3$:
   $f'(3) = 3(3^2) - (4 \times 3) + 1$
   $= 27 - 12 + 1$
   $= 16$ *[1 mark]*

   Use the fact that the tangent gradient multiplied by the normal gradient must equal –1 to find the gradient of the normal (n): $16 \times n = -1$ therefore $n = -\frac{1}{16}$ *[1 mark]*.
   Put n and $P(3, 10)$ into the formula for the equation of a line and rearrange until it's in the form $y = \frac{a - x}{b}$:

   $y - 10 = -\frac{1}{16}(x - 3)$ *[1 mark]*

   $y = \frac{3}{16} - \frac{x}{16} + 10$

   $y = \frac{163 - x}{16}$

   So $a = 163$ and $b = 16$. *[1 mark]*

7 The limits are the x-values when $y = 0$, so first solve
   $(x - 3)^2(x + 1) = 0$: *[1 mark]*
   $(x - 3)(x - 3)(x + 1) = 0$
   $x = 3$ *[1 mark]* and $x = -1$ *[1 mark]*
   Hence, to find the area, calculate:
   $\int_{-1}^{3}(x - 3)^2(x + 1)dx = \int_{-1}^{3}(x^3 - 5x^2 + 3x + 9)\,dx$ *[1 mark]*
   $= \left[\frac{x^4}{4} - \frac{5}{3}x^3 + \frac{3}{2}x^2 + 9x\right]_{-1}^{3}$ *[1 mark]*
   $= \left(\frac{3^4}{4} - \frac{5}{3}3^3 + \frac{3}{2}3^2 + (9 \times 3)\right) -$
   $\left(\frac{(-1)^4}{4} - \left(\frac{5}{3} \times (-1)^3\right) + \left(\frac{3}{2} \times (-1)^2\right) + (9 \times (-1))\right)$ *[1 mark]*
   $= 15\frac{3}{4} - -5\frac{7}{12}$ *[1 mark]*
   $= 21\frac{1}{3}$ *[1 mark]*

8 $\int_{2}^{7}(2x - 6x^2 + \sqrt{x})dx = \left[x^2 - 2x^3 + \frac{2\sqrt{x^3}}{3}\right]_{2}^{7}$
   [1 mark for each correct term]
   $= \left(7^2 - (2 \times 7^3) + \frac{2\sqrt{7^3}}{3}\right) - \left(2^2 - (2 \times 2^3) + \frac{2\sqrt{2^3}}{3}\right)$
   [1 mark]
   $= -624.6531605 - (-10.11438192)$
   $= -614.5387786 = -614.5388$ to 4 d.p. *[1 mark]*

9 a) (i) $h = \frac{8 - 2}{3} = 2$ *[1 mark]*
   $x_0 = 2$ $y_0 = \sqrt{(3 \times 2^3)} + \frac{2}{\sqrt{2}} = 6.31319$
   $x_1 = 4$ $y_1 = \sqrt{(3 \times 4^3)} + \frac{2}{\sqrt{4}} = 14.85641$
   $x_2 = 6$ $y_2 = \sqrt{(3 \times 6^3)} + \frac{2}{\sqrt{6}} = 26.27234$
   $x_3 = 8$ $y_3 = \sqrt{(3 \times 8^3)} + \frac{2}{\sqrt{8}} = 39.89894$ *[1 mark]*
   $\int_{2}^{8}y\,dx \approx \frac{2}{2}[6.31319 + 2(14.85641 + 26.27234)$
   $+ 39.89894]$ *[1 mark]*
   $= 128.46963 \approx 128.47$ to 2 d.p. *[1 mark]*

   (ii) $h = \frac{5 - 1}{4} = 1$ *[1 mark]*
   $x_0 = 1$ $y_0 = \frac{1^3 - 2}{4} = -0.25$
   $x_1 = 2$ $y_1 = \frac{2^3 - 2}{4} = 1.5$
   $x_2 = 3$ $y_2 = \frac{3^3 - 2}{4} = 6.25$
   $x_3 = 4$ $y_3 = \frac{4^3 - 2}{4} = 15.5$
   $x_4 = 5$ $y_4 = \frac{5^3 - 2}{4} = 30.75$ *[1 mark]*
   $\int_{1}^{5}y\,dx \approx \frac{1}{2}[-0.25 + 2(1.5 + 6.25 + 15.5) + 30.75]$
   [1 mark]
   ≈ 38.5 *[1 mark]*

   b) Increase the number of intervals calculated. *[1 mark]*

10 $n = 5$, $h = \frac{4 - 1.5}{5} = 0.5$ *[1 mark]*
   $x_1 = 2.0$, $x_2 = 2.5$, $x_3 = 3.0$ *[1 mark]*
   $y_0 = 2.8182$ *[1 mark]*, $y_3 = 6.1716$ *[1 mark]*,
   $y_4 = 7.1364$ *[1 mark]*
   $\int_{1.5}^{4}y\,dx \approx \frac{0.5}{2}[2.8182 + 2(4 + 5.1216 + 6.1716 + 7.1364) + 8]$
   [1 mark] $= 13.91935 = 13.9$ to 3 s.f. *[1 mark]*

11 a) $m = \frac{y_2 - y_1}{x_2 - x_1} = \frac{0 - -5}{-1 - 4} = -1$ *[1 mark]*
   $y - y_1 = m(x - x_1)$
   $y - -5 = -1(x - 4)$ so $y + 5 = 4 - x$
   $y = -x - 1$ *[1 mark]*

   b) Multiply out the brackets and then integrate:
   $(x + 1)(x - 5) = x^2 - 4x - 5$ *[1 mark]*
   $\int_{-1}^{4}(x^2 - 4x - 5)\,dx = \left[\frac{x^3}{3} - 2x^2 - 5x\right]_{-1}^{4}$ *[1 mark]*
   $= \left(\frac{4^3}{3} - 2(4^2) - (5 \times 4)\right)$
   $-\left(\frac{(-1)^3}{3} - 2(-1)^2 - (5 \times -1)\right)$ *[1 mark]*
   $= -30\frac{2}{3} - 2\frac{2}{3}$ *[1 mark]* $= -33\frac{1}{3}$ *[1 mark]*

   c) Subtract the area between the line and the x-axis from the area between the curve and the x-axis to leave the shaded region. The area under the line is a triangle (where $b = 5$ and $h = 5$), so use the formula for the area of a triangle to calculate it *[1 mark]*:
   $A = \frac{1}{2}bh = \frac{1}{2} \times 5 \times -5 = 12.5$ *[1 mark]*
   $A = 33\frac{1}{3} - 12\frac{1}{2}$ *[1 mark]*
   $= 20\frac{5}{6}$ *[1 mark]*
   You could also have integrated the line $y = -x - 1$ to find the area under the line — you'd have got the same answer.

Answers

C2 — Practice Exam One

1 a) The graph of $y = \tan 2t$ is going to be the same shape as $\tan x$, but squashed horizontally by a factor of 2. So the graph will be periodic with a period of 90° instead of 180°. It asks for solutions in the range $0° \leq t < 360°$ — so that would also be a suitable range for your sketch:

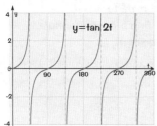

So, for any value of k there are 4 solutions.

[3 marks available — 1 mark for shape, 1 mark for 90° period, 1 mark for 4 solutions in range.]

b) Divide by $\cos 2t$ to get $\tan 2t = \sqrt{2}$ (as $\tan = \frac{\sin}{\cos}$):

$\sin 2t = \sqrt{2} \cos 2t$

$\Rightarrow \tan 2t = \sqrt{2}$ *[1 mark]*

$2t = \tan^{-1}\sqrt{2} = 54.7356...$

$t = 27.37°$ (to 2 d.p.)   *[1 mark]*

That's only one solution, but you know from part (a) that there's got to be four. You also know from part (a) that the graph repeats every 90°, so just add 90° on three times to get the other answers:

$t = 117.37°, 207.37°$ and $297.37°$ *[1 mark]*

2 a) In the laws of logs: $\log_a a = 1$. So $\log_3 3 = 1$.   *[1 mark]*

b) Use the laws of logs to rewrite the expression:

$\log_a 4 + 3\log_a 2 = \log_a(4 \times 2^3) = \log_a 32$.   *[1 mark]*

Therefore $\log_a \chi = \log_a 32$ so $\chi = 32$.   *[1 mark]*

3 a) c represents the coefficient of x^3, so find an expression for the coefficient of x^3 using the binomial expansion formula:

$(j + kx)^6 = j^6\left(1 + \frac{k}{j}x\right)^6$

Coefficient of $x^3 = j^6 \times \frac{6 \times 5 \times 4}{1 \times 2 \times 3} \times \left(\frac{k}{j}\right)^3$ *[1 mark]*

so $j^6 \times \frac{6 \times 5 \times 4}{1 \times 2 \times 3} \times \left(\frac{k}{j}\right)^3 = 20\,000$

$j^6 \times 20 \times \left(\frac{1}{j^3}\right) \times k^3 = 20\,000$

$j^6 \times j^{-3} \times k^3 = 1000$ *[1 mark]*

$= j^3 \times k^3 = 1000$

$(jk)^3 = 1000$ so $jk = \sqrt[3]{1000} = 10$ *[1 mark]*

b) Write an expression for the coefficient of x and then solve simultaneously with the equation $jk = 10$:

coefficient of $x = j^6 \times \frac{6}{1} \times \frac{k}{j} = 37\,500$

$= j^6 \times j^{-1} \times k \times 6 = 37\,500 \Rightarrow kj^5 = 6250$ *[1 mark]*

From a) $jk = 10$ so $k = \frac{10}{j}$

$kj^5 = \frac{10}{j} \times j^5 = 6250$ so $10 \times j^{-1} \times j^5 = 6250$ *[1 mark]*

$j^4 = 625$

$j = 5$ *[1 mark]*

Now input $j = 5$ into $jk = 10$ to find: $k = 2$ *[1 mark]*

Funny how part a) helps you work out part b).
It's almost as if the examiners are trying to help you… weird.

c) Coefficient of x^2, $b = 5^6 \times \frac{6 \times 5}{1 \times 2} \times \left(\frac{2}{5}\right)^2 = 37\,500$

[2 marks available — 1 mark for formula,
1 mark for correct answer]

4 a)

The bearing of C from B is $360° - 35° - x$, where x is the angle marked above. $x = 180° - 135° = 45°$ *[1 mark]*, so bearing of C from B $= 360° - 35° - 45° = 280°$ *[1 mark]*

b) Using cosine rule:

$AC^2 = 8^2 + 12^2 - 2 \times 8 \times 12 \times \cos 35°$ *[1 mark]*

$\Rightarrow AC^2 = 208 - 192\cos 35° = 50.7228...$

$\Rightarrow AC = 7.12199... = 7.12$ km (to 2 d.p.) *[1 mark]*

c) Using sine rule: $\frac{\sin BAC}{12} = \frac{\sin 35°}{7.122}$

$\Rightarrow \sin BAC = \frac{12\sin 35°}{7.122}$ *[1 mark]* $= 0.966$

$BAC = \sin^{-1}\left(\frac{12\sin 35°}{7.122}\right) = 75.1°$ (to 1 d.p.) *[1 mark]*

So angle ACB $= 180° - 35° - 75.1° = 69.9°$

So using ACB and the angles at B, the bearing of A from C

$= 180° - (35° + 45° + 69.9°)$ *[1 mark]*

$= 30.1°$ (to 1 d.p.) *[1 mark]*

5 a) The curve and the line intersect where:

$2x - 4 = (x - 2)(x - 4)$

$\Rightarrow 2x - 4 = x^2 - 6x + 8$

Rearrange to $= 0$ and then factorise:

$x^2 - 8x + 12 = 0$

$(x - 6)(x - 2) = 0$

$\Rightarrow x = 6$ and $x = 2$

To find the y-coordinates put the x-values in $y = 2x - 4$:

when $x = 2$, $y = (2 \times 2) - 4 = 0$

when $x = 6$, $y = (6 \times 2) - 4 = 8$

so the two points of intersection are $(2, 0)$ and $(6, 8)$.

Find where the line and the curve cut the axes by solving the equations for $y = 0$ (x-axis intersection) and $x = 0$ (y-axis intersection):

$2x - 4 = 0$ when $x = 2$. When $x = 0$, $y = -4$.

$(x - 2)(x - 4) = 0$ when $x = 2$ and $x = 4$. When $x = 0$, $y = -2 \times -4 = 8$.

The quadratic is U-shaped because the coefficient of x^2 is positive.

Now you're ready to sketch the graph.

Phew, at last. I thought we'd never get there…

Answers

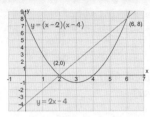

[3 marks available — 1 mark for intersection points, 1 mark for axes intercepts, 1 mark for shape.]

b) $\int_2^4 (x-2)(x-4)dx = \int_2^4 (x^2 - 6x + 8)\, dx$ *[1 mark]*

$= \left[\dfrac{x^3}{3} - 3x^2 + 8x\right]_2^4$ *[1 mark]*

$= \left(\dfrac{64}{3} - 48 + 32\right) - \left(\dfrac{8}{3} - 12 + 16\right)$

$= -\dfrac{4}{3}$ *[1 mark]*

The area's negative because it's below the x-axis.

c) Look at your sketch for part a):

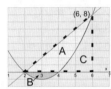

Area enclosed by line and curve = A + B, where B = $\dfrac{4}{3}$ (from part b)).

Triangle AC = $\dfrac{1}{2}$ × base × height

$= \dfrac{4 \times 8}{2} = 16$ *[1 mark]*

C is the area beneath $y = (x - 2)(x - 4)$ between $x = 4$ and $x = 6$:

$\int_4^6 (x^2 - 6x + 8)dx = \left[\dfrac{x^3}{3} - 3x^2 + 8x\right]_4^6$ *[1 mark]*

$= \left(\dfrac{216}{3} - 108 + 48\right) - \left(\dfrac{64}{3} - 48 + 32\right)$

$= \dfrac{20}{3}$ *[1 mark]*

So A = $16 - \dfrac{20}{3} = \dfrac{28}{3}$,

Total area: A + B = $\dfrac{28}{3} + \dfrac{4}{3} = \dfrac{32}{3}$.   *[1 mark]*

6 a) $360° = 2\pi$ radians.

So $120° = 120° \times \dfrac{2\pi}{360°}$ radians $= \dfrac{120°}{360°} \times 2\pi$ radians

$= \dfrac{2\pi}{3}$ radians   *[1 mark]*

b) Arc length S = $r\theta$, so

$40 = \dfrac{2\pi}{3} \times r$ *[1 mark]*

$r = 40 \div \dfrac{2\pi}{3} = 19.0985...$

$r = 19.1\,$cm (3 s.f.)   *[1 mark]*

c) $A = \dfrac{1}{2}r^2\theta$ *[1 mark]*

$= \dfrac{1}{2} \times (19.0985...)^2 \times \dfrac{2\pi}{3} = 381.9718...$

$= 382\,$cm^2 (to the nearest cm^2)   *[1 mark]*

7   $\int (4x^3 + 6x + 3)\, dx = \dfrac{4x^4}{4} + \dfrac{6x^2}{2} + 3x + C$

$= x^4 + 3x^2 + 3x + C$

[3 marks available in total — 1 mark for each of the first three terms, lose 1 mark if C is missing.]

8 a) $u_{n+1} = ru_n \Rightarrow u_2 = ru_1$

$\Rightarrow u_1 = \dfrac{u_2}{r}$

$u_1 = -2 \div -\dfrac{1}{2} = 4$

Using the nth term formula $u_n = ar^{(n-1)}$, where $a = u_1 = 4$:

$u_{13} = 4 \times \left(-\dfrac{1}{2}\right)^{12} = \dfrac{1}{1024}$

[3 marks available — 1 mark for a = 4, 1 mark for inputting u into nth term formula, 1 mark for correct value of u_{13}.]

b) The sum to infinity of a converging geometric series is given

by: $S_\infty = \dfrac{a}{1-r}$ *[1 mark]*

So just plug in the numbers to get:

$S_\infty = \dfrac{4}{1-\left(-\frac{1}{2}\right)} = 4 \div \dfrac{3}{2} = 4 \times \dfrac{2}{3}$ *[1 mark]*

$= 2\dfrac{2}{3}$ *[1 mark]*

To infinity and $2\frac{2}{3}$! Hmm... doesn't sound quite so adventurous when you put it like that...

9 a) Multiply out the brackets and rearrange to get zero on one side:

$(x - 1)(x^2 + x + 1) = 2x^2 - 17$

$\Rightarrow x^3 - 1 = 2x^2 - 17$ *[1 mark]*

$\Rightarrow x^3 - 2x^2 + 16 = 0$ *[1 mark]*

b) To show whether $(x + 2)$ is a factor of f(x) you need the factor theorem, which says that $(x - a)$ is a factor of a polynomial f(x) if and only if f(a) = 0. So if $(x + 2)$ is a factor of f(x), f(–2) = 0.   *[1 mark]*

$f(x) = x^3 - 2x^2 + 16$

$f(-2) = (-2)^3 - 2 \times (-2)^2 + 16$

$= -8 - 8 + 16$

$= 0$ *[1 mark]*

f(–2) = 0, therefore $(x + 2)$ *is* a factor of f(x)   *[1 mark]*

c) From part b) you know that $(x + 2)$ is a factor of f(x). Dividing f(x) by $(x + 2)$ gives:

$x^3 - 2x^2 + 16 - \underline{x^2}(x + 2) = x^3 - 2x^2 + 16 - x^3 - 2x^2$

$= -4x^2 + 16$

$-4x^2 + 16 - (\underline{-4x})(x + 2) = -4x^2 + 16 + 4x^2 + 8x = 8x + 16$

$8x + 16 - \underline{8}(x + 2) = 0$.

So $x^3 - 2x^2 + 16 = (x + 2)(x^2 - 4x - 8)$

[3 marks available — 1 mark for each correct term in the quadratic.]

d) From b) you know that $x = -2$ is a root. From c), $f(x) = (x + 2)(x^2 - 4x + 8)$. So for f(x) to equal zero, either $(x + 2) = 0$ (so $x = -2$) or $(x^2 - 4x + 8) = 0$ *[1 mark]*. Completing the square of $(x^2 - 4x + 8)$ gives

$x^2 - 4x + 8 = (x - 2)^2 + something$

$= (x - 2)^2 + 4$

The equation $(x - 2)^2 + 4 = 0$ has no real roots. So f(x) = 0 has no solutions other than $x = -2$. *[1 mark]*

You could also have shown that $x^2 - 4x + 8$ has no real roots by finding the discriminant — the discriminant is $(-4)^2 - (4 \times 1 \times 8)$ $= 16 - 32 = -16$, which is < 0 so it has no real roots.

Answers

e) To find $(x^3 - 2x^2 + 3x - 3) \div (x - 1)$ keep subtracting lumps of $(x - 1)$ to get rid of all powers of x.

First get rid of the x^3 term by subtracting x^2 lots of $(x - 1)$:
$(x^3 - 2x^2 + 3x - 3) - \underline{x^2}(x - 1)$
$= x^3 - 2x^2 + 3x - 3 - x^3 + x^2$
$= -x^2 + 3x - 3$

Now do the same with the bit you've got left to get rid of the x^2 term:
$-x^2 + 3x - 3 + \underline{x}(x - 1)$
$= -x^2 + 3x - 3 + x^2 - x$
$= 2x - 3$

Finally, get rid of the x term in the bit that's left:
$2x - 3 - \underline{2}(x - 1) = 2x - 3 - 2x + 2$
$= -1$

Which all means that $(x^3 - 2x^2 + 3x - 3) \div (x - 1)$
$= x^2 - x + 2$ with a remainder -1.

[4 marks available — 1 mark for each correct term and 1 mark for remainder.]

10 a) Use the information given and the general expression for the nth term in a sequence: $u_n = a + (n - 1)d$
to formulate expressions for the 3rd and 7th term:
$u_3 = a + 2d = 9$
$u_7 = a + 6d = 33$ *[1 mark]*

Now solve them as simultaneous equations:
$u_7 - u_3 = a + 6d - a - 2d = 33 - 9$
$4d = 24$
$d = 6$ *[1 mark]*
$a + 2d = 9$
$a + (2 \times 6) = 9$
$a + 12 = 9$
$a = 9 - 12 = -3$ *[1 mark]*

So the first term is −3 and the common difference is 6.

b) $S_n = \frac{n}{2}[2a + (n - 1)d]$

So $S_{12} = \frac{12}{2}[(2 \times -3) + 6(12 - 1)]$ *[1 mark]*
$= 6[-6 + 66]$ *[1 mark]*
$= 6 \times 60$
So $S_{12} = 360$ *[1 mark]*

c) $(6n + 1)$ is the rule for finding the nth term, so jot down the first few terms:
$u_1 = (6 \times 1) + 1 = 7$
$u_2 = (6 \times 2) + 1 = 13$
$u_3 = (6 \times 3) + 1 = 19$

So you can see that $d = 6$ and $a = 7$ *[1 mark]*
It's the same as the sequence before, except the first term is 7 instead of −3. So...
$\sum_{1}^{12}(6n + 1) = S_{12} = \frac{12}{2}[(2 \times 7) + (11 \times 6)]$
$= 6(14 + 66) = 6 \times 80 = 480$ *[1 mark]*

(Or you could note that each term is 10 more than the equivalent term in part b), so just add 10 × 12 to your answer for part b).)

C2 — Practice Exam Two

1 a) $\cos(3x)$ is the graph of $\cos x$, squashed horizontally by a factor of 3:

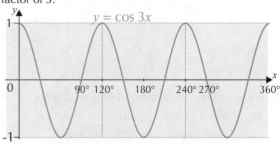

[2 marks available — 1 mark for shape, 1 mark for squashed horizontally by factor of 3.]

b) Remember that $\sin^2 x + \cos^2 x \equiv 1$ so with a little rearranging you can replace the $\sin^2$ with a $1 - \cos^2$:
$\sin^2(3x) + \cos^2(3x) = 1$
$\sin^2(3x) = 1 - \cos^2(3x)$ *[1 mark]*

Replace $\sin^2(3x)$ in the original equation:
$2[1 - \cos^2(3x)] = 1 + \cos(3x)$ *[1 mark]*

Now multiply out the bracket and rearrange:
$2[1 - \cos^2(3x)] = 1 + \cos(3x)$
$\Rightarrow 2 - 2\cos^2(3x) = 1 + \cos(3x)$ *[1 mark]*
$\Rightarrow 2\cos^2(3x) + \cos(3x) - 1 = 0$ *[1 mark]*

c) Rewrite the quadratic so it looks a bit friendlier. Substitute y for $\cos(3x)$ and the quadratic becomes:
$2y^2 + y - 1 = 0$.

This factorises to give: $(2y - 1)(y + 1) = 0$
so $y = \frac{1}{2}$ or $y = -1$ *[1 mark]*

Remember that $y = \cos(3x)$, so $\cos(3x) = \frac{1}{2}$ or $\cos(3x) = -1$
And by taking the inverse cosine of these you get:
$3x = \cos^{-1}(0.5) = 60°$
$\Rightarrow x = 20°$ *[1 mark]*
$3x = \cos^{-1}(-1) = 180°$
$\Rightarrow x = 60°$ *[1 mark]*

The graph from part a) shows there are nine possible solutions — the curve intersects the line $y = \frac{1}{2}$ six times, and touches the line $y = -1$ three times.
So the nine solutions are:
$x = 20°$, $x = 60°$, $x = 100°$, $x = 140°$, $x = 180°$, $x = 220°$, $x = 260°$, $x = 300°$ and $x = 340°$.   *[1 mark]*

2 a) Using the binomial expansion formula:
$(1 + x)^n =$
$1 + \frac{n}{1}x + \frac{n(n - 1)}{1 \times 2}x^2 + \frac{n(n - 1)(n - 2)}{1 \times 2 \times 3}x^3 + ... + x^n$
Expand the expression $(1 + ax)^{10}$ into this form:
$1 + \frac{10}{1}(ax) + \frac{10 \times 9}{1 \times 2}(ax)^2 + \frac{10 \times 9 \times 8}{1 \times 2 \times 3}(ax)^3 + ...$ *[1 mark]*

Then simplify each coefficient:
$(1 + ax)^{10} = 1 + 10ax + 45a^2x^2 + 120a^3x^3 + ...$ *[1 mark]*

Answers

b) *Pay attention to the number at the front of the bracket. If it's not a 1, you have to rearrange everything so it is a 1. Fiddly but important.*

First take a factor of 2 to get it in the form $(1 + ax)^n$:

$(2 + 3x)^5 = \left[2\left(1 + \frac{3}{2}x\right)\right]^5 = 2^5\left(1 + \frac{3}{2}x\right)^5 = 32\left(1 + \frac{3}{2}x\right)^5$

Now expand:

$32\left[1 + \frac{5}{1}\left(\frac{3}{2}x\right) + \frac{5 \times 4}{1 \times 2}\left(\frac{3}{2}x\right)^2 + ...\right]$ *[1 mark]*

You only need the x^2 term, so simplify that one:

$32 \times \frac{20}{2} \times \left(\frac{3}{2}\right)^2 \times x^2 = 720x^2$

So the coefficient of x^2 is 720   *[1 mark]*

c) Look back to the x^2 term from part a) — $45a^2x^2$. This is equal to $720x^2$ so just rearrange the formula to find a:

$45a^2 = 720$

$a^2 = 16$

$a = \pm 4$ *[1 mark]*

And remember that part a) tells you that $a > 0$, so $a = 4$.
[1 mark]

3 a) Look up the trapezium formula in the nice formula booklet they give you:

$\int_a^b y\,dx \approx \frac{1}{2}h[(y_0 + y_n) + 2(y_1 + y_2 + ...y_{n-1})]$

and remember that n is the number of intervals (in this case 4), and h is the width of each strip:

$h = \frac{b - a}{n} = \frac{2 - 0}{4} = 0.5$ *[1 mark]*

Work out each y value:

$x_0 = 0 \qquad y_0 = 2^{0^2} = 2^0 = 1$

$x_1 = 0.5 \qquad y_1 = 2^{0.5^2} = 2^{0.25} = 1.189\,(3\,d.p.)$

$x_2 = 1 \qquad y_2 = 2^{1^2} = 2^1 = 2$

$x_3 = 1.5 \qquad y_3 = 2^{1.5^2} = 2^{2.25} = 4.757\ (3\,d.p)$

$x_4 = 2 \qquad y_4 = 2^{2^2} = 2^4 = 16$ *[1 mark]*

And put all these values into the formula:

$\int_0^2 2^{x^2}dx$

$\approx \frac{1}{2} \times 0.5[(1 + 16) + 2(1.189 + 2 + 4.757)]$ *[1 mark]*

$= \frac{1}{4}(17 + 15.892)$

$= 8.22\,(3\,s.f.)$ *[1 mark]*

b) Look at the diagram of the curve — it's U-shaped. A trapezium on each strip goes higher than the curve and has a greater area than that under the curve. *[1 mark]*
So the trapezium rule gives an overestimate for the area.
[1 mark]

4 a) First put the two known terms into the formula for the nth term of a geometric series: $u_n = ar^{n-1}$:

$u_3 = ar^2 = \frac{5}{2} \qquad u_6 = ar^5 = \frac{5}{16}$

Divide the expression for u_6 by the expression for u_3 to get an expression just containing r and solve it:

$\frac{ar^5}{ar^2} = \frac{5}{16} \div \frac{5}{2} \Rightarrow r^3 = \frac{5}{16} \times \frac{2}{5} = \frac{10}{80}$ *[1 mark]*

$r^3 = \frac{1}{8} \qquad r = \sqrt[3]{\frac{1}{8}} \qquad r = \frac{1}{2}$ *[1 mark]*

Put this value back into the expression for u_3 to find a:

$a\left(\frac{1}{2}\right)^2 = \frac{5}{2} \Rightarrow \frac{a}{4} = \frac{5}{2} \Rightarrow a = 10$ *[1 mark]*

The nth term is $u_n = ar^{n-1}$, where $r = \frac{1}{2}$ and $a = 10$

$u_n = 10 \times \left(\frac{1}{2}\right)^{n-1} = 10 \times \frac{1}{2^{n-1}} = \frac{10}{2^{n-1}}$ *[1 mark]*

b) This asks you to find the sum of the first ten terms, so input the known values of n, a and r (from part a)) into the formula for the sum of the first n terms:

$S_n = \frac{a(1 - r^n)}{1 - r}, \ S_{10} = \frac{10(1 - (\frac{1}{2})^{10})}{1 - \frac{1}{2}}$ *[1 mark]*

$= 10 \times 2 \times \left(1 - \frac{1}{2^{10}}\right)$

$= 20\left(1 - \frac{1}{1024}\right) = 20 \times \frac{1023}{1024} = 5 \times \frac{1023}{256}$ *[1 mark]*

$= \frac{5115}{256}$ *[1 mark]*

c) Just pop the known values of a and r into the formula for the sum to infinity:

$S_\infty = \frac{a}{1 - r} = \frac{10}{1 - \frac{1}{2}}$ *[1 mark]*

$= 10 \div \frac{1}{2} = 10 \times 2$

$= 20$ *[1 mark]*

5 a) Use the cosine rule: $a^2 = b^2 + c^2 - 2bc\,cosA$, where $b = 10$, $c = 7$ and angle $A = 60°$:

$a^2 = 10^2 + 7^2 - 2 \times 10 \times 7 \times \cos 60°$ *[1 mark]*

$\Rightarrow a^2 = 149 - 140\cos 60°$

$\Rightarrow a^2 = 149 - 140(0.5)$

$\Rightarrow a^2 = 79$

$\Rightarrow a = \sqrt{79} = 8.89$ cm to 3 s.f.   *[1 mark]*

b) Now you can use the sine rule to find the angles:

$\frac{a}{sinA} = \frac{b}{sinB} = \frac{c}{sinC}$

θ is the angle opposite the 10 cm side. So if we call the 10 cm side 'side b', then θ = angle B. Putting the known values into the sine rule gives:

$\frac{\sqrt{79}}{\sin 60°} = \frac{10}{\sin \theta}$ *[1 mark]*

$\sin \theta = \frac{10 \times \sin 60°}{\sqrt{79}} = 0.9744$

$\Rightarrow \theta = \sin^{-1}0.9744 = 77.0°$ to 3 s.f.   *[1 mark]*

Now, you know 2 of the angles in the triangle, and as the angles in a triangle add up to 180°,

$\phi = 180 - 60 - 77 = 43°$ *[1 mark]*.

To summarise: $\theta = 77°$ and $\phi = 43°$.

Answers

6 a) (i) In the diagram, x is the adjacent side of a right-angled triangle with an angle θ and hypotenuse r — so use the cos formula:

$$\cos\theta = \frac{\text{adjacent}}{\text{hypotenuse}} = \frac{x}{r}$$
and so $x = r\cos\theta$ **[1 mark]**

(ii) As the stage is symmetrical, you know that distance y is the same on both triangles. Distance y is the opposite side of the right-angled triangle — so use the sine formula:

$$\sin\theta = \frac{\text{opposite}}{\text{hypotenuse}} = \frac{y}{r}$$
and so $y = r\sin\theta$ **[1 mark]**

b) Looking at the diagram, most of the perimeter is simple — $q + q + 2r$. But the top and curved lengths need a bit of thinking.
First the top length — you can see this is $2x$ so, using the expression for x found in a), you can write this as $2r\cos\theta$.
For the curved lengths — the shaded areas are sectors of circles, and the formula for the length of one arc is given by: $r\theta$

Now add them all up to get the total perimeter:
$q + q + 2r + 2r\cos\theta + r\theta + r\theta = 2[q + r(1 + \theta + \cos\theta)]$.

And do the same sort of thing for the area — break it down into a rectangle, a triangle and two sectors:
Area of rectangle = width × height = $2qr$

Area of triangle = $\frac{1}{2}$ × width × height = $\frac{1}{2}(2r\cos\theta)(r\sin\theta)$
$= r^2\cos\theta\sin\theta$

Area of 1 shaded sector = $\frac{1}{2}r^2\theta$

So the total area = $2qr + r^2\cos\theta\sin\theta + r^2\theta$
$= 2qr + r^2(\cos\theta\sin\theta + \theta)$.

[4 marks available — 1 mark for all individual lengths correct, 1 mark for all individual areas correct, 1 mark for each correct expression.]

Crumbs, that looked very intimidating. The best thing to do with questions like that is stay calm and break them into small chunks. And knowing all the formulas doesn't hurt...

c) Substitute the given values of P and θ into the equation for the perimeter: $P = 2[q + r(1 + \theta + \cos\theta)]$

$\Rightarrow 40 = 2\left[q + r\left(1 + \frac{\pi}{3} + \cos\frac{\pi}{3}\right)\right]$

$\Rightarrow 20 = q + r\left(\frac{3}{2} + \frac{\pi}{3}\right)$ **[1 mark]**

And then into the equation for the area:

$A = 2qr + r^2(\cos\theta\sin\theta + \theta)$

$\Rightarrow A = 2qr + r^2\left(\cos\frac{\pi}{3}\sin\frac{\pi}{3} + \frac{\pi}{3}\right)$

$= 2qr + r^2\left(\frac{\sqrt{3}}{4} + \frac{\pi}{3}\right)$ **[1 mark]**

To rearrange this formula for area into the form shown in the question, you need to get rid of q. Rearrange the perimeter formula to get an expression for q in terms of r, then substitute that into the area equation:

$q = 20 - r\left(\frac{3}{2} + \frac{\pi}{3}\right)$

$A = 2qr + r^2\left(\frac{\sqrt{3}}{4} + \frac{\pi}{3}\right)$

$= 2r\left[20 - r\left(\frac{3}{2} + \frac{\pi}{3}\right)\right] + r^2\left(\frac{\sqrt{3}}{4} + \frac{\pi}{3}\right)$

$= 40r - 2r^2\left(\frac{3}{2} + \frac{\pi}{3}\right) + r^2\left(\frac{\sqrt{3}}{4} + \frac{\pi}{3}\right)$

$= 40r - r^2\left[2\left(\frac{3}{2} + \frac{\pi}{3}\right) - \left(\frac{\sqrt{3}}{4} + \frac{\pi}{3}\right)\right]$ **[1 mark]**

And since $\left[2\left(\frac{3}{2} + \frac{\pi}{3}\right) - \left(\frac{\sqrt{3}}{4} + \frac{\pi}{3}\right)\right] = 3.614$ to 3 d.p.
this means: $A = 40r - 3.614r^2$ **[1 mark]**

7 a) (i) Remainder = f(–3) = $(-3)^3 - 6(-3)^2 - (-3) + 30$ **[1 mark]**
$= -48$ **[1 mark]**.

(ii) Remainder = $f\left(\frac{1}{4}\right) = \left(\frac{1}{64}\right) - 6\left(\frac{1}{16}\right) - \left(\frac{1}{4}\right) + 30$ **[1 mark]**
$= 29.4$ (3 s.f.) **[1 mark]**.

b) If $(x - 3)$ is a factor then f(3) = 0.
$f(3) = (3)^3 - 6(3)^2 - (3) + 30$ **[1 mark]**
$= 27 - 54 - 3 + 30 = 0$,
so $(x - 3)$ is a factor of f(x). **[1 mark]**

c) $(x - 3)$ is a factor, so divide $x^3 - 6x^2 - x + 30$ by $x - 3$:
$x^3 - 6x^2 - x + 30 - \underline{x^2}(x - 3) = x^3 - 6x^2 - x + 30 - x^3 + 3x^2$
$= -3x^2 - x + 30$.
$-3x^2 - x + 30 - (\underline{-3x})(x - 3) = -3x^2 - x + 30 + 3x^2 - 9x$
$= -10x + 30$. Finally $-10x + 30 - (\underline{-10})(x - 3) = 0$.
so $x^3 - 6x^2 - x + 30 = (x^2 - 3x - 10)(x - 3)$.

This is the method from p.54.

Factorising the quadratic expression gives:
$f(x) = (x - 5)(x + 2)(x - 3)$.

[4 marks available — 1 mark for dividing by x – 3 to find quadratic factor, 1 mark for correct quadratic factor, 1 mark for attempt to factorise quadratic, 1 mark for correct factorisation of quadratic.]

8 a) $\frac{1}{x^2}$ tends towards infinity as x gets closer to 0, and $\frac{1}{x^2}$ gets smaller as x gets bigger. So the graph looks like this:

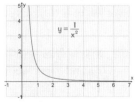

[1 mark]

b) $\int_1^\infty \frac{1}{x^2}dx = \int_1^\infty x^{-2}dx$

$= \left[\frac{x^{-1}}{-1}\right]_1^\infty = \left[-\frac{1}{x}\right]_1^\infty$ **[1 mark]**

$= (-0) - \left(-\frac{1}{1}\right) = 1$ **[1 mark]**

Answers

c) The tangent's gradient will be the same as the curve's gradient, so find $\frac{dy}{dx}$ at $x = 1$:

$y = \frac{1}{x^2} = x^{-2}$

$\frac{dy}{dx} = -2x^{-3} = -\frac{2}{x^3}$

when $x = 1$:

$= -\frac{2}{1^3} = -2$ **[1 mark]**

When $x = 1$, $y = \frac{1}{1^2} = 1$, so the tangent goes through the point (1, 1) and has a gradient of –2. Using the equation of a straight line: $y - y_1 = m(x - x_1)$, to find f(x):

$y - 1 = -2(x - 1)$

$y = -2x + 2 + 1$

$\Rightarrow f(x) = 3 - 2x$ **[1 mark]**

d) Find a value less than 1 for k.

Just do the integration normally, but write k instead of a number:

$\int_0^k f(x)\,dx = \int_0^k (3 - 2x)\,dx$

$= [3x - x^2]_0^k$

$= (3k - k^2) - 0$

$= 3k - k^2$

This integral has to be equal to 1, so you need to solve:

$3k - k^2 = 1$

$\Rightarrow k^2 - 3k + 1 = 0$ **[1 mark]**

This is a quadratic but it doesn't look like it's going to factorise, so using the quadratic formula:

$k = \frac{3 \pm \sqrt{(-3)^2 - 4 \times 1 \times 1}}{2 \times 1}$

$= \frac{3 \pm \sqrt{5}}{2}$ **[1 mark]**

The question asks for a value of less than 1 for k, but using surds. So use a calculator to find which is < 1 but leave in its surd form:

$\frac{3 + \sqrt{5}}{2} = 2.618$ $\frac{3 - \sqrt{5}}{2} = 0.382$

therefore $k = \frac{3 - \sqrt{5}}{2}$ **[1 mark]**

9 a) In an arithmetic sequence, the nth term is defined by the formula $a + (n - 1)d$. The 12th term is 79, so the equation is $79 = a + 11d$ **[1 mark]**, and the 16th term is 103, so the other equation is $103 = a + 15d$ **[1 mark]**. Solving these simultaneously (by taking the first equation away from the second) gives $24 = 4d$, so $d = 6$ **[1 mark]**. Putting this value of d into the first equation gives $79 = a + (11 \times 6)$, so $a = 13$ **[1 mark]**.

b) The formula to find the sum, S_n, is $S_n = \frac{n}{2}[2a + (n - 1)d]$ **[1 mark]**. Putting in the values of a and d from above gives the formula

$S_n = \frac{n}{2}[(2 \times 13) + 6(n - 1)]$ **[1 mark]**

$= \frac{n}{2}[20 + 6n]$ or $10n + 3n^2$ **[1 mark]**

c) $S_{15} = (10 \times 15) + 3(15^2)$

$= 150 + 675$

$= 825$ **[1 mark]**

Gee to the whizzle, I thought we'd never finish C2, but hurrah! Run for your lives, before the maths sucks you back in again...

Answers

S1 Section 1 — Representation of Data

Warm-up Questions

1)

Length of call	Lower class boundary (lcb)	Upper class boundary (ucb)	Class width	Frequency	Frequency density = Height of column
0 - 2	0	2.5	2.5	10	4
3 - 5	2.5	5.5	3	6	2
6 - 8	5.5	8.5	3	3	1
9 - 15	8.5	15.5	7	1	0.143

Lots of fiddly details here — a table helps you get them right.

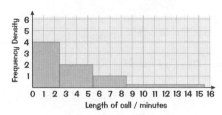

2) 12.8, 13.2, 13.5, 14.3, 14.3, 14.6, 14.8, 15.2, 15.9, 16.1, 16.1, 16.2, 16.3, 17.0, 17.2 (all in cm)

3) $\Sigma f = 16$, $\Sigma fx = 22$, so mean = 22 ÷ 16 = 1.375
Median position = 17 ÷ 2 = 8.5, so median = 1
Mode = 0.

4)

Speed	mid-class value x	Number of cars f	fx
30 - 34	32	12 (12)	384
35 - 39	37	37 (49)	1369
40 - 44	42	9	378
45 - 50	47.5	2	95
	Totals	60	2226

Estimated mean = 2226 ÷ 60 = <u>37.1 mph</u>
Median position is 61 ÷ 2 = 30.5.
This is in class 35 - 39.
30.5 – 12 = 18.5, so median is 18.5th value in class.
Class width = 5, so estimated median is:

$$34.5 + \left(18.5 \times \frac{5}{37}\right) = \underline{37\text{ mph}}$$

Modal class is <u>35 - 39 mph</u>.

Easy eh? It doesn't hurt to double-check your mid-class values though.

5) Put the 20 items of data in order:
1, 4, 5, 5, 5, 5, 5, 6, 6, 7, 7, 8, 10, 10, 12, 15, 20, 20, 30, 50
Then the median position is 10.5, and since the 10th and the 11th items are both 7, the median = <u>7</u>.
Lower quartile = <u>5</u>.
Upper quartile = (12 + 15) ÷ 2 = <u>13.5</u>.

6) Find the upper class boundaries and the cumulative frequencies:

Distance	Upper class boundary (ucb)	f	Cumulative frequency (CF)
< 0	0	0	0
0 - 2	2	10	10
2 - 4	4	5	15
4 - 6	6	3	18
6 - 8	8	2	20

Now draw the cumulative frequency diagram:

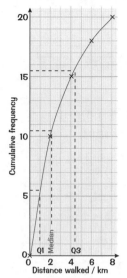

Now you can read off the values of the median (the 10.5th value) and the quartiles (the 5.5th and 15.5th values). This gives a value for the median of <u>2.1 km</u>, and values for Q_1 and Q_3 of 1.0 km and 4.3 km respectively. So the interquartile range is 4.3 – 1.0 = <u>3.3 km</u>.

Because you have grouped data, you could also use the 10th value for the median and the 5th and 15th values for the quartiles. Either would be okay in the exam, but make sure you understand why.

7) a) Mean $= \dfrac{11 + 12 + 14 + 17 + 21 + 23 + 27}{7}$

$= \dfrac{125}{7} = 17.9$ to 3 sig. fig.

b) $s.d. = \sqrt{\dfrac{11^2 + 12^2 + 14^2 + 17^2 + 21^2 + 23^2 + 27^2}{7} - \left(\dfrac{125}{7}\right)^2}$

$= \sqrt{30.98} = 5.57$ to 3 sig. fig.

Just numbers and a formula. Simple.

8)

Score	Mid-class value, x	x^2	f	fx	fx^2
100 - 106	103	10609	6	618	63654
107 - 113	110	12100	11	1210	133100
114 - 120	117	13689	22	2574	301158
121 - 127	124	15376	9	1116	138384
128 - 134	131	17161	2	262	34322
	Totals		50 (= Σf)	5780 (= Σfx)	670618 (= Σfx^2)

Mean $= \dfrac{5780}{50} = 115.6$

Variance $= \dfrac{670\,618}{50} - 115.6^2 = 49$

9) Let $y = x - 20$.
Then
$\bar{y} = \bar{x} - 20$ or $\bar{x} = \bar{y} + 20$
$\sum y = 125$ and $\sum y^2 = 221$
So $\bar{y} = \dfrac{125}{100} = 1.25$ and $\bar{x} = 1.25 + 20 = \underline{21.25}$

Variance of $y = \dfrac{221}{100} - 1.25^2 = 0.6475$,
and so s.d. of $y = 0.805$ to 3 sig. fig.
Therefore <u>s.d. of x = 0.805</u> to 3 sig. fig.

If you got in a muddle, look back at stuff about coding.

Answers

10)

Time	Mid-class x	$y = x - 35.5$	f	fy	fy^2
30 - 33	31.5	-4	3	-12	48
34 - 37	35.5	0	6	0	0
38 - 41	39.5	4	7	28	112
42 - 45	43.5	8	4	32	256
		Totals	20 (= Σf)	48 (= Σfy)	416 (= Σfy^2)

$\bar{y} = \frac{48}{20} = 2.4$

So $\bar{x} = \bar{y} + 35.5 = 2.4 + 35.5 = \underline{37.9 \text{ minutes}}$

Variance of $y = \frac{416}{20} - 2.4^2 = 15.04$,

and so s.d. of $y = 3.88$ minutes, to 3 sig. fig.

But s.d. of x = s.d. of y,

and so s.d. of $x = \underline{3.88 \text{ minutes}}$, to 3 sig. fig.

Even if you did the coding differently, your answer should be the same.

Exam Questions

1 a) Let $y = x - 30$.

$\bar{y} = \frac{228}{19} = 12$ and so $\bar{x} = \bar{y} + 30 = \underline{42}$ *[1 mark]*

Variance of $y = \frac{3040}{19} - 12^2 = 16$ *[1 mark]*,

and so s.d. of $y = 4$.

But s.d. of x = s.d. of y, and so s.d. of $x = \underline{4}$ *[1 mark]*

b) $\bar{x} = \frac{\sum x}{19} = 42$

And so $\sum x = 42 \times 19 = \underline{798}$ *[1 mark]*

Variance of $x = \frac{\sum x^2}{19} - \bar{x}^2 = \frac{\sum x^2}{19} - 42^2 = 16$ *[1 mark]*

And so $\sum x^2 = (16 + 42^2) \times 19 = \underline{33\,820}$ *[1 mark]*

A bit harder...

c) New $\sum x = 798 + 32 = \underline{830}$ *[1 mark]*

So new $\bar{x} = \frac{830}{20} = \underline{41.5}$ *[1 mark]*

New $\sum x^2 = 33\,820 + 32^2 = \underline{34\,844}$ *[1 mark]*

So new variance $= \frac{34\,844}{20} - 41.5^2 = 19.95$

and new s.d. $= \underline{4.47}$ to 3 sig. fig. *[1 mark]*

2 a) (i) Times = 2, 3, 4, 4, 5, 5, 5, 7, 10, 12

Median position = 5.5, so median = 5 minutes
[1 mark]

(ii) Lower quartile = 4 minutes *[1 mark]*

Upper quartile = 7 minutes *[1 mark]*

b) Worker A

Worker B

0 2 4 6 8 10 12 time in mins

*[6 marks available overall — 1 mark for each
median in the right place, 1 mark for each pair of
quartiles shown correctly, and 1 mark for each pair
of lines showing the extremes correctly drawn.]*

c) Various statements could be made,
e.g. the times for Worker B are longer than those for Worker A, on average.
The IQR for both workers is the same — generally they both work with the same consistency.

The range for Worker A is larger than that for Worker B. Worker A had a few items he/she could iron very quickly and a few which took a long time.
[1 mark for any sensible answer]

d) Worker A would be better to employ. The median time is less than for Worker B, and the upper quartile is less than the median of Worker B. Worker A would generally iron more items in a given time than worker B.
[1 mark for any sensible answer]

Don't be put off by these questions — you just have to show you understand what the data is telling you

3 a) $\bar{a} = \frac{60.3}{20} = 3.015\,g$ *[1 mark]*

b) Variance of brand A $= \frac{219}{20} - 3.015^2$ *[1 mark]*

$= 1.860\,g^2$ *[1 mark]*

So s.d. of brand A $= 1.36\,g$ to 3 sig. fig. *[1 mark]*

c) Brand A chocolate drops are heavier on average than brand B. Brand B chocolate drops are much closer to their mean weight than brand A.
[1 mark for each of 2 sensible statements]

"Mmm, chocolate drops" does not count as a sensible statement...

d) Mean of A and B $= \frac{\sum a + \sum b}{50} = \frac{60.3 + (30 \times 2.95)}{50}$

$= 2.976\,g$ *[1 mark]*

$\frac{\sum b^2}{30} - 2.95^2 = 1$, and so $\sum b^2 = 291.075$ *[1 mark]*

Variance of A and B $= \frac{\sum a^2 + \sum b^2}{50} - 2.976^2$

$= \frac{219 + 291.075}{50} - 2.976^2$

$= 1.3449$ *[1 mark]*

So $s.d. = \sqrt{1.3449} = 1.16\,g$ to 3 sig. fig. *[1 mark]*

Work through each step carefully so you don't make silly mistakes and lose any lovely marks.

4 a) Total number of people = 38
Median position = (38 + 1) ÷ 2 = 19.5 *[1 mark]*
19th value = 15; 20th value = 16,
so median = $\underline{15.5 \text{ hits}}$ *[1 mark]*.
Mode = $\underline{15 \text{ hits}}$ *[1 mark]*

b) The value of 25 looks like it could be an outlier. The median is less affected by outliers than the mean, so it's a better measure of location when the data set includes outliers *[1 mark]*.

c)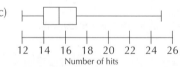

12 14 16 18 20 22 24 26
Number of hits

[1 mark]

Box-and-whisker plots... everyone's favourite.

d) If 25 was removed then the right-hand 'tail' of the box plot would be much shorter, and the distribution would be more symmetrical *[1 mark]*.

5 a)

Profit	Class width	Frequency	Frequency density = Height of column
4.5 - 5.0	0.5	24	48
5.0 - 5.5	0.5	26	52
5.5 - 6.0	0.5	21	42
6.0 - 6.5	0.5	19	38
6.5 - 8.0	1.5	10	6.67

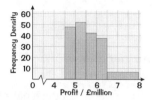

[1 mark for correct axes, plus 2 marks if all bars drawn correctly, or 1 mark for at least 3 bars correct.]

b) For example:
The modal profit is between £5 million and £5.5 million.
The range of the profits is at most £3.5 million.
Businesses with profits over £6.5 million are much less common than those making less than £6.5 million.
[1 mark per sensible comment, up to a maximum of 2.]

Not too tricky — not too tricky at all.

6 a) There are 30 males, so median is in 31 ÷ 2 = 15.5th position. Take the mean of the 15th and 16th readings to get median = (62 + 65) ÷ 2 = 63.5 *[1 mark]*

b) The female median is 64.5 (halfway between the 8th and 9th readings). The female median is higher than the male median. The females scored better than the males on average.
Female range = 79 – 55 = 24.
Male range = 79 – 43 = 36
The female range is less than the male range. Their scores are more consistent than the males'.
[Up to 2 marks available for any sensible comments]

7 Find the total area underneath the histogram using the grid squares *[1 mark]*:
2 + 1.5 + 2 + 2 + 1.5 + 4 + 5 + 3 + 4 = 25 *[1 mark]*
So each grid square represents 2 lions *[1 mark]*.
The number of squares for lengths above 220 cm is 7 *[1 mark]*, which represents 7 × 2 = 14 lions *[1 mark]*.

S1 Section 2 — Probability

Warm-up Questions

1) a) The sample space would be as below:

		Dice				
		1	2	3	4	5	6
Coin	H	2	4	6	8	10	12
	T	5	6	7	8	9	10

b) There are 12 outcomes in total, and 9 of these are more than 5, so P(score > 5) = 9/12 = 3/4

c) There are 6 outcomes which have a tail showing, and 3 of these are even, so P(even score given that you throw a tail) = 3/6 = 1/2

Hmm, a bit fiddly but not too bad.

2) a) 20% of the people eat chips, and 10% of these is 2% — so 2% eat both chips and sausages.
Now you can draw the Venn diagram:

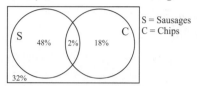

By reading the numbers in the appropriate sets from the diagram you can see...

b) 18% eat chips but not sausages.

c) 18% + 48% = 66% eat chips or sausages, but not both.

These questions do make you work up an appetite... mmm, sausages...

3) Draw a sample space diagram

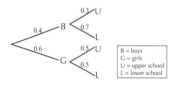

There are 36 outcomes altogether.

a) 15 outcomes are prime (since 2, 3, 5, 7 and 11 are prime), so P(prime) = 15/36 = 5/12

b) 7 outcomes are square numbers (4 and 9), so P(square) = 7/36

c) Being prime and a square number are exclusive events, so P(prime or square) = 15/36 + 7/36 = 22/36 = 11/18

You have to think outside the probability box for this one, but it's basic maths really.

4) a)

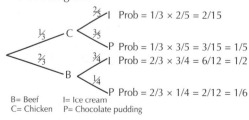

b) Choosing an upper school pupil means either 'boy and upper' or 'girl and upper'.
P(boy and upper) = 0.4 × 0.3 = 0.12.
P(girl and upper) = 0.6 × 0.5 = 0.30.
So P(Upper) = 0.12 + 0.30 = 0.42.

5) Draw a tree diagram:

2/5 I   Prob = 1/3 × 2/5 = 2/15
1/3 C
3/5 P   Prob = 1/3 × 3/5 = 3/15 = 1/5
3/4 I   Prob = 2/3 × 3/4 = 6/12 = 1/2
2/3 B
1/4 P   Prob = 2/3 × 1/4 = 2/12 = 1/6

B= Beef   I= Ice cream
C= Chicken   P= Chocolate pudding

Answers

a) P(chicken or ice cream but not both) = P(C∩P) + P(B∩I)
   = 1/5 + 1/2 = 7/10

b) P(ice cream) = P(C∩I) + P(B∩I) = 2/15 + 1/2 = 19/30

c) P(chicken|ice cream) = P(C∩I) ÷ P(I)

   = (2/15) ÷ (19/30) = 4/19

   You aren't asked to draw a tree diagram, but it makes it a lot easier if you do.

6) STATISTICS has 10 letters, 3 repeated S's, 3 repeated T's and 2 repeated I's.
   This gives 10! ÷ (3! × 3! × 2!) = 50 400 arrangements.

7) a) The 6 people can sit in 6! = 720 ways.

   b) Put Mr & Mrs Brown together as one object — you can do this in two ways. Then there are 5 objects to rearrange (which can be done in 5! ways) and for each of these, there are 2 "Brown arrangements".
      This means there are 2 × 5! = 240 ways to seat the Browns together.

   c) The number of ways the Browns sit apart is
      720 – 240 = 480. So P(Browns sit apart) = 480 ÷ 720 = 2/3

Exam Questions

1 a) The order in which the team members are picked doesn't matter, so we need a combination:

   $${}^{10}C_6 = \binom{10}{6} = \frac{10!}{4!6!} = \frac{3\,628\,800}{24 \times 720} = 210$$ *[1 mark]*

   b) The probability of a team of 3 boys and 3 girls is
      $\frac{\text{number of possible teams of 3 boys and 3 girls}}{\text{total number of possible teams}}$ *[1 mark]*

      The number of possible teams of 3 boys and 3 girls
      = (number of ways of picking 3 boys from 4)
         × (number of ways of picking 3 girls from 6)
      = ${}^4C_3 \times {}^6C_3$
      = 4 × 20 = 80 *[1 mark]*

      So P(3 boys and 3 girls) = $\frac{80}{210}$
      = 0.381 (to 3 sig.fig.) *[1 mark]*

   c) There are 6! = 720 ways to arrange the team. Treat the captain and vice-captain as one object, because you're interested in when they sit together.
      So now we have to arrange 5 objects —
      this can be done in 5! = 120 ways *[1 mark]*.
      The captain and vice-captain can be swapped around in each of these arrangements, so multiply this by 2.
      The total number of ways to arrange the team with the captain and vice captain sitting together is
      120 × 2 = 240 *[1 mark]*. So the probability that the captain and vice captain sit together is = $\frac{240}{720} = \frac{1}{3}$ *[1 mark]*.

2 a)

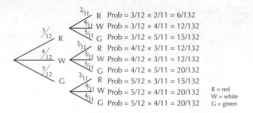

   R = red
   W = white
   G = green

   [3 marks available — 1 mark for each set of 3 branches on the right-hand side correct]

   b) The second counter is green means one of three outcomes 'red then green' or 'white then green' or 'green then green'.
      So P(2nd is green) = 15/132 + 20/132 + 20/132 *[1 mark]*
      = 55/132 = 5/12 *[1 mark]*

   c) For both to be red there's only one outcome: 'red then red' *[1 mark]*. P(both red) = 6/132 = 1/22 *[1 mark]*

   d) 'Both same colour' is the complementary event of 'not both same colour'. So P(not same colour) = 1 – P(both same colour) *[1 mark]*. Both same colour is either R and R or W and W or G and G.
      P(not same colour) = 1 – [6/132 + 12/132 + 20/132]
      [1 mark] = 1 – 38/132 = 94/132 = 47/66 *[1 mark]*
      (Alternatively, 1 mark for showing P(RW or RG or WR or WG or GR or GW), 1 mark for adding the 6 correct probabilities and 1 mark for the correct answer.)

   Ooh, that was a long one. Shouldn't be too tricky though, as long as your tree diagram was nice and clear.

3 a) (i) J and K are independent, so
         P(J ∩ K) = P(J) × P(K) = 0.7 × 0.1 = 0.07 *[1 mark]*

      (ii) P(J ∪ K) = P(J) + P(K) – P(J ∩ K) *[1 mark]*
         = 0.7 + 0.1 – 0.07 = 0.73 *[1 mark]*

   b) Drawing a quick Venn Diagram often helps:

   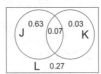

   P(L|K') = P(L ∩ K') ÷ P(K')
   Now L ∩ K' = L — think about it — all of L is contained in K', so L ∩ K' (the 'bits in both L and K') are just the bits in L.
   Therefore P(L ∩ K') = P(L) = 1 – P(K ∪ J) = 1 – 0.73 = 0.27
   [1 mark]
   P(K') = 1 – P(K) = 1 – 0.1 = 0.9 *[1 mark]*
   And so P(L|K') = 0.27 ÷ 0.9 = 0.3 *[1 mark]*

   That was a bit complicated — you just need to put your thinking cap on and DON'T PANIC.

Answers

4   Draw a tree diagram:

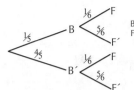

B = Biased dice shows 6
F = Fair dice shows 6

a) P(B′) = 0.8 *[1 mark]*

b) Either at least one of the dice shows a 6 or neither of them do, so these are complementary events. Call F the event 'the fair dice shows a 6'.
Then P(F ∪ B) = 1 – P(F′ ∩ B′) *[1 mark]*
= 1 – (4/5 × 5/6) = 1 – 2/3 = 1/3 *[1 mark]*

c) P(exactly one 6 | at least one 6)
= P(exactly one 6 ∩ at least one 6) ÷ P(at least one 6).
The next step might be a bit easier to get your head round if you draw a Venn diagram:

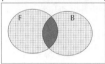

'exactly one 6' ∩ 'at least one 6' = 'exactly one 6'
(Look at the diagram — 'exactly one 6' is the cross-hatched area, and 'at least one 6' is the cross-hatched area <u>plus</u> the grey bit. So the bit in common to both is just the cross-hatched area.)
Now, that means P(exactly one 6 ∩ at least one 6) =
P(B∩F′) + P(B′∩F) — this is the cross-hatched area in the Venn diagram,
i.e. P(exactly one 6 ∩ at least one 6) = (1/5 × 5/6) + (4/5 × 1/6) = 9/30 = 3/10 (using the fact that B and F are independent) *[1 mark]*
P(at least one 6) = 1/3 (from b)).

And all of this means P(exactly one 6 | at least one 6)
= 3/10 ÷ 1/3 *[1 mark]* = 9/10 *[1 mark]*

Blauuurgh — the noise of a mind boggling. Part c is difficult to get your head round, but it's just a matter of remembering the right conditional probability formula, breaking it down into separate parts and working through it step by step. Yay.

S1 Section 3 —
Discrete Random Variables

Warm-up Questions

1) a) All the probabilities have to add up to 1.
So $0.5 + k + k + 3k = 0.5 + 5k = 1$, i.e. $5k = 0.5$, i.e. $k = 0.1$.

   b) P(Y < 2) = P(Y = 0) + P(Y = 1) = 0.5 + 0.1 = 0.6.

2) a) As always, the probabilities have to add up to 1, so
$$k = 1 - \left(\frac{1}{6} + \frac{1}{2} + \frac{5}{24}\right) = 1 - \frac{21}{24} = \frac{3}{24} = \frac{1}{8}$$

   b) $E(X) = \left(1 \times \frac{1}{6}\right) + \left(2 \times \frac{1}{2}\right) + \left(3 \times \frac{1}{8}\right) + \left(4 \times \frac{5}{24}\right)$
$$= \frac{4 + 24 + 9 + 20}{24} = \frac{57}{24} = \frac{19}{8}$$

$E(X^2) = \left(1^2 \times \frac{1}{6}\right) + \left(2^2 \times \frac{1}{2}\right) + \left(3^2 \times \frac{1}{8}\right) + \left(4^2 \times \frac{5}{24}\right)$
$$= \frac{4 + 48 + 27 + 80}{24} = \frac{159}{24} = \frac{53}{8}$$

$Var(X) = E(X^2) - [E(X)]^2 = \frac{53}{8} - \left(\frac{19}{8}\right)^2$
$$= \frac{424 - 361}{64} = \frac{63}{64}$$

3) a) E(X) = (1 × 0.1) + (2 × 0.2) + (3 × 0.25) + (4 × 0.2)
            + (5 × 0.1) + (6 × 0.15) = 3.45

   b) Var(X) = E(X²) – (E(X))²
E(X²) = (1 × 0.1) + (4 × 0.2) + (9 × 0.25) + (16 × 0.2)
        + (25 × 0.1) + (36 × 0.15) = 14.25
So Var(X) = 14.25 – 3.45² = 2.3475

4)   P(X = 15) = 0.9¹⁴ × 0.1 = 0.0229 (to 3 sig. fig.).
The expected value of X is 1 ÷ 0.1 = 10.

5) a) $P(5 \text{ heads}) = 0.5^5 \times 0.5^5 \times \binom{10}{5}$
$$= 0.5^{10} \times \frac{10!}{5!5!} = 0.246 \text{ (to 3 sig.fig.).}$$

   b) $P(9 \text{ heads}) = 0.5^9 \times 0.5 \times \binom{10}{9}$
$$= 0.5^{10} \times \frac{10!}{9!1!} = 0.00977 \text{ (to 3 sig.fig.).}$$

6) a) Binomial — there are a fixed number of independent trials (30) with two possible results ('prime' / 'not prime'), a constant probability of success, and the random variable is the total number of successes.

   b) Binomial — there are a fixed number of independent trials (however many students are in the class) with two possible results ('heads' / 'tails'), a constant probability of success, and the random variable is the total number of successes.

   c) Not binomial — the probability of being dealt an ace changes each time, since the total number of cards decreases as each card is dealt.

   d) Not binomial — the number of trials is not fixed.

It's weird to have to write actual sentences in a maths exam, but be ready for it.

7) a) Use tables with $n = 10$ and $p = 0.5$.
If X represents the number of heads, then:
P(X ≥ 5) = 1 – P(X < 5) = 1 – P(X ≤ 4)
= 1 – 0.3770 = 0.6230

   b) P(X ≥ 9) = 1 – P(X < 9) = 1 – P(X ≤ 8)
            = 1 – 0.9893 = 0.0107

You do have to be prepared to monkey around with the numbers the tables give you.

Answers

8) a) You can't use tables here (because they don't include $p = 0.27$), so you have to use the probability function.

$$P(X = 4) = \binom{14}{4} \times 0.27^4 \times (1 - 0.27)^{10}$$
$$= 0.229 \text{ (to 3 sig.fig.)}$$

b) $P(X < 2) = P(X = 0) + P(X = 1)$
$$= \binom{14}{0} \times 0.27^0 \times (1 - 0.27)^{14}$$
$$+ \binom{14}{1} \times 0.27^1 \times (1 - 0.27)^{13}$$
$$= 0.012204... + 0.063195...$$
$$= 0.0754 \text{ (to 3 sig.fig.)}$$

c) $P(5 < X \le 8) = P(X = 6) + P(X = 7) + P(X = 8)$
$$= \binom{14}{6} \times 0.27^6 \times (1 - 0.27)^8$$
$$+ \binom{14}{7} \times 0.27^7 \times (1 - 0.27)^7$$
$$+ \binom{14}{8} \times 0.27^8 \times (1 - 0.27)^6$$
$$= 0.093825... + 0.039660... + 0.012835...$$
$$= 0.146 \text{ (to 3 sig.fig.)}$$

9) For parts a)-c), use tables with $n = 25$ and $p = 0.15$.

a) $P(X \le 3) = 0.4711$

b) $P(X \le 7) = 0.9745$

c) $P(X \le 15) = 1.0000$

For parts d)-f), use tables with $n = 16$ and $p = 0.65$.

d) $P(Y \le 3) = 0.0002$

e) $P(Y \le 7) = 0.0671$

f) $P(Y \le 16) = 1$ (since 16 is the maximum possible value).
Make sure you get lots of practice at all this.

10) From tables:

a) $P(X \le 15) = 0.9997$

b) $P(X < 4) = P(X \le 3) = 0.7202$

c) $P(X > 7) = 1 - P(X \le 7) = 1 - 0.0639 = 0.9361$

d) $P(X \ge 10) = 1 - P(X < 10) = 1 - P(X \le 9)$
$$= 1 - 0.4417 = 0.5583$$

e) $P(X = 20) = P(X \le 20) - P(X \le 19)$
$$= 0.4112 - 0.2696 = 0.1416$$

f) $P(X = 7) = P(X \le 7) - P(X \le 6) = 0.4744 - 0.2241 = 0.2503$

Or you could use the formula for parts e) and f):
$$P(X = r) = \binom{n}{r} \times p^r \times (1 - p)^{n-r}$$

11) a) mean = $20 \times 0.4 = 8$; variance = $20 \times 0.4 \times 0.6 = 4.8$

b) mean = $40 \times 0.15 = 6$; variance = $40 \times 0.15 \times 0.85 = 5.1$

c) mean = $25 \times 0.45 = 11.25$;
variance = $25 \times 0.45 \times 0.55 = 6.1875$

d) mean = $50 \times 0.8 = 40$; variance = $50 \times 0.8 \times 0.2 = 8$

e) mean = $30 \times 0.7 = 21$; variance = $30 \times 0.7 \times 0.3 = 6.3$

f) mean = $45 \times 0.012 = 0.54$;
variance = $45 \times 0.012 \times 0.988 = 0.53352$

Exam Questions

1 a) $P(X = 1) = a$, $P(X = 2) = 2a$, $P(X = 3) = 3a$.
Therefore the total probability is $3a + 2a + a = 6a$.
This must equal 1, so $a = \frac{1}{6}$. *[1 mark]*

b) $E(X) = \left(1 \times \frac{1}{6}\right) + \left(2 \times \frac{2}{6}\right) + \left(3 \times \frac{3}{6}\right) = \frac{1 + 4 + 9}{6}$ *[1 mark]*
$= \frac{7}{3}$ *[1 mark]*

c) $E(X^2) = Var(X) + [E(X)]^2 = \frac{5}{9} + \left(\frac{7}{3}\right)^2 = \frac{5 + 49}{9}$ *[1 mark]*
$= \frac{54}{9} = 6$ *[1 mark]*

2 a) The probability of getting 3 heads is: $\frac{1}{2} \times \frac{1}{2} \times \frac{1}{2} = \frac{1}{8}$
[1 mark]

The probability of getting 2 heads is: $3 \times \frac{1}{2} \times \frac{1}{2} \times \frac{1}{2} = \frac{3}{8}$
(multiply by 3 because any of the three coins could be the tail — the order in which the heads and the tail occur isn't important).
[1 mark]

Similarly the probability of getting 1 head is:
$3 \times \frac{1}{2} \times \frac{1}{2} \times \frac{1}{2} = \frac{3}{8}$

And the probability of getting no heads is $\frac{1}{2} \times \frac{1}{2} \times \frac{1}{2} = \frac{1}{8}$

So the probability of 1 or no heads $= \frac{3}{8} + \frac{1}{8} = \frac{1}{2}$ *[1 mark]*

Hence the probability distribution of X is:

x	20p	10p	*nothing*
$P(X = x)$	$\frac{1}{8}$	$\frac{3}{8}$	$\frac{1}{2}$

[1 mark]

b) You need the probability that X >10p *[1 mark]*
This is just $P(X = 20p) = \frac{1}{8}$ *[1 mark]*
Easy peasy. The difficult question is — why would anyone play such a rubbish game?

3 a) (i) $P(X < 8) = P(X \le 7) = 0.5618$ *[1 mark]*

(ii) $P(X = 5) = P(X \le 5) - P(X \le 4)$ *[1 mark]*
$= 0.1582 - 0.0573 = 0.1009$ *[1 mark]*

Or you could use the probability function for part (ii):
$$P(X = 5) = \binom{12}{5} \times 0.6^5 \times 0.4^7 = 0.1009$$

(iii) $P(3 < X \le 7) = P(X$ is greater than 3 *and* less than or equal to 7) $= P(X \le 7) - P(X \le 3)$ *[1 mark]*
$= 0.5618 - 0.0153$ *[1 mark]*
$= 0.5465$ *[1 mark]*

b) (i) $P(Y = 4) = 0.8^4 \times 0.2^7 \times \frac{11!}{4!7!}$ *[1 mark]*
$= 0.00173$ (to 3 sig. fig.) *[1 mark]*

(ii) $E(Y) = 11 \times 0.8 = 8.8$ *[1 mark]*

(iii) $Var(Y) = 11 \times 0.8 \times 0.2 = 1.76$ *[1 mark]*

4 a) When you throw two dice, there are 36 possible outcomes and 6 of these will be doubles, which means that
P(throw a double) $= \frac{6}{36} = \frac{1}{6}$. So if X is the random variable 'number of throws till you get a double', then
$X \sim \text{Geo}(\frac{1}{6})$ *[1 mark].*
Then the mean number of throws needed to start the game is $1 \div \frac{1}{6} = 6$ *[1 mark].*

Answers

b) (i) $P(X = 4) = \left(\frac{5}{6}\right)^3 \times \frac{1}{6} = \frac{125}{1296}$ *[1 mark]*

$= 0.0965$ (to 3 sig.fig.) *[1 mark]*.

(ii) $P(X \geq 3) = 1 - P(X = 1) - P(X = 2)$ *[1 mark]*

$= 1 - \frac{1}{6} - \frac{5}{6} \times \frac{1}{6} = \frac{25}{36}$ *[1 mark]*

$= 0.694$ (to 3 sig.fig.) *[1 mark]*.

5 a) (i) Let X represent the number of apples that contain a maggot. Then $X \sim B(20, 0.15)$ *[1 mark]*.

$P(X < 6) = P(X \leq 5) = 0.9327$ *[1 mark]*

(ii) $P(X > 2) = 1 - P(X \leq 2)$ *[1 mark]*

$= 1 - 0.4049 = 0.5951$ *[1 mark]*

(iii) $P(X = 7) = P(X \leq 7) - P(X \leq 6)$ *[1 mark]*

$= 0.9941 - 0.9781 = 0.0160$ *[1 mark]*

Or you could use the probability function for part (iii):

$P(X = 7) = \binom{20}{7} \times 0.15^7 \times 0.85^{13} = 0.0160$

b) The probability that a crate contains more than 2 apples with maggots is 0.5951 (from part a) (ii)).

So define a random variable Y, where Y is the number of crates that contain more than 2 apples with maggots.

Then $Y \sim B(3, 0.5951)$ *[1 mark]*.

You need to find $P(Y = 2) + P(Y = 3)$. This is:

$0.5951^2 \times (1 - 0.5951) \times \binom{3}{2}$

$+ 0.5951^3 \times (1 - 0.5951)^0 \times \binom{3}{3}$ *[1 mark]*

$= 0.4302 + 0.2108 = 0.641$(to 3 d.p.) *[1 mark]*

6 a) (i) The probability of Simon being able to solve each crossword needs to remain the same *[1 mark]*, and all the outcomes need to be independent (i.e. Simon solving or not solving a puzzle one day should not affect whether he will be able to solve it on another day) *[1 mark]*.

(ii) The total number of puzzles he solves (or the number he fails to solve) *[1 mark]*.

b) $P(X = 4) = p^4 \times (1 - p)^{14} \times \frac{18!}{4!14!}$ *[1 mark]*

$P(X = 5) = p^5 \times (1 - p)^{13} \times \frac{18!}{5!13!}$ *[1 mark]*

So $p^4 \times (1 - p)^{14} \times \frac{18!}{4!14!} = p^5 \times (1 - p)^{13} \times \frac{18!}{5!13!}$ *[1 mark]*

Dividing by $p^4, (1 - p)^{13}$ and $\frac{18!}{4!13!}$ gives:

$\frac{1 - p}{14} = \frac{p}{5}$ *[1 mark]*, or $5 = 19p$.

This means $p = \frac{5}{19}$ *[1 mark]*.

S1 Section 4 — Bivariate Data

Warm-up Questions

1) a)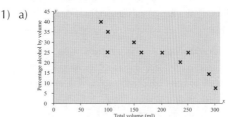

b) First you need to find these values:

$\sum x = 1880, \sum y = 247, \sum x^2 = 410\,400,$
$\sum y^2 = 6899$ and $\sum xy = 40\,600.$

Then put these values into the PMCC formula:

$$\frac{40\,600 - \dfrac{[1880][247]}{10}}{\sqrt{\left(410\,400 - \dfrac{[1880]^2}{10}\right)\left(6899 - \dfrac{[247]^2}{10}\right)}}$$

$$= \frac{40\,600 - 46\,436}{\sqrt{(410\,400 - 353\,440)(6899 - 6100.9)}}$$

$$= \frac{-5836}{\sqrt{56\,960 \times 798.1}} = \frac{-5836}{6742.3865} = -0.866 \text{ (to 3 sig.fig.)}$$

c) The PMCC tells you that there is a strong negative correlation between drink volume and alcohol concentration — cocktails with smaller volumes tend to have higher concentrations of alcohol.

Don't panic about that nasty ol' PMCC equation. You need to know how to USE it, but they give you the formula in the exam, so you don't need to REMEMBER it. Hurrah.

2) a) **Independent**: the annual number of sunny days
Dependent: the annual number of volleyball-related injuries

b) **Independent**: the annual number of rainy days
Dependent: the annual number of Monopoly-related injuries

c) **Independent**: a person's disposable income
Dependent: a person's spending on luxuries

d) **Independent**: the number of cups of tea drunk per day
Dependent: the number of trips to the loo per day

e) **Independent**: the number of festival tickets sold
Dependent: the number of pairs of Wellington boots bought

3) a) (i) $S_{xx} = 26\,816.78 - \dfrac{517.4^2}{10} = 46.504$

(ii) $S_{xy} = 57\,045.5 - \dfrac{517.4 \times 1099}{10} = 183.24$

b) $b = \dfrac{S_{xy}}{S_{xx}} = \dfrac{183.24}{46.504} = 3.94$

c) $a = \bar{y} - b\bar{x}$, where $\bar{y} = \dfrac{\sum y}{10} = 109.9$

and $\bar{x} = \dfrac{\sum x}{10} = 51.74$

So $a = 109.9 - 3.94 \times 51.74 = -94.0$

d) The equation of the regression line is: $y = 3.94x - 94.0$

Answers

e) When $x = 60$, the regression line gives an estimate for y of:
$y = 3.94 \times 60 - 94.0 = 142.4$ g

f) This estimate might not be very reliable because it uses an x-value from outside the range of the original data.
It is extrapolation.

You'll be given the equations for finding a regression line — but you still need to know how to use them, otherwise the formula booklet will just be a blur of incomprehensible squiggles. Oh, and you need to practise USING them of course...

4)

Physics	54	34	23	57	56	58	13	65	69	52
English	16	73	89	83	23	81	56	62	61	37
Physics rank	6	8	9	4	5	3	10	2	1	7
English rank	10	4	1	2	9	3	7	5	6	8
d	4	4	8	2	4	0	3	3	5	1
d^2	16	16	64	4	16	0	9	9	25	1

So $\sum d^2 = 160$, and

$r_s = 1 - \dfrac{6\sum d^2}{n(n^2-1)} = 1 - \dfrac{6 \times 160}{10(10^2-1)}$

$= 1 - \dfrac{960}{990} = 0.0303$ (to 3 sig.fig.)

Exam Questions

1) a)
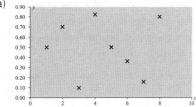

[2 marks for all points plotted correctly, or 1 mark if at least 3 points are plotted correctly.]

Aren't scatter diagrams pretty... Just make sure you're not so distracted by their artistic elegance that you forget to be accurate and lose easy marks.

b) You need to work out these sums:

$\sum x = 36, \sum y = 3.94,$
$\sum x^2 = 204, \sum y^2 = 2.4676, \sum xy = 17.66$

Then:

$S_{xx} = \sum x^2 - \dfrac{(\sum x)^2}{n} = 204 - \dfrac{36^2}{8} = 42$

$S_{yy} = \sum y^2 - \dfrac{(\sum y)^2}{n} = 2.4676 - \dfrac{3.94^2}{8} = 0.52715$

$S_{xy} = \sum xy - \dfrac{(\sum x)(\sum y)}{n} = 17.66 - \dfrac{36 \times 3.94}{8} = -0.07$

[3 marks available — 1 for each correct term]

This means:

$r = \dfrac{S_{xy}}{\sqrt{S_{xx}S_{yy}}} = \dfrac{-0.07}{\sqrt{42 \times 0.52715}} = -0.015$ (to 3 d.p.).

[1 mark]

c) This very small value for the correlation coefficient tells you that there appears to be only a very weak negative linear relationship between the two variables (or perhaps no linear relationship at all) *[1 mark]*.

2 a)
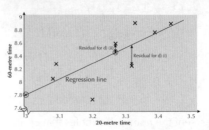

[2 marks for all points plotted correctly, or 1 mark if at least 3 points are plotted correctly.]

b) It's best to make a table like this one, first:

20-metre time, x	3.39	3.2	3.09	3.32	3.33	3.27	3.44	3.08	Totals
60-metre time, y	8.78	7.73	8.28	8.25	8.91	8.59	8.9	8.05	26.12
									67.49
x^2	11.4921	10.24	9.5481	11.0224	11.0889	10.6929	11.8336	9.4864	85.4044
xy	29.7642	24.736	25.5852	27.39	29.6703	28.0893	30.616	24.794	220.645

[2 marks for at least three correct sums, or 1 mark if one total found correctly.]

Then: $S_{xy} = 220.645 - \dfrac{26.12 \times 67.49}{8} = 0.29015$

[1 mark]

$S_{xx} = 85.4044 - \dfrac{26.12^2}{8} = 0.1226$

[1 mark]

Then the gradient b is given by:

$b = \dfrac{S_{xy}}{S_{xx}} = \dfrac{0.29015}{0.1226} = 2.3666$

[1 mark]

And the intercept a is given by:

$a = \bar{y} - b\bar{x} = \dfrac{\sum y}{n} - b\dfrac{\sum x}{n}$

$= \dfrac{67.49}{8} - 2.3666 \times \dfrac{26.12}{8} = 0.709$

[1 mark]

So the regression line has equation: $y = 2.367x + 0.709$

[1 mark]

To plot the line, find two points that the line passes through. A regression line always passes through $(\bar{x}, \bar{y})$, which here is (3.27, 8.44). Then put $x = 3$ (say) to find that the line also passes through (3, 7.81).
Now plot these points (in circles) on your scatter diagram, and draw the regression line through them
[1 mark for plotting the line correctly].

Hmm, lots of fiddly things to calculate there. Remember, you get marks for method as well as correct answers, so take it step by step and show all your workings. And don't fall into the old trap of using one of your data points to plot the regression line, since there's no guarantee that any of your data points will satisfy the regression equation (and so be on the regression line).

c) (i) $y = 2.367 \times 3.15 + 0.709 = 8.17$ (to 3 sig. fig.),
(8.16 if $b = 2.3666$ used) *[1 mark]*

This should be reliable, since we are using interpolation within the range of x for which we have data *[1 mark]*.

(ii) $y = 2.367 \times 3.88 + 0.709 = 9.89$ (to 3 sig. fig.)
[1 mark]

This could be unreliable, since we are extrapolating beyond the range of the data *[1 mark]*.

d) (i) residual = 8.25 − (2.367 × 3.32 + 0.709)
   = −0.317 (3 sig. fig.), (−0.316 if b = 2.3666 used)

   [1 mark for calculation, 1 mark for plotting residual correctly]

   (ii) residual = 8.59 − (2.367 × 3.27 + 0.709)
   = 0.141 (3 sig. fig.), (0.142 if b = 2.3666 used)

   [1 mark for calculation, 1 mark for plotting residual correctly]

3 a) Put the values into the correct PMCC formula:
   $$\text{PMCC} = \frac{S_{xy}}{\sqrt{S_{xx}S_{yy}}} = \frac{12\,666}{\sqrt{310\,880 \times 788.95}}$$
   $$= \frac{12\,666}{15\,661.059} = 0.809$$

   [1 mark for correctly substituting the values into the PMCC formula, and 1 mark for the correct final answer.]

b) There is a strong positive correlation between the miles cycled in the morning and calories consumed for lunch. Generally, the further they have cycled, the more they eat *[1 mark]*.

c) 0.809 *[1 mark]*

   Remember — the PMCC won't be affected if you multiply all the variables by a constant, so changing the data from miles to km doesn't change it.

4 a) (i) At x = 12.5, y = 211.599 + (9.602 × 12.5) = 331.624
   (ii) At x = 14.7, y = 211.599 + (9.602 × 14.7) = 352.748
   [1 mark for each value of y correctly calculated]

b) Using the equation: 'Residual = Observed y-value − Estimated y-value':
   At x = 12.5: Residual = 332.5 − 331.624 = 0.876 *[1 mark]*
   At x = 14.7: Residual = 352.1 − 352.748 = −0.648 *[1 mark]*

   And that's the end of that — Section 4 done and dusted. Bring on the practice exam papers...

S1 — Practice Exam One

1) a) 4.1 metres (the upper quartile) *[1 mark]*.

b)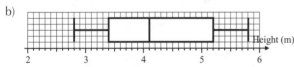

   [1 mark for the median shown correctly, 1 mark for the upper quartile, 1 mark for the lower quartile, and 1 mark for both the minimum and the maximum shown correctly.]

c) The giraffes in the zoo are generally taller, with a higher median *[1 mark]*, and higher upper and lower quartiles *[1 mark]*. The IQR for the giraffes in the zoo is greater than for the giraffes in the game reserve, so the data is more spread out *[1 mark]*, even though the game reserve giraffes have a greater total range *[1 mark]*.

2) a) The order the selections are made doesn't matter, so we're looking for the number of combinations of 4 items from a choice of 8:
   $$^8C_4 \text{ [1 mark]} = \frac{8!}{4!4!} = \frac{8 \times 7 \times 6 \times 5}{4 \times 3 \times 2 \times 1} = 70 \text{ [1 mark]}$$

b) (i) If two of the places in the selection are already taken by raisins and sultanas, that means there are 2 places to fill, from 6 choices. The number of ways this can be done is $^6C_2 = \frac{6!}{4!2!} = \frac{6 \times 5}{2 \times 1} = 15$ *[1 mark]*
   So P(selection contains both raisins and sultanas)
   $$= \frac{\text{number of combinations containing both}}{\text{total number of possible combinations}} = \frac{15}{70}$$
   = 0.214 (to 3 sig. fig.) *[1 mark]*

   (ii) If you're counting combinations with raisins but not sultanas, that means one place is taken, and there are 6 choices to fill the other 3 places.
   The number of ways this can be done is
   $$^6C_3 = \frac{6!}{3!3!} = \frac{6 \times 5 \times 4}{3 \times 2 \times 1} = 20 \text{ [1 mark]}$$
   Similarly, there are 20 selections that contain sultanas, but not raisins.
   P(selection contains exactly one of raisins and sultanas)
   $$= \frac{20 + 20}{70} = \frac{40}{70} \text{ [1 mark]}$$
   = 0.571 (to 3 sig. fig.) *[1 mark]*

3) a) The probabilities have to add up to 1,
   so $p = 1 - \left(\frac{7}{20} + \frac{1}{5} + \frac{3}{20} + \frac{3}{20}\right)$ *[1 mark]*
   $$= 1 - \frac{17}{20} = \frac{3}{20} \text{ [1 mark]}$$
   Easy.

b) $E(X) = \Sigma x P(X = x)$
   $$= \left(0 \times \frac{7}{20}\right) + \left(10 \times \frac{1}{5}\right)$$
   $$+ \left(20 \times \frac{3}{20}\right) + \left(50 \times \frac{3}{20}\right) + \left(100 \times \frac{3}{20}\right) \text{ [1 mark]}$$
   $$= 0 + 2 + 3 + 7.5 + 15$$
   $$= 27.5 \text{ [1 mark]}$$
   $\text{Var}(X) = \Sigma x^2 P(X = x) - [E(X)]^2$
   $$= \left(0 \times \frac{7}{20}\right) + \left(100 \times \frac{1}{5}\right) + \left(400 \times \frac{3}{20}\right)$$
   $$+ \left(2500 \times \frac{3}{20}\right) + \left(10\,000 \times \frac{3}{20}\right) - 27.5^2 \text{ [1 mark]}$$
   $$= 0 + 20 + 60 + 375 + 1500 - 756.25$$
   $$= 1198.75 \text{ [1 mark]}$$
   A bit harder.

c) X is a random variable that shows what's paid out. The expected value of X is 27.5p, so a charge of 30p will average a profit of 2.5p per game *[1 mark]*. This is unlikely to be sufficient to cover the owner's costs *[1 mark for any sensible comment]*.

   Ooh — easy again.

d) Probably not. It would be usual for smaller prizes to have much higher probabilities than bigger prizes.

   [1 mark for saying that this model is unlikely, and 1 mark for any sensible explanation as to why.]

   Sigh of relief — wasn't as bad as I thought.

4) a) 1. The probability P(chocolate bar contains a golden ticket) must be constant.
   2. Whether or not each individual chocolate bar contains a golden ticket must be independent of whether other chocolate bars contain a golden ticket.
   [1 mark for each correct condition]

Answers

b) (i) $P(X > 1) = 1 - P(X \leq 1)$.
From tables, $P(X \leq 1) = 0.5535$ *[1 mark]*.
So $P(X > 1) = 1 - 0.5535 = 0.4465$ *[1 mark]*.

(ii) $P(3 < X < 7) = P(3 < X \leq 6)$
$= P(X \leq 6) - P(X \leq 3)$ *[1 mark]*
$= 0.9994 - 0.9392$ *[1 mark]*
$= 0.0602$ *[1 mark]*

(iii) $E(X) = np = 30 \times 0.05 = 1.5$ *[1 mark]*.

c) Now we're looking at the number of trials until the first success, so it's a geometric distribution.
$W \sim \text{Geo}(0.05)$ *[1 mark]*
So $P(W = 6) = 0.05 \times 0.95^5$ *[1 mark]*
$= 0.0387$ (3 sig. fig.) *[1 mark]*

Often, the hardest bit of a question is spotting which distribution to use — and then once you've done that, you're off and running. So don't rush in when you first start a question — think it through carefully, otherwise you might start running in the wrong direction.

5) To calculate r_s, first we need to make a new table showing the ranks of the dancers, then find the difference between the ranks, d, for each pair of dancers, and calculate d^2:

Pair	A	B	C	D	E	F
Judges	2	6	1	5	4	3
Public	1	3	4	5	6	2
d	1	3	3	0	2	1
d^2	1	9	9	0	4	1

[3 marks available — 1 mark for a table with one column for each pair, 1 mark for judges' and public rankings correctly entered, 1 mark for correctly calculating values of d^2]

$r_s = 1 - \dfrac{6\Sigma d^2}{n(n^2 - 1)}$

$= 1 - \dfrac{6(1 + 9 + 9 + 0 + 4 + 1)}{6(6^2 - 1)}$ *[1 mark]*

$= 1 - \dfrac{6(24)}{6(35)} = 0.314$ (3 sig. fig.) *[1 mark]*

6) a) If C is the event 'has had a crash' and G is the event 'wears glasses', then the tree diagram is as follows:

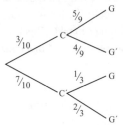

[1 mark for each correct pair of branches, but lose 1 mark for not cancelling down fractions.]

b) The easiest way is to work out the probabilities of the two branches ending in G by multiplying along each branch, and then adding the results
(i.e. $P(G) = P(G \cap C) + P(G \cap C')$).

$P(G \cap C) = \dfrac{3}{10} \times \dfrac{5}{9} = \dfrac{15}{90} = \dfrac{1}{6}$ *[1 mark]*,

and $P(G \cap C') = \dfrac{7}{10} \times \dfrac{1}{3} = \dfrac{7}{30}$ *[1 mark]*.

Adding these together you get:

$P(G) = \dfrac{1}{6} + \dfrac{7}{30} = \dfrac{5 + 7}{30} = \dfrac{12}{30} = \dfrac{2}{5}$ *[1 mark]*.

c) You need to find: $P(C \mid G) = \dfrac{P(C \cap G)}{P(G)}$ *[1 mark]*.

You've just worked out $P(C \cap G)$ and $P(G)$, so

$P(C \mid G) = \dfrac{1}{6} \div \dfrac{2}{5}$ *[1 mark]*

$= \dfrac{1}{6} \times \dfrac{5}{2} = \dfrac{5}{12}$ *[1 mark]*.

Tree diagrams are things you've definitely seen before, and they don't get any harder. The question may sound more complicated, but it's not really.

7) a) The mean (μ) is given by $\mu = \dfrac{\Sigma x}{10} = \dfrac{500}{10} = 50$ *[1 mark]*.

The variance (σ^2) is 'the mean of the squares minus the square of the mean'. And the standard deviation (σ) is just the square root of the variance.
So the variance is given by

$\sigma^2 = \dfrac{\Sigma x^2}{10} - 50^2$

$= \dfrac{25\,622}{10} - 2500 = 62.2$ *[1 mark]*

So $\sigma = \sqrt{62.2} = 7.89$ (to 3 sig. fig) *[1 mark]*.

b) (i) The mean will be unchanged *[1 mark]*, because the new value is equal to the original mean *[1 mark]*.

(ii) The standard deviation will decrease *[1 mark]*. This is because the standard deviation measures the deviation of values from the mean. So by adding a new value that's equal to the mean, you're not adding to the total deviation from the mean, but as you have an extra reading, you now have to divide by 11 (not 10) when you work out the variance *[1 mark]*.

Understanding what the standard deviation actually is can help you get your head round questions like this.

8) a) $S_{xx} = \Sigma x^2 - \dfrac{(\Sigma x)^2}{n}$

$= 847 - \dfrac{79^2}{8} = 66.875 = 66.9$ (to 3 sig. fig.) *[1 mark]*

$S_{yy} = \Sigma y^2 - \dfrac{(\Sigma y)^2}{n}$

$= 45\,884 - \dfrac{600^2}{8} = 884$ *[1 mark]*

$S_{xy} = \Sigma xy - \dfrac{\Sigma x \Sigma y}{n}$

$= 6143 - \dfrac{79 \times 600}{8} = 218$ *[1 mark]*

b) $r = \dfrac{S_{xy}}{\sqrt{S_{xx} \times S_{yy}}} = \dfrac{218}{\sqrt{66.875 \times 884}}$ *[1 mark]*

$= 0.897$ (to 3 sig. fig.) *[1 mark]*

c) The amount of revision (x) *[1 mark]*, since the exam mark depends on the amount of revision done, not the other way around *[1 mark]*.

The independent variable is also known as the explanatory variable (and the dependent variable as the response variable).

d) The correlation coefficient is very close to 1, so if the points were plotted on a scatter graph, they would all lie close to a straight line *[1 mark]*.

e) $b = \dfrac{S_{xy}}{S_{xx}} = \dfrac{218}{66.875} = 3.26$ (to 3 sig. fig.) *[1 mark]*

$a = \bar{y} - b\bar{x} = \dfrac{600}{8} - 3.26 \times \dfrac{79}{8}$ *[1 mark]*

$= 42.8$ (to 3 sig. fig.) *[1 mark]*

So $y = 42.8 + 3.26x$ *[1 mark]*.

f) Using the regression line to estimate the mark:
$y = 42.8 + 3.26 \times 4 = 55.84 \approx 56$ marks *[1 mark]*.

g) 4 is outside the range for which there is data — extrapolation is needed so the estimate is unreliable / This estimate may be unreliable, since this student may not fit the pattern generated by the others *[1 mark for any sensible comment]*.

S1 — Practice Exam Two

1) a) With this type of question, it usually helps to start by drawing a Venn diagram. Let H be hard centre, N be nutty and S be soft centre.

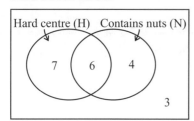

Hard centre (H)   Contains nuts (N)

7   6   4

3

(i) $P(S) = \dfrac{\text{Number of soft centres}}{\text{Total number of chocolates}}$

$= \dfrac{20 - 13}{20} = \dfrac{7}{20}$ *[1 mark]*

(ii) $P(H \mid N)$

$= \dfrac{\text{Number of chocolates in both H and N}}{\text{Number of chocolates in N}}$ *[1 mark]*

$= \dfrac{6}{10} = \dfrac{3}{5}$ *[1 mark]*

In part (ii), you're "given that the chocolate contains a nut", so you only need to look at the circle containing nutty chocolates — you can ignore the rest of the diagram.

b) P(pick hard centre with 1st pick) $= \dfrac{13}{20} \times \dfrac{7}{19} \times \dfrac{6}{18}$

$= \dfrac{546}{6840} = \dfrac{91}{1140}$ *[1 mark]*

This is P(HSS), but you also need to add P(SHS) and P(SSH). In fact, P(HSS) = P(SHS) = P(SSH), so you need to multiply the above answer by 3 *[1 mark]*.

So

P(pick exactly 1 hard centre) $= 3 \times \dfrac{91}{1140} = \dfrac{91}{380}$ *[1 mark]*.

Don't forget that the hard centre could be the first one picked out of the box, or the second or the third — and you need to take the fact that there are 'different arrangements' into account when you work out your probability.

2) a) $P(X \le 3) = P(X = 1) + P(X = 2) + P(X = 3)$ *[1 mark]*

$= \dfrac{1}{12} + \dfrac{1}{6} + \dfrac{1}{4}$

$= \dfrac{1}{12} + \dfrac{2}{12} + \dfrac{3}{12}$

$= \dfrac{6}{12} = \dfrac{1}{2}$ *[1 mark]*

b) $E(X) = \sum x P(X = x)$

$= \left(1 \times \dfrac{1}{12}\right) + \left(2 \times \dfrac{2}{12}\right) + \left(3 \times \dfrac{3}{12}\right)$

$\quad + \left(4 \times \dfrac{3}{12}\right) + \left(5 \times \dfrac{2}{12}\right) + \left(6 \times \dfrac{1}{12}\right)$ *[1 mark]*

$= \dfrac{1 + 4 + 9 + 12 + 10 + 6}{12} = \dfrac{42}{12} = 3.5$ *[1 mark]*

c) $\text{Var}(X) = E(X^2) - E(X)^2$

$E(X^2) = \left(1 \times \dfrac{1}{12}\right) + \left(4 \times \dfrac{2}{12}\right) + \left(9 \times \dfrac{3}{12}\right)$

$\quad + \left(16 \times \dfrac{3}{12}\right) + \left(25 \times \dfrac{2}{12}\right) + \left(36 \times \dfrac{1}{12}\right)$ *[1 mark]*

$= \dfrac{1 + 8 + 27 + 48 + 50 + 36}{12} = \dfrac{170}{12}$ *[1 mark]*

So $\text{Var}(X) = \dfrac{170}{12} - 3.5^2 = 1.92$ (to 3 s.f.) *[1 mark]*

3) a) This is a binomial distribution.
If X is the number of heads, then $X \sim B(9, p)$ *[1 mark]*
So $E(X) = np = 9p = 3$
$\Rightarrow p = \dfrac{3}{9} = \dfrac{1}{3}$ *[1 mark]*

b) $P(X = 4) = P(X \le 4) - P(X \le 3)$ *[1 mark]*
So using the binomial tables,
$P(X = 4) = 0.8552 - 0.6503$ *[1 mark]*
$= 0.205$ (to 3 s.f.) *[1 mark]*

4) a) The value of k must be between 11 and 20 *[1 mark]*, because SRCC can only equal 1 if y increases whenever x increases *[1 mark]*.

b) (i) $S_{xy} = \sum xy - \dfrac{\sum x \sum y}{n} = 45.6 + 1.2k - \dfrac{4.5 \times (42 + k)}{5}$

$= 45.6 + 1.2k - 37.8 - 0.9k$

$= 7.8 + 0.3k$ *[1 mark]*

So $S_{xy} = 12 \Rightarrow 0.3k = 12 - 7.8 = 4.2$

$\Rightarrow k = 4.2 \div 0.3 = 14$ *[1 mark]*

(ii) $S_{xx} = \sum x^2 - \dfrac{(\sum x)^2}{n} = 4.95 - \dfrac{4.5^2}{5}$

$= 4.95 - 4.05$

$= 0.9$ *[1 mark]*

$\sum y = 42 + k = 42 + 14 = 56$

$\sum y^2 = 594 + k^2 = 594 + 196 = 790$

So $S_{yy} = \sum y^2 - \dfrac{(\sum y)^2}{n} = 790 - \dfrac{56^2}{5}$

$= 790 - 627.2$

$= 162.8$ *[1 mark]*

So $r = \dfrac{S_{xy}}{\sqrt{S_{xx} \times S_{yy}}}$

$= \dfrac{12}{\sqrt{0.9 \times 162.8}} = \dfrac{12}{\sqrt{146.52}}$

$= 0.991$ (to 3 s.f.) *[1 mark]*

Answers

5) a) If the same people are upgraded, but sit in different seats, that's a different way of filling the 5 seats.

So this is a permutation question:

Number of ways to fill 5 seats $= \frac{9!}{4!}$ *[1 mark]*

$= 9 \times 8 \times 7 \times 6 \times 5 = 15\,120$ *[1 mark]*

b) Number of permutations with at least one of Amy and Sam
= (total number of permutations)
      – (number of permutations with neither of them)

$= 15\,120 - \frac{7!}{2!}$ *[1 mark]* (if neither Amy nor Sam get upgraded, there's a choice of 5 from 7)

$= 15\,120 - (7 \times 6 \times 5 \times 4 \times 3)$
$= 15\,120 - 2520$
$= 12\,600$ *[1 mark]*

So P(At least one of Amy and Sam get upgraded)
$= \frac{12\,600}{15\,120} = \frac{5}{6}$ *[1 mark]*

c) The total number of ways to arrange the 5 upgraded passengers is $5! = 120$ *[1 mark]*.

If Amy and Sam are in the two seats together, then there are three remaining seats, which can be filled in $3! = 6$ ways. For each of these arrangements, there are 2 ways to arrange Amy and Sam, giving a total of $2 \times 6 = 12$ ways *[1 mark]*.

So P(Amy and Sam sit together given they're upgraded)
$= \frac{12}{120} = \frac{1}{10}$ *[1 mark]*

6) a) Mean $= \frac{\sum x}{n} = \frac{66.5}{12}$ *[1 mark]*
    $= 5.54$ (or £5540) (to 3 sig. fig.) *[1 mark]*.

Variance $= \frac{\sum x^2}{n} - \left(\frac{\sum x}{n}\right)^2 = \frac{390.97}{12} - \left(\frac{66.5}{12}\right)^2$ *[1 mark]*
    $= 1.87$ (to 3 sig. fig.) *[1 mark]*.

b) The ordered list of the 12 data points is:
3.8, 4.1, 4.2, 4.6, 4.9, 5.5, 5.8, 5.9, 6.0, 6.2, 6.4, 9.1.

The position of the median is $\frac{1}{2}(n+1) = \frac{1}{2}(12+1) = 6.5$, so take the average of the 6th and 7th values.

So the median Q_2 is: $\frac{1}{2}(5.5 + 5.8) = 5.65$ *[1 mark]*.

Since $12 \div 4 = 3$, the lower quartile is the average of the 3rd and 4th values.

So the lower quartile Q_1 is: $\frac{1}{2}(4.2 + 4.6) = 4.4$ *[1 mark]*.

Since $12 \div 4 \times 3 = 9$, the upper quartile is the average of the 9th and 10th values.

So the upper quartile Q_3 is: $\frac{1}{2}(6.0 + 6.2) = 6.1$ *[1 mark]*.

c) E.g. Central tendency – the mean and median of both sets are quite similar, suggesting that the average weekly sales for both shops are quite similar (but a bit higher for the first shop).
Variation – the variance for the first shop is much greater than for the second, suggesting that there is a greater spread of values for the first shop.

[2 marks available — 1 mark for any sensible comment about central tendency, 1 mark for any sensible comment about variation]

d) E.g. If there is an outlier in the data, the mean is far more likely to be distorted by the outlier than the median is *[1 mark]*.

7) a) $P(S = 3) = 0.4 \times 0.6^2$ *[1 mark]* $= 0.144$ *[1 mark]*

b) $P(S < 4) = P(S = 1) + P(S = 2) + P(S = 3)$ *[1 mark]*
$= 0.4 + 0.4 \times 0.6 + 0.144$ *[1 mark]*
$= 0.4 + 0.24 + 0.144 = 0.784$ *[1 mark]*

c) $E(S) = \frac{1}{0.4}$ *[1 mark]* $= 2.5$ *[1 mark]*

8) a)

[2 marks for all points correctly plotted, or 1 mark if at least 4 points are correctly plotted.]

b) $S_{xx} = \sum x^2 - \frac{(\sum x)^2}{n} = 828 - \frac{64^2}{8} = 316$ *[1 mark]*

$S_{xy} = \sum xy - \frac{\sum x \sum y}{n} = 219.05 - \frac{64 \times 26.2}{8} = 9.45$ *[1 mark]*.

These formulas will be given to you on the formula sheet, but make sure you practise using them.

c) If $y = a + bx$, then

$b = \frac{S_{xy}}{S_{xx}} = \frac{9.45}{316} = 0.029905... = 0.0299$ (to 3 sig.fig.).
[1 mark].
And $a = \bar{y} - b\bar{x}$
    $= \frac{26.2}{8} - 0.0299 \times \frac{64}{8}$ *[1 mark]*
    $= 3.0358 = 3.04$ (to 3 sig. fig.) *[1 mark]*.

So the equation of the regression line is:
$y = 3.04 + 0.0299x$ *[1 mark]*

These formulas for the regression line coefficients will also be on your formula sheet.

d) a represents the length of the cable when it is not under tension (i.e. when $x = 0$) *[1 mark]*.
b represents the extra extension of the cable when the tension is increased by 1 kN *[1 mark]*.

e) $y = 3.04 + 0.0299x$, so when $x = 30$,
$y = 3.04 + 0.0299 \times 30 = 3.937$ *[1 mark]*
$= 3.94$ metres (to 3 sig. fig.) *[1 mark]*
(or 3.93 m if $a = 3.0358$ used)

f) This estimate may be unreliable as it involves extrapolating beyond the range of the experimental data *[1 mark]*.

278

S1 — ANSWERS

9) a) Because the cards are not being replaced, the probability of choosing a picture card does not remain constant *[1 mark]*.

  b) (i) Since the cards are now being replaced after each pick, Y will follow a binomial distribution.

   Since $\frac{12}{52} = \frac{3}{13}$, $Y \sim B(3, \frac{3}{13})$.

   $$P(Y = 2) = \binom{3}{2} \times \left(\frac{3}{13}\right)^2 \times \frac{10}{13} \text{ [1 mark]}$$
   $$= \frac{270}{13^3} = \frac{270}{2197}$$
   $$= 0.123 \text{ (to 3 sig. fig.) } \textit{[1 mark]}.$$

   (ii) $E(Y) = 3 \times \frac{3}{13} = \frac{9}{13} = 0.692$ (to 3 sig. fig.) *[1 mark]*.

   (iii) $Var(Y) = 3 \times \frac{3}{13} \times \frac{10}{13} = \frac{90}{169} = 0.533$ (to 3 sig. fig.)

   [1 mark]

  c) The probability of picking a red card is always 0.5. So the probability of any student picking exactly 3 red cards in 4 picks is:

   $$P(\text{pick 3 red cards}) = \binom{4}{3} \times 0.5^3 \times (1 - 0.5)$$
   $$= 4 \times 0.5^4 = 0.25 \textit{ [1 mark]}$$

   This means that Q follows a binomial distribution: $Q \sim B(20, 0.25)$ *[1 mark]*.

   You need to find $P(2 \leq Q \leq 8)$. $p = 0.25$ and $n = 20$ are in binomial tables, so:

   $P(2 \leq Q \leq 8) = P(Q \leq 8) - P(Q < 2)$
   $= P(Q \leq 8) - P(Q \leq 1)$ *[1 mark]*
   $= 0.9591 - 0.0243 = 0.9348$ *[1 mark]*

   You could do this question without tables. But it would take a while, because you'd need to find 7 individual probabilities, and add them together. That's the beauty of tables — they can tell you lots of information very quickly.

Answers

M1 Section 1 — Vectors and Forces

Warm-up Questions

1) Displacement = $(15 \times 0.25) - (10 \times 0.75) = -3.75$ km
Time taken = 1 hour

Average velocity = -3.75 kmh^{-1} (i.e. 3.75 kmh^{-1} south)

2) a) Small point mass, no air resistance, no wind, released from rest.

b) Small point mass, no air resistance, no wind, released from rest.

c) Same assumptions as in a) and b), although it might not be safe to ignore wind if outside as table tennis balls are very light.

You need to get familiar with modelling and all the terminology used in M1 — it's going to be really tricky to figure out M1 questions if you're not.

3) Assumptions: Point mass, one point of contact with ground, constant driving force D from engine, constant friction, F, includes road resistance and air resistance, acceleration = 0 as it's moving at 25mph (in a straight line).

4) a)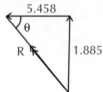
$R = \sqrt{4^2 + 3^3} = 5$ N
$\tan \theta = \frac{4}{3}$
$\theta = 53.1°$ (3 s.f.) below the horizontal

b)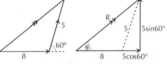
$R = \sqrt{(8 + 5\cos 60°)^2 + (5\sin 60°)^2} = 11.4$ N (3 s.f.)
$\tan \theta = \frac{5\sin 60°}{8 + 5\cos 60°} = 0.412...$
So $\theta = 22.4°$ (3 s.f.) above the horizontal

c) Total force up = $6 - 4\sin 10° - 10\sin 20° = 1.885$ N (4 s.f.)
Total force left = $10\cos 20° - 4\cos 10° = 5.458$ N (4 s.f.)
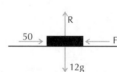
$R = \sqrt{1.885^2 + 5.458^2}$
$= 5.77$ N (3 s.f.)
$\theta = \tan^{-1}\frac{1.885}{5.458}$
$= 19.1°$ (3 s.f.) above the horizontal

5)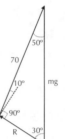

a) $\tan 30° = \frac{20}{T_B}$
$T_B = \frac{20}{\tan 30°}$
$= 34.6$ N (3 s.f.)

b) $\sin 30° = \frac{20}{mg}$
$mg = \frac{20}{\sin 30°}$
$m = 4.08$ kg (3 s.f.)

6)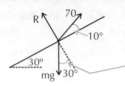

Huge hint: The angle of the plane to the horizontal (in this case 30°) will always be the angle in here.

Sine rule: $\frac{mg}{\sin 100°} = \frac{70}{\sin 30°}$

So $mg = \frac{70\sin 100°}{\sin 30°}$
$m = 14.1$ kg (3 s.f.)

$\frac{R}{\sin 50°} = \frac{70}{\sin 30°}$

So $R = \frac{70\sin 50°}{\sin 30°}$
$= 107$ N (3 s.f.)

Yet another example of how triangles might just save your ~~life~~ mark for the M1 module. Although you could also have solved it by resolving forces parallel and perpendicular to the slope if that floats your boat.

7)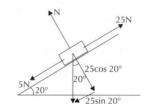

Force perpendicular to the slope: N = $25\cos 20°$
$= 23.5$ N (3 s.f.)

Force parallel to the slope: $25 - 25\sin 20° - 5$
$= 11.4$ N (3 s.f.)
So the resultant force is 11.4 N up the slope.

8) a)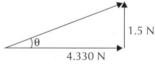

Resolve vertically: $R = 12g$
Use formula: $F \leq \mu R$
$F \leq \frac{1}{2}(12g)$
$F \leq 58.8$ N (3 s.f.)

50 N isn't big enough to overcome friction — so it has no overall motion.

b) Force would have to be > 58.8 N

Exam Questions

1 Resolve horizontally: $0 + 5\cos 30° = 4.330$ N (4 s.f.)
Resolve vertically: $4 - 5\sin 30° = 1.5$ N

$\theta = \tan^{-1}\left(\frac{1.5}{4.330}\right) = 19.1°$ (3 s.f.) above the horizontal
Magnitude = $\sqrt{1.5^2 + 4.330^2} = 4.58$ N (3 s.f.)

[4 marks available in total]:
- **1 mark for resolving horizontally**
- **1 mark for resolving vertically**
- **1 mark for calculating the direction**
- **1 mark for calculating the magnitude**

Triangles — how do I love thee? Let me count the ways...

...one big way, really. They're just super useful when resolving things.

2 a)

[2 marks available in total]:
- *1 mark for drawing 4 correct arrows*
- *1 mark for correctly labelling the arrows*

b) Resolve vertically:
$R = 39g + 140\sin20° = 430$ N (3 s.f.)
Resolve horizontally:
$F = 140\cos20° = 132$ N (3 s.f.)

[4 marks available in total]:
- *1 mark for resolving vertically*
- *1 mark for resolving horizontally*
- *1 mark for correct reaction magnitude*
- *1 mark for correct friction magnitude*

No need to panic if friction is involved — it's just another thing to consider when resolving (and an extra arrow to draw).

3 a)
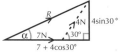

Resolve vertically:
$4\sin30° = 2$
Resolve horizontally:
$7 + 4\cos30° = 10.5$
$R = \sqrt{2^2 + 10.5^2}$
$= 10.7$ N (3 s.f.)

[4 marks available in total]:
- *1 mark for diagram*
- *1 mark for resolving vertically*
- *1 mark for resolving horizontally*
- *1 mark for correct magnitude*

b) $\tan\alpha = \dfrac{2}{7 + 4\cos30}$
$\alpha = 10.8°$ (3 s.f.)

[2 marks available in total]:
- *1 mark for correct workings*
- *1 mark for correct value of α*

4
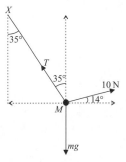

Resolving vertically: $mg = 10\sin14° + T\cos35°$
Need to find T.
Resolving horizontally: $T\sin35° = 10\cos14°$
So, $T = \dfrac{10\cos14°}{\sin35°} = 16.9$ N (3 s.f.)
So $mg = 10\sin14° + 16.9\cos35° = 16.3$ N
Therefore, the mass of $M = \dfrac{16.3}{g} = 1.66$ kg (3 s.f.)

[4 marks available in total]:
- *1 mark for resolving vertically*
- *1 mark for resolving horizontally*
- *1 mark for correct value of T*
- *1 mark for correct mass of M*

I think this question is sort of fun, but then I also think rods are sort of pretty... Anyway, a good clear diagram here will simplify matters no end.

5 a)

$\sin\theta = \dfrac{12}{15}$, so, $\theta = 53.1°$ (3 s.f.)

[2 marks available in total]:
- *1 mark for correct workings*
- *1 mark for the correct value of θ*

b) $15^2 = W^2 + 12^2$
$W = \sqrt{15^2 - 12^2} = 9$ N

[2 marks available in total]:
- *1 mark for correct workings*
- *1 mark for correct value of W*

c) Remove W and the particle moves in the opposite direction to W, i.e. upwards. This resultant of the two remaining forces is 9 N upwards, because the particle was in equilibrium beforehand.

[2 marks available in total]:
- *1 mark for correct magnitude*
- *1 mark for correct direction*

The word 'state' in an exam question means that you shouldn't need to do any extra calculation to answer it.

Answers

6

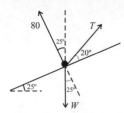 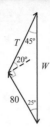 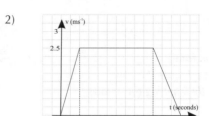

a) $\dfrac{T}{\sin 25^\circ} = \dfrac{80}{\sin 45^\circ}$

So, $T = \dfrac{80\sin 25^\circ}{\sin 45^\circ} = 47.8$ N (3 s.f.)

[3 marks available in total]:
- *1 mark for diagram*
- *1 mark for correct workings*
- *1 mark for correct value of T*

b) $\dfrac{W}{\sin 110^\circ} = \dfrac{80}{\sin 45^\circ}$

So, $W = \dfrac{80\sin 110^\circ}{\sin 45^\circ} = 106$ N (3 s.f.)

[2 marks available in total]:
- *1 mark for correct workings*
- *1 mark for correct value of W*

Do you remember the sine rule? If not, go and revise it (try p. 73)
— a bit of trigonometry never hurt anyone, and it'll serve you well
in M1. You can solve pretty much anything with triangles...

7 a) Resolving horizontally:

$T\cos 50^\circ = 58$ N

so, $T = \dfrac{58}{\cos 50^\circ} = 90.2$ N (3 s.f.)

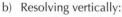

[3 marks available in total]:
- *1 mark for resolving horizontally*
- *1 mark for correct workings*
- *1 mark for correct value of T*

b) Resolving vertically:

$mg = T\sin 50^\circ = 90.2\sin 50^\circ$

so, $mg = 69.1$ and $m = 7.05$ kg (3 s.f.)

[3 marks available in total]:
- *1 mark for resolving vertically*
- *1 mark for correct workings*
- *1 mark for correct value of m*

8 Resolve horizontally: $S\cos 40^\circ = F$
Resolve vertically: $R = 2g + S\sin 40^\circ$
It's limiting friction so $F = \mu R$
So, $S\cos 40^\circ = \dfrac{3}{10}(2g + S\sin 40^\circ)$
$S\cos 40^\circ = 0.6g + 0.3S\sin 40^\circ$
$S\cos 40^\circ - 0.3S\sin 40^\circ = 0.6g$
$S(\cos 40^\circ - 0.3\sin 40^\circ) = 0.6g$
$S = 10.3$ N (3 s.f.)

[4 marks available in total]:
- *1 mark for resolving horizontally*
- *1 mark for resolving vertically*
- *1 mark for correct workings*
- *1 mark for correct value of S*

A ring on a rod — it might be a car on a road, or a sledge
on snow... it's all the same mathematically.

M1 Section 2 — Kinematics
Warm-up Questions

1) $u = 3; v = 9; a = a; s = s; t = 2$. Use $s = \frac{1}{2}(u + v)t$
$s = \frac{1}{2}(3 + 9) \times 2 \qquad s = \frac{1}{2}(12) \times 2 = 12$ m

2)

distance $= (5 \times 2.5) \div 2 + (20 \times 2.5) + (10 \times 2.5) \div 2$
$= 68.75$ m

3) displacement = area under (t, v) graph

a) $t = 3$,   displacement $= (3 \times 5) \div 2 = 7.5$ m

b) $t = 5$,   displacement $= 7.5 + (2 \times 5) = 17.5$ m

c) $t = 6$,   displacement $= 17.5 + (1 \times 5) \div 2 = 20$ m

4) a) $a = \dfrac{dv}{dt} = 16t - 2$

b) $s = \displaystyle\int v\,dt = \dfrac{8t^3}{3} - t^2 + c$

When $t = 0$, the particle is at the origin, i.e. $s = 0 \Rightarrow c = 0$
So, $s = \dfrac{8t^3}{3} - t^2$

Exam Questions

1 a) Using $u = v - at$
$u = 17 - (9.8 \times 1.2)$
So, $u = 5.24$ ms^{-1}

[3 marks available in total]:
- *1 mark for using appropriate equation*
- *1 mark for correct workings*
- *1 mark for correct value of u*

These kind of questions are trivial if you've memorised all
those constant acceleration equations. If you haven't, you
know what to do now (turn to p. 167).

b) Using $s = ut + \frac{1}{2}at^2$
$s = (17 \times 2.1) + \frac{1}{2}(9.8 \times 2.1^2)$
So, $s = 57.31$
$h = \dfrac{s}{14} = 4.09$ m (3 s.f.)

[4 marks available in total]:
- *1 mark for using appropriate equation*
- *1 mark for correct value of s*
- *1 mark for correct workings*
- *1 mark for correct value of h*

Answers

2 a)

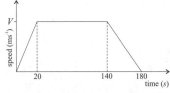

[3 marks available in total]:
- *1 mark for the correct shape*
- *1 mark for the correct times*
- *1 mark for correctly marking V on the vertical axis*

b) Area under graph (area of trapezium) = distance

$\frac{1}{2}(120 + 180)V = 2100$

$V = \frac{2100}{150} = 14$ ms⁻¹

[3 marks available in total]:
- *1 mark for using Area under graph = distance*
- *1 mark for correct workings*
- *1 mark for correct value of V*

The area could also be worked out in other ways, say, using two triangles and a rectangle. Best to use whatever's easiest for you.

c) Distance = area under graph

= ½ × 40 × 14 = 280 m

[2 marks available in total]:
- *1 mark for using Area under graph = distance*
- *1 mark for correct value*

d) $u = 0$, $v = V = 14$, $t = 20$, $a = ?$

Using $a = \frac{v - u}{t}$:

$a = (14 - 0) \div 20 = 0.7$ ms⁻².

[3 marks available in total]:
- *1 mark for using appropriate equation*
- *1 mark for correct workings*
- *1 mark for correct value of a*

3 a) $u = u$; $v = 20$, $a = 9.8$, $s = 8$.

Using $v^2 = u^2 + 2as$

$20^2 = u^2 + (2 \times 9.8 \times 8)$

$u = \sqrt{400 - 156.8}$

So $u = 15.59... = 15.6$ ms⁻¹ (3 s.f.)

[3 marks available in total]:
- *1 mark for using appropriate equation*
- *1 mark for correct workings*
- *1 mark for correct value of u*

b) Using $v = u + at$

$20 = -15.59 + 9.8t$

The initial velocity is negative, as the rocket is projected upwards.

So, $9.8t = 35.59$

hence $t = 3.63$ s (3 s.f.)

[3 marks available in total]:
- *1 mark for using appropriate equation*
- *1 mark for correct workings*
- *1 mark for correct value of t*

Constant use of those constant acceleration equations...
See, I wasn't fooling around — learn them.

4 a) $a = 0 \Rightarrow \frac{dv}{dt} = 0$.

So, in the interval $0 \le t \le 4$,

$a = \frac{dv}{dt} = 9 - 6t$ *[1 mark]*

Set $a = 0$:

$0 = 9 - 6t \Rightarrow t = 1.5$ s *[1 mark]*

b) $s = \int v\,dt$

$= \frac{9t^2}{2} - t^3 + c$ for $0 \le t \le 4$. *[1 mark]*

When $t = 0$, P is at the origin, i.e. $s = 0 \Rightarrow c = 0$ *[1 mark]*

So, at $t = 4$: $s = \frac{9}{2}(16) - 64 = 8$ m *[1 mark]*

c) $s = \int v\,dt = \int -12\,dt = -12t + k$ for $t > 4$. *[1 mark]*
From part b), when $t = 4$ s, $s = 8$ m. Use these as initial conditions to find k:

$8 = -12(4) + k \Rightarrow k = 8 + 48 = 56.$ *[1 mark]*

So $s = -12t + 56$. Set $s = 0$ to find when the particle is back at the origin:

$0 = -12t + 56 \Rightarrow t = 56 \div 12 = 4.67$ s (3 s.f.) *[1 mark]*

You could have done this without integrating, as the speed is constant — but a little light integration never hurt anybody now, did it?

5 a) $a = \dot{v} = 6 - 2t$ ms⁻². *[1 mark]*

b) $s = \int_0^3 v\,dt = \left[3t^2 - \frac{t^3}{3} \right]_0^3 = 3(3)^2 - \frac{3^3}{3} = 18$ m.

*[3 marks available in total — 1 mark for integrating,
1 mark for substituting in limits, 1 mark for correct answer]*

M1 Section 3 — Dynamics
Warm-up Questions

1) Resolve horizontally: $F_{net} = ma$

$2 = 1.5a$ so $a = 1\frac{1}{3}$ ms⁻²

$v = u + at$ $v = 0 + (1\frac{1}{3} \times 3) = 4$ ms⁻¹

And we're off. I hope that bit of resolving was simple enough (if not you might want to go revise).

2) Resolve horizontally:

$F_{net} = ma$ $P - 1 = 2 \times 0.3$

So, $P = 1.6$ N

Resolve vertically: $R = 2g$

Limiting friction: $F = \mu R$, so $1 = \mu \times 2g$,

which gives $\mu = 0.05$ (to 2 d.p.)

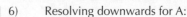

3) Resolving in ↖ direction:
$F_{net} = ma$
$R - 1.2g\cos25° = 1.2 \times 0$
$R = 1.2g\cos25°$
$R = 10.66$ N
Resolving in ↙ direction:
$F_{net} = ma$
$1.2g\sin25° - F = 1.2 \times 0.3$
So, $F = 1.2g\sin25° - 1.2 \times 0.3 = 4.610$ N
Limiting friction, so:
$F = \mu R$
$4.610 = \mu \times 10.66$
$\mu = 0.43$ (to 2 d.p.)
Assumptions:
i) brick slides down line of greatest slope
ii) acceleration is constant
iii) no air resistance
iv) point mass / particle

4) Resolving in ↖ direction:
$F_{net} = ma$
$R - 600\cos30° = \left(\frac{600}{g}\right) \times 0$
$R = 600\cos30°$
Sliding, so $F = \mu R$
$F = 0.5 \times 600\cos30° = 259.8$
Resolving in ↙ direction:
$600\sin30° - F = \left(\frac{600}{g}\right)a$
$600\sin30° - 259.8 = 61.22 \times a$
$a = 0.6566$ ms⁻²

$\left.\begin{array}{l} u = 0 \\ s = 20 \\ a = 0.6566 \\ v = ? \end{array}\right\}$ $\begin{array}{l} v^2 = u^2 + 2as \\ v^2 = 0^2 + 2 \times 0.6566 \times 20 \\ v = 5.12 \text{ ms}^{-1} \text{ (3 s.f.)} \end{array}$

5) Taking tractor and trailer together (and calling the resistance force on the trailer R):

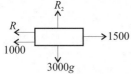

Resolving horizontally: $F_{net} = ma$
$1500 - R - 1000 = 3000 \times 0$
$R = 500$ N
For trailer alone:

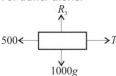

Resolving horizontally:
$F_{net} = ma$
$T - 500 = 1000 \times 0$
$T = 500$ N
T could be found instead by looking at the horizontal forces acting on the tractor alone.

6) Resolving downwards for A:
$F_{net} = ma$
$4g - T = 4 \times 1.2$
$T = 4g - 4.8$ ①
Resolving upwards for B:
$F_{net} = ma$
$T - W = \frac{W}{g} \times 1.2$ ②

Sub ① into ② :

$(4g - 4.8) - W = \frac{W}{g}(1.2)$

$4g - 4.8 = W(1 + \frac{1.2}{g})$

So $W = 30.6$ N

Here the particles are connected over a pulley, rather than in a straight line, but the key is still resolving — downwards and upwards instead of horizontally and vertically (or parallel and perpendicular to a plane, as in the next question). No need for any panic then. Phew.

7) For B, resolving vertically:
$F_{net} = ma$
$4g - T = 4a$
$T = 4g - 4a$ ①
For A , resolving in ↗ direction:
$F_{net} = ma$
$T - 3g\sin40° = 3a$ ②
Sub ① into ②:
$4g - 4a - 3g\sin40° = 3a$
$4g - 3g\sin40° = 7a$
$a = 2.90$ ms⁻²   (to 3 s.f.)
Sub into ① :
$T = 4g - (4 \times 2.9) = 27.6$ N   (to 3 s.f.)
If equilibrium, then for B:
$T = 4g$
Then for A:

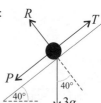

Resolving in ↗ direction:
$F_{net} = ma$
$T - 3g\sin40 - P = 0$
$4g - 3g \sin 40 = P$
$P = 20.3$ N (to 3 s.f.)

8) a) $(5 \times 3) + (4 \times 1) = (5 \times 2) + (4 \times v)$
$19 = 10 + 4v$
$v = 2¼$ ms⁻¹ to the right

b) $(5 \times 3) + (4 \times 1) = 9v$
$19 = 9v$
$v = 2\frac{1}{9}$ ms⁻¹ to the right

c) $(5 \times 3) + (4 \times -2) = (5 \times -v) + (4 \times 3)$
$7 = -5v + 12$
$5v = 5$
$v = 1$ ms⁻¹ to the left

Answers

d) $(m \times 6) + (8 \times 2) = (m \times 2) + (8 \times 4)$

$6m + 16 = 2m + 32$

$4m = 16$

$m = 4$ kg

Collision questions have me bouncing off the ceiling... Be careful with your directions (positive and negative) and it'll all be okay.

Exam Questions

1 a) Constant velocity, so, $a = 0$

Resolve horizontally:

$F_{net} = ma$

$T_2\cos40° - T_1\cos40° = 300 \times 0$

$T_2\cos40° = T_1\cos40°$

$T_2 = T_1$

Resolve vertically:

$F_{net} = ma$

$T_1\sin40° + T_2\sin40° - 300g = 300 \times 0$

Let $T_1 = T_2 = T$: $2T\sin40° = 300g$

$T = 2290$ N   (to 3 s.f.)

[4 marks available in total]:
- **1 mark for resolving horizontally**
- **1 mark for resolving vertically**
- **1 mark for substituting T_1 or T_2**
- **1 mark for the correct value of T**

More triangles, that's what I like to see...

b) Resolve horizontally: $F_{net} = ma$

$T_2\cos40° - T_1\cos40° = 300 \times 0.4$

$T_2 - T_1 = 156.65$ N   ①

Resolve vertically:

$F_{net} = ma$

$T_1\sin40° + T_2\sin40° - 300g = 300 \times 0$

$T_1\sin40° + T_2\sin40° = 300g$

So $T_1 + T_2 = 4573.83$ N   ②

from ①: $T_2 = T_1 + 156.65$

into ②: $T_1 + (T_1 + 156.65) = 4573.83$

so $2T_1 = 4417.18$

$T_1 = 2210$ N   (to 3 s.f.)

and, $T_2 = 2370$ N   (to 3 s.f.)

[6 marks available in total]:
- **1 mark for resolving horizontally**
- **1 mark for finding ①**
- **1 mark for resolving vertically**
- **1 mark for finding ②**
- **1 mark for correct value of T_1**
- **1 mark for correct value of T_2**

c) E.g. cables are inextensible, particle is considered as a point mass, there's no air resistance.

[2 marks available in total]:
- **1 mark each for any 2 relevant assumptions.**

If you got these right, I will make the assumption that you've done some revision...

2 a) Resolving in ↗ direction:

$F_{net} = ma$

$8\cos15° + F - 7g\sin15° = 7 \times 0$

$F = 7g\sin15° - 8\cos15°$

$F = 10.03$ N

Resolving in ↖ direction:

$F_{net} = ma$

$R - 8\sin15° - 7g\cos15° = 7 \times 0$

$R = 8\sin15° + 7g\cos15° = 68.33$ N

Limiting friction:

$F = \mu R$, i.e. $10.03 = \mu \times 68.33$,

which gives $\mu = 0.15$ (2 d.p.)

[5 marks available in total]:
- **1 mark for resolving in ↗ direction**
- **1 mark for correct value of F_{net} in ↗ direction**
- **1 mark for resolving in ↖ direction**
- **1 mark correct value of R**
- **1 mark for correct value of μ**

b) 8 N removed:

Resolving in ↙ direction:

$7g\sin15° - F = 7a$ ①

Resolving in ↖ direction:

$R - 7g\cos15° = 7 \times 0$

$R = 7g\cos15° = 66.26$ N

$F = \mu R$

$F = 0.147 \times 66.26 = 9.74$ N

①: $7g\sin15° - 9.74 = 7a$

$a = \dfrac{8.01}{7} = 1.14$ ms^{-2} (to 2 d.p.)

$s = 3$; $u = 0$; $a = 1.14$; $t = ?$ $s = ut + \frac{1}{2}at^2$

$3 = 0 + \frac{1}{2} \times 1.14 \times t^2$ $t = \sqrt{\dfrac{6}{1.14}} = 2.3$ s (to 2 s.f.)

[7 marks available in total]:
- **1 mark for resolving in ↙ direction**
- **1 mark for resolving in ↖ direction**
- **1 mark for correct value of R**
- **1 mark for correct value of F**
- **1 mark for correct value of a**
- **1 mark for appropriate calculation method for t**
- **1 mark for correct value of t**

3 a) (i) Considering the car and the caravan together:

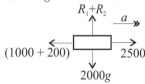

Resolving horizontally, taking right as positive:

$F_{net} = ma$

$2500 - 1200 = 2000a$

$a = 0.65$ ms^{-2}

[3 marks available in total]:
- **1 mark for resolving horizontally**
- **1 mark for correct workings**
- **1 mark for correct value of a**

Answers

(ii) Either: *Caravan*

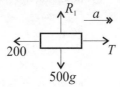

Resolving horizontally,
taking right as positive:
$F_{net} = ma$
$T - 200 = 500 \times 0.65$
$T = 525$ N

[2 marks available in total]:
*   **1 mark for resolving horizontally**
*   **1 mark for correct value of T**

Or: *Car*

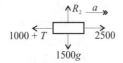

Resolving horizontally,
taking right as positive:
$F_{net} = ma$
$2500 - (1000 + T) = 1500 \times 0.65$
$2500 - 1000 - T = 975$
$1500 - 975 = T$
$T = 525$ N

[2 marks available in total]:
*   **1 mark for resolving horizontally**
*   **1 mark for correct value of T**

Two different methods, one correct answer. At the end of the day, it doesn't matter which you use (but show your diagrams and workings), although it's certainly a bonus if you manage to pick the simpler way and save a bit of time in the exam.

b) (i) Considering the car and the caravan together:

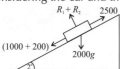

Resolving parallel to slope, taking up the slope as positive:
$F_{net} = ma$
$2500 - 1200 - (2000 \times 9.8 \times \sin 2°) = 2000a$
$a = 0.308$ ms^{-2} (3 s.f.)

[3 marks available in total]:
*   **1 mark for resolving parallel to slope**
*   **1 mark for correct workings**
*   **1 mark for correct value of a**

(ii) Consider the Caravan:
Resolving parallel to slope,
taking up the slope as positive:
$F_{net} = ma$
$T - 200 - (500 \times 9.8 \times \sin 2°) = 500a$
$T = 500a + 200 + (500 \times 9.8 \times \sin 2°)$
Using the exact value of *a* from part b) (i) gives
$T = 525$ N
i.e. the tension is unchanged

[3 marks available in total]:
*   **1 mark for resolving parallel to slope**
*   **1 mark for correct workings**
*   **1 mark for correct value of T**

4 a) For Q:
$F_{net} = ma$
Resolving vertically:
$mg - T = 0$, so $T = mg$
For P:
$F_{net} = ma$
Resolving in ↖ direction:
$R - 1g\cos 20° = 1 \times 0$, so $R = g\cos 20°$
Limiting friction:
$F = \mu R = 0.1 \times g\cos 20°$
Resolving in ↙ direction:
$1g\sin 20° - F - T = 1 \times 0$
$1g\sin 20° - 0.1g\cos 20° - mg = 0$
$\sin 20° - 0.1\cos 20° = m$
$m = 0.248$ kg (to 3 s.f.)

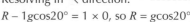

[5 marks available in total]:
*   **1 mark for resolving vertically**
*   **1 mark for resolving in ↖ direction**
*   **1 mark for correct value of F**
*   **1 mark for resolving in ↙ direction**
*   **1 mark for correct value of m**

b) If Q = 1kg:
$F_{net} = ma$
For Q:
Resolving vertically:
$1g - T = 1a$, so $T = g - a$ ①
For P:
Resolving in ↖ direction:
$R = g\cos 20°$
$F = \mu R = 0.1g\cos 20°$
Resolving in ↗ direction:
$T - 1g\sin 20° - F = 1a$
$T - 1g\sin 20° - 0.1g\cos 20° = 1a$ ②
Sub ① into ②:$(g - a) - g\sin 20° - 0.1g\cos 20° = a$
$g - g\sin 20° - 0.1g\cos 20° = 2a$
$5.527 = 2a$, so $a = 2.76$ ms^{-2} (to 3 s.f.)
i.e. the masses move with an acceleration of 2.76 ms^{-2}, with P moving up the slope and Q moving downwards.

[5 marks available in total]:
*   **1 mark for resolving vertically**
*   **1 mark for resolving in ↖ direction**
*   **1 mark for resolving in ↗ direction**
*   **1 mark for substituting ① into ②**
*   **1 mark for correct value of a**

5   Before   After

$(0.8 \times 4) + (1.2 \times 2) = (0.8 \times 2.5) + 1.2v$
$3.2 + 2.4 = 2.0 + 1.2v$
$v = 3$ ms^{-1}

Answers

Before   **After**

$(1.2 \times 3) + (m \times -4) = (1.2 + m) \times 0$

$3.6 = 4m$

$m = 0.9$ kg

[4 marks available in total]:
- *1 mark for using conservation of momentum*
- *1 mark for correct value of v*
- *1 mark for correct workings*
- *1 mark for correct value of m*

Diagrams are handy for collision questions too, partly because they make the question clearer for you, but they also make it easier for the examiner to see how you're going about answering the question.

6 a) Resolving forces acting on A:

$7g - T = 7a$

Resolving forces acting on B:

$T - 3g = 3a$, so $T = 3a + 3g$

Substituting T:

$7g - 3a - 3g = 7a$, so $4g = 10a$

hence $a = 3.92$ ms^{-2}

Using $t = \frac{(v - u)}{a}$:

$t = (5.9 - 0) \div 3.92 = 1.505...$

So, $t = 1.51$ s (to 3 s.f.)

[4 marks available in total]:
- *1 mark for resolving forces*
- *1 mark for correct value of a*
- *1 mark for correct workings*
- *1 mark for correct value of t*

b) Using $s = \frac{v^2 - u^2}{2a}$

$s = (5.9^2 - 0^2) \div (2 \times 3.92)$

$s = 4.44$ m (to 3 s.f.)

[2 marks available in total]:
- *1 mark for correct workings*
- *1 mark for correct value of s*

c) When A hits the ground, speed of A = speed of B = 5.9 ms^{-1}
B will then continue to rise, momentarily stop and then fall freely under gravity. String will be taut again when displacement of B = 0.

So, $a = -9.8$, $s = 0$, $u = 5.9$

Using $s = ut + \frac{1}{2}at^2$:

$0 = 5.9t + \frac{1}{2}(-9.8)t^2 = 5.9t - 4.9t^2$

Solve for t:

$4.9t^2 = 5.9t$, so $t(4.9t - 5.9) = 0$

and so $t = 0$ s or $t = 5.9 \div 4.9 = 1.20$ s

So the string becomes taut again at $t = 1.20$ s (to 3 s.f.)

[4 marks available in total]:
- *1 mark for using $s = ut + \frac{1}{2}at^2$*
- *1 mark for correct workings*
- *1 mark for solving for t*
- *1 mark for correct value of t*

7 a) **Before**   **After**

$(4000 \times 2.5) + (1000 \times 0) = 5000v$

$v = 2$ ms^{-1}

[2 marks available in total]:
- *1 mark for using conservation of momentum*
- *1 mark for correct value of v*

b) E.g. track horizontal; no resistance (e.g. friction) to motion; wagons can be modelled as particles.

[2 marks available in total]:
- *1 mark each for any of the above assumptions or any other relevant assumption*

If you've forgotten what 'any other valid assumption' might be, I recommend you have a look at the table on p. 158 again.

M1 — Practice Exam One

1 a) Find the horizontal and vertical components of the resultant by resolving horizontally and vertically *[1 mark]*:
Horizontal component: 11 + 4cos25° *[1 mark]*
Vertical component: 7 + 4sin25° *[1 mark]*
Now you can draw a 'triangle of forces':

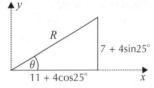

Where R is the resultant force and θ is the angle it makes with the horizontal.
Use Pythagoras to find the magnitude of R:

$R^2 = (7 + 4\sin25)^2 + (11 + 4\cos25)^2 = 289.4$ *[1 mark]*

$\Rightarrow R = 17.0$ N (3 s.f.) *[1 mark]*

b) Use trig on the above triangle:

$\tan\theta = \frac{7 + 4\sin25}{11 + 4\cos25} = 0.5942$ *[1 mark]*

$\Rightarrow \theta = \tan^{-1}(0.5942)$ *[1 mark]*

$= 30.7°$ (3 s.f.) *[1 mark]*

2 a) With uniform motion questions, always start by writing down the data you have and the data you need.

$u = 15$, $v = 40$, $a = ?$, $t = 4$, $s = ?$

You need to find a, so '$v = u + at$' is the equation you need.
Rearrange to make a the subject and substitute in:

$a = \frac{v - u}{t} = \frac{40 - 15}{4} = 6.25$ ms^{-2}

[2 marks available in total]:
- *1 mark for using '$v = u + at$' or equivalent*
- *1 mark for correct value of a*

b) $u = 40$, $v = 26$, $a = -2.8$, $t = ?$, $s = ?$

You need t, so it's '$v = u + at$'. Rearrange and substitute:

$t = \frac{v - u}{a} = \frac{26 - 40}{-2.8} = 5$ s

[2 marks available in total]:
- *1 mark for using '$v = u + at$' or equivalent*
- *1 mark for correct value of t*

Answers

c) You've now got all the other quantities except the two distances, so you can use any of the formulas with s in.

I'm going for '$s = \frac{1}{2}(u+v)t$' because it's nice and easy:

A to B: $s = \frac{1}{2}(u+v)t = \frac{1}{2}(15+40) \times 4 = 110$ m

B to C: $s = \frac{1}{2}(u+v)t = \frac{1}{2}(40+26) \times 5 = 165$ m

AC = 275 m

[3 marks available in total]:
- *1 mark for using '$s = \frac{1}{2}(u+v)t$' or equivalent*
- *1 mark for either intermediate distance correct*
- *1 mark for the correct value of AC*

You REALLY need to know those equations.

3 a) For collision questions, always decide at the start (and label) which direction you're going to use as positive.

Diagram:

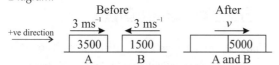

Use Conservation of Momentum to solve:

'total momentum of A and B before collision = momentum of combined trucks after collision'

$(3500 \times 3) + (1500 \times -3) = 5000v$ *[1 mark]*

So, $v = 6000 \div 5000 = 1.2$ ms⁻¹ in the positive direction. After the collision, the combined trucks move at 1.2 ms⁻¹ *[1 mark]* in the same direction as A was moving before the collision *[1 mark]*.

b)

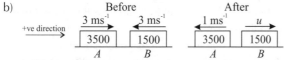

As in part a), use Conservation of Momentum to solve:

$(3500 \times 3) + (1500 \times -3) = (3500 \times -1) + (1500 \times u)$ *[1 mark]*

So $u = 9500 \div 1500 = 6.33$ ms⁻¹ (3 s.f.) *[1 mark]* in the same direction A was moving before the collision *[1 mark]*.

Not sure why, but I find these questions very satisfying when I've solved them. Maybe I'm just a freak.

4 a) It's usually a good idea to draw a diagram to make it clear what's going on:

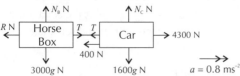

(Taking right as positive)

(i) Resolve forces acting on the car only:

$F_{net} = ma$ *[1 mark]*

$\Rightarrow 4300 - 400 - T = 1600 \times 0.8$ *[1 mark]*

$\Rightarrow T = 4300 - 400 - (1600 \times 0.8) = 2620$ N *[1 mark]*.

(ii) Resolve forces acting on the horse box only:

$F_{net} = ma$ *[1 mark]*

$T - R = 3000 \times 0.8$ *[1 mark]*

$\Rightarrow R = 2620 - (3000 \times 0.8) = 220$ N *[1 mark]*.

b) (i) $F_{net} = ma \Rightarrow -220 = 3000a$ *[1 mark]*

$\Rightarrow a = -220 \div 3000 = -0.0733$ ms⁻² (3 s.f.) *[1 mark]*.

So the deceleration of the horse box is 0.0733 ms⁻².

(ii) Use $v^2 = u^2 + 2as$: *[1 mark]*

$0 = 7^2 + (2 \times -0.0733 \times s)$ *[1 mark]*

$\Rightarrow s = -49 \div (2 \times -0.0733) = 334$ m (3 s.f.) *[1 mark]*.

5 a) Differentiate the velocity to find the acceleration:

$a = \frac{dv}{dt}$ *[1 mark]* $= 11 - 4t$ *[1 mark]*.

b) Integrate the velocity to find the displacement *[1 mark]*:

$s = \int v\,dt = \frac{11}{2}t^2 - \frac{2}{3}t^3 + c$ for $0 \le t \le 5$ *[1 mark]*.

When $t = 0$, $s = 0 \Rightarrow c = 0$ *[1 mark]*.

So, when $t = 5$:

$s = \frac{11}{2}(25) - \frac{2}{3}(125) = 54.2$ m (3 s.f.) *[1 mark]*

c) Maximum v occurs when $a = 0$ *[1 mark]*.

Differentiate to find a:

$a = \frac{dv}{dt} = 56 - 8t$ *[1 mark]*

$a = 0 \Rightarrow t = 56 \div 8 = 7$ *[1 mark]*.

When $t = 7$, $v = -175 + 56(7) - 4(7)^2 = 21$ ms⁻¹ *[1 mark]*.

Make sure you know the time interval each part of the question is asking about. Here, parts a) and b) ask about the motion for $0 \le t \le 5$, whereas part c) asks about the motion for $t > 5$. You don't want to end up using the wrong equation — that wouldn't be good at all.

6 a) $u = 0, v = ?, a = 1.5, t = 8, s = ?$

So you're going to need '$v = u + at$'

$v = 0 + (1.5 \times 8) = 12$ ms⁻¹

Greatest speed = 12 ms⁻¹

[2 marks available in total]:
- *1 mark for using '$v = u + at$' or equivalent*
- *1 mark for correct value of speed*

b) Use the information from part (a) to mark when the cyclist stops accelerating and travels at a constant speed:

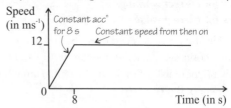

[2 marks available in total]:
- *1 mark for correct shape*
- *1 mark for correct numbers*

c) Speed

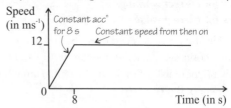

[2 marks available in total]:
- *1 mark for correct shape*
- *1 mark for correct numbers*

Answers

d) First work out how long the cyclist was travelling at a constant speed:

total time until overtaking = 24 s,

so cyclist travelled at a constant speed for 24 − 8 = 16 s.

Total distance travelled = area under speed-time graph.

The area is split into two simple shapes:

area of triangle = $\frac{1}{2} \times 12 \times 8 = 48$

area of rectangle = $12 \times 16 = 192$

Distance travelled = 48 + 192 = 240 m

[3 marks available in total]:
- *1 mark for using 'distance = area under graph' or equivalent*
- *1 mark for correct working*
- *1 mark for the correct value for distance travelled*

e) The cycle and car travel the same distance, so you can use the result from part (d). Again, the distance travelled is the area under the graph, so you can work back from there. This time the area under the graph is a simple triangle, so it's a bit easier.

distance = area under graph = $240 = \frac{1}{2} \times 24 \times V$

So, $V = 20$ ms^{-1}

[3 marks available in total]:
- *1 mark for 'distance = area under graph' or equivalent*
- *1 mark for recognising both cycle and car travelled the same distance*
- *1 mark for correct value of V*

This is as easy as Mechanics gets, so there's no excuse for getting questions like this wrong. If you found this hard, get it learnt before the exam. These questions never vary much — if you can do one, you can do them all.

7 a) Hold onto your hats — this is a long, long question...

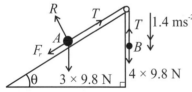

where $\theta = \tan^{-1}\frac{3}{4}$

[2 marks for adding all the correct forces]

b) Particle A remains on the angled plane, so the normal reaction must be equal to the component of the weight force in the opposite direction:

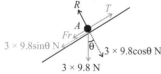

$\tan\theta = \frac{3}{4}$ so $\cos\theta = \frac{4}{5}$

So $R = 3 \times 9.8 \times \frac{4}{5} = 23.52$ N

So, normal reaction = 23.52 N

[2 marks available in total]:
- *1 mark for resolving perpendicular*
- *1 mark for correct value of R*

c) You don't know anything about the friction force on A yet, so start by looking at B, since that's only affected by weight and tension:

Use '$F = ma$' for B:

$(4 \times 9.8) - T = 4 \times 1.4$

So, $T = 33.6$ N

[2 marks available in total]:
- *1 mark for using '$F = ma$'*
- *1 mark for correct value of T*

d) We now know the tension, so we can use '$F = ma$' on particle A to find the friction (in case you get confused — the 'F' in '$F = ma$' means 'resultant force', not 'friction'). Start with a diagram (always helps):

For A: Resultant force = ma

$T - F_r - (3 \times 9.8 \sin\theta) = 3 \times 1.4$

Note that $\tan\theta = \frac{3}{4}$ so $\sin\theta = \frac{3}{5}$

Substitute in value of T from part (c):

$33.6 - F_r - 17.64 = 4.2$

So, $F_r = 11.76$ N

[3 marks available in total]:
- *1 mark for using '$F = ma$'*
- *1 mark for correct expression for resultant force*
- *1 mark for correct answer*

e) The system's moving, so friction is 'limiting', i.e. $F_r = \mu R$.

Rearranging and substituting values in gives:

$\mu = \frac{F_r}{R} = \frac{11.76}{23.52} = 0.5$

[2 marks available in total]:
- *1 mark for using '$F_r = \mu R$'*
- *1 mark for correct value of μ*

f) This is fairly straightforward — it's just uniform acceleration, so it's the usual equations:

Motion of B: $u = 0$, $v = ?$, $a = 1.4$, $s = ?$, $t = 2$

It's s you're after, so use '$s = ut + \frac{1}{2}at^2$':

$s = 0 + \left(\frac{1}{2} \times 1.4 \times 4\right) = 2.8$ m

Particle B moves 2.8 m before the string breaks.

[2 marks available in total]:
- *1 mark for using '$s = ut + \frac{1}{2}at^2$' or equivalent*
- *1 mark for correct value of s*

Answers

g) This is easier than it looks (phew). Remember, while A and B are attached, they move together at the same speed. So you can use the data from part (f) to find the speed of (both) A and B when the string breaks:
$v = u + at = 0 + 1.4 \times 2 = 2.8$ ms⁻¹
Then draw yourself another diagram to show particle A immediately after the string breaks:

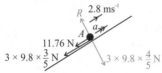

You need to work out the acceleration, so you need '$F = ma$':
$-11.76 - \left(3 \times 9.8 \times \frac{3}{5}\right) = 3a$
So, $a = -9.8$ ms⁻²
Don't stop there — now you've got to find how far A travels before it comes to rest. It's the usual equations:
For A: $u = 2.8$, $v = 0$, $a = -9.8$, $s = ?$, $t = ?$
You're after s, so use '$v^2 = u^2 + 2as$':
Rearrange to give:
$s = \frac{v^2 - u^2}{2a} = \frac{0 - 2.8^2}{2 \times -9.8} = 0.4$ m
So particle A moves 0.4 m from the instant the string breaks until it comes to rest.

[5 marks available in total]:
- *1 mark for correct value for speed*
- *1 mark for using 'F = ma'*
- *1 mark for correct value for acceleration*
- *1 mark for using 'v² = u² + 2as' or equivalent*
- *1 mark for correct answer*

That was one beast of a question. But you made it. And honestly — this is the best kind of practice you can get. There's balancing forces, resolving forces, Newton's 2nd law and friction. All in one big question. It might feel like you've gone through the mill a bit, but if you got that question all right, I reckon you've got a pretty good understanding of mechanics.

M1 — Practice Exam Two

1 a) Resolve along x-axis:
$P\sin40° - 20\cos(105-90)° = 0$
so, $P = \frac{20\cos15°}{\sin40°} = 30.054... = 30.1$ N (3 s.f.)
[2 marks available in total]:
- *1 mark for correct workings*
- *1 mark for correct value of P*

Something simple to get you started. I bet you'd never have guessed it would involve resolving forces.

b) Resolve along y-axis:
$R = 30.05\cos40° + 35 - 20\sin15° = 52.846...$
$= 52.8$ N (3 s.f.) up the y-axis
[3 marks available in total]:
- *1 mark for correct workings*
- *1 mark for correct value of R*
- *1 mark for correct direction*

c) Use $F_{net} = ma$:
$R = ma \Rightarrow a = R \div m = 52.846... \div 5 = 10.569...$
$= 10.6$ ms⁻² (3 s.f.)
[2 marks available in total]:
- *1 mark for correct working*
- *1 mark for correct answer*

d) Use $s = ut + \frac{1}{2}at^2$, with $u = 0$, $a = 10.569...$ and $s = 6$:
$6 = \frac{1}{2}(10.569...)t^2$
$\Rightarrow t^2 = \frac{6 \times 2}{10.569...} = 1.135...$
$\Rightarrow t = 1.07$ s (3 s.f.)
[3 marks available in total]:
- *1 mark for using constant acceleration equation*
- *1 mark for correct working*
- *1 mark for correct final answer*

2 a) Just plug $t = 1$ into the equation for x:
$x = 1 + 6 - 24 + 1 = -16$ m *[1 mark]*.

b) Differentiate the displacement to find the velocity:
$v = \frac{dx}{dt}$ *[1 mark]* $= 4t^3 + 18t^2 - 48t$ *[1 mark]*
$t = 2 \Rightarrow v = 4(8) + 18(4) - 48(2) = 8$ ms⁻¹ *[1 mark]*.

c) (i) Differentiate the velocity to find the acceleration:
$a = \frac{dv}{dt}$ *[1 mark]* $= 12t^2 + 36t - 48$ *[1 mark]*.
$a = 0 \Rightarrow 12t^2 + 36t - 48 = 0$
$\Rightarrow t^2 + 3t - 4 = 0$ *[1 mark]*
$\Rightarrow (t - 1)(t + 4) = 0$ *[1 mark]*
$\Rightarrow t = 1, t = -4$ *[1 mark]*.
$t = -4$ has no meaning in this context, so the particle has zero acceleration at time $t = 1$ *[1 mark]*.

(ii) Plug $t = 1$ into the expression for velocity:
$v = 4(1)^3 + 18(1)^2 - 48(1)$ *[1 mark]* $= -26$ ms⁻¹ *[1 mark]*.

3 a)

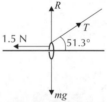

[2 marks available in total]:
- *1 mark for correct force arrows*
- *1 mark for correctly labelling the forces*

b) Resolving horizontally:
$F = T\cos51.3°$ so $T = \frac{1.5}{\cos51.3} = 2.40$ N
Resolving vertically:
$mg = R + T\sin51.3°$
$R = \frac{F}{\mu} = 1.5 \div 0.6 = 2.5$ N
so $mg = 2.5 + 2.40\sin51.3°$
and $m = 0.446$ kg (3 s.f.)

[6 marks available in total]:
- *1 mark for resolving horizontally*
- *1 mark for correct value of T*
- *1 mark for resolving vertically*
- *1 mark for using F = μR*
- *1 mark for correct workings*
- *1 mark for correct value of m*

Answers

4   a)

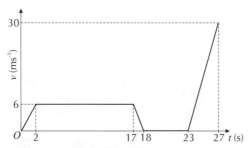

[2 marks available in total]:
- **1 mark for correct shape**
- **1 mark for correct numbers**

b) a = gradient of graph
$t = 0 - 2$ s: $a = 6 \div 2 = 3$ ms^{-2}
$t = 17 - 18$ s: $a = -6 \div 1 = -6$ ms^{-2}
$t = 23 - 27$ s: $a = 30 \div 4 = 7.5$ ms^{-2}
Greatest acceleration is 7.5 ms^{-2}.

[3 marks available in total]:
- **1 mark for finding gradients or equivalent**
- **1 mark for correct workings**
- **1 mark for correct statement of greatest acceleration**

c)   Distance = area under the graph
$t = 0 - 2$ s: $s = \frac{1}{2}(6)2 = 6$ m   (triangle: area = $\frac{1}{2}bh$)
$t = 2 - 17$ s: $s = 6 \times 15 = 90$ m   (rectangle)
$t = 17 - 18$ s: $s = \frac{1}{2}(6)1 = 3$ m   (triangle)
$t = 18 - 23$ s: $s = 0 \times 5 = 0$ m   (rectangle)
$t = 23 - 27$ s: $s = \frac{1}{2}(30)4 = 60$ m   (triangle)
Total distance = $6 + 90 + 3 + 0 + 60 = 159$ m

[3 marks available in total]:
- **1 mark for using distance = area under graph**
- **1 mark for correct workings**
- **1 mark for correct value of total distance**

I don't really like roller coasters, but they do have some great maths involved. I'd give up writing books to go and design them, unless I had to test them. I feel sick thinking about that.

5   a)   Using conservation of momentum:
$m_A u_A + m_B u_B = m_A v_A + m_B v_B$
$(4 \times 4) + (m \times -10) = (4 \times -2) + (m \times v)$ *[1 mark]*
$16 - 10m = -8 + mv$ *[1 mark]*
$\Rightarrow mv = 24 - 10m$ *[1 mark]*, as required.

b) B has velocity v ms^{-1} immediately before impact, so, using conservation of momentum:
$m_B u_B + m_C u_C = m_{(B + C)} v_{(B + C)}$
$(m \times v) + (1 \times 0) = (m + 1) \times 7$ *[1 mark]*
$\Rightarrow mv = 7(m + 1)$ *[1 mark]*

c)   (i)   Solve the simultaneous equations from parts a) & b):
$mv = 24 - 10m$
$mv = 7(m + 1)$
$\Rightarrow 24 - 10m = 7(m + 1)$
$24 - 7 = 7m + 10m$
$17 = 17m$
$\Rightarrow m = 1$ kg.

[3 marks available in total]:
- **1 mark for attempting to solve simultaneous equations**
- **1 mark for correct working**
- **1 mark for correct value of m**

(ii)   Sub $m = 1$ into one of the equations from a) and b):
$mv = 24 - 10m$
$\Rightarrow v = \dfrac{24 - 10m}{m} = \dfrac{24 - 10}{1}$ *[1 mark]*
$= 14$ ms^{-1} *[1 mark]*.

Momentum questions can sometimes be a bit wordy — you'll need to read the question carefully to find out all of the information you need. Watch out for things like 'their directions are reversed' and 'goes on to collide with' — this will tell you the speed and direction of the particles at different stages during the collision.

6   a)   Using $F_{net} = ma$ and resolving vertically:
$34\,000\,000 - (1\,400\,000 \times 9.8) = (1\,400\,000 \times a)$
So, $a = \dfrac{34\,000\,000 - 13\,720\,000}{1\,400\,000}$
$= 14.485... = 14.5$ ms^{-2} (3 s.f.)

[2 marks available in total]:
- **1 mark for resolving vertically**
- **1 mark for correct value of a**

b)   Again, using $F_{net} = ma$ and resolving vertically:
$34\,000\,000 - 13\,720\,000 - R = 1\,400\,000 \times 12$
so, $R = 34\,000\,000 - 13\,720\,000 - 16\,800\,000$
$= 3\,480\,000$ N

[2 marks available in total]:
- **1 mark for resolving vertically**
- **1 mark correct value of R**

c) $u = 0$; $a = 12$; $s = 20\,000$; $t = ?$
Using $s = ut + \frac{1}{2}at^2$:
$20\,000 = (0 \times t) + \frac{1}{2}(12 \times t^2)$
so, $t^2 = 20\,000 \div 6$ and $t = 58$ s (to the nearest second)

[2 marks available in total]:
- **1 mark for using 's = ut + $\frac{1}{2}$at²'**
- **1 mark for correct value of t**

d)   Use $v^2 = u^2 + 2as$ and the values from c)
to find the speed at 20 km:
$v^2 = 0^2 + 2(12 \times 20\,000)$
$\Rightarrow v^2 = 480\,000$ *[1 mark]*
The acceleration of the rocket is now $-g$,
so using $v^2 = u^2 + 2as$:
$0 = 480\,000 + (2 \times -9.8 \times s)$ *[1 mark]*
At its maximum height, the rocket's velocity will be O ms^{-1}.

So $s = 24\,500$ m (3 s.f.) *[1 mark]*

Add to initial height:
$20\,000 + 24\,500 = 44\,500$ m $= 44.5$ km (3 s.f.) *[1 mark]*

You could have used other motion equations here, but it's best to use one which includes the values that you're given in the question, not values that you've found yourself.

e)   e.g. g is constant/R is constant up to 20 km/the force from the engines is constant/the mass of the rocket is constant.

[1 mark for any valid assumption]

Answers

7 a)

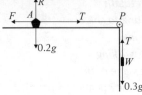

For W, $F_{net} = ma$:
$0.3g - T = 0.3(4)$
$T = 2.94 - 1.2 = 1.74$ N
For A, $F_{net} = ma$:
$T - F = 4(0.2) = 0.8$
$F = T - 0.8 = 1.74 - 0.8 = 0.94$ N
Resolving vertically: $R = 0.2g = 1.96$ N
$F = \mu R$ so $\mu = \dfrac{F}{R} = \dfrac{0.94}{1.96} = 0.480$ (3 s.f.)

[5 marks available in total]:
- *1 mark for resolving forces on A and W*
- *1 mark for correct value of T*
- *1 mark for correct value of F*
- *1 mark for correct value of R*
- *1 mark for correct value of μ*

b) Find speed of A when string goes slack (this will be the same as the speed of W when it hits the floor):
$u = 0$; $v = ?$; $a = 4$; $s = h$
Use $v^2 = u^2 + 2as$:
$v^2 = 0^2 + 2(4 \times h)$ *[1 mark]*
$v^2 = 8h \Rightarrow v = \sqrt{8h}$ *[1 mark]*
Find the acceleration of A once the string has gone slack by resolving forces horizontally:
$F_{net} = ma \Rightarrow -F = 0.2a$, *[1 mark]*
where $F = 0.94$ N (from part a) *[1 mark]*
So, $-0.94 = 0.2a \Rightarrow a = -4.7$ ms^{-2} *[1 mark]*
For the motion of A between the point where the string goes slack and P:
$u = \sqrt{8h}$; $v = 3$; $a = -4.7$; $s = \dfrac{7}{4}h - h = \dfrac{3}{4}h$
Use $v^2 = u^2 + 2as$:
$9 = 8h - (2 \times 4.7 \times 0.75h) = 0.95h$ *[1 mark]*
So $h = 9.47$ m (3 s.f.) *[1 mark]*
Tricky. And a little bit sticky.

c) The fact that string is inextensible means that A and W have the same acceleration when W is falling.

[1 mark for correct explanation]

A simple question to finish off. Well, you deserved a break after part b). That's M1 in the bag, so practise, practise and practise some more until the exam. If the next thing you have to do is the exam, then good luck — Mechanics loves you.

Answers

D1 Section 1 — Algorithms
Warm-up Questions

1) a) Input: raw ingredients (e.g. vegetables, water etc.)
Output: vegetable soup.

   b) Input: starting point (Leicester Square)
Output: final destination (the Albert Hall)

   c) Input: components (e.g. shelves, screws etc.)
Output: finished TV cabinet (*in theory — I'm not much good at flat-pack*)

2)

x	y
17	56
~~8~~	~~112~~
~~4~~	~~224~~
~~2~~	~~448~~
1	896
Total	952

So $17 \times 56 = 952$.

3) Diamond-shaped boxes are used for decisions — they'll ask a question.

4) $a = 16$

n	b	Output	n = a?
1	16	1	No
2	8	2	No
3	$5\frac{1}{3}$		No
4	4	4	No
5	$3\frac{1}{5}$		No
6	$2\frac{2}{3}$		No
7	$2\frac{2}{7}$		No
8	2	8	No
9	$1\frac{7}{9}$		No
10	$1\frac{3}{5}$		No
11	$1\frac{5}{11}$		No
12	$1\frac{1}{3}$		No
13	$1\frac{3}{13}$		No
14	$1\frac{1}{7}$		No
15	$1\frac{1}{15}$		No
16	1	16	Yes

So the factors of 16 are 1, 2, 4, 8 and 16.

5)
<u>72, 57</u>, 64, 54, 68, 71	swap
57, <u>72, 64</u>, 54, 68, 71	swap
57, 64, <u>72, 54</u>, 68, 71	swap
57, 64, 54, <u>72, 68</u>, 71	swap
57, 64, 54, 68, <u>72, 71</u>	swap
57, 64, 54, 68, 71, 72	end of first pass.

At the end of the second pass, the list is:
57, 54, 64, 68, 71, 72.
At the end of the third pass, the list is:
54, 57, 64, 68, 71, 72.
There are no swaps on the fourth pass, so the list is in order.
It took 3 passes to get the list in order.

6) The maximum number of comparisons is $9 + 8 + 7 + 6 + 5 + 4 + 3 + 2 + 1 = 45$ (or $\frac{1}{2} \times 9 \times 10 = 45$).

7) $60 = 20 \times 3$, and as the algorithm is quadratic, it'll take approx. $3^2 = 9$ times as long for 60 numbers. $0.4 \times 9 = 3.6$ s.

8)
First pass:	<u>21, 11</u>, 23, 19, 28, 26	swap
Second pass:	11, <u>21, 23</u>, 19, 28, 26	no swap
Third pass:	11, 21, <u>23, 19</u>, 28, 26	swap
	11, <u>21, 19</u>, 23, 28, 26	swap
	<u>11, 19</u>, 21, 23, 28, 26	no swap
Fourth pass:	11, 19, 21, <u>23, 28</u>, 26	no swap
Fifth pass:	11, 19, 21, 23, <u>28, 26</u>	swap
	11, 19, 21, <u>23, 26</u>, 28	no swap

9) a)
Box 1: 5, 8	space left: ~~10 kg~~ 2 kg
Box 2: 11	space left: 4 kg
Box 3: 9	space left: 6 kg
Box 4: 12	space left: 3 kg
Box 5: 7	space left: 8 kg.

Total space wasted = $2 + 4 + 6 + 3 + 8 = 23$ kg

   b) First, reorder the numbers in descending order:
12, 11, 9, 8, 7, 5. Then,
Box 1: 12	space left: 3 kg
Box 2: 11	space left: 4 kg
Box 3: 9, 5	space left: ~~6 kg~~ 1 kg
Box 4: 8, 7	space left: ~~7 kg~~ 0 kg

Total space wasted = $3 + 4 + 1 + 0 = 8$ kg

Exam Questions

1 a)
First pass:	<u>77, 83</u>, 96, 105, 78, 89	swap
		1 comparison 1 swap
		[1 mark]
Second pass:	83, <u>77, 96</u>, 105, 78, 89	swap
	<u>83, 96</u>, 77, 105, 78, 89	swap
		2 comparisons 2 swaps
		[1 mark]
Third pass:	96, 83, <u>77, 105</u>, 78, 89	swap
	96, <u>83, 105</u>, 77, 78, 89	swap
	<u>96, 105</u>, 83, 77, 78, 89	swap
		3 comparisons 3 swaps
		[1 mark]
Fourth pass:	105, 96, 83, <u>77, 78</u>, 89	swap
	105, 96, <u>83, 78</u>, 77, 89	no swap
		2 comparisons 1 swap
		[1 mark]
Fifth pass:	105, 96, 83, 78, <u>77, 89</u>	swap
	105, 96, 83, <u>78, 89</u>, 77	swap
	105, 96, <u>83, 89</u>, 78, 77	swap
	105, <u>96, 89</u>, 83, 78, 77	no swap
		4 comparisons 3 swaps
		[1 mark]

   b) (i) After the first pass, the final (6th) number in the list (77) will be in the correct position. *[1 mark]*

   (ii) There are 6 items, so the maximum number of passes is $6 - 1 = 5$ *[1 mark]*. The maximum number of swaps is $5 + 4 + 3 + 2 + 1 = 15$ *[1 mark]*.

Answers

2 a)

N	C	D	Output	$N = A$?
1	8	12	1	No
2	4	6	2	No
3	$2\frac{2}{3}$	4		No
4	2	3	4	No
5	$1\frac{3}{5}$	$2\frac{2}{5}$		No
6	$1\frac{1}{3}$	2		No
7	$1\frac{1}{7}$	$1\frac{5}{7}$		No
8	1	$1\frac{1}{2}$		Yes

The results are 1, 2 and 4.

[3 marks available in total:

- ***1 mark for correct values of C;***
- ***1 mark for correct values of D;***
- ***1 mark for correct outputs (there should be 3 outputs)]***

b) (i) This algorithm produces the common factors of the inputs. ***[1 mark]***

(ii) The output would be 1 ***[1 mark]***, as 19 and 25 have no common factors. ***[1 mark]***

3 a) Plank 1: 1.2, 0.6, 0.8 space left: ~~1.8~~ ~~1.2~~ 0.4
Plank 2: 2.3 space left: 0.7
Plank 3: 1.5, 1.0 space left: ~~1.5~~ 0.5
Plank 4: 0.9 space left: 2.1
Plank 5: 2.5 space left: 0.5 ***[1 mark]***
So 5 planks are used ***[1 mark]*** and there is 0.4 + 0.7 + 0.5 + 2.1 + 0.5 = 4.2 m wasted wood. ***[1 mark]***

b) 120 = 30 × 4, and as the algorithm is quadratic, it will take approximately $4^2 = 16$ times as long ***[1 mark]*** when there are 4 times as many numbers. 16 × 2.1 = 33.6 s ***[1 mark]***.

5 a)

First pass:	1.3, 0.8, 1.8, 0.5, 1.2, 0.2, 0.9	swap
Second pass:	0.8, 1.3, 1.8, 0.5, 1.2, 0.2, 0.9	no swap
Third pass:	0.8, 1.3, 1.8, 0.5, 1.2, 0.2, 0.9	swap
	0.8, 1.3, 0.5, 1.8, 1.2, 0.2, 0.9	swap
	0.8, 0.5, 1.3, 1.8, 1.2, 0.2, 0.9	swap
		[1 mark]
Fourth pass:	0.5, 0.8, 1.3, 1.8, 1.2, 0.2, 0.9	swap
	0.5, 0.8, 1.3, 1.2, 1.8, 0.2, 0.9	swap
	0.5, 0.8, 1.2, 1.3, 1.8, 0.2, 0.9	no swap
		[1 mark]
Fifth pass:	0.5, 0.8, 1.2, 1.3, 1.8, 0.2, 0.9	swap
	0.5, 0.8, 1.2, 1.3, 0.2, 1.8, 0.9	swap
	0.5, 0.8, 1.2, 0.2, 1.3, 1.8, 0.9	swap
	0.5, 0.8, 0.2, 1.2, 1.3, 1.8, 0.9	swap
	0.5, 0.2, 0.8, 1.2, 1.3, 1.8, 0.9	swap
		[1 mark]
Sixth pass:	0.2, 0.5, 0.8, 1.2, 1.3, 1.8, 0.9	swap
	0.2, 0.5, 0.8, 1.2, 1.3, 0.9, 1.8	swap
	0.2, 0.5, 0.8, 1.2, 0.9, 1.3, 1.8	swap
	0.2, 0.5, 0.8, 0.9, 1.2, 1.3, 1.8	no swap
		[1 mark]

There are 7 numbers, so there must be 7 – 1 = 6 passes ***[1 mark]***.

b) On the first pass, there was 1 comparison and 1 swap ***[1 mark]***.

D1 Section 2 — Graph Theory Warm-up Questions

1) a) A graph which has a number associated with each edge.

b) A graph in which one or more of the edges have a direction associated with them.

c) A connected graph with no cycles.

d) A subgraph which contains all the vertices of the original graph and is also a tree.

2) E.g.

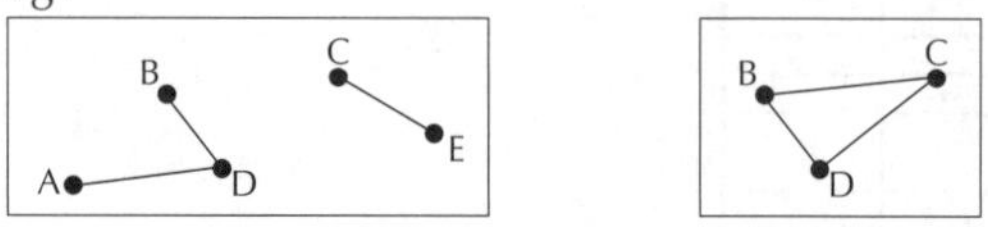

3) a) Arcs do not cross at all, so definitely planar.

Planar graphs can be drawn so that the arcs only cross at nodes.

b) No multiple arcs between any pair of nodes.
No nodes connected to themselves directly.

4) Path: E.g. ADBC, cycle: E.g. BCDB

5) E.g.

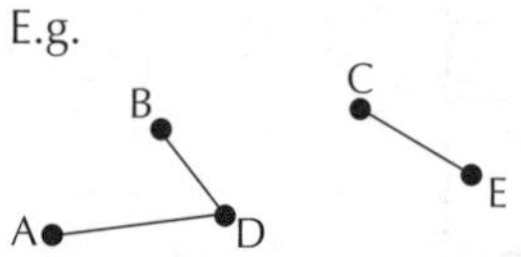

6) A = 1, B = 2, C = 3, D = 3, E = 1
Sum of orders = double number of edges

7) A, D, C and E are all odd nodes, so an arc between any two of them will make them even, leaving just two odd nodes.

8)

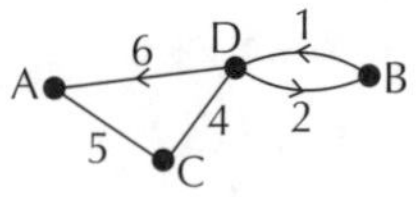

9) a) ABDEF. Shortest route A to F is 9.

Trace back from F to A on the final diagram on page 206. The weight of each arc you go along must equal the difference in the permanent labels of the vertices at each end of the arc.

b)

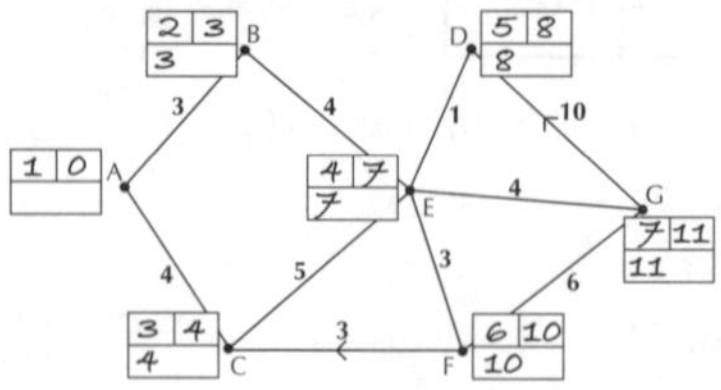

ABEG (11)

Exam Questions

1 a) DG (22) – add; EF (24) – add; BE (25) – add; DE (25) – add; EG (26) – don't add; AB (26) – add; BD (27) – don't add; BF (28) – don't add; FH (28) – add; CF (30) – add; AC (32) – don't add; GH (33) – don't add. Vertices of equal length can be considered in either order.

[3 marks available — 1 mark for edges in correct order, 2 marks for all added edges correct. Lose 1 mark for each error.]

b) 22 + 24 + 25 + 25 + 26 + 28 + 30 = £180 *[1 mark]*

c)

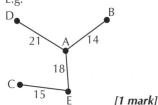

[2 marks for correct edges. Lose 1 mark for each error.]

d) FC / CF.
Order edges added: EF, EB, ED, DG (or ED, DG, EB), BA, FH, FC.

[2 marks available. 1 mark for correct edge, 1 mark for evidence that Prim's algorithm has been applied.]

e) E.g. Prim's algorithm can be applied to data in matrix form; you don't have to check for cycles using Prim's; the tree grows in a connected way using Prim's.
[2 marks — 1 mark for each, up to a total of 2.]

2 a) 6 (AD, AE, BD, BE, CD, CE) (*[1 mark]*

b) 1 *[1 mark]*

You just need to add one edge to join one part of the graph to the other part, e.g. AD.

c) 4 (number of nodes – 1) *[1 mark]*

d) 8 (2 × number of edges) *[1 mark]*

e) The sum of the orders is double the number of edges, so is always even *[1 mark]*. There are 5 vertices, and the sum of 5 odd numbers is always odd *[1 mark]*.

3 a)

	Ⓐ	Ⓑ	Ⓒ	Ⓓ	Ⓔ
A	–	14	22	21	18
B	14	–	19	21	20
C	22	19	–	21	15
D	21	21	21	–	24
E	18	20	15	24	–

Order arcs added: AB, AE, EC, AD/BD/CD
(You only need one of AD, BD or CD — they're interchangeable.)

[3 marks available — 2 marks for arcs in correct order (1 mark if one error). 1 mark for correct use of matrix.]

Each time you circle a number, write down which arc it represents by reading the row and column labels. Don't leave it until the end, or you'll have forgotten the order you added them in. Doh.

b) E.g.

```
   D●              ●B
      21     A   14
             18
   C●
      15    ●E        [1 mark]
```

D may be connected to B or C instead of A.
weight = 68 *[1 mark]*.

c) 2 (using any of the alternatives AD, BD and CD) *[1 mark]*.

4 a) 8 (no. of vertices – 1) *[1 mark]*

b)

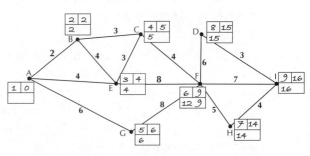

Fastest route = ABCFI, 16 minutes

[6 marks available — 1 mark for route, 1 mark for 16 minutes, 4 marks for all vertices correctly completed in diagram, lose 1 mark for each error.]

Find the fastest route by tracing back from the final destination. You know if a path is on the route because its weight is the difference between the permanent labels at either end of it.

c) Fastest route from A to G is 6. Fastest route from H to I is 4.
Total route AGHI must be less than 16 minutes.
$6 + x + 4 < 16, x < 6$
[2 marks available — 1 mark for 6 + x + 4 as new route length, 1 mark for solving inequality for x.]

d) Dijkstra's algorithm is quadratic ($O(n^2)$, where n is the number of vertices). Repeating it n times gives an order of $O(n^2 \times n) = O(n^3)$, or cubic.
[2 marks available — 1 mark for implying that Dijkstra's algorithm is quadratic and 1 mark for identifying new order as cubic.]

D1 Section 3
— The Route Inspection Problem
Warm-up Questions

1) a) Eulerian

b) semi-Eulerian

c) semi-Eulerian

d) neither

Eulerian. It's my new favourite word. In fact, I think I'll name my first child "Eulerian".

2) A, B, F, J
AB + FJ, AF + BJ, AJ + BF

3) a) It's Eulerian, so length = weight of network = 36.

b) It's semi-Eulerian, so length = 31 (weight of network) + 4 (distance AB) = 35

c) 4 odd vertices: A, B, D, F
AB + DF = 7 + 8 = 15
AD + BF = 5 + 3 = 8 (minimum)
AF + BD = 4 + 7 = 11
length = 42 (weight of network) + 8 = 50

Answers

4) a) 36, any vertex.

b) 31, start and end at A and B

c) BF is shortest distance between odd vertices, so start and end at A and D. Length = 42 + 3 = 45.

5) a) A, B, F, I, J, K

AB = 7, AF = 8, AI = 9, AJ = 8, AK = 10, BF = 9, BI = 4, BJ = 5, BK, 7, FI = 7, FJ = 6, FK = 4, IJ = 1, IK = 3, JK = 2

b) IJ and FK have the lowest total, so repeat the paths between them. This means starting at A or B (and finishing at the other).

IJ and FK have distinct vertices. You couldn't have picked IJ and JK, because they share vertex J (even though they are the minimum pairs).

Exam Questions

1 a) Logo A = semi-Eulerian *[1 mark]*
Logo B = neither *[1 mark]*

b) (i) Logo A = 0 *[1 mark]*
Logo B = once *[1 mark]*

(ii) B or D *[1 mark]*

c) Logo A = 1 *[1 mark]*
Logo B = 2 *[1 mark]*

2 a) There are four odd vertices (A, D, I and J) so the network isn't traversable and some streets would need to be walked down more than once *[1 mark]*.

So it's not Eulerian. And there are four odd vertices, so it's not even semi-Eulerian.

b) Odd vertices are A, D, I, J *[1 mark]*
Pairings: AD + IJ = 180 + 100 = 280
AI + DJ = 440 + 310 = 750
AJ + ID = 490 + 340 = 830
[1 mark for pairings, 1 mark for lengths]
minimum pairing = AD + IJ *[1 mark]*
route length = 2740 + 280 *[1 mark]*
= 3020 m *[1 mark]*

The question says that you must start and end at K — but as you've made the graph effectively Eulerian, it doesn't actually matter which vertex you start and finish at.

c) (i) IJ is minimum distance between odd vertices *[1 mark]*
Length of route = 2740 + 100 = 2840 m *[1 mark]*

(ii) A or D *[1 mark]*

3 a) Odd vertices are B, G, L, M *[1 mark]*
Pairings: BL + GM = 41 + 26 = 67
BG + LM = 30 + 29 = 59
BM + GL = 30 + 28 = 58
[1 mark for pairings, 1 mark for times]
minimum pairing = BM + GL *[1 mark]*
route time = 336 + 58 *[1 mark]* = 394 mins *[1 mark]*

b) (i) GM is minimum *[1 mark]* so end at L *[1 mark]*

(ii) 336 + 26 = 362 minutes *[1 mark]*

4 a) Odd vertices are A, D, E, F *[1 mark]*
Pairings: AD + EF = 12 + 15 = 27
AE + DF = 12 + 21 = 33
AF + DE = 18 + 6 = 24
[1 mark for pairings, 1 mark for distances]
minimum pairing = AF + DE *[1 mark]*
route length = 106 + 24 *[1 mark]* = 130 miles *[1 mark]*

b) Example route = ABFG<u>E</u>FBA<u>C</u>B<u>E</u>D<u>EC</u>DA *[1 mark]*
so 5 times *[1 mark]*.

Alternatively, you could say that C has four edges connected to it, so must be passed through twice. E has six edges connected to it (including the extra pass along DE) so must be passed through three times, so 2 + 3 = 5 times past an ice-cream shop.

c) 106 × 2 = 212 miles *[1 mark]*

You've effectively doubled the edges and made the graph Eulerian. You have to traverse it twice, so the distance is just double the network's weight.

D1 Section 4
— Travelling Salesperson Problem
Warm-up Questions

1) a) E.g. ABCDEA, ACEBDA, AEBDCA

Your routes must start and end at A and contain B, C, D and E.

b) From A: ACEBDA (weight = 31)
From B: BECADB (weight = 31)
From C: CEBADC (weight = 30)
From D: DCEBAD (weight = 30)
From E: ECADBE (weight = 31)

Best upper bound = 30

c) Deleting A:

x = 4, y = 7, W = 14, Lower bound = 25

Deleting B:

x = 5, y = 7, W = 13, Lower bound = 25

Deleting C:

x = 3, y = 4, W = 20, Lower bound = 27

Answers

Deleting D:

$x = 6$, $y = 7$, $W = 12$, Lower bound = 25

Deleting E:

$x = 3$, $y = 5$, $W = 17$, Lower bound = 25

Best lower bound = 27

d) $27 \leq$ optimum solution ≤ 30

2) a) FCEBADF, upper bound = 38

b) Deleting B:

	Ⓐ	B	Ⓒ	Ⓓ	Ⓔ	Ⓕ
A		4	6	5	8	12
B	4		11	22	6	11
C	Ⓖ	14		18	3	5
D	⑤	22	18		13	15
E	8	6	③	13		20
F	12	11	⑤	15	20	

$x = 4$, $y = 6$, $W = 6 + 5 + 3 + 5 = 19$

Lower bound = 29

3) a) C (CEFABDC), D (DBAFECD), E (EFABDCE)

b) CEFABDC = 7 + 2 + 3 + 5 + 4 + 8 = 29
DBAFECD = 4 + 5 + 3 + 2 + 7 + 8 = 29
EFABDCE = 2 + 3 + 5 + 4 + 8 + 7 = 29
So best upper bound = 29

These routes are all essentially the same (the one starting at D is in the opposite direction from the first two).

c) Deleting E and all arcs incident to it, then applying Prim's algorithm to the reduced network:
From A: AF, FD, DB, DC.

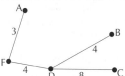

$x = 2$, $y = 5$, $W = 19$, Lower bound = 26

Exam Questions

1 a) EG (15) – add; DE (17) – add; AB (18) – add; AF (20) – add; AE (24) – add; BC (25) – add. That's all vertices joined, so don't need to consider any more. *[3 marks available — 1 mark for edges in correct order, 2 marks for all added edges correct, otherwise 1 mark for all but one edge correct.]*

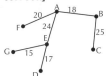

[1 mark]

Weight = 15 + 17 + 18 + 20 + 24 + 25 = 119 *[1 mark]*

b) Weight of reduced network = 119 – 25 = 94 *[1 mark]*
Shortest edges incident to C = 25 + 30 = 55 *[1 mark]*
Lower bound = 94 + 55 = 149 *[1 mark]*

c) DEGFABCD *[1 mark]*
Weight = 17 + 15 + 37 + 20 + 18 + 25 + 34 *[1 mark]*
= 166, so upper bound = 166 *[1 mark]*

d) CBAFEG *[1 mark]*. Algorithm stalls at G/can't get to D *[1 mark]*.

2 a) CABFE, then method stalls *[1 mark]*
There's no path to remaining unused vertex D.

b) ACDFEBA *[1 mark]*
= 80 + 100 + 140 + 100 + 150 + 90 *[1 mark]*
= 660 m *[1 mark]*

c) 90 + 120 + 100 + 140 + 100 + 300 *[1 mark]*
= 850 m *[1 mark]*

d) 660 m *[1 mark]*

e) Apply either Prim's or Kruskal's algorithm to get MST for reduced network.
Shortest edges incident to D = 100 + 140 = 240 m *[1 mark]*
E.g. Prim's applied from A: AC (80), AB (90), BF (130), EF (100). Weight = 80 + 90 + 130 + 100 = 400 m

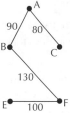

[4 marks — 1 mark for attempting to apply appropriate algorithm or 2 marks for correct application, 1 mark for correct edges, 1 mark for MST.]
Lower bound = 400 + 240 = 640 m *[1 mark]*

3) a) There are a few possible MSTs here. Only 1 is shown:

E.g.	Ⓐ	Ⓑ	Ⓒ	Ⓓ	E	Ⓕ	Ⓖ
A	—	15	10	7	6	7	4
B	15	—	8	⑤	12	13	14
C	10	8	—	6	15	18	②
D	7	5	⑥	—	7	5	13
E	6	12	15	7	—	③	10
F	7	13	18	⑤	3		6
G	④	14	2	13	10	6	—

[4 marks — 1 mark for attempting to apply appropriate algorithm or 2 marks for correct application, 1 mark for correct edges, 1 mark for MST.]

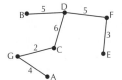

[1 mark]

Weight = 4 + 2 + 6 + 5 + 5 + 3 = 25 mins *[1 mark]*

You could have included AE (6) or FG (6) instead of CD (6). It doesn't change the weight though. Also, your tree might look completely different, depending on how you arranged your vertices.

Answers

b) Weight = 25 – 5 = 20 *[1 mark]*
Shortest edges incident to B = 5 + 8 = 13 *[1 mark]*
Lower bound = 20 + 13 = 33 mins *[1 mark]*

c) FEAGCDBF *[1 mark]*

	A	B	C	D	E	F	G
A	–	15	10	7	6	7	④
B	15	–	8	5	12	⑬	14
C	10	8	–	⑥	15	18	2
D	7	⑤	6	–	7	5	13
E	⑥	12	15	7	–	3	10
F	7	13	18	5	③	–	6
G	4	14	②	13	10	6	–

Weight = 3 + 6 + 4 + 2 + 6 + 5 + 13 *[1 mark]*
= 39 mins, so upper bound = 39 mins *[1 mark]*

d) 33 mins $\leq$ optimum weight of tour *[1 mark]* $\leq$ 39 mins
[1 mark]

D1 Section 5 — Linear Programming
Warm-up Questions

1) a) Decision variables represent the quantities of the things being produced in a linear programming problem.

   b) The objective function is the thing you're trying to optimise — a function in terms of the decision variables that you want to maximise or minimise.

   c) The optimal solution is a feasible solution that optimises the objective function (i.e. maximises or minimises it).

2) A dotted line represents a strict (< or >) inequality. You don't include this line in the feasible region.

3) An objective line is a line in the form $Z = ax + by$, which represents all solutions of the objective function that have the same value of Z.

4) E.g. A linear programming problem involving liquid doesn't need integer solutions — e.g. mixing vinegar and oil to make vinaigrette. You can have fractions of a litre. E.g. A linear programming problem about making musical instruments needs integer solutions — you can't make half a trumpet.

5) a) The decision variables are the number of large posters and the number of small posters, so let x = number of large posters and y = number of small posters.
   The constraints are the different amounts of time available. Printing a large poster takes 10 minutes, so printing x large posters takes $10x$ minutes. Printing a small poster takes 5 minutes, so printing y small posters takes $5y$ minutes. There are 250 minutes of printing time available, so the inequality is $10x + 5y \leq 250 \Rightarrow 2x + y \leq 50$. Using the same method for laminating time produces the inequality $6x + 4y \leq 200 \Rightarrow 3x + 2y \leq 100$. The company wants to sell at least as many large posters as small posters, so $x \geq y$, and at least 10 small posters, so $y \geq 10$. (These last two cover $x, y \geq 0$, the trivial constraints). The objective function is $P = 6x + 3.5y$ (profit) which needs to be maximised.

You could use x for the number of small posters and y for the number of large posters instead — so x and y in each inequality would just swap round.

b)
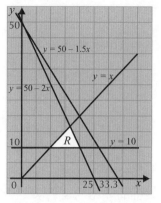

The line y = 50 − 1.5x isn't actually used to form the feasible region.

c) E.g. starting with the objective line for $P = 42$ (which goes through (0, 12) and (7, 0)) and moving it towards R gives:

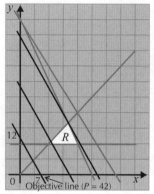

So the final point in the feasible region touched by the objective line is the point of intersection of the lines $y = x$ and $y = 50 - 2x$. Solving these simultaneous equations gives the point of intersection as $\left(\frac{50}{3}, \frac{50}{3}\right)$. Putting these values into the objective function gives a maximum profit of £158.33.
You can choose any value of P as a starting value — 42 makes it easy to draw the line. This answer uses the objective line method, but you could have used the vertex method instead.

d) From part c) above, the maximum profit is found at $\left(\frac{50}{3}, \frac{50}{3}\right)$. However, you can't have fractions of a poster, so an integer solution is required. The points with integer coordinates nearby are (16,16), (16,17), (17, 17) and (17, 16). (16, 17) doesn't satisfy the constraint $x \geq y$ and (17, 17) doesn't satisfy the constraint $y \leq 50 - 2x$. The value of the objective function at (16, 16) is £152 and at (17, 16) it's £158, so (17, 16) gives the maximum solution.

Answers

6) a) The objective function becomes $P - 6x - 12y = 0$.
Introducing slack variables to turn the constraints into equalities gives $x + 3y + s = 7$ and $2x + 3y + t = 8$, where $s, t \geq 0$. Putting this into the Simplex tableau gives:

P	x	y	s	t	RHS	
1	−6	−12	0	0	0	(a)
0	1	3	1	0	7	(b)
0	2	3	0	1	8	(c)

b) First, choose your pivot (start with the x-column):
$7 \div 1 = 7$, $8 \div 2 = 4$, so the pivot is 2.

P	x	y	s	t	RHS	
1	0	−3	0	3	24	(d) = (a) + 3(c)
0	0	1.5	1	−0.5	3	(e) = (b) − 0.5(c)
0	1	1.5	0	0.5	4	(f) = (c) ÷ 2

Now choose a pivot from the new y-column:
$3 \div 1.5 = 2$, $4 \div 1.5 = 2.67$, so the pivot is 1.5 in row (e).

P	x	y	s	t	RHS	
1	0	0	2	2	30	(g) = (d) + 2(e)
0	0	1	0.67	−0.33	2	(h) = (e) ÷ 1.5
0	1	0	−1	1	1	(i) = (f) − (e)

So the maximum value of P is 30, found at $x = 1$, $y = 2$.
You could have started with the y-column instead if you wanted to.

Exam Questions

1 The objective function is to minimise the cost *[1 mark]*, $C = 0.75x + 0.6y$ in £ (or $C = 75x + 60y$ in pence) *[1 mark]* (where x is the number of red roses and y is the number of white roses), subject to the constraints:
$x, y > 0$ *[1 mark]* (from the statement that she will sell both red and white roses — x and y can't be 0).
$x > y$ *[1 mark]* (from the statement that she will sell more red roses than white roses).
$x + y \geq 100$ *[1 mark]* (from the statement that she will sell a total of at least 100 flowers).
$x \leq 300$ *[1 mark]* and $y \leq 200$ *[1 mark]* (from the statement that the wholesaler has 300 red roses and 200 white roses).
Don't waste time trying to solve these inequalities — the question doesn't ask you to find a solution. Just write them down and run.

2 a) There are 6 sheets of foil in a gold pack, so in x gold packs there will be $6x$ sheets of foil. There are 2 sheets of foil in a silver pack, so in y silver packs there will be $2y$ sheets of foil. There is 1 sheet of foil in a bronze pack, so in z bronze packs there will be z sheets of foil. There are 30 sheets of foil available, so the inequality is $6x + 2y + z \leq 30$ *[2 marks — 1 mark for LHS, 1 mark for correct inequality sign and RHS]*. Using the same method for sugar paper produces the inequality $15x + 9y + 6z \leq 120$ *[1 mark]*, which simplifies to give $5x + 3y + 2z \leq 40$ *[1 mark]*. For tissue paper, the inequality is $15x + 4y + z \leq 60$ *[2 marks — 1 mark for LHS, 1 mark for correct inequality sign and RHS]*. Finally, the amount of foil used is $6x + 2y + z$,

and the amount of sugar paper used is $15x + 9y + 6z$. The amount of sugar paper used needs to be at least three times the amount of foil, so the inequality for this constraint is
$15x + 9y + 6z \geq 3(6x + 2y + z)$ *[1 mark]*
$15x + 9y + 6z \geq 18x + 6y + 3z$
$3y + 3z \geq 3x$
$y + z \geq x$ *[1 mark]*

b) (i) If the number of silver packs sold is equal to the number of bronze packs, then $y = z$. Substituting this into the inequalities from part (a) gives:
$6x + 2y + y \leq 30 \Rightarrow 6x + 3y \leq 30 \Rightarrow 2x + y \leq 10$
$5x + 3y + 2y \leq 40 \Rightarrow 5x + 5y \leq 40 \Rightarrow x + y \leq 8$
$15x + 4y + y \leq 60 \Rightarrow 15x + 5y \leq 60 \Rightarrow 3x + y \leq 12$
$y + y \geq x \Rightarrow 2y \geq x$. *[3 marks available — 1 mark for making the correct substitution, 1 mark for correctly forming the inequalities and 1 mark for simplifying the inequalities.]*

(ii)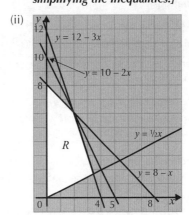

[5 marks available — 1 mark for each of the four inequality lines (with equations as shown on the graph) and 1 mark for correct feasible region]

(iii) Using the vertex method, the feasible region has vertices (0, 0) (the origin), (0, 8) (intersection of the y-axis and $y = 8 - x$), (2, 6) (intersection of $y = 8 - x$ and $y = 10 - 2x$) and $\left(\frac{24}{7}, \frac{12}{7}\right)$ (intersection of $y = \frac{1}{2}x$ and $y = 12 - 3x$) *[1 mark]*. The number of packs made on Monday is $x + y + z = x + 2y$, so the numbers made at each vertex are 0, 16, 14 and $\frac{48}{7} = 6\frac{6}{7}$, so the maximum number of packs made that day is 16 = 8 silver and 8 bronze *[1 mark]*.
You could have used the objective line method instead, using the line $Z = x + y + z = x + 2y$ to find the maximum.

(iv) The objective function is $P = 3.5x + 2y + z$ $= 3.5x + 2y + y = 3.5x + 3y$, which needs to be maximised. The value of P for each of the vertices found in part (iii) is £0, £24, £25 and £17.14 *[1 mark]*. The maximum value is £25 *[1 mark]*, which occurs at (2, 6), so the company needs to sell 2 gold packs, 6 silver packs and 6 bronze packs (as the number of bronze packs is equal to the number of silver packs) *[1 mark]*.

Answers

3 a) First, the trivial constraints are $x, y \geq 0$. The solid line that passes through $(0, 6)$ and $(3, 0)$ has equation $y = 6 - 2x$, and as the area below the line is shaded, the inequality is $2x + y \geq 6$. The dotted line that passes through $(2, 0)$ has equation $y = x - 2$, and as the area below the line is shaded, the inequality is $x - y < 2$. The horizontal solid line that passes through $(0, 4)$ has the equation $y = 4$, and as the area above the line is shaded, the inequality is $y \leq 4$.

[5 marks available — 1 mark for trivial constraints, 1 mark for each line equation and 1 mark for all inequality signs correct]

   b) The coordinates of the vertices of R are $(1, 4)$ (the intersection of the lines $y = 4$ and $y = 6 - 2x$) *[1 mark]*, $(6, 4)$ (the intersection of the lines $y = 4$ and $y = x - 2$) *[1 mark]* and $\left(\frac{8}{3}, \frac{2}{3}\right)$ *[1 mark]* (the intersection of the lines $y = 6 - 2x$ and $y = x - 2$) *[1 mark for solving the simultaneous equations]*.

   c) The value of C at $(1, 4)$ is 8, the value of C at $(6, 4)$ is 28 *[1 mark if both are correct]* and the value of C at $\left(\frac{8}{3}, \frac{2}{3}\right)$ is $\frac{34}{3} = 11\frac{1}{3}$ *[1 mark]*. Hence the minimum value of C is 8, which occurs at the point $(1, 4)$ *[1 mark]*.

   This answer uses the vertex method, but you could also have used the objective line method to answer this question — pick whichever method you prefer.

4 a) The objective function becomes $P + 2x - 4y + 3z = 0$. Introducing slack variables to the other equations gives: $x + y + z + s = 16$, $3x + 2y - z + t = 20$, $4x - 5y + z + u = 25$, where $s, t, u \geq 0$. Putting this into the tableau gives:

P	x	y	z	s	t	u	RHS	
1	2	−4	3	0	0	0	0	(a)
0	1	1	1	1	0	0	16	(b)
0	3	2	−1	0	1	0	20	(c)
0	4	−5	1	0	0	1	25	(d)

[4 marks available — 1 mark for each correct row of the tableau.]

   b) The y-column is the only column with a negative value in the top row, so the pivot must come from there *[1 mark]*. $16 \div 1 = 16$ and $20 \div 2 = 10$. $10 < 16$, so the pivot is 2 *[1 mark]* (ignore the final row, as this doesn't give a positive value).

   c)

P	x	y	z	s	t	u	RHS	
1	8	0	1	0	2	0	40	(e)
0	−0.5	0	1.5	1	−0.5	0	6	(f)
0	1.5	1	−0.5	0	0.5	0	10	(g)
0	11.5	0	−1.5	0	2.5	1	75	(h)

where (e) = (a) + 2(c), (f) = (b) − 0.5(c), (g) = (c) ÷ 2, (h) = (d) + 2.5(c).
At this point, the value of $P = 40$.

   [5 marks available — 1 mark for each correct row of the tableau (obtained using correct method), 1 mark for corresponding value of P.]

5 a) Let x = number of small rooms and y = number of large rooms. The constraint on painting time is $x + 3y \leq 15$ *[1 mark]*. The constraint on wallpapering time is $2x + 4y \leq 22$ *[1 mark]*. The trivial constraints are $x, y \geq 0$ *[1 mark]*.

   b) The objective function is $P = 50x + 120y$ *[1 mark]*.

   c) The objective function becomes $P - 50x - 120y = 0$. Adding the slack variables to the constraints gives: $x + 3y + s = 15$ and $2x + 4y + t = 22$, where $s, t \geq 0$.

P	x	y	s	t	RHS	
1	−50	−120	0	0	0	(a)
0	1	3	1	0	15	(b)
0	2	4	0	1	22	(c)

[3 marks available — 1 mark for each correct row of the tableau.]

   d) Choose a pivot from the x-column: $15 \div 1 = 15$, $22 \div 2 = 11$. $11 < 15$, so the pivot is 2.

P	x	y	s	t	RHS	
1	0	−20	0	25	550	(d) = (a) + 25(c)
0	0	1	1	−0.5	4	(e) = (b) − 0.5(c)
0	1	2	0	0.5	11	(f) = (c) ÷ 2

Now choose a pivot from the new y-column: $4 \div 1 = 4$, $11 \div 2 = 5.5$. $4 < 5.5$, so the pivot is 1.

P	x	y	s	t	RHS	
1	0	0	20	15	630	(g) = (d) + 20(e)
0	0	1	1	−0.5	4	(h) = (e)
0	1	0	−2	1.5	3	(i) = (f) − 2(e)

s and t are non-basis columns, so $s, t = 0$.
Reading off the values for the basis columns P, x and y:
$P = 630$, $y = 4$ and $x = 3$.
So the maximum profit is £630, which occurs when the company decorates 3 small rooms and 4 large rooms.

[8 marks available — 1 mark choosing correct x-pivot, 1 mark for correct pivot row in first tableau, 1 mark for obtaining other rows in first tableau, 1 mark choosing correct y-pivot, 1 mark for correct pivot row in second tableau, 1 mark for obtaining other rows in second tableau, 1 mark for correct P value and 1 mark for correct interpretation of x- and y-values.]

Answers

D1 — Practice Exam 1

1 a) First iteration: A = 2, N = 1.
P = A ÷ N = 2 ÷ 1 = 2
Q = P + N = 2 + 1 = 3
R = Q ÷ 2 = 3 ÷ 2 = 1.5 *[1 mark for P, Q and R correct]*
|R − N| = |1.5 − 1| = 0.5 > 0.01, so go to Step 8.
N = R = 1.5 *[1 mark]*.
Second iteration: A = 2, N = 1.5.
P = 2 ÷ 1.5 = 1.33333...
Q = 1.33333... + 1.5 = 2.83333...
R = 2.83333... ÷ 2 = 1.41666... *[1 mark for P, Q and R correct]*
|R − N| = |1.4166... − 1.5| = 0.0833... > 0.01, so go to Step 8.
N = R = 1.4166... *[1 mark]*.
Third iteration: A = 2, N = 1.4166...
P = 2 ÷ 1.4166... = 1.4117...
Q = 1.4117... + 1.4166... = 2.8284...
R = 2.8284... ÷ 2 = 1.4142... *[1 mark for P, Q and R correct]*
|R − N| = |1.4142... − 1.4166...| = 0.0024... < 0.01
So R = 1.41 *[1 mark]*.
The square root of 2 to 2 d.p. is 1.41.

b) The algorithm calculates square roots to 2 decimal places, so for A = 9, the output would be 3.00 *[1 mark]*.

2 a)
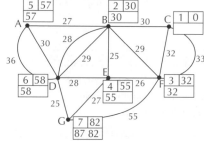
Route = CBEG, length = 82 miles

[7 marks available — 1 mark for route, 1 mark for length, 5 marks for all vertices correctly completed, alternatively 4 marks for 6 vertices correct, 3 marks for 5 vertices, 2 marks for 4 vertices, 1 mark for 2 or 3 vertices.]

b) (i) AB and BF *[1 mark]*

This is the shortest route between the other odd vertices, A and F. AB is 27 miles and BF is 29 miles — so A to F is 56 miles.

(ii) 460 + 56 = 516 miles *[1 mark]*

3 a) Box 1: 1.8, 3.5   space left: 4.2 0.7
Box 2: 2.6, 1.2, 0.8   space left: 3.4 2.2 1.4
Box 3: 4.1   space left: 1.9
Box 4: 2.0, 2.4   space left: 4.0 1.6
Box 5: 3.1   space left: 2.9   *[1 mark]*
5 boxes are used *[1 mark]* and there is:
0.7 + 1.4 + 1.9 + 1.6 + 2.9 = 8.5 kg wasted space *[1 mark]*.

b) In decreasing order, the weights of the items are:
4.1, 3.5, 3.1, 2.6, 2.4, 2.0, 1.8, 1.2, 0.8 *[1 mark]*.
Using the first fit method on this new list gives:
Box 1: 4.1, 1.8   space left: 1.9 0.1
Box 2: 3.5, 2.4   space left: 2.5 0.1
Box 3: 3.1, 2.6   space left: 2.9 0.3
Box 4: 2.0, 1.2, 0.8   space left: 4.0 2.8 2.0
[1 mark] 4 boxes are used and there is:
0.1 + 0.1 + 0.3 + 2.0 = 2.5 kg wasted space *[1 mark]*.

c) E.g. the boxes in part a) are lighter so will be easier to carry *[1 mark]*.

4 a) Order paths added:
GF, FB, BC, CA, GH/CH, HI, ID, IK, KL, KJ, IE

[5 marks for answer fully correct. Lose 1 mark for each mistake.]

b)
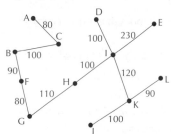
(CH is an alternative to GH.)
Length = 1200 metres
[3 marks available. 1 mark for 9 or 10 correct edges, 2 marks for 11 correct. 1 mark for length of spanning tree.]

c) [AC – add; FG – add]; [BF – add; KL – add]; [BC – add; DI – add; HI – add; JK – add]; [AB – don't add; GH/CH – add; CH/GH – don't add]; IK – add; [HJ – don't add; HK – don't add; IL – don't add]; CD – don't add; EI – add; GJ – don't add; DE – don't add; EL – don't add; FJ – don't add. (The edges in square brackets can be considered in any order.)

The tenth and eleventh edges are IK and EI.

[3 marks available — 1 mark for each correct edge, 1 mark for evidence that Kruskal's algorithm has been applied.]

5 a) Simple:
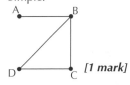
[1 mark]

Not simple, e.g.:

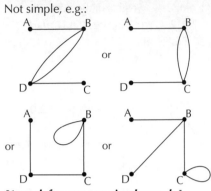

[1 mark for any non-simple graph.]

A loop counts as 1 arc but it adds 2 to the order of the vertex it's attached to. There are other possible 'not simple' graphs with a loop — just check you've drawn one with 4 nodes, 4 arcs, and that A has an order of 1 and B has an order of 3.

b) E.g. BCDB *[1 mark]*

c) It goes through vertex B more than once. *[1 mark]*

6 a) AFECBDA *[1 mark]*
Weight = 4 + 5 + 4 + 3 + 10 + 5 *[1 mark]* = 31,
so the upper bound is 31 *[1 mark]*.

b) BC (3) — add; CE (4) — add; AF (4) — add; AD (5) — add;
EF (5) — add *[2 marks — 1 mark for correct edges, 1 mark for adding edges in correct order]*.

All the vertices are joined so stop. Edges with equal weight can be added in any order (i.e. you could have added CE and AF the other way round, and AD and EF the other way round.

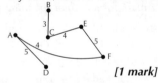

[1 mark]

Weight = 3 + 4 + 4 + 5 + 5 = 21 *[1 mark]*.

c) Weight of reduced network = 21 – 3 = 18 *[1 mark]*
Shortest edges incident to B = 3 + 6 = 9 *[1 mark]*
Lower bound = 18 + 9 = 27 *[1 mark]*

d) 27 ≤ length of optimum tour ≤ 31 *[1 mark]*

7 a) $0.4x + 0.5y \leq 8$ or $4x + 5y \leq 80$ *[1 mark]*
$x + y \leq 18$ *[1 mark]*

b) $P = 0.75x + 1.5y$ *[1 mark]*

c) The objective function becomes $P - 0.75x - 1.5y = 0$.
Adding the slack variables to the constraints gives:
$4x + 5y + s = 80$ and $x + y + t = 18$, where $s, t \geq 0$.

P	x	y	s	t	RHS	
1	–0.75	–1.5	0	0	0	(a)
0	4	5	1	0	80	(b)
0	1	1	0	1	18	(c)

[3 marks available — 1 mark for each correct row of the tableau.]

d) Choose a pivot from the y-column: 80 ÷ 5 = 16,
18 ÷ 1 = 18. 16 < 18, so the pivot is 5.

P	x	y	s	t	RHS	
1	0.45	0	0.3	0	24	(d) = (a) + 0.3(b)
0	0.8	1	0.2	0	16	(e) = (b) ÷ 5
0	0.2	0	-0.2	1	2	(f) = (c) – 0.2(b)

x column is non-basis, so $x = 0$.
Reading off other values $P = 24$, $y = 16$.
So the maximum profit is £24, which is achieved when John makes no birthday cards and 16 blank cards.

[6 marks available — 1 mark for choosing correct y-pivot, 1 mark for each correct row in the tableau, 1 mark for correct P, x and y values and 1 mark for correct interpretation of values.]

e) Natalie can make no more than 8 blank cards
[1 mark]. Also, the number of blank cards made must be no more than number of birthday cards made *[1 mark]*.

f)

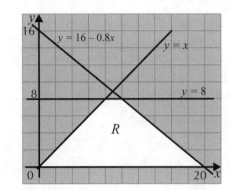

[4 marks available — 1 for each correct line (with equations as shown on graph), 1 for correct feasible region]

g) Using the vertex method, the vertices of the feasible region are (0,0), (8, 8) (the intersection of $y = x$ and $y = 8$), (10, 8) (the intersection of $y = 16 – 0.8x$ and $y = 8$) and (20, 0) *[2 marks for all 4 correct, or 1 mark for 2 correct vertices]*.
Putting these values into the objective functions gives P values of £0, £18, £19.50 and £15 *[1 mark]*, so the maximum profit is £19.50 *[1 mark]*, which occurs at (10, 8), so Natalie must make 10 birthday cards and 8 blank cards *[1 mark]* to maximise her profit.

You could have used the objective line method instead, using the line P = 0.75x + 1.5y to find the maximum.

Answers

D1 — Practice Exam 2

1 a) First pass:
<u>281, 276</u>, 255, 290, 263, 287   swap
Order after pass 1: 276, 281, 255, 290, 263, 287
1 comparison, 1 swap *[1 mark]*

Second pass:
276, <u>281, 255</u>, 290, 263, 287   swap
<u>276, 255</u>, 281, 290, 263, 287   swap
Order after pass 2: 255, 276, 281, 290, 263, 287
2 comparisons, 2 swaps *[1 mark]*

Third pass:
255, 276, <u>281, 290</u>, 263, 287   no swap
Order after pass 3: 255, 276, 281, 290, 263, 287
1 comparisons, 0 swaps *[1 mark]*

Fourth pass:
255, 276, 281, <u>290, 263</u>, 287   swap
255, 276, <u>281, 263</u>, 290, 287   swap
255, <u>276, 263</u>, 281, 290, 287   swap
<u>255, 263</u>, 276, 281, 290, 287   no swap
Order after pass 4: 255, 263, 276, 281, 290, 287
4 comparisons, 3 swaps *[1 mark]*

Fifth pass:
255, 263, 276, 281, <u>290, 287</u>   swap
255, 263, 276, <u>281, 287</u>, 290   no swap
Order after pass 5: 255, 263, 276, 281, 287, 290
2 comparisons, 1 swap *[1 mark]*

b) Using a bubble sort on 6 numbers, the maximum number of comparisons needed would be ½ × 5 × 6 = 15 *[1 mark]* and the maximum number of passes would be 6 − 1 = 5 *[1 mark]*.

2 a) (i) 213 *[1 mark]*

(ii) 217 *[1 mark]*

Remember — you want the biggest lower bound and the smallest upper bound.

(iii) 213 ≤ weight of optimum tour ≤ 217 *[1 mark]*

b) (i) BCAFEDB *[1 mark]*

	A	B	C	D	E	F
Ⓐ	–	6	7	5	11	②
Ⓑ	6	–	④	12	8	6
Ⓒ	⑦	4	–	9	10	13
Ⓓ	5	12	9	–	③	7
Ⓔ	11	8	10	③	–	1
Ⓕ	2	6	13	7	①	–
[1 mark]

Weight = 4 + 7 + 2 + 1 + 3 + 12 = 29 *[1 mark]*, so an upper bound is 29 minutes *[1 mark]*.

(ii) Here is a possible MST for the network:

	Ⓐ	Ⓑ	Ⓒ	Ⓓ	Ⓔ	Ⓕ
A	–	⑥	7	5	11	2
B	6	–	④	12	8	6
C	7	4	–	9	10	13
D	5	12	9	–	③	7
E	11	8	10	3	–	①
F	②	6	13	7	1	–

[2 marks — 1 mark for applying algorithm correctly and 1 mark for correct edges]

Order edges added: CB, BA, AF, FE, ED *[1 mark]*.
The MST looks like this:

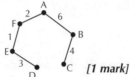 *[1 mark]*

Weight = 4 + 6 + 2 + 1 + 3 = 16 mins *[1 mark]*

You could have added edge BF (6) instead of BA (6). This wouldn't change the weight of the MST.

(iii) Weight = 16 − 3 = 13 *[1 mark]*
Shortest edges incident to D = 3 + 5 = 8 *[1 mark]*
Lower bound = 13 + 8 = 21 mins *[1 mark]*

3 a)

A	B	B = 1 digit?	B = 9?	Output
977	23	No		
	5	Yes	No	
978	24	No		
	6	Yes	No	
979	25	No		
	7	Yes	No	
980	17	No		
	8	Yes	No	
981	18	No		
	9	Yes	Yes	981

The result is 981.

[4 marks available in total. 4 marks if all correct, lose 1 mark for each mistake.]

b) 981 *[1 mark]*. This starting value would produce the same trace table as in part a), but starting one row down.

c) The next multiple of 9 is at most 8 numbers away from the starting value, so no more than 9 passes will be needed *[1 mark]*.

4 a) Odd vertices are B, D, F, G *[1 mark]*
Pairings: BF + DG = 190 + 100 = 290
             BD + FG = 180 + 110 = 290
             BG + DF = 80 + 210 = 290
[1 mark for pairings, 1 mark for lengths]
minimum pairing = any of above *[1 mark]*
route length = 2200 + 290 *[1 mark]*
= 2490 metres *[1 mark]*

Answers

b) (i) D and F *[1 mark]*. B and G are the pair of odd vertices with the shortest path between them, so that's the path that should be repeated, which means the route must start and finish at the other odd vertices *[1 mark]*.

(ii) $2200 + 80 = 2280$ m *[1 mark]*

c)

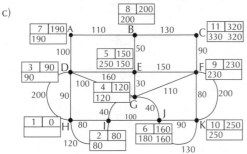

Distance = 320 metres

Route = HIGFC

[6 marks available — 1 mark for distance, 1 mark for route, 4 marks for all vertices correctly completed, alternatively 3 marks for 9 or 10 vertices correct, 2 marks for 7 or 8 vertices, 1 mark for 5 or 6 vertices.]

5 a) The graph is Eulerian *[1 mark]* because all its vertices are of even degree *[1 mark]*.

b) To make the graph semi-Eulerian, Scott would have to make two of the vertices odd. He could do this by removing one of the edges *[1 mark]*.

c) $8 - 1 = 7$ edges *[1 mark]*.

6 a) (i) Number of tickets: $5x + 10y \leq 300 \Rightarrow x + 2y \leq 60$ *[1 mark]*. Number of bottles of wine: $2x + 8y \leq 160 \Rightarrow x + 4y \leq 80$ *[1 mark]*.

(ii) $x \geq 5$, $y \geq 5$ *[1 mark]*.

There have to be at least 5 business class packages and at least 5 premier packages sold.

$x + y \geq 20$ *[1 mark]*.

The total number of packages sold has to be 20 or more.

b) (i)

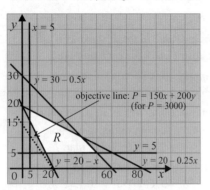

[6 marks available — 1 for each correct line (with equations as shown on graph — 4 in total), 1 for correct feasible region and 1 for objective line with correct gradient.]

(ii) Using the objective line, the last point in the feasible region it touches is the point (50, 5), the intersection of the lines $y = 5$ and $y = 30 - 0.5x$. At this point, $P = £8500$ *[1 mark]*, so this is the maximum profit possible, achieved when 50 business class packages and 5 premier packages are sold *[1 mark]*.

(iii) Using the objective line, the first point in the feasible region it touches is the point (15, 5), the intersection of the lines $y = 5$ and $y = 20 - x$. At this point, $P = £3250$ *[1 mark]*, so this is the minimum profit possible, achieved when 15 business class packages and 5 premier packages are sold *[1 mark]*.

7 a) The objective function becomes $P - 4x - 3y - 2z = 0$. Adding the slack variables to the constraints gives: $x - y + 3z + s = 6$ and $2x - 4y - 5z + t = 20$, where s, $t \geq 0$.

P	x	y	z	s	t	RHS	
1	−4	−3	−2	0	0	0	(a)
0	1	−1	3	1	0	6	(b)
0	2	−4	−5	0	1	20	(c)

[3 marks available — 1 mark for each correct row of the tableau.]

b) The values in the y column are all negative, so dividing the RHS by each value gives negative values, none of which can be used as the pivot *[1 mark]*.

c) Choose a pivot from the x-column: $6 \div 1 = 6$, $20 \div 2 = 10$. $6 < 10$, so the pivot is 1.

P	x	y	z	s	t	RHS	
1	0	−7	10	4	0	24	(d) = (a) + 4(b)
0	1	−1	3	1	0	6	(e) = (b)
0	0	−2	−11	−2	1	8	(f) = (c) − 2(b)

$P = 24$, $x = 6$, $y = 0$, $z = 0$

[6 marks available — 1 mark choosing correct x-pivot, 1 mark for each correct row in the tableau, 1 mark for correct P, and 1 mark for correct x, y, z values.]

d) y can increase without limit, and increasing y increases P, so there's no limit to P. *[1 mark]*

OR: the only negative in the objective row is in the y-column, but all the other numbers in this column are negative too. You can't have a pivot from this column, so y has no maximum.

If you read the top row in the tableau in c), you get $P = 7y - 10z - 4s + 24$, so as y increases, so does P.

Index

A

acceleration 167, 171, 172
acceleration-time graphs 169
algebraic division 54
algebraic fractions 6
algorithms 191–196, 202–206, 210,
        211, 215–217
  bin packing 196
  bubble sort 194
  Dijkstra's 205, 206
  efficiency 192
  first-fit 196
  first-fit decreasing 196
  greedy 202
  Kruskal's 202
  lower bound 215, 217
  Nearest Neighbour 215, 216
  order 192
  Prim's 203, 204
  route inspection 210, 211
  Russian Peasant 191
  shuttle sort 195
'almost' quadratic equations 19
approximation
  area under a curve 92
arc length 71, 72
arcs (graphs) 199
areas
  between curve and x-axis 91
  between curves 94
  under curves 92
arithmetic
  progressions 59, 60, 64
  series 59, 60
arrangements 120–122, 129
assumptions 158, 159, 168
asymptotes 32

B

bases 84
basis columns 226, 227
binomial coefficients 121, 129
binomial cumulative distribution
        function 131
binomial distribution 130–133
binomial expansions 65–67
binomial probability function 129
binomial tables 131, 150–155
bin packing algorithms 196
bivariate data 137–141
Blackadder 60
box-and-whisker plots 111
bubble sort algorithm 194

C

cake 226, 227
CAST diagram 77
central tendency 104, 105, 109
chickens 35
Chinese postman problem 210
circles 34, 35, 71
  properties 35
class boundaries 102
coalesce 181
coding 110
coefficient of friction 163
combinations 121, 122
common denominators 6
common factors 5
comparing distributions 111
complement of an event 116
complete graphs 199
completing the square 13, 14
complexity of an algorithm 192
components of forces 160
component vectors 157
conditional probability 118
connected graphs 199
connected particles 178–180
conservation of momentum 181
constant acceleration equations 167, 168
constant of integration 89, 90
constants 1
constraints 220–222, 225, 227
convergent series 62
coordinate geometry 29, 30
correlation 137, 138, 141
$\cos x$ 72, 75
cosine rule 73, 74
cows 18
cubic functions 53
  graphs 32
cumulative frequency 107
curve sketching 32, 44
cycles in graphs 200

D

decision variables 220, 224, 226
decreasing functions 43
definite integrals 91
degrees of
  angles 71
  nodes 201
dependent variables 139
differentiation 39–45
  of displacement and velocity 171
digraphs 199
Dijkstra's algorithm 205, 206
directed graphs 199
discrete random variables 125–127

discriminant 16, 17
disguised quadratics 19
displacement 167, 171, 172
displacement-time graphs 169
distance matrices 201, 204
divergent series 63
division 1
dynamics 175–181

E

edges (graphs) 199
efficiency of an algorithm 192
elimination method (simultaneous
        equations) 24
equations 1
  of circles 34, 35
  of motion 176
  of straight lines 29, 31
equilibrium 161
Eulerian graphs 209, 210, 212
events 115, 116
exclusive events 116
expected values 127
experimental error 140
experiments 115
explanatory variables 139
exponentials 85, 86
  graphs 85
  growth and decay 86
extrapolation 141

F

factorials 120
factorising
  cubics 53
  quadratics 11, 12
Factor Theorem 55
feasible regions/solutions 220–224
finite sequences 58
first-fit algorithm 196
first-fit decreasing algorithm 196
flow charts 193
forces 158–162, 175
frequency density 102
frequency tables 102, 104
friction 158, 163, 179, 180
  and inclined planes 176, 177
functions 1
  increasing and decreasing 43

Index

G

geometric distribution 128
geometric interpretations 26
geometric progressions 61–64
gradients 30, 40–44
graphs 75, 76, 199–206, 209–211
  exponential 85
  quadratic 10
  sketching 32
  transformations 33
  trig functions 75
gravity 167
greedy algorithms 202
grouped data 105, 109

H

Hardy, Oliver 178
histograms 102

I

identities 1
inclined planes 162, 176, 177, 180
increasing functions 43
indefinite integrals 89
independent
  events 119
  variables 139
indices 2
inequalities
  linear 22
  quadratic 23
infinite sequences 58
integer solutions (linear programming)
  224
integration 89–91, 94
  acceleration and velocity 171, 172
  adding and subtracting integrals 94
interpolation 141
interquartile range 106
intersection of events 115

K

kinematics 167–172
Kruskal's algorithm 202

L

Laurel, Stan 178
least squares regression 140
limiting friction 163
limiting motion 177
limits (integration) 91
linear inequalities 22
linear interpolation 105
linear programming 220–227
linear regression 139, 140
line segments 31
lines of best fit 139–141
location 104, 105
logs 84–86
lower bound algorithm 215, 217
lower class boundaries 102
lower quartile 106

M

magnitude of forces 160
magnitude of vectors 156
masses on strings 159, 162
matrices (graphs) 201
maximum
  of a graph 42
  volume and area 45
mean 104, 105
  of binomial distribution 132
  of random variables 127
median 104, 105, 107, 111
mid-class values 105, 109
mid-points of lines 31
minimum
  of a graph 42
  volume and area 45
minimum connectors 202
minimum spanning trees 202–204
modal class 105
mode 104, 105
modelling 158, 159, 168
momentum 181
motion graphs 169, 170
motion under gravity 167
multiplication and brackets 1, 4
mutilating soft toys 224
mutually exclusive events 116

N

natural numbers 60
Nearest Neighbour algorithm 215, 216
negative correlation 137
networks 199
Newton's laws of motion 175
nodes (graphs) 199
non-basis columns 226
non-negativity constraints 220, 221
normal reaction 158, 163
normals 30, 41
n-shaped graphs 10

O

objective functions 220, 222, 223, 225
objective line method (linear programming)
  222, 224
optimal integer solution 224
optimal solutions 220, 222–224
order
  of an algorithm 192
  of a node 201, 209
outcomes 115
outliers 109, 141

P

packing algorithms 196
parallel lines 30
Pascal's triangle 65
passes (sorting algorithms) 194, 195
paths in graphs 200
pegs 178, 179
permutations 121, 122
periodic sequences 58
perpendicular lines 30
pivots (Simplex method) 226, 227
planar graphs 201
PMCC 137, 138
polynomials 1
positive correlation 137
Prim's algorithm 203, 204, 217
probability 115–119, 122
probability distributions 125, 126
probability functions 125
product-moment correlation coefficient
  (PMCC) 137, 138
pseudo-code 192
pulleys 159, 178, 180

Index

Q

quadratic
  equations 10–17, 19, 25, 64
  formula 15, 16
  graphs 10
  inequalities 17, 23
quartiles 106, 107, 111

R

radians 71
random events 115, 116
random variables 125, 130
range 106
ranks 141
rates of change 40
rationalising the denominator 3
real-life problems 45, 86
recurrence relations 57
reflections (graphs) 33
regression lines 139–141
relative frequencies 115
Remainder Theorem 55
residuals 140
resolving
  forces 161, 175
  vectors 157
response variables 139
resultant
  forces 160
  vectors 156
roughness of a surface 163
rough planes 179, 180
route inspection problem 209–212
ruler method (linear programming) 222
Russian Peasant algorithm 191

S

sample space 115
sampling with replacement 117
scalars 156
scatter diagrams 137, 138
sector area 71, 72
selections 120–122
semi-Eulerian graphs 209, 210
sequences 57–64
series 59–64
shortcuts (Travelling Salesperson
      problems) 215
shuttle sort algorithm 195
sigma notation 60
simple graphs 199
Simplex method 225–227
simplifying expressions 5, 7
simultaneous equations 24–26, 64
  geometric interpretation 26

sin x 72, 75
sine rule 73, 74
slack variables 225–227
solving trig equations 77–80
sorting algorithms 194, 195
spanning trees 200
spare capacities 223, 226, 227
Spearman's rank correlation coefficient
      (SRCC) 141
speed-time graphs 170
squashed trig graphs 76
SRCC 141
standard deviation 108
stationary points 42, 44
statistical tables 150–155
stem and leaf diagrams 103
straight lines 29–31
stretches
  graphs 33
  trig graphs 76
subgraphs 200
substitution (simultaneous equations) 25
summarised data 110
sum to infinity 62
surds 3
sweeping statements 138

T

tableaux 225–227
tan x 72, 75, 79
tangents 41
  to circles 35
tension 158, 162, 177–179
thrust 158
trace tables 191, 193
transformed trig graphs 76
translations of graphs 33
trapezium rule 92, 93
Travelling Salesperson problems 215–217
traversable graphs 209, 210
tree diagrams 117
trees (the graphical type of tree that is) 200
trials 115
triangles 72–74
  area 73
  of forces 161
trig
  equations 77–80
  formulas 73
  functions 75
  graphs 75
  identities 73, 79, 80
  values from triangles 72

U

union 115
upper bound (Travelling Salesperson
      problems) 215
upper class boundaries 102
upper quartiles 106
u-shaped graphs 10
uvast variables 167, 168

V

valency of a node 201
variables 1
variance 108
  of a binomial distribution 132
  of random variables 127
variation 106, 108, 109, 111
vectors 156, 157, 160–162
velocity 171, 172
velocity-time graphs 169, 170
Venn diagrams 115, 116
vertex method (linear programming)
      223, 224
vertices (graphs) 199

W

weight 158
weighted graphs 199